UN SIECLE DE LITTERATURE CANADIENNE

A CENTURY OF CANADIAN LITERATURE

UN SIÈCLE DE LITTÉRATURE CANADIENNE
A CENTURY OF CANADIAN LITERATURE

Guy Sylvestre

H. Gordon Green

Éditions HMH
Montréal

The Ryerson Press
Toronto

"Published on the occasion of the Centennial of Canadian Confederation and subsidized by the Centennial Commission".

"Ouvrage publié à l'occasion du Centenaire de la Confédération Canadienne, grâce à une subvention de la Commission du Centenaire".

1867 | 1967

maquette / design: Raymond Bellemare, Gilles Robert & associés

FOREWORD

It must be immediately evident to anyone well acquainted
with our literature that a book of this size
can no longer hope to include all of the Canadian authors worthy
of the recognition afforded by an anthology.
Even if our coverage were to include
only those who are writing today and in English,
a volume of 600 pages would still be forced to leave out
some very notable names. Only half of this book
is allotted to the English language, however,
and that half must cover a century.
The reader who searches in vain here for some favourite
of his might remember this when he is tempted
to damn us for our sins of omission.

Since it was so painfully clear at the very outset that
we could not hope to offer anything more than a random
sampling of our literary achievement,
it was decided that the English section of our book
would attempt a sort of Canadian exploration
rather than a judgment of what constitutes
the absolute best in our writing.
Our search then was not only for authors
of outstanding accomplishment, but for those who
had some special ability to tell us what manner of men
we Canadians are and how we got that way.
We follow these authors now on a literary rambling through
one hundred years of this nation's history
and over 3500 miles of its geography.

Anthology compilers have an understandable tendency
to become increasingly timid about their own judgments
as a project progresses. It is much easier and safer perhaps
to merely maintain an awed reverence for the judgments
of those compilers who have gone before.
We hope that we have been properly irreverent in our choosing,
and whatever its other faults, we trust that this book

PRÉFACE

Nulle anthologie ne saurait satisfaire pleinement "tout le monde
et son père". Celle-ci pas plus qu'une autre. Ceux qui en ont eu l'idée,
comme ceux qui ont collaboré à sa compilation, en sont conscients.
Néanmoins, on peut espérer que cette anthologie décevra moins
qu'une autre la majorité de ses lecteurs parce que,
pour les raisons que j'indiquerai ici,
elle approche le plus possible d'un *consensus omnium*.

En effet, lorsque la Commission du Centenaire a accordé
une subvention à la Canadian Authors Association
et à la Société des Ecrivains canadiens pour permettre
la préparation, et la publication à un prix raisonnable,
d'une anthologie de nos deux littératures nationales
depuis cent ans, la Commission a suggéré
que le choix des textes ne soit pas fait par un ou deux auteurs,
mais par deux équipes d'écrivains, de critiques
et de professeurs afin qu'il réunisse des textes sur lesquels
on aura pu faire le plus large accord possible.
En fait, seize personnes ont participé au choix
des textes français reproduits ici et,
pour chaque genre littéraire,
de cinq à sept spécialistes de nos lettres ont été consultés.

La Société des Ecrivains canadiens m'a fait l'honneur
de me confier la direction de la partie française
de cette entreprise. J'ai eu la bonne fortune de réunir
une équipe remarquable d'experts qui m'ont accordé leur entière
collaboration et à qui je tiens à exprimer ici
ma plus vive gratitude. Si cette entreprise considérable
a pu être menée à bonne fin, c'est à leur dévouement
et à leurs lumières qu'on le doit.
Je tiens à exprimer aussi ma gratitude à Claire Martin,
sous la présidence de qui ce projet a été approuvé
par la Société des Ecrivains, et qui a continué à assurer
la liaison entre la Société, la Commission du Centenaire,

la Canadian Authors Association, les éditeurs et le soussigné.
will not be an anthology of other anthologies.

Certainly we set about the making of our part
of this collection determined to recognize new names
and new developments in Canadian letters.
We have given a place to radio writing. We have not subscribed
to the tradition that pessimism is essential
to lasting significance. And since we are not entirely
convinced that the choice of the majority is reliable for nothing
more than the election of democratic governments,
we have included writers whose appeal has been to the millions
rather than to the professors.

We have, of course, several regrets about this survey.
In particular we are sorry that we could not possibly give
the Canadian novel the attention it deserves.
While Canada has not yet produced a Steinbeck or a Hemingway,
it has at least a score of novelists distinguished enough
to merit inclusion in any work of this kind.
Unfortunately, however, a novel is frequently
of such a nature that an editor cannot,
no matter how skillfully he carves,
do justice to the writer by means
of excerpts or disconnected chapters.

A casual look at the English titles of this effort
will indicate that we have devoted at least a half
of our space to the writing of the last 25 years,
and we think there is ample justification for this.
Not only have the earlier Canadian writers been honoured
quite adequately already by other anthologies,
but there seems little doubt that what has been written
in this country since 1940 will one day be regarded
as more important by far than anything which preceded it.

It will also be noted that at least four of our authors
discuss some aspect of the French-English difference
in our nationality. It was inevitable of course
that Canada's first bilingual anthology
should be particularly anxious to explore that difference
and to achieve a measure of that greater understanding
which must come between our two breeds of Canadians
if we are to survive a second century as one nation.

It may be in order here to say something
about the method by which the English language half of this book
was accumulated. In general the task of selecting was entrusted
to three separate committees, one each for fiction, non-fiction and poetry.
Each of these committees had almost unlimited freedom
to choose and suggest. Naturally they turned first

Un premier choix de textes a été fait par des spécialistes dans chacun des six genres suivants.

POÉSIE — M. Jacques BRAULT, professeur à la faculté de Philosophie de l'Université de Montréal;
le Frère Clément LOCKQUELL, m.s.r.c., professeur à la faculté des Lettres de l'Université Laval;
M. Gilles MARCOTTE, professeur à la faculté des Lettres de l'Université de Montréal;

ROMAN — M. Gérard BESSETTE, m.s.r.c., professeur de littérature à la faculté des Arts de la Queen's University;
Mlle Cécile CLOUTIER, professeur de littérature à la faculté des Arts de la University of Toronto;
le Père Réjean ROBIDOUX, professeur de littérature à la faculté des Arts de l'Université d'Ottawa;

THÉÂTRE — M. Roger DUHAMEL, m.s.r.c.,
Imprimeur de la Reine à Ottawa;
le Père Bernard JULIEN, professeur de littérature à la faculté des Arts de l'Université d'Ottawa;

CRITIQUE — M. Jean MARCEL,
critique littéraire à l'*Action Nationale;*
M. Paul WYCZYNSKI, professeur de littérature à la faculté des Arts de l'Université d'Ottawa;

HISTOIRE — M. Jean HAMELIN, professeur d'histoire à la faculté des Lettres de l'Université Laval;
le Père Benoît LACROIX, professeur à l'Institut d'Etudes médiévales de l'Université de Montréal;

AUTRES GENRES — M. Jean-Ethier BLAIS, professeur de littérature à la McGill University et critique littéraire au *Devoir;*
M. Jean-Charles BONENFANT, m.s.r.c., conservateur de la Bibliothèque de la Législature de Québec;
M. Fernand DUMONT, m.s.r.c., professeur à la faculté des Sciences sociales de l'Université Laval.

Cette équipe, dont les membres n'appartiennent pas tous à la même génération et qui représentent des tendances diverses, a retenu pour étude 391 textes de 156 auteurs (140 poèmes; 163 extraits de romans ou nouvelles; 16 scènes tirées de 12 pièces; 23 essais critiques; 20 extraits d'oeuvres historiques et 37 autres essais). Nous avions en mains cinq fois plus de textes que nous ne pouvions en publier dans les quelque trois cents pages dont nous disposions. Si on considère que l'anthologie ne renferme que 89 textes de 78 auteurs de langue française, on aura une idée de la somme de travail et de réflexion

to the best works of our best known authors.
But since it had been resolved to make this anthology distinctively
different from its predecessors, a special effort was made
to find good writing which is not yet so widely known.
Not only did we attempt to make rediscoveries
in the works of long-established authors but we also let it be known
that we would consider material written by those who are not yet famous.
The press and the various branches
of the Canadian Authors' Association were especially helpful
in publicizing this policy and as a result we received
hundreds of submissions either from the writers themselves
or from their readers and editors.

Ultimately the nominations submitted by each
of the three chairmen totalled about a third more than was enough
to fill the allotted space. The main function of the editor
and the top committee therefore was to select approximately two-thirds
of the titles given them by each of the chairmen and thus
to finally establish the English language content of the book.

It should be clear then that the research and judgment
of many minds have gone into the making of this anthology,
and that no author has been included
because he happened to be a favourite of a single critic.

Finally, due credit should be given to the Centennial Commission.
The Commission not only provided the financial assistance
which made this project possible but
also gave us valuable criticism and advice.

H. GORDON GREEN,
Canadian Authors' Association

qui a été nécessaire pour en arriver au choix définitif.
Les 391 textes ont été photocopiés et distribués, avec les commentaires
de ceux qui les avaient suggérés, aux quatre membres du comité
qui fut chargé d'établir le dernier choix :
MM. Bonenfant, Duhamel, Marcotte et le soussigné.
Après un abondant échange de correspondance qui a permis
des éliminations successives, le comité a tenu
deux longues réunions au cours desquelles ses membres ont pu faire
l'accord sur les textes qu'on trouvera ici. Ai-je besoin de dire
que les quatre membres de ce comité ont tenu
à s'exclure eux-mêmes de ce florilège ?

On pourra critiquer ce choix, on ne pourra pas dire
qu'il a été fait à la légère. Cette anthologie n'est pas la mienne
— on en a exclu des textes auxquels je tenais
et on y a inclus des textes qui n'avaient pas ma préférence
— et tous ceux qui y ont collaboré pourraient en dire autant.
Tous regretteront qu'il ait fallu en exclure certains auteurs
— trois d'entre eux s'en sont exclus d'eux-mêmes en refusant
l'autorisation de reproduire leurs textes — mais je crois
que tous seront d'accord pour dire que ceux qui en sont méritent d'y être.
Nous avons désormais trop de bons auteurs pour qu'il ait été
possible de leur donner à tous une place dans ce livre
(ni de donner parfois à ceux qui y sont
autant d'espace qu'ils en mériteraient).

Nous devons nous réjouir qu'il y ait autant d'absents;
il n'y a pas si longtemps, on aurait pu se demander, au contraire,
si on pouvait trouver assez de textes de qualité pour en constituer
une anthologie digne d'intérêt. Quoi qu'il en soit,
j'espère que ce produit de nos efforts concertés démontrera,
si c'est encore nécessaire, que nous avons au Canada deux littératures
qui, au cours des derniers cent ans, n'ont cessé de progresser
et de se renouveler pour devenir peu à peu ce double patrimoine
riche et divers dont cette anthologie donne une idée
certes réduite mais que je crois néanmoins fidèle.

GUY SYLVESTRE, m.s.r.c.
de l'Académie canadienne-française

BEFORE 1867

The first writing to be done in Canada was that of the early missionaries
and explorers, and many of the memoirs, diaries and letters
of these men are doubtless as fascinating today
as they were when America was still as far distant as another
planet. The adventures of probing countless miles of unknown
geography and of confronting natives who had every right to be hostile
were so inescapably dramatic as they actually happened that even
the most artless account of those lonely battles contained all
of the elements of suspense. They needed neither the craft of the
creative writer nor his imagination to give them a permanent place
in Canadian letters. In even the humblest of those historic reports
one may see all three of the basics of the human struggle — man
against nature, man against man and man against himself.

But because these writings were not the work of writers at all but
of history-makers, there has long been a supposition that
pre-Confederation Canada was rather lacking in serious literary
pretension. This is unfortunate. The first printing press to operate
on what is now Canadian soil was set up in Halifax in 1752
and was soon followed by other presses in Quebec City,
Montreal and Niagara. And while these early printing houses
were for many years fully occupied turning out news-sheets,
notices and official gazettes, they eventually made possible some rather
notable periodicals. The year 1789 saw John Howe producing the
Nova-Scotia Magazine, this to be followed in the days
of his son Joseph Howe by the *Acadian Magazine* (1826-28) and
the *Halifax Monthly* (1830-31). Montreal meanwhile had made its
first acknowledgment of the growing need for expression by launching
the bilingual *Quebec Magazine* (1792-94) and several other
publications which were equally short lived.
The Scribbler (1821-27), the *Canadian Magazine* (1823-25) and
the *Canadian Review* (1824-26) were somewhat more successful.
In 1838, however, John Gibson began publication of the
Literary Garland, a periodical which, though its writing often lacked

INTRODUCTION

Cette anthologie couvre un siècle de littérature canadienne.
Le plus ancien texte français qu'on y trouve est tiré
d'une lettre que Crémazie écrivait à Casgrain en 1867
et dans laquelle il se montrait fort pessimiste
sur l'avenir de nos lettres. Une anthologie comme celle-ci démontre
combien le poète était mauvais prophète. On peut y faire,
en raccourci, ce voyage depuis Crémazie jusqu'à Gatien Lapointe,
de Laure Conan à Marie-Claire Blais,
d'Arthur Buies à Fernand Dumont.
Un siècle, ce n'est pas très long dans la vie d'un peuple.
Et pourtant, en comparant les premiers aux seconds,
on a vite fait de constater qu'un monde les sépare.
L'homme de 1966 n'est pas l'homme de 1867. Il y a certes des traits
communs à l'un et à l'autre : d'ailleurs l'atavisme existe
et les hommes sont aussi marqués par l'histoire.
Néanmoins, les idées ont évolué considérablement depuis cent ans,
et aussi les préoccupations, les aspirations, la sensibilité, le goût,
l'art d'écrire. Les textes réunis ici illustrent de maintes manières
cette évolution, qui a d'ailleurs subi récemment l'accélération
de l'histoire. Un livre comme celui-ci permet de vérifier
le chemin parcouru, de faire le point et, peut-être, d'entrevoir
la sorte d'hommes et de peuples que nous sommes en train de devenir.
Le style de vie a autant changé que le style écrit ;
ce dernier n'est que le reflet du premier.

   Je n'ai pas l'intention de réécrire ici
l'histoire de notre littérature. Cela a été fait ailleurs.
Il me semble nécessaire, toutefois, de soumettre aux lecteurs,
quelques remarques très générales — dont certaines ne sont
que des approximations — qui pourraient
les aider à mieux situer les textes qui suivent.

   On a certes écrit au Canada avant 1867. Les relations de Cartier,
de Champlain, des Jésuites ; les lettres de Marie de l'Incarnation,
les poésies que Lescarbot écrivit dès 1606 à Port Royal

distinction, was nevertheless a very important outlet for creative effort then badly in need of encouragement.

Upper Canada meanwhile had tried unsuccessfully to sustain such ventures as Egerton Ryerson's *Christian Guardian* (1829), *Barker's Canadian Monthly* (Kingston, *1846-47)* and *The Victoria Magazine* (Belleville, 1847-48). Nevertheless after 1850 Toronto began to declare itself the cultural centre of English-speaking Canada and within the next decade such a cluster of magazines appeared there that only a few had any hope of survival.

No good purpose will be served here by cataloguing the list of periodicals published in British North America before 1867, or by trying to discover some long-hidden greatness in them. Their chief importance is simply that they were a first voice from the wilderness which was about to become a nation. It was in the *Acadian Magazine* for instance that Joseph Howe and Thomas Chandler Haliburton first demanded attention. Here too Oliver Goldsmith published his *Rising Village,* a long poem which may be regarded as the first major effort by a Canadian-born poet. Margaret Blennerhasset of Montreal and Adam Hood Burwell of Col. Talbot's settlement in Upper Canada published their verse in *The Scribbler.* One of the more enduring writers of the period, Mrs. Susanna Moodie, was contributing to the *Literary Garland* for some years before she wrote her pioneering classic *Roughing it in the Bus*h (1852).

But not all of the more significant writing of those early days went into such periodicals. Mrs. Frances Brooke's book *The History of Emily Montague* appeared in 1769 when the English novel was only beginning to emerge as a distinct literary form. This novel was published in England but its background was Quebec City where Mrs. Brooke's husband served as chaplain of the British garrison during the Seven Years' War. It pretends to be a series of letters exploring love as "an intellectual pleasure," and while its style is very obviously patterned after that of Samuel Richardson, a personal friend of the Brookes, it must be admitted that this is not only the first novel to come out of Canada, but one of the very first to be written in America.

But *The History of Emily Montague* was actually no more Canadian than John Galt's novels *Laurie Todd* (1830) and *Bogle Corbet* (1831), or Anna Jameson's *Winter Studies and Summer Rambles* or the satirical humour of Dr. "Tiger" Dunlop, or even the frontier life chronicles of Susanna Moodie and her sister Catherine Parr Traill. None of these writers was Canadian-born: few of them even wished to be regarded as belonging here. It wasn't until after 1800 that Canada began to produce its own authors.

appartiennent à notre histoire ; elles ne constituent pas
une première littérature canadienne. Ces écrits vénérables
sont l'oeuvre de Français, non de Canadiens.
L'intérêt des chroniques et récits que nous ont laissés
les explorateurs, les missionnaires et les administrateurs
des dix-septième et dix-huitième siècles
est historique et non littéraire.

Après la conquête et l'occupation de la colonie par les Anglais,
on trouve une littérature de résistance, une littérature
d'action qui est une source historique qu'on ne peut ignorer,
mais dont la qualité littéraire reste médiocre.
Cette littérature de journalistes, d'orateurs et de juristes
a aidé les *Canadiens* à rester fidèles à leurs origines
et à résister victorieusement aux tentatives que multipliaient
les nouveaux *Canadians* pour les dominer ou les assimiler.
Ces efforts littéraires souvent gauches
des défenseurs de notre langue, de nos lois et de nos institutions
ont préparé la naissance d'une littérature digne
de ce nom vers le milieu du dix-neuvième siècle.

Cette première génération d'écrivains vécut au moment
où le romantisme régnait en Europe. Nos auteurs y prirent le goût
de l'histoire et de la couleur locale.
Ils furent tous influencés d'ailleurs par leur maître à tous,
François-Xavier Garneau (1809-1866) dont l'*Histoire du Canada*
reste notre plus grand livre du dix-neuvième siècle
et fut pour nos poètes, romanciers et conteurs la source de la plupart
de leurs sujets et de leur inspiration. Aucun écrivain canadien
n'a exercé une aussi grande influence que lui.
Cette première génération d'écrivains comprenait encore
le journaliste Etienne Parent, le conteur Philippe Aubert de Gaspé
— *Les Anciens Canadiens* possèdent un charme qui nous touche encore;
Octave Crémazie qui a su, par ses poésies patriotiques,
toucher l'âme populaire; d'autres encore comme Antoine Gérin-Lajoie,
Joseph-Charles Taché ou Henri-Raymond Casgrain qui,
avec les premiers, appartenaient à ce qu'on a appelé
l'Ecole patriotique de Québec, ou l'Ecole de 1860.
Cette école portait bien son nom :
la littérature était alors en service commandé.

Elle allait le rester encore longtemps;
il y a d'ailleurs à toutes les époques des écrivains d'action,
une littérature engagée. On le constate en retrouvant
au début du siècle la littérature nationaliste de Bourassa,
Asselin et Fournier; un peu plus tard,
les essais du chanoine Groulx, d'Edouard Montpetit
et de Victor Barbeau; et aujourd'hui les écrits polémiques

Most versatile of all the early homegrown writers was Joseph Howe — Loyalist, orator, politician, humorist, story-teller and poet. That he was a formidable crusader as well is indicated by the fact that he is generally credited with winning freedom of the press in Canada through a single magnificent speech. Finally Howe was publisher of a newspaper called *The Novascotian* and one of the writers he brought to light in this paper was his fellow Loyalist, Haliburton, whose witty Clockmaker series was to make him the first Canadian to win international acclaim. Some critics even declare Sam Slick's author to be the father of American humour.

It was a writer from Upper Canada however who wrote the first truly Canadian novel. Major John Richardson volunteered as a soldier in the War of 1812 when he was 15, and what he saw with his own eyes of that struggle was later to form the historically accurate background for his three-volume *Wacousta* (1832). It is a well-planned tale and in spite of its melodramatic tendencies still quite readable. A later Canadian historical romance by Rosanna Eleanor Leprohon, *Antoinette de Mirecourt* (1864), was more realistic and more compactly managed.

There was even a serious attempt at producing Canadian drama in the first half of the century, with a Montreal cabinet maker, Charles Heavysege, winning the praise of such famous men as Hawthorne and Longfellow for his efforts. Heavysege produced a laboured Shakespearian type of play but even the best of these, *Jephthah's Daughter* (1865), is now almost completely forgotten.

As earthy as Heavysege was erudite, Alex McLachlan wrote verses which were so exclusively concerned with the soil and the struggle of the common man that he was often called "the Canadian Burns." The first full volume of Canadian verse was published in 1840, the highly fanciful *Hamilton and Other Poems* by William A. Stevens of Owen Sound.

But the first Canadian poet to win universal acclaim was Charles Sangster, then with the *Kingston Whig*. Sangster's narrative poem *The St. Lawrence and the Saguenay and Other Poems* (1856) was so brimming with pride in the Canadian scene that he was hailed as our "national poet" ten years before we were even a nation. Another poet of his day, Thomas D'Arcy McGee, did more than offer up a tribute of poetry to the cause of a unified Canada for he was destined to become one of the Fathers of Confederation and, only a year after union, our first political martyr.

It is worth noting that McGee was by no means the first of our nation's makers who were also competent writers. Novelist John

du groupe de *Parti pris* qui sont plus des actes que des oeuvres.
Mais à côté de cette littérature d'action,
on a vu paraître peu à peu une littérature gratuite.
Il est significatif que l'Ecole *littéraire* de Montréal
ait succédé à l'Ecole *patriotique* de Québec.
Certes, à cette époque-là, Nérée Beauchemin renouvelait
la poésie du terroir chère à LeMay, et Mgr Camille Roy préconisait
"la nationalisation de la littérature".
Mais, en même temps, Emile Nelligan et Albert Lozeau
trouvaient la matière et l'inspiration de leurs oeuvres,
non dans l'histoire ni dans leur milieu, mais au fond de leur coeur.
Le *moi* prenait sa place dans notre littérature
dominée jusque là par le *nous*. Un peu plus tard,
réagissant encore violemment contre le régionalisme littéraire,
Paul Morin n'écrira que des poèmes délibérément exotiques.
Dans certains milieux, cette forme de littérature
fut considérée comme une trahison. Mais le goût avait changé et,
après avoir subi longtemps l'influence de Victor Hugo,
nos poètes avaient puisé chez Baudelaire et Verlaine
le goût de la musique et des symboles.

Nos prosateurs étaient alors beaucoup plus timides et,
après la première grande guerre, en ces années où on tenait Bourget
pour un très grand romancier,
on a vu Jean-Charles Harvey, Harry Bernard,
le chanoine Groulx et quelques autres pratiquer le roman à thèse et
aborder dans leurs récits des problèmes moraux, sociaux et économiques.
On n'était pas si loin d'Antoine Gérin-Lajoie qu'on le croyait.

Depuis les années 30, toutefois, notre littérature
s'est constamment diversifiée tout en s'élevant à un niveau moyen
de plus en plus élevé. Qu'il suffise de rappeler les noms de romanciers
comme Ringuet, Grignon, Desrosiers et Savard; des poètes comme
Desrochers, Choquette, Grandbois et Saint-Denys-Garneau,
pour le prouver. C'est alors que notre littérature
a commencé à retenir l'attention de l'étranger.
Gallimard publie en 1938 *Les Engagés du Grand Portage* et,
la même année, *Trente arpents,* paru chez Flammarion,
obtient à Ringuet le prix des Vikings.
Quelques années plus tard, Gabrielle Roy recevra le prix Femina
pour *Bonheur d'occasion;* aujourd'hui, plusieurs de nos écrivains
publient leurs oeuvres simultanément à Montréal et à Paris.
Nous existons non seulement à nos propres yeux, mais aussi à ceux des
autres.

En lisant les textes des auteurs contemporains réunis ici,
on pourra constater combien chacun a une voix différente de celle des
autres. La luxuriance de Rina Lasnier fera mieux sentir le laconisme

Galt was a superintendent of the colonization project known as
The Canada Company. Joseph Howe, the poet and story writer,
became Nova Scotia's leading politician. Humorist Thomas
Haliburton was also a politician, and later a judge. Perhaps it is only
coincidence that we should have numbered so many writers
among our first great men. Or perhaps it was the power which then
grew out of oratory which made them aware of the fact that the
written word too has its magic.

In any case it would be wrong to conclude that pre-Confederation
Canada, uncouth and disjointed though it may have been, was
inarticulate. It had no lack of men who could think clearly
as well as dream. Which is, briefly, all that a writer is.

H.G.G.

ACKNOWLEDGEMENTS

The Canadian Authors' Association is deeply indebted to Professor
W.G. Hardy, Head of the Department of Classics, University of Alberta,
who first conceived the central idea of this unique anthology,
and who, perhaps more than any other, is responsible for its
creation.

It is also indebted to the three men, writers all, who worked for
over a year with the Editor to gather the selections for the
English language section of this book. These are : poetry —
Professor Fred Cogswell, University of New Brunswick; fiction —
John Patrick Gillese, Edmonton; non-fiction — Professor Earle
Beattie, University of Western Ontario.

Also its sincere appreciation goes to the following, each of whom
had a part in the shaping of this book: John Robert Colombo,
the late John Drainie, Dorothy Needles, Vernon Pope, Hugh Shaw,
Craig Ballantyne, Guy Sylvestre, H.R. Percy, Phyllis Blakeley,
Gladys Taylor, Lynda Muir, George Bowering, Fred Swayze.

Also to the editors of *Maclean's,* the editors *of Reader's
Digest,* the editors of *The Star Weekly* and to each of the Branch
Presidents of its own Association.

de Jean-Guy Pilon, le goût de la clarté de Pierre Baillargeon contraste
avec le désordre intérieur de Réal Benoit;
l'humanisme classique de Paul Toupin est aux antipodes
du spiritualisme tourmenté de Jean Le Moyne.
Ce ne sont là que quelques exemples de la multiplicité des tendances
et des styles qu'on peut observer aujourd'hui dans nos lettres
et qui ajoute à leur intérêt. On y trouve un peu de tout :
surréalisme et nouveau roman, néo-classicisme et théâtre d'avant-garde.
C'est la littérature d'un monde en transition,
d'une société qui cherche un nouvel équilibre, d'individus qui mettent
en question les valeurs traditionnelles sur lesquelles leurs pères ont vécu
Elle nous donne de l'homme une image complexe.

Cette littérature américaine écrite en français
dans un pays britannique a une saveur unique.
Elle n'est peut-être pas des plus grandes :
elle existe. On n'en pouvait dire autant en 1867.

G.S.

Ottawa, Ontario
le 12 juillet 1966.

ACKNOWLEDGEMENTS

Canadian Author & Bookman for *And Mercy Mild* by Isabel LeBourdais. Canadian Broadcasting Corporation for *Passing of the Big M* by Vinia Hoogstraten. Canadian Forum for *And Mercy Mild* by Isabel LeBourdais and *The First Armistice* by Violet Lang. Clarke, Irwin & Company Limited for the excerpt from *Homebrew and Patches* by Harry Boyle. Contact Press for *Spilled Plaster* by Louis Dudek, *Entomology* by Eli Mandel, *By the Church Wall* by John Newlove and *Déménagement* by Peter Miller. J.M. Dent & Sons (Canada) Limited for an excerpt from *The Law Marches West* by the late Sir Cecil E. Denny. Dodd, Mead & Company, N.Y.C., for *My Madonna* by Robert Service. Faber and Faber Limited for *Graveyard on a Cliff of White Sand* by Wilfred Watson. Family Herald for *The Reluctant Genius* by Vicki Branden, *Especially Worthy* by John Patrick Gillese, *Isses Net Peculiar* by Jane Van Every and *Babiche Land* by Gwen Lewis. The Fiddlehead for *In Memory of Elizabeth* by Joan Finnigan, *The Genealogy of Morals* by Alden Nowlan, *Water and the Rock* by Fred Cogswell, *The North Wind Doth Blow* by Fred Swayze, *Age-Old Wisdom* by Louis Ginsberg and *Beaver Pond* by Anne Marriott McLellan. W.J. Gage Limited for *A Penny in the Dust* by Ernest Buckler. Klanak Press for *In the Yukon* by Ralph Gustafson. Lethbridge Herald for *The Chinese Café* by Ed Arrol.

Longmans Canada Limited for the excerpt from *Home Made Banners* by Ralph Allen, and *Ma Parsons* by R.D. Symons from his book *Many Trails*. Maclean's for *Sunrise for Peter* by Will R. Bird, *Overland from Signal Hill to Victoria* by Edward McCourt, *The Day Canada Became a Nation* by D.J. Goodspeed, *Front Line Letters to My Son* by Donald Pearce and *The Secret Life of Mackenzie King* by Blair Fraser. Macmillan Company of Canada Limited and the following authors for excerpts from *Two Solitudes* by Hugh MacLennan, *Who Has Seen the Wind* by W.O. Mitchell, *The Donnellys Must Die* by Orlo Miller, *Ringing the Changes* by Mazo de la Roche (with permission from The Estate of Mazo de la Roche), and *Dear Enemies* by Gwethalyn Graham (with permission from Gwethalyn Graham's Estate), *From Flores* by Ethel Wilson, *Overland from Signal Hill to Victoria* by Edward McCourt, *Memories That Live* by S. Morgan Powell, *When the Steel Went Through* by P.T. Bone, *Front Line Letters to My Son* by Donald Pearce, and *Newfoundland* by E.J. Pratt. McClelland and Stewart Limited for *The Crisis* from *Glengarry School Days* by Ralph Connor, *The Crop* from *Fruits of the Earth* by Philip Grove, the excerpt from *Sarah Binks* by Paul Hiebert, *Adventures of a Columnist* by Pierre Berton, the excerpt from *A Choice for Canada* by Walter Gordon, *The Struggle for National Broadcasting in Canada* by Austin Weir the excerpt from *A Voice from the Attic* by Robertson Davies,

On Amaryllis, A Tortoyse by Marjorie Pickthall, *Song for Naomi* by Irving Layton, *Dark Lagoon* by James Reaney, *For E.J.P.* by Leonard Cohen, *The Country North of Belleville* by Alfred Purdy and *Photos of a Salt Mine* by P.K. Page. Musson Book Company, Toronto for *Marshlands* by E. Pauline Johnson. Thomas Nelson & Sons for *A Social Departure* by Sara Jeannette Duncan. Oxford University Press for *Running to Paradise* by Kildare Dobbs, *The St. Lawrence* by William Toye, *Case of Psychasthenia in a School Teacher* from *A Divided Voice* by Francis Sparshott, *Field of Long Grass* from *A.J.M. Smith Collected Poems, Death of Don Quixote* from *A Point of Sky* by John Glassco, *Storm* from *The Boatman* by Jay Macpherson and *Mr. Goon* by George Johnston. Pan # 2 and Allan Brilliant for *Noel* by Anne Wilkinson. Reader's Digest for *Canada Game Scores Abroad* by David MacDonald. Reilly Lee Co. of Chicago for *Nesting Canada Geese* by Jack Miner. Ryerson Press for *Do Seek Their Meat from God* from *Earth's Enigmas* by Sir Charles G.D. Roberts, *Anne Says Her Prayers* from *Anne of Green Gables* by L.M. Montgomery, *Sunrise for Peter* by Will R. Bird, *Sense and Nonsense* by Eric Nicol, *The Four Jameses* by William Arthur Deacon, *A Great Champion* from *Tales Retold Under The Old Town Clock* by William Borrett, *Confessions of an Immigrant's Daughter* by Laura Goodman Salverson, *We Keep a Light* by Evelyn Richardson, *Quebec Now* by Miriam Chapin, *Eve* by F.R. Scott, *White Cat* from *Collected Poems* by Raymond Knister, *Grain Elevator* from *The Rocking Chair* by A.M. Klein, *On Looking into Henry Moore* from *Selected Poems* by Dorothy Livesay, *Flux* from *The Sea is Also a Garden* by Phyllis Webb, *The North Wind Doth Blow* from *And See Penelope Plain* by Fred Swayze and *The Water and the Rock* from *Descent from Eden* by Fred Cogswell.

Saturday Evening Post for *It's Gotta Rain Sometime* by R. Ross Annett. Swan Publications for *William Lyon Mackenzie* by John Colombo. Tamarack Review for *Running to Paradise* by Kildare Dobbs, and *Red Boots* by George Bowering. University of Toronto Press for *A Conversation* by Margaret Avison and *Survivors* by Robert Finch. Vancouver Sun for *The British Columbian* by Barry Mather. Viking Press for *Wolf Willow* by Wallace Stegner. Weekend Magazine for *The Schemer* from *Kettle Cove and the Industrial Revolution* by Michael Francis Harrington, and *La Mer* by Gregory Clark. Willing and Williamson for *The Political Destiny of Canada* by Goldwin Smith. William Morrow & Co. Inc. for the selection from *On the Highest Hill* by Roderick Haig-Brown.

REMERCIEMENTS

Nous remercions les auteurs, les éditeurs et les autres personnes qui nous ont gracieusement autorisés à reproduire les textes qui suivent :
Pierre Baillargeon, Jovette Bernier, Michel Brunet, Cécile Chabot, Robert Charbonneau, Robert Choquette, Mme Simone Drouin (Simone Routier), Marcel Dubé, Mme Michèle Duchastel de Montrouge (Michèle Lalonde), Roland Giguère, André Giroux, Claude-Henri Grignon, Germaine Guèvremont, Jean-Charles Harvey, Paul-Marie Lapointe, Rina Lasnier, Roger Lemelin, Fernand Ouellette, Albert Pelletier, Jean-Jules Richard, Marcel Trudel, Medjé Vézina;
M. Pierre Asselin (pour l'essai d'Olivar Asselin); M. le juge André Montpetit (pour l'essai d'Edouard Montpetit); M. Bernard Moore (pour le poème de René Chopin); Mlle Cécile Saint-Jorre (pour le poème de Pamphile LeMay); Mr. Joseph D. Seers (pour l'essai de Louis Dantin); le Conseil du Séminaire de Québec (pour l'essai de Camille Roy), l'Académie canadienne-française (pour l'essai de Victor Barbeau); les Editions à la Page (pour le texte de Claude Jasmin); les Editions du Bien Public (pour le poème de Nérée Beauchemin); les Editions Beauchemin (pour les textes de Gabrielle Roy et l'extrait du *Journal* de Saint-Denys-Garneau); le Cercle du Livre de France (pour les textes de Hubert Aquin, Réal Benoit, Gérard Bessette, Eugène Cloutier, Albert Laberge, André Langevin, Jacques Languirand, Claire Martin, Jean Simard, Paul Toupin); la Librairie Déom (pour le poème de Sylvain Garneau); les Editions de la Diaspora française (pour le poème de François Hertel); les Publications Didac, Inc. (pour le texte d'Adrienne Choquette); les Editions Fides (pour les textes de Laure Conan, Alfred Desrochers, Jules Fournier, Guy Frégault, Saint-Denys-Garneau, Alain Grandbois, Lionel Groulx, Paul Morin, Emile Nelligan, Robert de Roquebrune, Félix-Antoine Savard); la Librairie Ernest Flammarion (pour le texte de Ringuet); les Editions Gallimard (pour le texte de Léo-Paul Desrosiers); la Librairie Garneau (pour les textes de Thomas Chapais et de Suzanne Paradis); les Editions Bernard Grasset (pour le texte d'Yves Thériault); les Editions H M H (pour les textes de Fernand Dumont, Anne Hébert, Jean Le Moyne et Pierre Trottier); les Ecrits du Canada français (pour le texte de Robert Elie); les Editions de l'Hexagone (pour les poèmes d'Alain Grandbois et de Gilles Hénault); *L'Ingénieur* (pour le texte de Léon Gérin); les Editions du Jour (pour les textes de Marie-Claire Blais, Gustave Lanctôt, Gatien Lapointe et Solange Chaput-Rolland); l'Imprimerie Populaire (pour les poèmes d'Albert Lozeau); les Editions Seghers (pour le poème de Jean-Guy Pilon) et les Editions du Seuil (pour les poèmes d'Anne Hébert).

TABLE DES MATIÈRES / TABLE OF CONTENTS

D.J. Goodspeed (Born in 1919)

A respected historian, now with the Army Historical Section in Ottawa, his recent book, *The Conspirators,* was acclaimed.

THE DAY CANADA BECAME A NATION

On the first of July, 1867, Upper and Lower Canada, New Brunswick, and Nova Scotia were united as provinces in the Dominion of Canada, but not by the democratic decision of the people. Passions ran so high that the fathers of Confederation never dared submit the issue to a vote. Newfoundland, Prince Edward Island, and British Columbia remained outside the union. In each of the four original provinces of Canada some people bitterly opposed the creation of the new nation : apart from Quebec, all the provinces were more British than the British — and Quebec, not to be outdone in vicarious patriotism, was more French than France and considerably more Catholic than the Pope.

In most of the twelve cities of the new Dominion the streets were unpaved, gas lighting extended no further than the main streets, and the board sidewalks were in frequent disrepair. There were no public libraries, no art galleries, and few theatres but, in compensation, every town had its Mechanics' Institute, Loyal Orange Lodge, and YMCA, Freemasons, Odd Fellows, Sons of Temperance, Sons of St. Patrick, Sons of St. Andrew, and Sons of St. George.

Every Sunday morning in Toronto, Montreal and Halifax, long lines of hansom cabs carried top-hatted and frock-coated citizens and their families to church. Canadian cities were filled with churches, and the respectable classes patronized them almost as assiduously as the lower orders patronized the taverns. Almost, but not quite. The number of taverns was fantastic. Kingston, with a population of about 13,000, had more than 220 legal liquor outlets. Yet the hard drinking didn't go unopposed. Temperance societies flourished and in New Brunswick Prime Minister S. L. Tilley had actually imposed a short-lived era of prohibition.

Servants were plentiful and cheap. Workmen had no unions; labour troubles were few ; and even radical political reformers like Ontario's George Brown stopped well short of demands which would encourage the lower classes to leave the station in life to which God had called them. Important as politics and religion were, however, the chief mark of the colonial Victorian was his profound veneration for money. As Professor A. R. M. Lower has remarked, the Canadian middle class regarded the man who had lost his capital with the same moral disapproval as the woman who had lost her virtue.

Money, then, was the root of much of the opposition to Confederation. The Maritimes looked sourly at the debts incurred by Canada's railways and feared the competition of Canadian industries. Ontario businessmen, who had never liked the legislative union with Quebec, feared Confederation would tie them to other industrially backward partners. And the fiery A. A. Dorion, leader of Lower Canada's *parti rouge,* declared that the whole scheme was no more than a plot by English capitalists who hoped to profit from the extension of the Grand Trunk Railway. The opposition was so strong, in fact, that Confederation would probably never have come about if it had not been for the American Civil War.

For generations rabid republicans in the northern United States had felt that the American Revolution was somehow incomplete so long as any part of the continent remained under the British crown, and the British colonies might actually have been annexed before if the South hadn't bitterly opposed anything which would upset the careful balance between slave states and free. But as soon as General Beauregard's guns opened up on Fort Sumter on April 12, 1861, the restraining influence of the South disappeared. The British provinces were in danger and they knew it. Thomas D'Arcy McGee, the shrewd Irish member for Montreal, advocated Confederation as a measure of defence. But McGee was always advancing fresh reasons in favour of Confederation, and it was a little while before he was taken seriously.

The *New York Herald* was soon calling stridently for annexation — "peaceably if possible, forcibly if necessary" — and the British government hurriedly dispatched nearly 15,000 reinforcements to Canada. New militia battalions were raised in Ontario and Quebec, and Canadian politicians at last began to discuss Confederation in earnest.

Their task was the more urgent because political deadlock had developed in the Canadas. The Liberal-Conservatives led by John A. Macdonald and the Reform Party led by George Brown faced each other with almost equal forces in the legislature. The two leaders had almost nothing in common except mutual dislike. Macdonald was a jaunty, convivial man, perhaps overly fond of a glass of whisky, but with a keen sense of humour and an even keener sense of political realities. His large nose, twinkling eyes, and thick mop of hair curling over his collar were recognized, generally with affection, in every village in the colony.

George Brown, the huge, humourless and opinionated editor of the Toronto *Globe,* was a teetotaller and not on speaking terms with Macdonald, to whom he referred as an unscrupulous opportunist.

Nevertheless, George Brown had some vision of a great Canadian empire in the west, and necessity drove him to compromise with the one man in Canada he most hated. Canadians were incredulous when Macdonald and Brown met in the St. Louis Hotel in Quebec City in 1864 and agreed to a coalition.

That summer when delegates from the Maritime colonies met in Charlottetown to consider the possibility of a Maritime union, Canada asked if she could send representatives. On September 1 eight Canadian ministers arrived at Charlottetown. They had difficulty finding accommodation because the capital was filled with people who had come to see a travelling circus. However, the Canadian proposal for a complete confederation of British North America dominated the Charlottetown conference.

The next month, in wet weather, the delegates met again at the Citadel in Quebec City and drew up the seventy-two resolutions which were to result in the formation of the Dominion of Canada.

By now, however, the anti-Confederates had rallied *their* forces. In Quebec, Dorion and the *parti rouge* declared that French language and culture would be submerged in the new Canada and George Cartier, Macdonald's lifelong friend and the Conservative leader in Lower Canada, lost some of his influence when he was publicly denounced as a traitor for supporting Confederation. Some of the English-speaking minority in Quebec fought Confederation for quite different reasons. Many of Montreal's English-speaking businessmen believed they would profit if the U.S. simply seized the whole continent.

The Montreal Telegraph Company discovered that one of its employees was a correspondent for the annexationist *New York Herald.* For months this enterprising journalist had been filing virulent dispatches, telling how Confederation was being forced on the people against their will. The telegraph company dismissed him. Ontario papers suggested he be deported to the United States.

In Nova Scotia, Joseph Howe stormed against the union and demanded that Nova Scotians observe the first Dominion Day "with fastings and humiliations." He declared that if it weren't for the presence of British soldiers in Halifax he would counsel his countrymen to resist openly, and he promised to "drive a coach and six through the Act of Union."

Ironically enough, although Charlottetown has since come to be regarded as the birthplace of Confederation, Prince Edward Island now flatly refused to join the new Dominion. Newfoundland didn't seriously consider the possibility. In Nova Scotia Prime Minister Charles Tupper dared not put Confederation to the vote in the face of Howe's barnstorming opposition. In New Brunswick, S. L. Tilley, who did put it to the vote, was decisively defeated. It looked for a time as though Confederation would have to be abandoned.

The British Government, however, was anxious to reduce colonial defence costs, and British officials did everything possible to influence the outcome of a new election called in New Brunswick in 1866. The railways and the Canadian political parties also poured money in to help Tilley. He was re-elected.

On December 4, 1866, delegates from the provinces met in the Westminster Palace Hotel in London to draft the British North America Act. The British Parliament passed the Act of Union in March, 1867, and the Queen decreed that the first self-governing Dominion would come into being on the first of July.

In what is now the Canadian West, in the land ruled by the Hudson's Bay Company, a handful of half-breed settlers on the Red River watched the union of the eastern provinces nervously. Further west yet, the new colony of British Columbia had closer ties with California than with Ontario or Quebec. Trade flowed north and south and a gold strike on the Lower Fraser in 1858 had drawn thousands of Americans into B.C. Their duels, lynchings, vigilante justice, and tradition of miners' self-government threatened the independence of the colony. The alternative to joining Confederation appeared to be annexation by the United States, but before B.C. could effectively become part of the Dominion an awesomely expensive railroad would have to be pushed through the Rockies.

Indeed, the union of any of the provinces would be economically feasible only if more railways were constructed, and by 1867 even the existing lines were in trouble. They had been hurt by American competition and had failed to achieve anything like the predicted volume of traffic.

Times had been none too good in British North America since the depression of 1857. In the Maritimes the brave days of clipper ships and windjammers were drawing to a close; worse still, all the British colonies had been hit hard by the refusal of the United States to renew its Reciprocity Treaty with Canada in 1865.

In June more than six hundred delegates attended a great Reform Convention in Toronto to hear George Brown denounce the scoundrels who were misruling Canada and promise that in the first Dominion parliament the Reform Party would have no part of any coalition. And yet, for all the argument and trouble in the air, 1867 was in many ways little different from previous years.

A cold, rainy spring had given way to a lovely summer. Steamboat companies operated regular excursions between Collingwood and Fort William, Toronto and Rochester and Montreal and Quebec City. In June and July a Confederation excursion ran from Montreal to Halifax and Saint John, with return tickets selling for $16. In Montreal, the heat made businessmen forget convention and they walked to and from work with their jackets over their arms. In Ontario, farm horses dropped dead from heat exhaustion, but in spite of the weather Toronto haberdashers did a brisk business with Confederation Specials in silk toppers.

The Hamilton races were poorly attended that summer, but this may have been due more to heat than hard times. In May, when the G. F. Bailey & Co. Menagerie and Circus toured eastern Ontario, people came from miles around to see the "colossal hippopotamus."

Garrison cricket matches were held in Halifax, Saint John, Quebec City, Toronto and London, and in most cities of the new Dominion lacrosse, tennis and lawn bowling were popular. That spring for the first time baseball clubs were formed in Toronto, Hamilton (where the team was called the "Maple Leafs"), London and Guelph. At the more disreputable taverns, well-known customers could find cockfights.

American affairs were closely followed in the British provinces. The Civil War was over and the threatened invasion had not materialized, but most Canadians still regarded the United States as their natural enemy. Jefferson Davis, the former president of the Confederacy, was spending the summer in Canada in a cottage on the Niagara River, and there were rumours that a secret society of Union veterans, known as the Andersonville League, planned to assassinate him.

The Fenians, of course, were still on everyone's mind, and were one reason why Ontario was the province most strongly in favour of Confederation. This Irish-American group, dedicated to the cause of an independent Ireland, had recruited an alarming number of battle-hardened Civil War veterans. Only the previous year the Fenians had invaded Canada at Fort Erie and defeated a small force of Canadian militia near Ridgeway.

In border-town taverns Fenian agents were sometimes found late at night, leading groups of local toughs and drunkards in the chorus :

> We are a Fenian brotherhood,
>   skilled in the arts of war,
>
> And we're going to fight for Ireland,
>   the land that we adore.

> Many battles have we won
> along with the boys in blue,
> And we'll go and capture Canada,
> for we've nothing else to do.

But, although the Fenians had threatened to interfere with the Dominion Day celebrations, they didn't. In Ottawa, the capital, the birthday of the new nation was hailed at the stroke of midnight with fireworks, a huge bonfire, the playing of bands, the ringing of bells, and a hundred-and-one-gun salute. Crowds thronged the boardwalks until dawn, and dozens of all-night garden parties were held by Chinese-lantern light on the lawns of the larger houses.

Ottawa's historic moment came at eleven o'clock that morning when the governor-general, Lord Monck, arrived at the East Block of the new parliament buildings for the official ceremony. Prime Minister Macdonald was disappointed to find that his lordship had seen fit to turn up in plain civilian clothes.

For his part, Monck was irritable because Rideau Hall was not ready for him to move in. The building was undergoing extensive repairs, and his lordship had no intention of taking up residence until they were completed. He would "camp out," as he put it, in Rideau Hall just long enough to get the new government started. Then he would return to the Citadel of Quebec where he could live in comfort.

Two days earlier he had refused to see a delegation of Ottawa citizens who had wished to congratulate him on his appointment. He was still in no mood for ceremonial. Therefore, although a guard of honour was provided by the Rifle Brigade and a salute was fired by the Ottawa Field Battery, the proceedings in the Council Chamber on Canada's First Dominion Day were drab.

Lord Monck repeated the oath of office after Chief Justice Draper in a matter-of-fact voice; the first cabinet was sworn in; and then the governor-general sprang the only surprise of the morning. He announced that John A. Macdonald had been awarded the KCB and would henceforth be Sir John. Six other fathers of Confederation were made Companions of the Bath; they would have initials after their names but no Sir in front of them. They were Cartier, Galt, Tilley, Tupper, Howland and McDougall.

Later, Cartier and Galt, outraged that Macdonald had been honoured above themselves, refused the award angrily. But no shadow of this quarrel darkened Confederation day itself. In all four provinces there were parades, band concerts, and fireworks displays.

But some Maritimers had listened to Joseph Howe. A few Halifax shops remained defiantly open and some houses displayed black funeral crepe in mourning for Nova Scotia's lost independence. In Saint John, an anti-Confederation doctor flew his Union Jack at half-mast until a party of uniformed volunteers good-naturedly raised it for him. Such incidents were rare, even in areas where opposition to Confederation was strongest.

Lower Canada seemed surprisingly enthusiastic about Dominion Day. The Archbishop of Quebec issued a pastoral letter supporting Confederation. Montreal, long an annexationist stronghold, was more apathetic than Quebec City. On June 26 the mayor and committee of citizens responsible for the celebrations had resigned because no one would co-operate with them. Nevertheless, a fireworks display was staged that night at Viger Square and St. Denis Street. (There were some acid comments that the fireworks were "niggardly" and had cost only $1,000.)

The small towns and villages of Quebec's eastern counties celebrated more wholeheartedly than most French-speaking communities. Mr. Laberge, the *rouge* mayor of Dorchester, refused to take any part in a civic celebration and called Confederation "a public monstrosity" — but in most places throughout Lower Canada houses and town halls were bright with bunting and flags.

Ontario was jubilant. As the largest province, she expected to have a dominant influence in Confederation; her defence problems would be simplified; and her entrepreneurs looked forward greedily to the opening up of the West. In Toronto a whole ox was roasted at the foot of Church Street, there was a balloon ascension from Queen's Park, and the Thirteenth Hussars, the British regiment renowned as the "noble six hundred" of the Light Brigade at Balaklava, galloped past on review in all the pride of their blue and silver uniforms. In Hamilton, as darkness fell, four large fires were lit on the crest of the mountain.

The reeves of dozens of Ontario villages read the Queen's proclamation sharp at 11 A.M. The quiet streets, lined with maple trees, were decorated with arches, and under these passed in long procession the buggies of visitors from the outlying farms. Militia battalions paraded; politicians made speeches and the afternoon was given over to races and field sports. Picnic grounds filled up; there were heaping platters of sandwiches and cakes, lemonade for the children, and great granite-ware pots of tea and coffee for their parents. In the evening volunteer firemen held torchlight processions and, of course, the politicians made more speeches.

By and large, the day went off well everywhere in the Dominion.

Once Confederation was achieved, Macdonald and Brown stopped speaking to each other again, and party politics were resumed with all the old bitterness. On an April night in 1868 Thomas D'Arcy McGee, the eloquent prophet of union, was murdered on Sparks Street in Ottawa by P. J. Whelan, a Fenian fanatic. The following February a crowd turned out to witness Whelan's hanging, the last public execution in Canada.

Joseph Howe and the anti-Confederates swept Nova Scotia at the next general election and for a time Howe continued to rail at "the scoundrels who betrayed us." Within two years, however, Macdonald was able to talk him around. Howe never became a Canadian at heart, but he did stop threatening the dissolution of the Dominion.

The resentment of Cartier and Galt at Macdonald's KCB was overcome by the simple expedient of offering Cartier a baronetcy and Galt a KCMG. Henceforth, in the Dominion they had helped to build, they too would be called Sir.

Charles G. D. Roberts (1860-1943)

Roberts explored new territory in his animal stories, relating the psychologies of man and beast. He wrote on pioneer life in New Brunswick, and his knowledge of wildlife and the outdoors was extensive. This story is adapted from a piece in *Earth's Enigmas.*

DO SEEK THEIR MEAT FROM GOD

There was a solitary cabin in the thick of the woods a mile or more from the nearest neighbour, a substantial frame house in the midst of a large and well-tilled clearing. The owner of the cabin, a shiftless fellow who spent his days for the most part at the corner tavern three miles distant, had suddenly grown disgusted with a land wherein one must work to live, and had betaken himself with his seven-year-old boy to seek some more indolent clime.

The five-year-old son of the prosperous owner of the frame house and the older boy had been playmates. The little boy, unaware of his comrade's departure, had stolen away, late in the afternoon, along the lonely stretch of wood road, and had reached the cabin only to find it empty. As the dusk gathered, he grew afraid to start for home and crept trembling into the cabin, whose door would not stay shut. Desperate with fear and loneliness, he lifted up his voice piteously. In the terrifying silence, he listened hard to hear if anyone or anything were coming. Then again his shrill childish wailings arose, startling the unexpectant night, and piercing the forest depths, even to the ears of two great panthers which had set forth to seek their meat from God.

The lonely cabin stood some distance, perhaps a quarter of a mile, back from the highway connecting the settlements. Along this main road a man was plodding wearily. All day he had been walking, and now as he neared home his steps began to quicken with anticipation of rest. Over his shoulder projected a double-barrelled fowling-piece, from which was slung a bundle of such necessities as he had purchased in town that morning. It was the prosperous settler, the master of the frame house, who had chosen to make the tedious journey on foot.

He passed the mouth of the wood road leading to the cabin and had gone perhaps a furlong beyond, when his ears were startled by the sound of a child crying in the woods. He stopped, lowered his burden to the road, and stood straining ears and eyes in the direction of the sound. It was just at this time that the two panthers also stopped, and lifted their heads to listen. Their ears were keener than those of the man, and the sound had reached them at a greater distance.

Presently the settler realized whence the cries were coming. He called to mind the cabin; but he did not know the cabin's owner had departed. He cherished a hearty contempt for the drunken squatter; and on the drunken squatter's child he looked with small favour, especially as a playmate for his own boy. Nevertheless he hesitated before resuming his journey.

"Poor little fellow!" he muttered, half in wrath. "I reckon his precious father's drunk down at 'the Corners,' and him crying for loneliness!" Then he re-shouldered his burden and strode on doggedly.

But louder, shriller, more hopeless and more appealing, arose the childish voice, and the settler paused again, irresolute, and with deepening indignation. In his fancy he saw the steaming supper his wife would have awaiting him. He loathed the thought of retracing his steps, and then stumbling a quarter of a mile through the stumps and bog of the wood road. He was foot-sore as well as hungry, and he cursed the vagabond squatter with serious emphasis; but in that wailing was a terror which would not let him go on. He thought of his own little one left in such a position, and straightway his heart melted. He turned, dropped his bundle behind some bushes, grasped his gun, and made speed back for the cabin.

"Who knows," he said to himself, "but that drunken idiot has left his youngster without a bite to eat in the whole miserable shanty? Or maybe he's locked out, and the poor little beggar's half scared to death. Sounds as if he was scared." And at this thought the settler quickened his pace.

As the hungry panthers drew near the cabin, and the cries of the lonely child grew clearer, they hastened their steps, and their eyes opened to a wider circle, flaming with a greener fire. It would be thoughtless superstition to say the beasts were cruel. They were simply keen with hunger, and alive with the eager passion of the chase. They were not ferocious with any anticipation of battle, for they knew the voice was the voice of a child, and something in the voice told them the child was solitary. Theirs was no hideous or unnatural rage, as it is the custom to describe it. They were but seeking with the strength, the cunning, the deadly swiftness given them to that end, the food convenient for them. On their success in accomplishing that for which nature had so exquisitely designed them, depended not only their own, but the lives of their blind and helpless young, now whimpering in the cave on the slope of the moonlit ravine. They crept through a wet alder thicket, bounded lightly over the ragged brush fence, and paused to reconnoitre on the edge of the clearing, in the full glare of the moon. At the same moment, the settler emerged from the darkness of the wood road on the opposite side of the clearing. He saw the two great beasts, heads down and snouts thrust forward, gliding towards the open cabin door.

For a few moments the child had been silent. Now his voice rose again in pitiful appeal, a very ecstasy of loneliness and terror. There was a note in the cry that shook the settler's soul. He had a vision of his own boy, at home with his mother, safeguarded from even the thought of peril. And here was this little one left to the wild beasts ! "Thank God ! Thank God I came !" murmured the settler, as he dropped on one knee to take a surer aim. There was a loud report (not like the sharp crack of a rifle), and the female panther, shot through the loins, fell in a heap, snarling furiously and striking with her forepaws.

The male walked around her in fierce and anxious amazement. Presently, as the smoke lifted, he discerned the settler kneeling for a second shot. With a high screech of fury, the lithe brute sprang upon his enemy, taking a bullet full in his chest without seeming to know he was hit. Ere the man could slip in another cartridge the beast was upon him, bearing him to the ground and fixing keen fangs in his shoulder. Without a word, the man set his strong fingers desperately into the brute's throat, wrenched himself partly free, and was struggling to rise, when the panther's body collapsed upon him all at once, a dead weight he easily flung aside. The bullet had done its work just in time.

Quivering from the swift and dreadful contest, bleeding profusely from his mangled shoulder, the settler stepped up to the cabin door and peered in. He heard sobs in the darkness.

"Don't be scared, sonny," he said, in a reassuring voice. "I'm going to take you home along with me. Poor little lad, I'll look after you, if folks that ought to don't."

Out of the dark corner came a shout of delight, in a voice which made the settler's heart stand still. "Daddy, Daddy," it said, "I knew you'd come. I was so frightened when it got dark !" And a little figure launched itself into the settler's arms, and clung to him trembling. The man sat down on the threshold and strained the child to his breast. He remembered how near he had been to disregarding the far-off cries, and great beads of sweat broke out upon his forehead.

Not many weeks afterwards the settler was following the fresh trail of a bear which had killed his sheep. The trail led him at last along the slope of a deep ravine, from whose bottom came the brawl of a swollen and obstructed stream. In the ravine he found a shallow cave, behind a great white rock. The cave was plainly a wild beast's lair, and then he entered circumspectly. There were bones scattered about, and on some dry herbage in the deepest corner of the den, he found the dead bodies of two small panther cubs.

(Earth's Enigmas)

Goldwin Smith (1823-1910)

Historian, political journalist and professor at the University of Toronto, Smith is regarded as being Canada's first essayist.

THE POLITICAL DESTINY OF CANADA

Canadian nationality being a lost cause, the ultimate union of Canada with the United States appears now to be morally certain; so that nothing is left for Canadian patriotism but to provide that it shall be a union indeed, and not an annexation; an equal and honourable alliance like that of Scotland and England, not a submission of the weaker to the stronger; and at the same time that the political change shall involve no change of any other kind in the relations of Canada with her mother country. The filaments of union are spreading daily, though they may be more visible to the eye of one who sees Canada at intervals than to that of a constant resident. Intercourse is being increased by the extension of railways; the ownership and management of the railways themselves are forming an American interest in Canada; New York is becoming the pleasure, and, to some extent, even the business, capital of Canadians; American watering-places are becoming their summer resort; the periodical literature of the States, which is conducted with extraordinary spirit and ability, is extending its circulation on the northern side of the line; and the Canadians who settle in the States are multiplying the links of family connection between the two countries. To specify the time at which a political event will take place is hardly ever possible, however assured the event itself may be; and in the present instance the occurrence depends not only on the circumstances of Canada, where, as we have seen, there is a great complication of secondary forces, but on the circumstances of the United States. If the commercial depression which at present prevails in Canada continues or recurs; if Canadian manufacturers are seen to be dying under the action of the customs-line; if owing to the depression or to over-costly undertakings, such as the Pacific Railway, financial difficulties arise; if, meantime, the balance of prosperity, which is now turning, shall have turned decisively in favour of the United States, and the reduction of their debt shall have continued at the present rate — the critical moment may arrive, and the politicians, recognizing the voice of Destiny, may pass in a body to the side of continental union. It will be fortunate if a misunderstanding between the Canadian Government and Downing Street, about some question such as that respecting the pecuniary claims of British Columbia, which is now assuming such exaggerated proportions, does not supervene to make the final dissolution of the political tie a quarrel instead of an amicable separation.

To Canada the economical advantages of continental union will be immense; to the United States its general advantages will not be less so. To England it will be no menace, but the reverse; it will be the introduction into the councils of the United States, on all questions, commercial as well as diplomatic, of an element friendly to England, the influence of which will be worth far more to her than the faint and invidious chance of building up Canada as a rival to the United States. In case of war, her greatest danger will be removed. She will lose neither wealth nor strength; probably she will gain a good deal of both.

(The Political Destiny of Canada)

Ralph Connor (1860-1937)

Connor was the pen name of Charles William Gordon, clergyman. His Glengarry novels of pioneer life in Ontario were so popular that he made a small fortune from his writing, some fifteen novels in all. His work was noted for its pioneer challenge and optimism.

THE CRISIS

The new master was quick of temper, and was determined at all costs to exact full and prompt obedience. There was more flogging done those first six days than during any six months of Archie Munro's rule. Sometimes the floggings amounted to little, but sometimes they were serious, and when those fell upon the smaller boys, the girls would weep and the bigger boys would grind their teeth and swear.

The situation became so acute that Murdie Cameron and the big boys decided that they would quit the school. They were afraid the temptation to throw the master out would some day be more than they could bear, and for men who had played their part, not without credit, in the Scotch River fights, to carry out the master would have been an exploit hardly worthy of them. So, in dignified contempt of the master and his rules, they left the school after the third day.

Their absence did not help matters much; indeed, the master appeared to be relieved, and proceeded to tame the school into submission. It was little Jimmie Cameron who precipitated the crisis. Jimmie's nose, upon which he relied when struggling with his snickers, had an unpleasant trick of failing him at critical moments, and of letting out explosive snorts of the most disturbing kind. He had finally been warned that upon his next outburst punishment would fall.

It was Friday afternoon, the drowsy hour just before recess, while the master was explaining to the listless Euclid class the mysteries of the forty-seventh proposition, that suddenly a snort of unusual violence burst upon the school. Immediately every eye was upon the master, for all had heard and had noted his threat to Jimmie.

"James, was that you, sir?"

There was no answer, except such as could be gathered from Jimmie's very red and very shamed face.

"James, stand up!"

Jimmie wriggled to his feet, and stood, a heap of various angles.

"Now, James, you remember what I promised you? Come here, sir!"

Jimmie came slowly to the front, growing paler at each step, and stood with a dazed look on his face, before the master. He had never been thrashed in all his life. At home the big brothers might cuff him good-naturedly, or his mother thump him on the head with her thimble, but a serious whipping was to him an unknown horror.

The master drew forth his heavy black strap with impressive deliberation and ominous silence. The preparations for punishment itself would not amount to much. Not so Jimmie. He stood numb with fear and horrible expectation. The master lifted up the strap.

"James, hold out your hand !"
Jimmie promptly clutched his hand behind his back.

"Hold out your hand, sir, at once !" No answer.

"James, you must do as you are told. Your punishment for disobedience will be much severer than for laughing." But Jimmie stood pale, silent, with his hands tight clasped behind his back.

The master stepped forward, and grasping the little boy's arm, tried to pull his hand to the front; but Jimmie, with a roar like that of a young bull, threw himself flat on his face on the floor and put his hands under him. The school burst into a laugh of triumph, which increased the master's embarrassment and rage.

"Silence !" he said, "or it will be a worse matter for some of you than for James."

Then turning his attention to Jimmie, he lifted him from the floor and tried to pull out his hand. But Jimmie kept his arms folded tight across his breast, roaring vigorously the while, and saying over and over, "Go away from me ! Go away from me, I tell you ! I'm not taking anything to do with you."

The big boys were enjoying the thing immensely. The master's rage was deepening in proportion. He felt it would never do to be beaten. His whole authority was at stake.

"Now, James," he reasoned, "you see you are only making it worse for yourself. I cannot allow any disobedience in the school. You must hold out your hand."

But Jimmie, realizing that he had come off best in the first round, stood doggedly sniffing, his arms still folded tight.

"Now, James, I shall give you one more chance. Hold out your hand."

Jimmie remained like a statue.

Whack ! came the heavy strap over his shoulders. At once Jimmy set up his refrain, "Go away from me, I tell you ! I'm not taking anything to do with you !"

Whack! whack! whack! fell the strap with successive blows, each heavier than the last. There was no longer any laughing in the school. The affair was growing serious. The girls were beginning to sob, and the bigger boys to grow pale.

"Now, James, will you hold out your hand? You see how much worse you are making it for yourself," said the master, who was heartily sick of the struggle, which he felt to be undignified, and the result of which he feared was dubious.

But Jimmie only kept up his cry, now punctuated with sobs, "I'm-not-taking-anything-to-do-with-you."

"Jimmy, listen to me," said the master. "You must hold out your hand. I cannot have boys refusing to obey me in this school." But Jimmie caught the entreaty in the tone, and knowing that the battle was nearly over, kept obstinately silent.

"Well, then," said the master, suddenly, "you must take it," and lifting the strap, he laid it with such sharp emphasis over Jimmie's shoulders that Jimmie's voice rose in a wilder roar than usual, and the girls burst into audible weeping.

Suddenly, above all the hubbub, rose a voice, clear and sharp.

"Stop!" It was Thomas Finch, of all people, standing with face white and tense, and regarding the master with steady eyes.

The school gazed thunderstruck at the usually slow and stolid Thomas.

"What do you mean, sir?" said the master, gladly turning from Jimmie. But Thomas stood silent, as much surprised as the master at his sudden exclamation.

He stood hesitating for a moment, and then said, "You can thrash me in his place. He's a little chap, and has never been thrashed."

The master misunderstood his hesitation for fear, pushed Jimmie aside, threw down his strap, and seized a birch rod.

"Come forward, sir! I'll put an end to your insubordination, at any rate. Hold out your hand!"

Thomas held out his hand till the master finished one birch rod.

"The other hand, sir!"

Another birch rod was used up, but Thomas neither uttered a sound nor made a move till the master had done, then he asked, in a strained voice, "Were you going to give Jimmie all that, sir?"

The master caught the biting sneer in the tone, and lost himself completely.

"Do you dare to answer me back?" he cried. He opened his desk, took out a rawhide, and without waiting to ask for his hand began to lay the rawhide about Thomas's shoulders and legs, till he was out of breath.

"Now, perhaps you will learn your place, sir," he said.

"Thank you", said Thomas, looking him steadily in the eye.

"You are welcome. And I'll give you as much more whenever you show that you need it." The slight laugh with which he closed this brutal speech made Thomas wince as he had not during his whole terrible thrashing, but still he had not a word to say.

"Now, James, come here!" said the master turning to Jimmie "You see what happens when a boy is insubordinate." Jimmie came trembling. "Hold out your hand!" Out came Jimmie's hand at once. Whack! fell the strap.

"The other!"

"Stop it!" roared Thomas. "I took his thrashing."

"The other!" said the master, ignoring Thomas.

With a curious savage snarl Thomas sprung at him. The master, however, was on the alert, and swinging round, met him with a straight facer between the eyes, and Thomas went to the floor.

"Aha! my boy! I'll teach you something you have yet to learn."

For answer came another cry, "Come on, boys!" It was Ranald Macdonald, coming over the seats, followed by Don Cameron, Billy Ross, and some smaller boys. The master turned to meet them.

"Come along!" he said, backing up to his desk. "But I warn you it's not a strap or a rawhide I shall use."

Ranald paid no attention to his words, but came straight toward him, and when at arm's length, sprung at him with the cry, "Horo, boys!"

But before he could lay his hands upon the master, he received a blow straight on the bridge of the nose that staggered him back, stunned and bleeding. By this time Thomas was up again, and rushing in was received in like manner, and fell back over a bench.

"How do you like it, boys?" smiled the master. "Come right along."

The boys obeyed his invitation, approaching him, but more warily, and awaiting their chance to rush. Suddenly Thomas, with a savage snarl, put his head down and rushed in beneath the master's guard, paid no attention to the heavy blow he received on the head and, locking his arms round the master's middle, buried his head close into his chest.

At once Ranald and Billy Ross threw themselves upon the struggling pair and carried them to the floor, the master underneath. There was a few moments of fierce struggling and then the master lay still, with the four boys holding him down for dear life.

It was Thomas who assumed command.

"Don't choke him so, Ranald," he said. "And clear out of the way, all you girls and little chaps."

"What are you going to do, Thomas ?" asked Don, acknowledging Thomas's new-born leadership.

"Tie him up," said Thomas.   "Get me a sash."

At once two or three little boys rushed to the hooks and brought one or two of the knitted sashes that hung there, and Thomas proceeded to tie the master's legs.

While he was thus busily engaged, a shadow darkened the door, and a voice exclaimed, "What is all this about ?" It was the minister, who had been driving past and had come upon the terrified, weeping children rushing home.

"Is that you, Thomas ?   And you, Don ?"

The boys let go their hold and stood up, shamed but defiant.

Immediately the master was on his feet, and with a swift, fierce blow, caught Thomas on the chin.   Thomas, taken off his guard, fell with a thud on the floor.

"Stop that, young man !" said the minister, catching his arm "That's a coward's blow."

"Hands off !" said the master, shaking himself free and squaring up to him.

"Ye would, would ye ?" said the minister, gripping him by the neck and shaking him as he might a child.   "Lift ye'r hand to me, would ye ?   I'll break ye'r back to ye, and that I will." So saying, the minister seized him by the arms and held him absolutely helpless.   The master ceased to struggle, and put down his hands.

"Ay, ye'd better, my man," said the minister, giving him a fling backward.

Meantime Don had been holding snow to Thomas's head, and had brought him round.

"Now, then," said the minister to the boys, "What does all this mean ?"

The boys were all silent, but the master spoke.

"It is a case of rank and impudent insubordination, sir, and I demand the expulsion of those impudent rascals."

"Well, sir," said the minister, "be sure there will be a thorough investigation, and I greatly misjudge the case if there are not faults on both sides. And for one thing, the man who can strike such a cowardly blow as you did a moment ago would not be unlikely to be guilty of injustice and cruelty."

"It is none of your business," said the master, insolently.

"You will find that I shall make it my business," said the minister. "And now, boys, be off to your homes, and be here Monday morning at nine o'clock, when this matter shall be gone into."

(Glengarry School Days)

William Arthur Deacon (Born in 1890)

For many years Deacon was literary editor of the *Mail and Empire*, and later of the *Globe and Mail*. He had also written for *Saturday Night*. His books include *The Four Jameses, My Vision of Canada*, and *Poteen*.

THE FOUR JAMESES

James McIntyre was living in Ingersoll when cheese-making began there, and he witnessed the triumphant expansion of the industry in the late seventies and eighties. Then it was that the farmers, exuberant over the new-found source of wealth, were at the pitch of their enthusiasm for the enterprise. Probably more cheese is now made in Ingersoll than McIntyre ever dreamed of — and he was bold in prophecy — but the inhabitants take it more prosaically. They are busier now in scientific merchandising than in trying to make monuments that, in their assault on the eye, may capture the imagination also, and impress the world with the jubilant news of their economic salvation. Then, however, in their delirious ecstasy, it was most natural that they should have endeavoured to manufacture for display the largest cheese ever moulded by man; and history does not say they failed. This monster production weighed over seven thousand pounds. It doubtless accomplished the object of its makers ; but it is doubtful whether it would have been widely remembered if it had not thrilled James McIntyre to the point of composing his immortal :

QUEEN OF CHEESE

We have seen thee, queen of cheese,
Lying quietly at your ease,
Gently fanned by evening breeze,
Thy fair form no flies dare seize.

All gaily dressed soon you'll go
To the great Provincial show,
To be admired by many a beau
In the city of Toronto.

Cows numerous as a swarm of bees,
Or as the leaves upon the trees
It did require to make thee please,
And stand unrivaled, queen of cheese.

May you not receive a scar as
We have heard that Mr. Harris
Intends to send you off as far as
The great world's show at Paris.

Of the youth beware of these,
For some of them might rudely squeeze
And bite your cheek, then songs or gless
We could not sing, Oh ! queen of cheese.

Wert thou suspended from balloon,
You'd cast a shade even at noon,
Folks would think it was the moon
About to fall and crush them soon.

This monstrous lump of edible matter was a constant inspiration to McIntyre, for his poet's eye rightly saw it as a symbol of the glory of his community ; and in another poem he explains just why a big cheese represents virtues that a little cheese cannot.

The romance that underlay this development, that was perceived by the poet, and caused him to dedicate his pen to its expression, began with the wretched state of agriculture in that section about the middle of the nineteenth century. The forests had been wiped out ; the land had been long tilled, and was suffering badly from unscientific over-production of wheat. The hopes of the pioneers seemed, for the time, to have been misplaced. The farmers were discouraged. Also, when matters were at their worst, disturbing rumours came back to them from those who had gone to the Canadian West.

The problem was to find some cheap fertilizer for the depleted soil. Cheese offered the ideal solution. Canada then imported it in great quantities. A man by the name of Ranney, who "began with just two cows" in 1856, soon had a large herd, plenty of natural fertilizer, and a most valuable by-product in the cheese he made on his farm on the dairy plan. Ten years after Ranney's start Farrington, in 1866, at the time plans for Confederation were in final shape, was the first to make this form of manufacturing his sole business, and thus spread the prosperity that had come to Ranney.

This move revolutionized agriculture in that part of Ontario, and brought the farmers suddenly from despair to affluence.

Octave Crémazie (1827-1879)

Considéré comme le père de la poésie canadienne, ce libraire de Québec s'est acquis au milieu du siècle dernier une célébrité considérable par ses poésies historiques et patriotiques. Il dut s'exiler en 1862 pour fuir la justice et vécut pauvrement en France jusqu'à sa mort. Casgrain a publié en 1882 ses *Oeuvres complètes,* y compris sa correspondance dont est tiré le texte qui suit.

LETTRE À CASGRAIN

29 janvier 1867

Plus je réfléchis sur les destinées de la littérature canadienne, moins je lui trouve de chances de laisser une trace dans l'histoire. Ce qui manque au Canada, c'est d'avoir une langue à lui. Si nous parlions iroquois ou huron, notre littérature vivrait. Malheureusement nous parlons et écrivons d'une assez piteuse façon, il est vrai, la langue de Bossuet et de Racine. Nous avons beau dire et beau faire, nous ne serons toujours, au point de vue littéraire, qu'une simple colonie; et quand bien même le Canada deviendrait un pays indépendant et ferait briller son drapeau au soleil des nations, nous n'en demeurerions pas moins de simples colons littéraires. Voyez la Belgique, qui parle la même langue que nous. Est-ce qu'il y a une littérature belge ? Ne pouvant lutter avec la France pour la beauté de la forme, le Canada aurait pu conquérir sa place au milieu des littératures du vieux monde, si parmi ses enfants il s'était trouvé un écrivain capable d'initier, avant Fenimore Cooper, l'Europe à la grandiose nature de nos forêts, aux exploits légendaires de nos trappeurs et de nos voyageurs.

Aujourd'hui, quand bien même un talent aussi puissant que celui de l'auteur du *Dernier des Mohicans* se révélerait parmi nous, ses oeuvres ne produiraient aucune sensation en Europe, car il aurait l'irréparable tort d'arriver le second, c'est-à-dire trop tard. Je le répète, si nous parlions huron ou iroquois, les travaux de nos écrivains attireraient l'attention du vieux monde. Cette langue mâle et nerveuse, née dans les forêts de l'Amérique, aurait cette poésie du cru qui fait les délices de l'étranger. On se pâmerait devant un roman ou un poème traduit de l'iroquois, tandis que l'on ne prend pas la peine de lire un livre écrit en français par un colon de Québec ou de Montréal. Depuis vingt ans, on publie chaque année, en France, des traductions de romans russes, scandinaves, roumains. Supposez ces mêmes livres écrits en français, ils ne trouveraient pas cinquante lecteurs.

La traduction a cela de bon, c'est que si un ouvrage ne nous semble pas à la hauteur de sa réputation, on a toujours la consolation de se dire que ça doit être magnifique dans l'original.

Mais qu'importe après tout que les oeuvres des auteurs canadiens soient destinées à ne pas franchir l'Atlantique. Ne sommes-nous pas un million de Français oubliés par la mère patrie sur les bords du Saint-Laurent ? N'est-ce pas assez pour encourager tous ceux qui tiennent une plume que de savoir que ce petit peuple grandira et qu'il gardera toujours le nom et la mémoire de ceux qui l'auront aidé à conserver intact le plus précieux de tous les trésors : la langue de ses aïeux ?

Quand le père de famille, après les fatigues de la journée, raconte à ses nombreux enfants les aventures et les accidents de sa longue vie, pourvu que ceux qui l'entourent s'amusent et s'instruisent en écoutant ses récits, il ne s'inquiète pas si le riche propriétaire du manoir voisin connaîtra ou ne connaîtra pas les douces et naïves histoires qui font le charme de son foyer. Ses enfants sont heureux de l'entendre, c'est tout ce qu'il demande.

Il en doit être ainsi de l'écrivain canadien. Renonçant sans regret aux beaux rêves d'une gloire retentissante, il doit se regarder comme amplement récompensé de ses travaux s'il peut instruire et charmer ses compatriotes, s'il peut contribuer à la conservation, sur la jeune terre d'Amérique, de la vieille nationalité française.

Maintenant, parlons un peu de M. Thibault et de sa critique de mes oeuvres. Le jeune écrivain a certainement du talent, et je le félicite d'avoir su blâmer franchement ce qui lui a semblé mauvais dans mon petit bagage poétique. Dans une de mes lettres je vous disais que ce qui manquait à notre littérature, c'était une critique sérieuse. Grâce à M. Thibault, qui a su faire autrement et mieux que ses prédécesseurs, la critique canadienne sortira bientôt de la voie ridicule dans laquelle elle a marché jusqu'à ce jour. M. le professeur de l'Ecole normale n'a que des éloges pour toutes les pièces qui ont précédé la *Promenade de trois morts*. Ses appréciations ne sont pas toutes conformes aux miennes, mais comme un père ne voit pas les défauts de ses enfants, je confesse humblement que le critique qui est tout à fait désintéressé dans la question doit être un meilleur juge que moi. Pour M. Thibault, comme pour beaucoup de mes compatriotes, *le Drapeau de Carillon* est un *magnifique poème historique*. Je crois vous l'avoir déjà dit : à mon avis, c'est une pauvre affaire, comme valeur littéraire, que ce *Drapeau* qui a *volé sur toutes les lèvres,* d'après mon bienveillant critique. Ce qui a fait la fortune de ce petit poème, c'est l'idée seule, car, pour la forme, il ne vaut pas cher. Il faut bien le dire, dans notre pays on n'a pas le goût très délicat en fait de poésie. Faites rimer un certain nombre de fois *gloire* avec *victoire, aïeux* avec *glorieux, France* avec *espérance;* entremêlez ces rimes de quelques mots sonores comme notre *religion,* notre *patrie,* notre *langue,* nos *lois,* le *sang de nos pères;* faites chauffer le tout à la flamme du patriotisme, et servez chaud. Tout le monde dira que c'est magnifique. Quant à moi, je crois que si je n'avais pas autre chose pour me recommander comme poète que ce malheureux *Drapeau de Carillon,* il y a longtemps que ma petite réputation serait morte et enterrée aux yeux des littérateurs sérieux. A la vogue du *magnifique poème historique,* comparez l'accueil si froid qui fut fait à la pièce intitulée *les Morts.* Elle parut, 1er novembre 1856, dans le *Journal de Québec.* Pas une seule autre feuille n'en souffla mot, et pourtant, c'est bien ce que j'ai fait de moins mal. L'année suivante, Chauveau reproduisit cette pièce dans le *Journal de l'Instruction publique,* et deux ou trois journaux en parlèrent dans ce style de réclame qui sert à faire l'éloge d'un pantalon nouveau tout aussi bien que d'un poème inédit.

M. Thibault me reproche de n'avoir pas donné, dans *la Fiancée du marin,* plus de vigueur d'âme à mes héroïnes et de ne pas leur faire supporter plus chrétiennement leur malheur. Si la mère et la jeune fille trouvaient dans la religion une consolation à leur désespoir, ce serait plus moral, sans doute, mais où serait le drame ? Cette légende n'en serait plus une, ce ne serait plus que le récit d'un accident comme il en arrive dans toutes les familles. On ne fait pas de poèmes, encore bien moins des légendes, avec les faits journaliers de la vie. D'ailleurs, la mère tombe à l'eau par accident et la fiancée ne se précipite dans les flots que lorsque son âme a déjà sombré dans la folie. Où donc la morale est-elle méconnue dans tout ce petit poème ? La morale est une grande chose, mais il ne faut pas essayer de la mettre là où elle n'a que faire. M. Thibault doit bien savoir que lorsque la folie s'empare d'un cerveau malade, cette pauvre morale n'a plus qu'à faire son paquet.

Si le critique du *Courrier du Canada* est tout miel pour mes premiers écrits, ce n'est que pour mieux tomber à bras raccourci sur mes pauvres *Trois morts,* qui n'en peuvent mais.

Les dieux littéraires de M. Thibault ne sont pas les miens; cramponné à la littérature classique, il rejette loin de lui cette malheureuse école romantique, et c'est à peine s'il daigne reconnaître qu'elle a produit quelques oeuvres remarquables. Pour moi, tout en admirant les immortels chefs-d'oeuvre du XVIIe siècle, j'aime de toutes mes forces cette école romantique qui a fait éprouver à mon âme les jouissances les plus douces et les plus pures qu'elle ait jamais senties. Et encore aujourd'hui, lorsque la mélancolie enveloppe mon âme comme un manteau de plomb, la lecture d'une méditation de Lamartine ou d'une nuit d'Alfred de Musset me donne plus de calme et de sérénité que je ne saurais en trouver dans toutes les tragédies de Corneille et de Racine. Lamartine et Musset sont des hommes de mon temps. Leurs illusions, leurs rêves, leurs aspirations, leurs regrets trouvent un écho sonore dans mon âme, parce que moi, chétif, à une distance énorme de ces grands génies, j'ai caressé les mêmes illusions, je me suis bercé dans les mêmes rêves et j'ai ouvert mon coeur aux mêmes aspirations pour adoucir l'amertume des mêmes regrets. Quel lien peut-il y avoir entre moi et les héros des tragédies ? En quoi la destinée de ces rois, de ces reines peut-elle m'intéresser ? Le style du poète est splendide, il flatte mon oreille et enchante mon esprit; mais les idées de ces hommes d'un autre temps ne disent rien ni à mon âme, ni à mon coeur.

Le romantisme n'est après tout que le fils légitime des classiques; seulement les idées et les moeurs n'étant plus au XIXe siècle ce qu'elles étaient au XVIIe, l'école romantique a dû nécessairement adopter une forme plus en harmonie avec les aspirations modernes, et les éléments de cette forme nouvelle, c'est au XVIe siècle qu'elle est allée les demander. Le classique, si je puis m'exprimer ainsi, c'est le grand-père que l'on vénère, parce qu'il est le *père de votre père,* mais qui ne peut prétendre à cette tendresse profonde que l'on réserve pour celui qui aida notre mère à guider nos premiers pas dans le chemin de la vie . . .

(Oeuvres complètes, 1882)

Louis Dantin (1865-1945)

Eugène Seers fut prêtre, Père du Saint-Sacrement, perdit la foi et s'exila aux Etats-Unis où il vécut pauvrement.

Poète et romancier, il est surtout connu comme critique et il a exercé une grande influence sur les poètes de la génération de Desrochers.

LA LANGUE FRANÇAISE
NOTRE INSTRUMENT D'EXPRESSION
LITTÉRAIRE

On m'a prié d'adresser à cette réunion quelques brèves paroles comportant, m'a-t-on dit, quelques conseils sur l'art d'écrire. C'est une tâche qui, à première vue, semble aisée entre toutes. Est-il chose plus facile que donner des conseils ? Il suffit d'énoncer, avec la gravité qu'il faut, quelques principes généraux, reconnus de tous, traînant déjà dans des traités et des manuels sans nombre. S'il s'agit de littérature, on se rappelle assez d'Horace, de Bouhours et de Verniolles pour former un bouquet de loyaux préceptes dont chacun est aussi solide que les commandements de Moïse. Mais ce genre de conseils est stérile autant que facile; ce n'est pas, j'en suis sûr, celui que vous attendez de moi. Vous voulez que je prenne, parmi des questions définies, des problèmes actuels intéressant la littérature canadienne, quelque point circonscrit qui mérite d'être élucidé, où un bon conseil montrant la voie immédiate à nos écrivains, serait pratiquement et spécifiquement utilisable.

Vous surprendrais-je en vous disant qu'à mon avis aucune question n'est aussi opportune, aussi importante pour nos lettres que celle de notre langue littéraire ? C'est une cause, il est vrai, qu'on pourrait croire toute décidée. Mais depuis quelque temps, des doutes et des équivoques l'obscurcissent et tendraient à en faire un sujet de dispute. C'est ce qui me suggère de la reprendre en ce moment et d'en faire la matière d'un unique conseil. Et ce conseil est celui-ci :

« Quels que soient les chemins où s'engage notre littérature, qu'elle garde comme son instrument d'expression, qu'elle protège contre toute corruption intime ou étrangère la langue du Canada français, autrement dit la langue française. »

Les jeunes littérateurs qui appellent vaguement je ne sais quelle évolution, je ne sais quelle transformation de notre langage au profit d'idéals strictement nationaux, sont animés d'excellentes intentions — je le sais, car j'en compte parmi mes meilleurs amis; — mais je crois qu'ils caressent une dangereuse chimère. Une littérature ne brise pas impunément avec tout son passé. Elle ne recommence pas, à peine adulte, un effort qui lui a déjà tant coûté. Il n'y a pour elle qu'un salut, qu'un gage d'avenir : tracer plus profond et plus large le sillon déjà entrouvert; continuer avec les mêmes armes la lutte jusqu'ici soutenue. Cela manque tout à fait de nouveauté, n'est-ce pas ? Mais la marche d'une littérature n'est pas une suite de sensations : c'est le progrès d'un travail patient et accumulé. Notre race est née, a grandi, liée au langage de la France, défendue et sauvée par lui. Le français qu'elle parlait, c'est ce qui, plus que tout le reste, lui a gardé son individualité, sa permanence distincte parmi les autres races qui l'entouraient et la débordaient. Le jour où ce langage se diluera, acceptera un amalgame quelconque, ce jour verra la fin de notre identité ethnique, et notre survivance tant vantée ne sera plus qu'un souvenir. La langue, la littérature et la race auront péri ensemble.

Quelle confusion pourtant on arrive à jeter dans un axiome si certain ! Quels curieux prétextes l'on donne à ces projets rénovateurs !

D'aucuns partent de l'assertion que la France d'outre-mer nous est devenue étrangère, que ses traits, ses tendances ne répondent plus aux nôtres. Et dès lors, concluent-ils, sa tutelle sur nous se trouve de plein droit périmée. Il nous faut désormais un canadianisme indépendant et intégral.

Mais qui songe à baser notre attitude envers notre langue sur une vassalité quelconque à l'égard de la France lointaine ? On est libre d'avoir pour celle-ci tous les sentiments que l'on veut, libre même d'oublier que son sang persiste en nos veines. Mais ce n'est pas pour elle que cette cause est plaidée. — Il nous faut garder notre langue simplement parce que c'est la nôtre, celle de la France américaine que nous sommes et que définissait si bien le poète que nous regrettons :

Ma France, c'est mon pays.

N'est-ce pas assez que cette langue ait été parlée par nos aïeux et par nos mères; qu'elle règne encore maîtresse parmi leurs deux millions de fils ? N'est-elle pas à ce titre seul la vraie, l'unique langue canadienne ?

Cela n'implique envers la France que cette dépendance très restreinte, dépendance de logique, de nécessité intrinsèque, que notre langue, dans son accroissement, suive l'évolution de la souche-mère, garde avec elle assez de liaison, d'échange, pour que l'unité essentielle ne soit pas brisée. Il ne peut y avoir deux langues françaises notablement diverses; et ce sera toujours Paris, et non Montréal ou Sherbrooke, qui devra dire le dernier mot sur ce qui est français et ce qui ne l'est pas. — Mais cette régence n'impose aucune servitude. Dans notre monde moderne, où toutes les nations sont voisines, il se fera naturellement par le voyage, le commerce et le livre, une pénétration réciproque qui, d'elle seule, maintiendra l'unité linguistique entre la France et nous. — N'est-ce pas de cette façon que notre langue évolue, en fait, depuis cent cinquante ans ? Notre français n'est plus celui de Champlain ou d'Etienne Parent : il a suivi spontanément, et sans aucune pression externe, tous les courants qui, depuis eux, ont entraîné la langue de France. Quand je lis une page historique de l'abbé Groulx ou une strophe d'Alfred Desrochers ou de Robert Choquette, j'y retrouve toutes les formes, toutes les inflexions du français vingtième siècle. Ainsi la langue des nôtres s'enrichit, se transforme, mais en accord à son verbe d'origine; elle le fait sans effort, inconsciemment presque, et elle n'a pour cela qu'à suivre son instinct.

D'autres doutent que la langue française, privée ainsi d'évolution distincte, puisse exprimer adéquatement l'âme et la pensée de chez nous. Mais, de grâce, ne nous faisons pas d'inquiétude là-dessus. La

langue française, comme toutes les langues modernes, mais mieux
encore qu'aucune autre, est un outil universel apte à toutes les besognes,
un instrument multiple capable de rendre tous les sons. Elle n'a pas
été faite pour les Français tout seuls; elle est cosmopolite; elle s'exerce
depuis des siècles à accumuler des symboles embrassant toute l'échelle
des êtres, toute la vision, toute l'émotion que puisse éprouver l'âme
humaine. Ses génies ne sont pas enclos dans le cercle des choses françaises : ils ont exprimé l'univers par la philosophie, la poésie, la découverte, la science. N'ayez donc crainte que nos spectacles ne trouvent
pas assez de couleurs dans la palette de Gautier ou de Loti; que notre
âme éprouve des élans que n'eussent pu exprimer Pascal, Rousseau,
Hugo ou Léon Bloy; que notre vie ait des détours qui eussent embar-
rassé Daudet ou Barrès. Si vous n'avez pas trouvé dans Larousse le
mot exact qu'il vous fallait pour peindre un coin de notre sol, une
nuance de notre être intime, soyez sûrs que vous n'avez pas assez
cherché. Vous avez d'ailleurs la ressource, dans des thèmes qui le
comportent, d'appeler au secours notre langue populaire, où certains
aspects sociaux se refléteront plus vivement. Mais notez que ces mots
normands, picards ou poitevins, seront eux-mêmes des mots de France,
ne seront devenus canadiens qu'en passant par vos lèvres; qu'il n'y
a pas cent mots de notre dialecte qui soient vraiment de notre cru et
esquivent tout à fait notre dette française. Car vous ne comptez pas
pour créations originales des emprunts maladroits, grossiers, à la langue britannique, simples aveux d'ignorance ou de paresse, greffes
hybrides qui corrompent la sève au lieu de l'enrichir.

Surtout, ne donnez pas dans cette effarante équivoque qui con-
fondrait d'emblée la langue de nos champs, de nos rues et de nos
usines avec celle de nos lettres, qui voudrait que tous nos écrits adop-
tassent l'idiome natif comme moyen normal d'expression. — Tous les
peuples ont une langue populaire et une langue littéraire qu'ils tiennent à distance l'une de l'autre, qu'ils n'entremêlent qu'incidemment
pour des besoins d'art. Il y a encore aujourd'hui en France des patois
poitevins, normands et picards; mais les journaux, les livres ne s'écri-
vent pas dans ces patois. Il y a l'« assent » de Marseille, mais on ne
s'en vante pas. Les patois continuent à vivre par la force des traditions, mais on ne les enseigne pas à l'école. Il existe aux Etats-Unis
un « slang » courant, parfois très pittoresque; mais un livre sérieux
ne s'écrit pas en « slang » : il s'écrit en très bon anglais, identique, à
des vétilles près, à l'anglais de Londres. Et vous voyez qu'une grande
nation, tout aussi étrangère que nous à ses origines premières, croit pouvoir s'exprimer pourtant dans la langue de ses origines, ne cherche pas
pour elle d'évolution indépendante, et n'a jamais, à aucun moment,
rêvé d'une langue nationale.

Une langue nationale pour nous ? Il nous faudrait la créer de toutes pièces, d'un noyau primitif de quelques centaines de vocables. Il nous faudrait refaire ce travail de dix siècles qui a élaboré les langues modernes. Et cela quand nous possédons sous la main un instrument de précision et de splendeur que nous savons manier déjà. Cela quand une langue étrangère, complète aussi, nous guette et nous attire, a déjà commencé à nous envahir ! Non, il n'est qu'une alternative : ou bien nous garderons notre langage traditionnel en le préservant de toute tache, en l'enrichissant à ses sources légitimes, — ou bien notre langue future, par la loi de résistance moindre, sera l'anglais, tout simplement. Mais alors aura disparu la plus ferme barrière à l'absorption de notre race; alors nos trois cents ans de culture nationale auront avorté misérablement. Nous voguerons vers des destins nouveaux, mais où ni vous ni moi, messieurs, ni la mémoire d'aucun de nos écrivains et de nos poètes n'occuperont la moindre place.

Ce n'est sûrement pas cette déchéance que nous voulons. Alors, mettons donc en question dans nos théories littéraires tout ce qu'il nous plaira, excepté ce premier principe. Aimons ou non la France moderne, mais usons sans scrupule de sa langue, qui est la nôtre, et pour qu'elle puisse nous exprimer, apprenons-la de mieux en mieux. Que ceux à qui il faut le canadianisme intégral le réalisent au moyen du français intégral : leur succès en cela ne dépendra que de leur génie, car, en puissance et en richesse, la langue française suffit à tout.

Me permettez-vous, en réponse à votre si cordial accueil, de vous offrir ce simple conseil ?

(*Gloses critiques,* 1931)

Camille Roy (1870-1943)

Professeur de philosophie, puis de littérature, puis recteur de l'Université Laval; président de la Société royale du Canada en 1928, il fut le premier à étudier systématiquement la littérature canadienne-française sur laquelle il nous a laissé de nombreux essais. Suit le début d'un des plus longs d'entre eux.

LA NATIONALISATION DE LA LITTÉRATURE CANADIENNE

Il y a quarante ans Crémazie se demandait si une littérature nationale était ici possible; il désespérait, pour sa part, que l'on vît jamais en notre pays se constituer une telle littérature, et entre autres mauvaises raisons dont il essayait d'étayer sa thèse, il y avait celle-ci, très grave, que nous parlons et que nous écrivons en français. N'ayant pas, pour exprimer nos idées, une langue qui soit exclusivement la nôtre, nous ne pouvons donc créer et développer chez nous une littérature qui soit vraiment distincte de la française. Poussant jusqu'au paradoxe, et jusqu'à la boutade, cette opinion personnelle, il regrettait, avec larmes, que nous, gens du Canada, nous ne parlions pas plutôt le huron ou l'iroquois : ce qui, assurément, mettrait en notre langage une saveur originale, en nos oeuvres un parfum nouveau, vierge, le seul qui pourrait faire goûter des autres peuples nos discours et nos livres.

Le temps, qui brise et renverse tant de théories, n'a pas eu de peine à détruire celle-là. Notre littérature se développe, et cela suffit pour qu'il ne soit plus permis de douter de son existence. Au surplus, ce ne sont pas ces messieurs de Lorette et de Caughnawaga qui ont accompli cette merveille, et nous n'avons pas même dérobé à leurs lèvres ce parler et ce miel indiens qui devaient faire si alléchante la littérature canadienne. C'est notre langue française qui exprime, pénètre de sa vertu, et comme de son arôme subtil, nos pensées, et c'est avec toutes les qualités précieuses qui en sont inséparables, et que nous avons héritées de nos pères, que l'on a composé les oeuvres les plus délicieuses et les plus substantielles que l'on voit dans notre bibliothèque nationale. Et loin que nous songions à changer ce langage, notre *Société du Parler français* n'a pas d'autre but que de l'étudier pour le mieux connaître, et de le mieux connaître pour le mieux conserver. Elle souhaite en même temps, avec combien d'ardeur, que notre littérature se développe dans la proportion où l'on connaîtra mieux notre langue, et que cette littérature, aussi bien que cette langue, conservent l'une et l'autre leur caractère propre et leur vigoureuse originalité.

Si donc c'est une question aujourd'hui que de savoir comment il convient de protéger notre langue contre les influences qui la pourraient corrompre, c'en est une autre qui s'y rattache par plus d'un lien, que de découvrir comment il ne faut pas égarer sur des sujets étrangers, ou gâter par des procédés exotiques notre littérature canadienne. En d'autres termes, et puisque le mot a été créé pour les besoins de la sociologie et ceux de la politique, un problème a été en ces derniers temps et souvent posé, qui est celui de la *nationalisation* de notre littérature. Et puisque nos revues et certains journaux qui veulent étendre à toutes les fibres de l'âme canadienne le mouvement nationaliste, sont revenus avec quelque insistance sur ce sujet, il ne sera peut-être pas inutile d'essayer ce soir de préciser un peu les don-nées du problème, et de dire d'abord ce que par *nationalisation* de la littérature il ne faut pas entendre, pour comprendre mieux ensuite et définir ce qu'il en faut penser.

Traiter des sujets canadiens, et les traiter d'une façon canadienne : tel est le mot d'ordre, ou le refrain que s'en vont répétant nos publicistes et nos critiques. Qu'est-ce que cela veut donc dire ? et le doit-on prendre en un sens si rigoureux qu'il faille blâmer ceux qui exerceraient autrement leur activité littéraire, et s'occuperaient, par exemple, à écrire sur des questions qui relèvent d'une autre histoire que la nôtre ? et faut-il aussi condamner tous ceux qui chercheraient à utiliser en leurs livres les ressources d'un art qui ne serait pas le fruit spontané de notre génie national ? Certes, il est sûr que, à cette heure de l'histoire de notre littérature, notre principale occupation, à nous Canadiens, ne doit pas être de faire des romans de moeurs où s'étale la vie des Topinambous, ni non plus d'apprendre au monde comment, en Chine, s'est développée et affermie la dynastie régnante que fonda, au dix-septième siècle, Choun-Tchi. Et ce n'est peut-être pas, non plus, le péril qui menace notre littérature nationale. Mais d'autre part, est-il nécessaire que l'écrivain canadien s'enferme tellement dans l'étude de l'histoire, des moeurs, de la nature de son pays, qu'il ne puisse s'appliquer à d'autres sujets, à des sujets qui dépassent notre vie canadienne et nos frontières ? Si c'est cela que l'on veut dire, c'est sans doute un autre excès et c'est une autre erreur.

Il ne peut être absolument interdit à nos romanciers de situer leurs personnages dans un autre milieu que celui où nous nous mouvons nous-mêmes, et de les faire vivre d'une autre vie que la nôtre; il ne peut être condamnable à nos philosophes d'étudier les problèmes les plus généraux de la psychologie, et de nous dire en notre langage français leurs conclusions; il ne peut être mauvais que nos moralistes essaient de comprendre l'homme « ondoyant » tel qu'il existe partout, et qu'ils tracent dans leurs livres la ligne fuyante de ses contradictions, et nous ne devons pas leur déclarer d'avance que, pour nous Canadiens,

> *. . . c'est folie à nulle autre seconde*
> *De vouloir se mêler de corriger le monde;*

il ne peut être défendu à nos poètes lyriques d'exprimer de leur âme tous ces sentiments, à coup sûr internationaux, et communs à toutes les âmes, que la vie et la mort, la joie et la tristesse, l'amour et la haine éveillent en nous tous : thèmes perpétuels que depuis Orphée jusqu'à M. Louis Fréchette et depuis Stésichore jusqu'à M. Pamphile LeMay, on a tour à tour repris et sans cesse accordés avec la lyre. Non, tout cela et bien d'autres choses encore qui intéressent l'humanité,

ne peuvent être proscrits de notre littérature; les bannir serait maladroit aussi bien que contraire à toutes les traditions de l'esprit français. Il n'y a pas d'écrivains qui aient plus et mieux fréquenté tous
les lieux communs de la pensée humaine que les grands écrivains du
dix-septième siècle, à moins que ce ne soit Montesquieu, Diderot, Vol-
taire, Rousseau : et c'est justement ce qui explique la fortune des uns
et des autres, de leurs livres et de leurs doctrines à travers le monde.
Ils nous intéressent par tout ce qui, dans leurs oeuvres, dépasse la vie
nationale, et jaillit du fond éternel de la conscience humaine.

Il ne faudrait donc pas fermer aux écrivains canadiens un champ
aussi vaste, où il y a place pour tous les talents et pour toutes les
ambitions. Pour nous, comme pour ce personnage de Térence, rien
de ce qui est humain ne doit être étranger. Nous portons nous-mêmes,
en nos personnes, toute la substance et les accidents de la commune
nature. Le mot de Joseph de Maistre est pour le moins paradoxal,
qui déclare qu'il n'y a pas d'hommes dans le monde mais seulement
des Français, des Russes, des Italiens et peut-être des Persans. Tous
ces individus, et quelques autres, comme par exemple, les Canadiens,
ne servent qu'à couvrir et envelopper ce qu'il y a de plus général en
notre espèce, et vous savez, et vous pouvez expérimenter encore tous
les jours qu'il ne faut pas ici gratter longtemps son voisin pour trouver,
dessous, l'homme. Laissons donc nos écrivains pénétrer jusqu'en ce
fond, et apporter ensuite à notre littérature philosophique, morale,
sociologique quelque utile contribution. Et s'ils s'y emploient, ne nous
en plaignons pas trop, puisqu'un pareil dessein nous a déjà valu quelques-unes des meilleures pages de notre littérature, et que le profond
et sage penseur que fut Etienne Parent n'a mérité qu'on l'appelle le
Victor Cousin du Canada que parce qu'un jour il s'est avisé de nous
dire ce qu'il pensait de l'*Intelligence dans ses rapports avec la société*.[1]

Et de même que l'on ne peut exiger de nos écrivains qu'ils se can-
tonnent en un répertoire de sujets qui soient exclusivement canadiens,
l'on ne doit pas leur reprocher de soumettre parfois leur esprit, leur
goût, leurs habitudes de penser, leur art, et, pour ainsi parler, leur
conscience littéraire aux influences qui viennent de l'étranger. Laissons-les assez volontiers demander aux écrivains de France quelques
conseils sur l'art d'écrire et de composer un livre; et, pour énoncer
ici un principe plus général, laissons-les s'assimiler tout ce qui dans
les oeuvres étrangères à notre pays, qu'il s'agisse du fond ou de la
forme, peut être profitable à l'art canadien. Outre que la langue que
nous écrivons est, d'ordinaire, assez pauvre, et manque de beaucoup

---

(1) Titre assez mal trouvé d'une solide étude présentée sous forme de discours à l'auditoire de l'Institut Canadien de Québec, en janvier et février 1852.

de mots qu'il faudrait avoir pour bien marquer toutes les nuances de la pensée, outre que notre goût littéraire n'est pas toujours très sûr, ni peut-être encore assez affiné, rien n'est plus susceptible de transformations et de progrès que les procédés de l'art littéraire; il n'y a pas de formules définitives qui les puissent retenir et emprisonner tout à fait, et l'on n'a jamais épuisé non plus toutes les façons de comprendre et de traduire par le livre la vie morale et la vie intellectuelle de nos semblables. Et c'est pourquoi il est bon que l'écrivain s'inquiète de savoir ce que l'on pense en d'autres pays que le sien, et comment on l'écrit; et c'est pour cela aussi, sans doute, que les littératures ont toujours beaucoup voisiné, et que les modernes, en particulier, se sont toujours communiqué les unes aux autres ce qu'elles avaient une fois conçu comme une loi du bon goût, ou comme une manifestation réelle de la beauté littéraire.

(*Essais sur la littérature canadienne*, 1907)

Albert Pelletier (Né en 1895)

Notaire, critique littéraire exigeant et virulent, il fonda la revue *Les Idées* qui fut une revue d'avant-garde (1931-1939). Suit un extrait de ses essais : l'auteur nous autorise à le reproduire pourvu que nous signalions que le vocabulaire de nos "habitants" d'avant 1930 était, selon lui, bien plus précis et français, et leur syntaxe généralement plus correcte, que la langue de nos professeurs et écrivains, et que tout cela s'est plus appauvri et abâtardi durant les 35 dernières années que dans les trois siècles précédents.

LITTÉRATURE NATIONALE ET NATIONALISME LITTÉRAIRE

On voudra bien admettre que sans écrivains nationaux, il est assez difficile de faire une littérature nationale. Or, produits déracinés et cultivés dans une serre, nos écrivains doivent subir l'artifice de la greffe sur un arbre étranger, presque inaccessible.

Dans cette province où il suffit de semer des affirmations et des négations sans les motiver pour prendre immédiatement figure dominante de statue sur un piédestal, on a toujours obligé nos littérateurs à traduire leurs manières de penser et leurs impressions originales de Canadiens (lorsqu'ils en ont) en langage parisien, — eux qui n'ont jamais vécu à Paris, ou qui ne connaissent de Paris que ce que les entremetteurs des agences maritimes ou de la Maison des Etudiants veulent bien leur montrer.

Il y a des Français vivant chez nous depuis un quart de siècle qui, en aucune manière, ne se sont assimilé nos expressions particularistes. Ils ont raison d'ailleurs : ces expressions nous sembleraient mortes sur leurs lèvres. Il y a des Américains et des Anglo-Canadiens de talent, gens très observateurs, qui ont pratiqué avec beaucoup de soins et de sympathie nos moeurs et notre langue; et on peut voir un spécimen de leurs insuccès, de leurs décalques tirés par les cheveux et sans vie, dans le volume du bienveillant W. H. Drummond, « The Habitant ».

Alors, si imitateurs et assimilateurs que nous soyons, comment pouvons-nous avoir cette certitude d'exprimer et de faire exprimer nos sentiments de façon originale et vivante dans une langue académique que nous ne parlons pas, que nous n'avons jamais pratiquée que dans les livres ? C'est imposer à nos écrivains l'obligation de substituer à leur original une mauvaise traduction, de rendre ce qu'ils voient, éprouvent, ressentent de neuf et de singulier, par des souvenirs livresques.

Je sais bien qu'on a la prétention de se figurer, dans ce pays où le ridicule ne tue pas, que nos pédagogues du « bon parler français » sont aussi français que des Parisiens. Si on ne manquait pas totalement d'esprit d'observation, l'évidence nous aurait depuis longtemps prouvé qu'ils ne sont en réalité ni canadiens, ni français, et qu'ils ont simplement l'air de sapins racornis épinglés de feuilles sèches.

C'est que la province de Québec n'est pas la France, et ne pourra jamais l'être. Pour parler et écrire comme les Français, il nous faudrait d'abord penser, sentir et vivre comme les Français. Pour penser, sentir et vivre comme les Français, il nous faudrait avoir toujours eu, et avoir encore aujourd'hui, la même situation géographique qu'eux, le même climat, les mêmes moeurs, les mêmes occupations, les mêmes ambiances, les mêmes facilités de vie sociale, littéraire, artistique, économique, les mêmes sentiments, les mêmes impressions, les mêmes aspirations, la même âme. Le calcul est très élémentaire : c'est une impossibilité.

J'espère bien, et je n'hésite pas à le dire, que nos professeurs de mauvais parler perdront toujours aussi risiblement leur temps que dans le passé. Car le jour où l'on obligera notre peuple à apprendre et à parler une autre langue que la sienne, ce sera l'anglaise qui l'emportera; eh oui, pour la simple raison qu'elle nous est plus utile que le vocabulaire de l'Académie française. Et l'on touche peut-être ici du doigt la raison principale de l'anglicisation continuelle, et sans arrêt depuis cent soixante-dix ans, de notre classe instruite et formée, non pas suivant les dispositions de notre caractère indigène, mais exclusivement « à la française ».

Les bonnes gens qui font des gorges chaudes sur la pauvreté de notre langage et trouvent « horribles » des expressions comme « Il file pas bien aujourd'hui » — qu'ils décrochent des lèvres de leur mère pour livrer à la risée du public —, seraient mieux inspirés, je crois, de nous donner des dictionnaires de ces mots savoureux et expressifs qui n'ont pas de sens en français, ou auxquels on donne chez nous une acception différente de celle qu'ils ont en France. S'adonner à notre vocabulaire alourdi par trois siècles d'inculture complète, ça serait, il me semble, faire oeuvre plus utile que de pratiquer petit à petit l'amputation de ce qui nous reste d'originalité et de vivacité. Car ces expressions au sens particulier valent infiniment mieux pour nous que les expressions académiques équivalentes, d'abord parce qu'elles sont à nous, ensuite parce qu'elles expriment les nuances de notre pensée dans leur forme originale, tandis que la meilleure expression française n'est qu'une traduction plus ou moins infidèle.

Et si notre « patois » devient trop difficile aux académiciens, eh bien, tant mieux : c'est que nous aurons une langue à nous; et qu'elle aura perdu sa vérité et sa valeur cette raison fondamentale que Crémazie invoquait, il y a soixante ans déjà, contre la possibilité d'une littérature canadienne. Si les Français veulent nous lire, ils nous traduiront, comme ils traduisent la littérature provençale; et ils y réussiront bien mieux que nous, soyons-en sûrs, parce qu'ils possèdent bien mieux leur langue que nous ne pourrons jamais, nous, la connaître.

Si les idéologues dénués de toute psychologie et de toute observation étaient habiles à apprécier du langage autre chose que ce qui est codifié dans les dictionnaires, ils se rendraient compte, je crois, que notre parler populaire est savoureux, imagé, vivant, et ils auraient bientôt fini cette tentative d'y substituer leurs produits desséchés. Tentative plutôt fâcheuse même pour eux d'ailleurs, parce qu'elle leur donne l'air de croire qu'on confectionne et rapièce une langue comme une paire de bottes. Tentative illogique et contradictoire aussi avec le nationalisme que la plupart de ces apôtres professent, car il est difficile de faire autre chose que copier Marc Sangnier et ses disciples, il est difficile d'être vraiment canadien en pratique, si l'on condamne et ridiculise au préalable le langage qui révèle, qui exprime, qui constitue cet état d'esprit canadien.

Nous avons tellement honte de notre langue, c'est-à-dire de nous-mêmes, que des hommes d'esprit libre comme Louis Dantin (ne parlons pas de Mgr Camille Roy, qui ne voit guère au pays que « bonguienne », « verrat », « torrieu ») disent un « non » catégorique, sans prendre la peine d'émettre aucune explication, à la seule pensée que dans un roman « la trame du récit, l'évolution des caractères, le dialogue entre gens instruits, s'énoncent en *langage canadien* ». N'est-ce pas sommaire, à la fin, ces notes affirmatives ou négatives en marge de tout ?

Cela m'étonne d'autant plus que Louis Dantin connaît la littérature des pays où l'on n'emploie pas le papier pour faire du simple parangonnage comme dans la province de Québec, et qu'il ne devrait pas ignorer Guy de Maupassant, Anatole Le Braz, Alphonse de Chateaubriant, Marion Gilbert, Charles Silvestre, Emile Pouvillon et les meilleurs romanciers de la France contemporaine qu'on lui nomme comme exemples. Puisqu'on est si dur d'entendement, crions-le donc à pleins poumons, afin que nul n'en ignore : il ne s'agit pas de mettre le pic et la pioche dans le génie même de la langue française, qui consiste dans sa grammaire et sa syntaxe. Nous demandons simplement que les écrivains canadiens, pour faire une littérature moins livresque, plus personnelle, plus humaine, plus vivante, se servent avec bon sens, avec goût, avec art, du vocabulaire canadien. Les peuples civilisés n'ont jamais, que je sache, refusé cette liberté élémentaire à leurs romanciers et à leurs poètes. Et d'autre part, si l'oeuvre de M. Alfred DesRochers nous remue et commande à la critique les appréciations les plus élogieuses, qu'on ait donc la droiture de reconnaître que ce n'est pas à cause des termes exotiques, artificiels, pauvres, qui la déparent, mais peut-être beaucoup à cause de nos archaïsmes, de nos anglicismes, de nos canadianismes, dont M. DesRochers fait un usage exemplaire, et qui rendent sa poésie plus copieusement expressive, plus véritablement humaine, plus originalement artistique. Enfin, je ne tiens pas le moins du monde à faire fausse route, et Louis Dantin est bien capable d'avoir raison. Pourquoi commence-t-il la riposte enfantine, qui n'aboutit à rien, des « oui » et des « non » ?

Eh bien, j'ai un peu envie de lui donner tort ! . . . Supposons qu'on lui *prête* à traduire en français académique ce chef-d'oeuvre d'émotion littéraire intitulé « La chanson javanaise », et qu'il y mette toute sa bonhomie, toute sa simplicité, toute sa finesse, tout son art, toute sa virtuosité, — c'est un expert. J'en réponds pour les Canadiens surtout, et aussi pour tous ceux qui peuvent le comprendre sans traduction : il ne resterait pas de ce livret le quart de son charme et de sa saveur.

C'est que pour produire en français moderne des oeuvres équivalentes à celles des bons écrivains de France, il nous aurait fallu recevoir notre éducation en France, et vivre ensuite la vie française pendant quinze à cinquante ans. Le français parisien n'est pas notre langue. Et surtout le seul français moderne que nous connaissons, le français livresque, séparé de son organisme et de sa vie, est impuissant à rendre les formes diverses de nos pensées, les nuances de nos sentiments. Ses formules et ses mots n'ont pas la vertu de représenter avec exactitude les choses réelles de notre pays, soit parce que les choses qu'ils désignent n'existent pas chez nous, soit parce qu'elles sont ici plus ou moins différentes de ce qu'elles sont en France, soit parce que ces choses et ces objets étant pourtant les mêmes là-bas que dans notre province, ont été vus et reproduits par des écrivains qui n'ont pas notre état d'esprit et ne voient pas de la même manière que nous. Avec cette langue livresque et artificielle, comment voulez-vous que nous puissions rendre autre chose que nos apparences, les à-peu-près superficiels de nous-mêmes, de notre existence, de notre pays ?

Je ne dis pas que nous sommes absolument inhabiles à écrire en français d'outremer d'il y a cinquante à trois cents ans nos dissertations par exemple, qui sont toujours plus ou moins calquées, par le fond et par la forme, à notre insu ou malgré nous, sur les réminiscences de nos manuels et les souvenirs de nos lectures. Et encore, dans ce genre imitatif, quel est celui de nos grammairiens, de nos puristes, de nos éplucheurs, qui ne puisse être épluché à son tour ? Si je ne fais pas de critique grammaticale, ce n'est pas que j'y sois plus inapte qu'un autre : c'est que cet exercice de collégien me semble d'autant plus vain et prétentieux, malicieux et injuste à l'égard de nos auteurs, que dans le sentier battu, nous ne pouvons nous garder nous-mêmes de trébucher.

Cela nous aide à reconnaître qu'il est très difficile à nos poètes et à nos romanciers qui, sous peine de ne rien valoir, doivent avec constance tracer une route neuve, de peindre les nuances de leurs impressions et de faire de la littérature subjective qui compte, aussi bien que de dégager les particularités de notre vie et de faire de la littérature objective qui soit vraie, dans une langue qu'ils n'ont pas vécue, et qui n'est elle-même qu'un rameau détaché du sol français, de son suc et de sa sève.

(*Carquois,* 1931)

Victor Barbeau (Né en 1896)

Journaliste, professeur de littérature française, pamphlétaire et essayiste, il a fondé la Société des Ecrivains canadiens en 1937 et, en 1944, l'Académie canadienne-française dont il dirige les *Cahiers,* où a paru l'essai remarquable dont on trouvera ici la conclusion.

LA DANSE AUTOUR DE L'ÉRABLE

Les problèmes-clés de la littérature canadienne-française semblent se ramener à deux. Le premier, de fond; le second, d'expression. Mais il suffit de les creuser un peu pour leur découvrir un sens beaucoup plus grave. Sous ces apparences se dissimule, en réalité, le point névralgique de notre dualité ethnique. En quoi sommes-nous canadiens ? En quoi sommes-nous français ? Quel que soit l'idiome dans lequel ils s'expriment, les Suisses sont des Suisses, les Belges des Belges. Nous seuls des peuples de langue française portons, de date assez récente, un trait d'union. Et c'est ce même petit signe grammatical qui, à l'examen, se révèle en filigrane dans nos oeuvres littéraires.

En effet, nous n'avons pas encore atteint à l'équilibre des influences dont nous devrions être l'harmonieuse résultante et dont nous ne sommes, pour l'instant, que le champ clos. Notre littérature « ne sait pas si elle doit être canadienne ou française; elle oscille constamment entre deux tendances, deux pôles d'attraction : ou elle regarde vers la France ou elle se renferme jalousement sur elle-même; elle hésite entre l'imitation et le régionalisme » [1]. C'est l'exacte vérité. Mais s'agit-il bien d'une antinomie irréductible ? Sommes-nous vraiment condamnés, si nous développons nos affinités françaises, à n'être qu'une copie ? Et, si nous nous ancrons au sol, le régionalisme étriqué serait-il notre seule issue ? Lesté de toute la rhétorique dont on l'hypertrophie, le coeur du problème tient-il en ce dilemme ?

Je crois, quant à moi, que cette question reflète moins l'embarras d'un choix hypothétique que notre incomplète, imparfaite soumission à la patrie charnelle. Je crains que nous ne soyons pas plus canadiens que nous ne sommes français. Est-on français parce qu'on fait ses études en français, qu'on lit des livres français (pas toujours écrits en français, hélas) et qu'on parle, avec plus ou moins de bonheur, français ? Est-on canadien parce que l'on situe l'action de ses oeuvres au Canada, que l'on chante l'heure des vaches ou que l'on ponctue de jurons le

---

(1) — Cf. Jean Seznec — *Le Travailleur* 5-6-41.

dialogue de ses personnages ? C'est se repaître de mots que de le croire. Entre le français qui est notre parler, notre signe indélébile, et la matière aux dimensions d'un continent qui s'offre à nous, il n'y a pas et il ne peut pas y avoir d'opposition, moins encore de contradiction. Seuls des esprits fumeux, enténébrés sont capables et coupables de telles cogitations. La vérité nue est qu'il ne s'agit point d'option mais uniquement de compénétration, d'alliage, de fusion.

Nos romantiques, je l'ai rappelé, étaient soudés à la France au point d'en partager les idéologies politiques, tradition qu'ont renouvelée nos intellectuels « évolués » en important le progressisme. Ils ne pensaient, les romantiques, ne jugeaient que par la France. Avec, comme conséquence, que la patrie canadienne dont ils chantent la naissance, dont ils sont les premiers bardes, ne nous émeut ni ne nous trouble. Les oripeaux français dans lesquels ils l'ont drapée l'étouffent, la paralysent. Tant de souffrances, tant d'épreuves ne méritaient pas le châtiment d'une pareille grandiloquence. La patrie dont ils entonnent la Marseillaise n'a pas encore gagné leur coeur, leur sens. Elle est un concept, une idée, une abstraction, un prétexte à des jeux oratoires, à la virtuosité verbale. Or, n'est-ce pas faute d'en subir, eux aussi, l'attraction qu'un si grand nombre d'écrivains canadiens-français demeurent étrangers à leur propre pays ? Ou provincialistes ou pasticheurs. Une fois pour toutes, en est-il ainsi d'une nécessité implacable, de par la nature des choses ? Ou, au contraire, l'explication s'en trouve-t-elle dans la méconnaissance de l'essentiel ?

Subjuguée comme le Canada, mendiante comme lui et, par surcroît s'exprimant dans une langue étrangère, est-ce que l'Irlande n'a pas donné à la littérature universelle de grands, de très grands écrivains ? La pauvreté ni le servage ne l'ont empêchée de produire Congreve, Swift, Sheridan, Yeats, Synge, Thomas Moore, George Russell, Joyce et j'en passe. Qu'avaient donc ces écrivains qui a manqué et manque aux nôtres ? Indépendamment de ce qui leur vient du fonds celtique et qui sans leur être exclusif leur est congénital, à savoir l'ironie, l'esprit, la fantaisie, la mystique — possédés de Dieu ou du diable — ils ont eu de leur patrie « femme royale, malheureuse et très fière » un amour absolu, passionné. C'est d'elle, de ses légendes, de ses malheurs, de ses gloires, de son incurable mélancolie, de ses chants, de ses mystères, de sa nature qu'ils ont extrait la chair et le sang de leurs oeuvres. Leurs plus beaux poèmes, leur théâtre, leurs romans leur sont montés de son passé et de son présent directement au coeur et aux lèvres. Pas un n'a eu à se battre les flancs pour les inventer. La terre et ses morts ont parlé en eux. Est-ce à dire qu'ils soient régionalistes ? Traduire les aspirations d'un peuple, donner cours à son histoire n'est pas, en soi, du régionalisme. Yeats qui rêvait de réunir les deux moitiés

de l'Irlande, la protestante et la catholique, par une « littérature nationale qui l'embellît dans la mémoire des hommes » y mettait comme
condition première « qu'elle fût préservée du provincialisme par un
esprit critique exigeant » et « par une position européenne ». Grâce
à quoi, tout en étant nationaux jusqu'à la moelle, les écrivains irlandais
ont pu devenir universels.

Quant à nous, jusqu'où devons-nous creuser pour trouver notre
âme au milieu de tant de scories littéraires ? On a écrit[2] que les dominantes de notre littérature sont l'histoire de notre peuple, la mère
patrie, l'Eglise, la langue et l'amour du sol. Telles sont bien, en effet,
les têtes de chapitre sous lesquelles nous pourrions en ranger les thèmes
majeurs. Mais cette abondante et diverse matière, l'avons-nous utilisée,
avons-nous su la façonner ? A la position européenne que réclamait
Yeats pour la littérature irlandaise afin de la protéger du provincialisme correspond géographiquement pour la nôtre la position américaine.
Qu'y a-t-il de continental dans nos lettres ? La question n'est pas oiseuse.
L'Amérique est notre habitat, notre ciel. Qu'y avons-nous emprunté ?
Qu'en avons-nous retenu ?

Je ne peux, ici, qu'effleurer en passant un sujet qui mériterait une
longue étude en soi et que Marine Leland a déjà entamée[3], à savoir
l'étroite parenté que présentent, en leurs commencements, la littérature
américaine et la nôtre. Les deux ont connu des phases identiques. Dans
la période coloniale, l'imitation prévaut ici et là. On est en présence
de deux peuples « qui s'agrippent opiniâtrement à la substance du vieux
monde et imitent, conscients de leur dépendance de provinciaux, les
moeurs et les modes de la mère patrie »[4]. Aux Etats-Unis comme
au Québec, la poésie et l'histoire sont les premiers genres à apparaître.
Puis, à l'âge colonial succède l'âge romantique avec, ou peu s'en manque, la même emphase. Là s'arrête le parallèle. Plus tôt que nous, les
Américains se sont tournés vers leur milieu géographique et social,
vers leurs légendes, leur particularisme. Plus tôt que nous, ils ont
modelé leurs oeuvres et à leur image et à leur ressemblance. Aussi,
longtemps avant nous sont-ils devenus autonomes. Fenimore Cooper,
Longfellow, Beecher-Stowe, Washington Irving ont été les premiers
exploitants du fonds nord-américain.[5]

Ils n'en ont extrait aucun chef-d'oeuvre universel, soit. Ils ont
néanmoins fait oeuvre de précurseurs, de pionniers. Après eux, c'est
à qui tournera et retournera la terre sachant qu'un trésor y est caché.

---

(2) — Cf. Ian Forbes Fraser — *The Spirit of French Canada*.
(3) — C. *The French Review* 1942.
(4) — Cf. Walter-C. Bronson — *A Short History of American Literature*.
(5) — Et qu'en est-il des débuts, à la fin du dix-neuvième, de la littérature
anglo-canadienne ?

Les mêmes richesses, sinon de plus fabuleuses, existent chez nous. Comptez ceux qui se sont lancés à leur découverte. La première de toutes, de dimensions et d'aspects insoupçonnés, est la nature. Déjà, en 1932, le Frère Marie-Victorin se demandait à son propos : qui a vu ? qui a vibré ? qui a peint ? Il se désolait que notre littérature ne fût pas racinée au sol et que l'école régionaliste qui eût dû, en bonne logique, découvrir nos paysages n'en avait retenu que « l'environnement domestique ». D'où, pour le reste, une collection de naïvetés, de méprises scientifiques impardonnables, de descriptions banales, empruntées, gauchement livresques[6]. Pour des fins rentables nous avons su ou, plutôt, nous avons vu capter les lacs, dompter les rivières, exploiter les forêts mais quelles images, quelles évocations en sont passées dans nos livres, ont sustenté, embelli nos livres ? Nos paysages, leur mystère, leur effarante grandeur, ce sont des écrivains français qui nous les ont révélés, Louis Hémon, Marie Le Franc, Frédéric Rouquette, Constantin-Weyer. A la nature que déjà nos ancêtres sacrifiaient à leur sécurité, que nos contemporains sacrifient à la tripaille et à l'architecture des vachers de l'ouest américain, nos écrivains applaudis par les ministres et auréolés par l'Université préfèrent les fonds de cour et la promiscuité des ruelles. C'est plus en harmonie avec nos moyens intellectuels et notre parler.

Autrement plus significative et plus douloureuse est l'absence dans nos lettres du sacré, du divin, de tout véritable sentiment religieux. Les ouvrages abondent de piété rose ou de piété grise, de dévotion, surtout de morale à l'usage des habitués des courriers du coeur et des illettrés de la télévision mais, on l'aura compris, ouvrages aux antipodes de la littérature. A nos romanciers, à nos dramaturges, la foi n'a pas inspiré grand-chose. Certains Anglo-Saxons prétendent que la domination de l'Eglise a entravé le libre essor du génie créateur au Canada français. Si, malgré son énormité, cela a pu être dans le passé — dérobade trop facile d'impuissants et de ratés — il y a belle lurette que cela n'est plus. Et aucun Gide, aucun Sartre, ces crabes de la faune française, ne pointent encore à notre horizon. Revenant à notre sujet, il reste que, dans un pays dont l'histoire se confond avec la foi catholique, il est pour le moins étrange que celle-ci ait si peu marqué, pénétré sa littérature sauf, heureuse exception, une part de sa poésie. Que de grandes et sublimes figures, que de vies exemplaires, que d'héroïsme et de vertus, que de fondateurs, de missionnaires sollicitent en vain d'être admis dans nos lettres. C'est une Américaine, Willa Cather, qui, à notre place, a sorti de l'ombre la recluse Jeanne LeBer. Au même niveau, humain et divin, nous n'avons à aligner que les pièces de Rina

---

(6) — Cf. *Le Devoir* 9-XI-31.

Lasnier dont *Le Jeu de la Voyagère* demeure la projection la plus émouvante d'un thème national sur le plan universel. Partout ailleurs, à une ou deux exceptions dont *Les Elus que vous êtes* du Frère Lockquell, ce ne sont que chromos ou silhouettes caricaturales de la vie religieuse. Des conflits entre la vocation religieuse et le monde, néant. Des épopées des missionnaires qu'ont entrouvertes à la littérature les Pères français Duchaussois (*Aux glaces polaires*) et Roger Buliard (*Inuk*), néant toujours.

Faut-il d'autres preuves de notre divorce d'avec la grandeur matérielle et spirituelle de notre pays ? D'autres témoignages de notre inaptitude ou de notre refus à y communier ? Un fait les résume tous. Aucun grand événement (grand relativement à nous) de notre pensée n'a trouvé d'expression dans nos lettres en dehors de l'histoire dont c'était le devoir de les consigner. La conquête du pouvoir politique, le républicanisme de 1837, et ses fièvres ardentes, la saignée de l'émigration, les luttes scolaires, la poussée nationaliste de Bourassa n'ont laissé aucun sillage dans nos lettres alors qu'en France le jansénisme, l'encyclopédisme, le sartrisme, l'existentialisme, le marxisme se sont transformés en formes d'art. Du répertoire des événements possibles dans la vie d'un homme et dans celle d'un peuple, quel usage avons-nous fait jusqu'ici ? Amour, énergie, ambition, famille, américanisation, déchristianisation sont autant de terres à peine grattées en surface et dont le tuf demeure intact. La vie d'aventures à la Curwood et à la Jack London nous échappe à nous peuple de coureurs de bois, comme nous ont échappé la guerre, à une ou deux expressions près, l'assimilation des Ecossais, des Irlandais, voire des Allemands venus avec les armées de Wolfe, la coexistence des deux peuples-souches du Canada emprisonnés chacun dans sa solitude, les conflits (« il semble, écrivait Bougainville, que nous soyons d'une nation différente, même ennemie ») entre l'ancienne et la Nouvelle-France, sans parler des hauts faits de l'histoire.

Comment douter, par conséquent, que le mal dont souffre la littérature canadienne-française c'est de n'être qu'une apparence du Canada français. Au sens humain et national, elle est irréaliste, sans point d'appui dans le charnel et le mystique. Qu'en son expression elle soit française, doive être française, la question ne se pose pas. Tel est son lourd, son écrasant destin. Qu'elle s'apparente par la facture, le dessin aux oeuvres françaises, qu'elle y cherche — à bon escient — des éléments d'ordre, de renouvellement, d'invention, trop d'affinités naturelles l'y inclinent pour qu'elle s'en prive. Que les maîtres français, de préférence mais sans exclusivisme, soient nos maîtres ou mieux nos compagnons de route, il y va, oserais-je dire, de notre santé intellectuelle. Tout nous lie donc à la France autant par propension naturelle, par atavisme que par intérêt. Il n'y a pas de clôture pour l'esprit.

Une fois reconnue, acceptée la nécessité non d'une subordination mais d'une filiation de nos lettres avec les lettres françaises sans pour cela, je le répète, les imperméabiliser contre tout apport étranger (et d'ailleurs, comment le pourrions-nous à nous en tenir à la seule pression des Etats-Unis ?) nous n'avons plus qu'à leur laisser suivre, selon le partage de l'histoire, leur pente naturelle. Leur aire est le Canada. Avec la géographie, l'essence de notre être le commande. Loin d'exclure le national, comme le supposent nos pêcheurs de lune, l'universel le contient ainsi qu'en témoignent les plus éminents chefs-d'oeuvre et quantité d'ouvrages d'un rang moins élevé. Je n'en veux pour preuve qu'un seul exemple en dehors de *Maria Chapdelaine*. Aucun livre des deux Canadas n'a conquis une audience aussi vaste que *Jalna* de Mazo de La Roche. La renommée en est mondiale. Quel en est le secret ? L'auteur y raconte avec humour et tendresse la vie d'une famille ontarienne. Tout y est de la plus grande simplicité, sans faux ornements, sans concessions fâcheuses au pittoresque de bric et de broc. Particulariste, *Jalna* l'est dans son décor, ses personnages; universel, il l'est dans sa psychologie, sa vérité. Il n'en faut pas davantage pour qu'un ouvrage (et celui-ci compte quatorze volumes) dépasse les frontières de son pays d'origine et excite partout une attachante curiosité.

Si tant de nos oeuvres moisissent à l'ombre de leur clocher, c'est qu'elles ne sont qu'un simili, un ersatz. Ou, encore, qu'elles ne sont qu'un instrument, qu'un auxiliaire maladroit, prêcheur, au service d'un idéal patriotique.[7] On ne lèvera l'hypothèque qui pèse sur notre littérature qu'à la condition expresse de la canadianiser jusqu'à l'âme. La prétendue antinomie de notre dualité ethnique n'a d'autre cause que notre déracinement, notre rupture d'avec nos forces de vie.
(Cahiers de l'Académie canadienne-française, I)

---

(7) — Cf. Je ne néglige pas le style, un autre chapitre à écrire, mais à propos de qui en parler ? La couleur, les images, la musique ne sont pas de nos richesses. Marcel Dugas est notre seul prosateur sensoriel. Il y a bien aussi Félix-Antoine Savard mais ne pourrait-on pas dire de son écriture ce qu'Emile Faguet disait de celle de Taine : « Il est un miracle de volonté. Il est tout artificiel. » Trouver la correction me suffit donc amplement.

Alfred Garneau (1836-1904)

Fils du célèbre historien, avocat, puis traducteur au Sénat à Ottawa. Poète surtout intime et souvent mélancolique à une époque où la poésie épique était à la mode ici, ses poésies n'ont été réunies en volume qu'en 1906, deux ans après sa mort.

DEVANT LA GRILLE DU CIMETIÈRE

La tristesse des lieux sourit, l'heure est exquise.
Le couchant s'est chargé des dernières couleurs,
Et devant les tombeaux que l'ombre idéalise,
Un grand souffle mourant soulève encor les fleurs.

Salut, vallon sacré, notre terre promise ! . . .
Les chemins sous les ifs, que peuplent les pâleurs
Des marbres, sont muets; dans le fond, une église
Dresse son dôme sombre au milieu des rougeurs.

La lumière au-dessus plane, longtemps vermeille . . .
Sa bêche sur l'épaule entre les arbres noirs,
Le fossoyeur repasse, il voit la croix qui veille.

Et de loin, comme il fait sans doute tous les soirs,
Cet homme la salue avec un geste immense . . .
Un chant très doux d'oiseaux vole dans le silence.

(*Poésies,* 1906)

Pamphile Lemay (1837-1918)

Avocat, bibliothécaire
de l'Assemblée législative
de Québec, poète et romancier,
il a laissé une oeuvre abondante
tant en prose qu'en vers,
y compris des traductions
d'*Evangéline* et du *Golden Dog*.
Son meilleur recueil de poésies
est *Les Gouttelettes* (1904),
dont est tiré le sonnet qui suit
et qui est une sorte de testament.

ULTIMA VERBA

Mon rêve a ployé l'aile. En l'ombre qui s'étend,
Il est comme un oiseau que le lacet captive.
Malgré des jours nombreux ma fin semble hâtive;
Je dis l'adieu suprême à tout ce qui m'entend.

Je suis content de vivre et je mourrai content.
La mort n'est-elle pas une peine fictive ?
J'ai mieux aimé chanter que jeter l'invective.
J'ai souffert, je pardonne, et le pardon m'attend.

Que le souffle d'hiver emporte, avec la feuille,
Mes chants et mes sanglots d'un jour ! Je me recueille
Et je ferme mon coeur aux voix qui l'ont ravi.

Ai-je accompli le bien que toute vie impose ?
Je ne sais. Mais l'espoir en mon âme repose,
Car je sais les bontés du Dieu que j'ai servi.

(*Les Gouttelettes,* 1904)

Louis Fréchette (1839-1908)

Successivement avocat, journaliste, député au Parlement, puis greffier du Conseil législatif de Québec; poète, conteur et dramaturge, il est surtout connu aujourd'hui comme le poète épique de *La Légende d'un peuple* (1887). Parmi ses meilleurs livres on trouve encore *Les Fleurs boréales* (1879) et le recueil de portraits en prose, *Originaux et détraqués* (1892).

LE CAP ÉTERNITÉ

C'est un bloc écrasant dont la crête surplombe
Au-dessus des flots noirs, et dont le front puissant
Domine le brouillard, et défie en passant
L'aile de la tempête ou le choc de la trombe.

Enorme pan de roc, colosse menaçant
Dont le flanc narguerait le boulet et la bombe,
Qui monte d'un seul jet dans la nue, et retombe
Dans le gouffre insondable où sa base descend !

Quel caprice a dressé cette sombre muraille ?
Caprice ! qui le sait ? Hardi celui qui raille
Ces aveugles efforts de la fécondité !

Cette masse nourrit mille plantes vivaces;
L'hirondelle des monts niche dans ses crevasses;
Et ce monstre farouche a sa paternité !

(*Les Fleurs boréales, Les Oiseaux de neige*, 1881)

Nérée Beauchemin (1850-1931)

Médecin à Yamachiche où il a vécu toute sa vie, il a laissé deux recueils de poésies d'inspiration religieuse et rustique : *Les Floraisons matutinales* (1897) et *Patrie intime* (1928), où l'on trouve un charme quelque peu suranné.

LA BRANCHE D'ALISIER CHANTANT

Je l'ai tout à fait désapprise
La berceuse au rythme flottant,
Qu'effeuille, par les soirs de brise,
La branche d'alisier chantant.

Du rameau qu'un souffle balance,
La miraculeuse chanson,
Au souvenir de mon enfance,
A communiqué son frisson.

La musique de l'air, sans rime,
Glisse en mon rêve, et, bien souvent,
Je cherche à noter ce qu'exprime
Le chant de la feuille et du vent.

J'attends que la brise reprenne
La note où tremble un doux passé,
Pour que mon coeur, malgré sa peine,
Un jour, une heure en soit bercé.

Nul écho ne me la renvoie,
La berceuse de l'autre jour,
Ni les collines de la joie,
Ni les collines de l'amour.

La branche éolienne est morte;
Et les rythmes mystérieux
Que le vent soupire à ma porte,
Gonflent le coeur, mouillent les yeux.

Le poète en mélancolie
Pleure de n'être plus enfant,
Pour ouïr ta chanson jolie,
O branche d'alisier chantant !

(*Patrie intime*, 1928)

Archibald Lampman (1861-1899)

Lampman's first book of poems was *Among the Millet,* in 1888. His work revealed a fondness for nature and reverie, and a flight from mechanized urban life. He wrote *Lyrics of Earth* (1895), and *Alcyone* was ready for press when he died (1899).

IN OCTOBER

Along the waste, a great way off, the pines
Like tall slim priests of storm, stand up and bar
The low long strip of dolorous red that lines
The under west, where wet winds moan afar.
The cornfields all are brown, and brown the meadows
With the blown leaves' wind-heaped traceries,
And the brown thistle stems that cast no shadows,
And bear no bloom for bees.

As slowly earthward leaf by red leaf slips,
The sad trees rustle in chill misery,
A soft strange inner sound of pain-crazed lips,
That move and murmur incoherently ;
As if all leaves, that yet have breath, were sighing,
So many low soft masses for the dying
Sweet leaves that live no more.

Here I will sit upon this naked stone,
Draw my coat closer with my numbed hands,
And hear the ferns sigh, and the wet woods moan,
And send my heart out to the ashen lands ;
And I will ask myself what golden madness,
What balmed breaths of dreamland spicery,
What visions of soft laughter and light sadness
Were sweet last month to me . . .

(The Poems of Archibald Lampman)

Bliss Carman (1861-1929)

Carman's first volume of poems was *Low Tide on Grand Pré,* in 1893, inspired by the Evangeline country of Nova Scotia. Other important works were *Behind the Arras, Ballads of Lost Haven, Sappho* and *Sanctuary*. He was honoured as poet and lecturer.

THE JUGGLER

Look how he throws them up and up,
The beautiful golden balls !
They hang aloft in the purple air,
And there never is one that falls.

He sends them hot from his steady hand,
He teaches them all their curves ;
And whether the reach be little or long,
There never is one that swerves.

Some, like the tiny red one there,
He never lets go far ;
And some he has sent to the roof of the tent
To swim without a jar.

So white and still they seem to hang,
You wonder if he forgot
To reckon the time of their return
And measure their golden lot.

Can it be that, hurried or tired out,
The hand of the juggler shook ?
O never you fear, his eye is clear,
He knows them all like a book.

And they will home to his hand at last,
For he pulls them by a cord
Finer than silk and strong as fate,
That is just the bid of his word.

Was ever there such a sight in the world ?
Like a wonderful winding skein,
The way he tangles them up together
And ravels them out again !

He has so many moving now,
You can hardly believe your eyes ;
And yet they say he can handle twice
The number when he tries.

You take your choice and give me mine,
I know the one for me,
It's that great bluish one low down
Like a ship's light out at sea.

It has not moved for a minute or more,
The marvel is that it can keep
As if it had been set there to spin
For a thousand years asleep !

If I could have him at the inn
All by myself some night,
Inquire his country, and where in the world
He came by that cunning sleight !

Where do you guess he learned the trick
To hold us gaping here,
Till our minds in the spell of his maze almost
Have forgotten the time of year?

One never could have the least idea.
Yet why be disposed to twit
A fellow who does such wonderful things,
With the merest lack of wit?

Likely enough, when the show is done
And the balls all back in his hand,
He'll tell us why he is smiling so,
And we shall understand.

(Ballads and Lyrics)

Charles G. D. Roberts (1860-1943)

In 1880 Roberts published his first book at Chatham, N.B., *Orion and Other Poems*. This volume, *In Divers Tones* (1886) and *Songs of the Common Day* (1893), contain his best poetry. He was knighted, and awarded the Lorne Pierce Medal.

THE HERRING WEIR

Back to the green deeps of the outer bay
The red and amber currents glide and cringe,
Diminishing behind a luminous fringe
Of cream-white surf and wandering wraiths of spray.
Stealthily, in the old reluctant way,
The red flats are uncovered, mile on mile,
To glitter in the sun a golden while.
Far down the flats, a phantom, sharply grey,
The herring weir emerges quick with spoil.
Slowly the tide forsakes it. Then draws near,
Descending from the farm-house on the height,
A cart, with gaping tubs. The oxen toil
Somberly o'er the level to the weir,
And drag a long black trail across the light.

(Selected Poems of Charles G. D. Roberts)

Duncan Campbell Scott (1862-1947)

Scott was a lifelong civil servant in the Department of Indian Affairs, and some of his best work shows a concern for the Canadian Indian. One of the Confederation poets, his first book, *The Magic House and Other Poems,* was published in 1893. His *Poems* came out in 1926. His two prose works are *In the Village of Viger,* a group of sketches, and *The Witching of Elspie.*

THE MAD GIRL'S SONG

My mother was a shy child,
The daughter of a king,
A stranger stole and married her
With a grass ring.

So pay me not for loving
With silver or gold,
Or with a fur mantle
To keep away the cold,

Or with a crimson petticoat,
Or a diamond stone,
Or a carved necklace
Of ivory bone,

Or with pearls for my ear-bobs,
Or a ruby star,
Or with anything that's near and dear
Or precious from afar :

All these are often given
And taken in good part,
They're not enough for loving
With a broken heart :

But just say, "You sweet thing" !
Or maybe a few words more,
A tender say that was never thought
And never said before;

So pay me with a whisper,
With a kiss on the breast,
And a prayer, if ever you make one,
That I may find rest.

(The Poems of Duncan Campbell Scott)

Marjorie Pickthall (1883-1922)

Miss Pickthall was a short-story writer and novelist as well as poet. Her poems and stories appeared early in her career in *Harper's, Scribner's,* the *Atlantic.* Her first book of poems was *The Drift of Pinions* (1913). In 1922 *The Woodcarver's Wife* came out.

ON AMARYLLIS, A TORTOYSE

My name was Amaryllis. I
From a harde Shell put forthe to fly;
No Bird, alas; with Beautie prim'd,
Hath Death th'inconstant Fowler lim'd.
No antick Moth on Blossoms set
Hath Judgement taken in a Net.
So dull, so slowe, so meeke I went
In my House-Roof that pay'd no Rent,
E'en my deare Mistresse guess'd no Spark
Could e'er enlight'n my dustie Dark.

> Judge not, ye Proud. Each lowlie Thing
> May lack the Voyce, not Heart, to sing.
> The Worme that from the Moulde suspires
> May be attun'd with heavenlie Quires,
> And I, a-crawling in my Straw,
> Was moved by Love, and made by Law.

So all ye wise, who 'neath your Clod
Go creeping onwards up to God,
Take Heart of me, who by His Grace,
Slough'd off my Pris'n and won my Race.

(The Selected Poems of Marjorie Pickthall)

Isabella Valancy Crawford (1850-1887)

Miss Crawford was born in Ireland, and grew up in Ontario. She wrote poems, short stories and novels, with a fondness for the West (her best-known poem, "Old Spookses' Pass," features a stampede). Her *Collected Poems* came out in 1905, and at last her work gained due recognition.

A BATTLE

Slowly the Moon her banderoles of light
Unfurls upon the sky; her fingers drip
Pale, silvery tides; her armoured warriors
Leave Day's bright tents of azure and of gold,
Wherein they hid them, and in silence flock
Upon the solemn battlefield of Night
To try great issues with the blind old king,
The Titan Darkness, who great Pharaoh fought
With groping hands, and conquered for a span.

The starry hosts with silver lances prick
The scarlet fringes of the tents of Day,
And turn their crystal shields upon their breasts,
And point their radiant lances, and so wait
The stirring of the giant in his caves.

The solitary hills send long, sad sighs
As the blind Titan grasps their locks of pine
And trembling larch to drag him toward the sky,
That his wild-seeking hands may clutch the Moon
From her war-chariot, scythed and wheeled with light,
Crush bright-mailed stars, and so, a sightless king,
Reign in black desolation ! Low-set vales
Weep under the black hollow of his foot,
While sobs the sea beneath his lashing hair
Of rolling mists, which, strong as iron cords,
Twine round tall masts and drag them to the reefs.

Swifter rolls up Astarte's light-scythed car;
Dense rise the jewelled lances, groves of light;
Red flouts Mars' banner in the voiceless war
(The mightiest combat is the tongueless one);
The silver dartings of the lances prick
His fingers from the mountains, catch his locks

And toss them in black fragments to the winds,
Pierce the vast hollow of his misty foot,
Level their diamond tips against his breast,
And force him down to lair within his pit
And thro' its chinks thrust down his groping hands
To quicken Hell with horror — for the strength
That is not of the Heavens is of Hell.

(The Collected Poems of Isabella Valancy Crawford)

Orlo Miller (Born in 1919)

A feature writer who has spent most of his life in London, Ontario, Miller has always had a special interest in the history of south-western Ontario.

THE DONNELLYS MUST DIE

Foreword

The brutal murder of an old farmer named James Donnelly and four members of his family near the village of Lucan in southwestern Ontario in 1880 has long fascinated the public and students of crime. The murders were the climax of a feud that is unique in Canadian crime and almost unparalleled in recent times in the western world.

The story has been told so often that it is now almost in the realm of legend. Legend has been recited as fact for so long that the truth lies buried fathoms deep.

I have attempted to reveal that truth.

The sole source of facts for all previously published accounts has been the newspaper reports of the trial of six of the suspected murderers in London, Ontario, in November, 1880, and January, 1881. Many articles and books have been based on this source, including W. Stewart Wallace's scholarly résumé in *Canadian Murders and Mysteries*.

In addition to telling the story of the Canadian feud I have tried to describe its origins in Ireland. It began in Tipperary in 1766, came to Canada with the great Irish migrations of the 1830s and 1840s, and reached its climax on the night of February 3, 1880. On that night, a gang of men killed James, Johannah, Thomas, Bridget, and John Donnelly. Although eyewitnesses identified the killers in court, there were no convictions because the feud filled the jury with fear.

There are in this book a few outbursts of personal anger which I trust will be considered justified. There is no question that upon occasion the members of the Donnnelly family committed misdemeanours. There can equally be no question that they did *not* merit the savage punishment meted out to them by their neighbours. I consider their unavenged deaths an unexpunged blot on the Canadian judicial system.

A Night's Work

The work of murder began shortly after midnight.

Entry to the Donnelly home presented no problem. The door had been left on the latch for Jim Feeheley.

It appears that the man identified by Johnny O'Connor as Constable James Carroll entered first, alone. The rest of the Vigilantes waited outside.

Carroll found a lamp and lit it. He may first have gone to Tom Donnelly's room, wakened him and placed a pair of handcuffs on his wrists. This is conjecture, but in view of the timing of events it seems probable. His next move was witnessed.

Carrying the lamp, he entered the bedroom off the kitchen to wake the old man. There was an exchange of words between them which wakened the O'Connor lad. He heard only the tail-end of the conversation, but what he heard makes it easy to reconstruct the unrecorded part. It must have begun with the usual Biddulph gambit about having a warrant for arrest.

At this stage Jim Donnelly seems to have had no inkling of what was to come. He was irritated at being awakened, but apparently assumed the visit to be a legitimate legal call. As he struggled into his trousers under the eyes of the intruder he growled:

"What charge have you got against me now?"

"I've got another charge against you," the visitor said; then, apparently convinced that the old man suspected nothing, he went into the kitchen while Donnelly finished putting on his boots. Johnny heard him walking back and forth there, whistling. He seemed still to be alone.

A moment or two later Jim Donnelly went into the kitchen and Johnny O'Connor heard him exclaim:

"Tom! Are you handcuffed?"

Tom Donnelly's voice answered:

"Yes. He thinks he's smart."

The old man immediately returned to the bedroom to get his coat. Carroll may have suspected he was after a weapon; in any case he followed him with the lamp.

The O'Connor boy was using Donnelly's coat as a pillow. He dragged it from under his head and offered it to his host.

"It's here," he said.

If we are to believe Johnny's evidence, this by-play took place in full view of the Vigilante leader. It makes Johnny's later escape from that house of death very remarkable indeed.

By now Mrs. Donnelly was awake, dressed and in the kitchen. Her first concern was a housewifely one. Going to the door of her bedroom she called out:

"Bridget! Get up and light the fire!"

Jim's niece had apparently been wakened by the voices. She came from the bedroom immediately. Johnny heard her lifting off the stove lids.

There was a murmur of voices in the kitchen. Then Tom spoke:

"All right. Now read your warrant."

"There's lots of time for that," the constable said.

At that point, someone shouted. It was the signal. The outside door burst open and the Vigilantes entered.

The rest is utter confusion.

Johnny O'Connor said that when the men poured into the house, Bridget Donnelly raced up the stairs, and he after her. When she reached the top, she closed the door in his face. He ran back down the stairs, dived under the bed in the old man's room and hid behind a laundry basket.

While this was going on, the Donnellys were being assaulted. Johnny says the Viligantes were "hammering them with sticks." It is impossible to say for certain who died first, or who last. However, the two old people were probably dead when the Vigilantes dragged Bridget down the stairs and killed her.

Tom Donnelly gave them the most trouble. Beaten, battered and bleeding, he broke away from his captors and ran outside. The blood draining from many wounds created a pool that was still visible in the snow near the house the following morning. With his hands manacled, he was no match for his attackers. They dragged him back into the kitchen and threw him on the floor.

A voice said:

"Hit him with a spade and break his skull open."

Johnny did not see the blow fall. Local legend says the spade decapitated its victim, and that until the end of his days one of the Vigilantes was known by the nickname "Spadey."

Nothing was now to be heard except the heavy breathing of the murderers. Some of them came to Jim Donnelly's bedroom, poured kerosene on the bed and set it afire. Then they all left.

Some moments later Johnny crawled out of his hiding-place. As he fled from the burning bedstead he inadvertently stepped on the body of Mrs. Donnelly. Another of the victims was still breathing. He saw also the body of Tom Donnelly and near it, something that "looked like a dog's head." He did not see the body of Bridget.

A few moments later he was seeking refuge at the home of Pat Whelan.

The Donnelly homestead was a substantial structure. The flames of its burning must have been visible for a considerable distance in all directions. When Pat Ryder's barns burned on January 10, people came from all points of the compass to see the fire. Nobody visited the pyre of James, Johannah, Tom and Bridget Donnelly in the early morning hours of February 4, 1880, except Pat Whelan and his sons.

They would not have gone either had it not been for the unexpected presence and unplanned escape of little Johnny O'Connor.

II

When the murderers had finished at the Donnelly homestead they made their way to Will Donnelly's house at Whalen's Corners, three and a half miles distant.

Some of the Vigilantes may have defected before they got there. There were not as many engaged in the work at Will's home.

They could not have known of Will Donnelly's two guests — his brother John, and Martin Hogan. Hogan, John and Will had talked late. They had been asleep only a little over an hour when the Vigilantes arrived, at a quarter past two.

The murderers went first to the stable where Will's prize stallion was bedded. In one of the most savage acts of a night of unmitigated horror, they beat the poor animal with clubs, apparently in the hope that its screams would bring Will from the house. When this failed of its object, some of them began pounding on Will's door and shouting "Fire!" while others prepared their weapons for the ambush.

Inside the house it was John Donnelly who wakened first. He roused Will and then went to the door to investigate the racket. When he opened it there were two shots — one from a shotgun, the other from a rifle — at point-blank range. He fell back into the house and died within five minutes.

Satisfied that they had killed Will Donnelly, the Vigilantes left after firing a triumphant volley of shots into the air. According to some witnesses they intended one more call that night — at the home of Jim Keeffe. They left clear evidence in the snow that they had started in that direction, had hesitated and then dispersed to their homes.

After five murders, their blood lust had been sated.

Unfortunately for them, they had left two living witnesses to the night's work. Johnny O'Connor had by now already told his story to the Whelan family. Will Donnelly was keeping his own counsel.

L. M. Montgomery (1874-1942)

Few Canadian writers have ever been so affectionately regarded outside of their own country as L. M. Montgomery. Her childhood classic *Anne of Green Gables* has remained a best seller for over fifty years. Mark Twain calls its imaginative Prince Edward Island heroine "the dearest and most lovable child in fiction since the immortal Alice." The following chapter from the book takes place after Marilla and her brother finally decide not to send Anne back to the Orphans' Home.

ANNE SAYS HER PRAYERS

When Marilla took Anne up to bed that night she said stiffly :

"Now, Anne, I noticed last night that you threw your clothes all about the floor when you took them off. That is a very untidy habit, and I can't allow it at all. As soon as you take off any article of clothing fold it neatly and place it on the chair. I haven't any use at all for little girls who aren't neat."

"I was so harrowed up in my mind last night that I didn't think about my clothes at all," said Anne. "I'll fold them nicely to-night. They always made us do that at the asylum. Half the time, though, I'd forget, I'd be in such a hurry to get into bed nice and quiet and imagine things."

"You'll have to remember a little better if you stay here," admonished Marilla. "There, that looks something like. Say your prayers now and get into bed."

"I never say any prayers," announced Anne.

Marilla looked horrified astonishment.

"Why, Anne, what do you mean ? Were you never taught to say your prayers ? God always wants little girls to say their prayers. Don't you know who God is, Anne ?"

" 'God is a spirit, infinite, eternal and unchangeable in His being, wisdom, power, holiness, justice, goodness, and truth,' " responded Anne promptly and glibly.

Marilla looked rather relieved.

"So you do know something then, thank goodness ! You're not quite a heathen. Where did you learn that ?"

"Oh, at the asylum Sunday-school. They made us learn the whole catechism. I liked it pretty well. There's something splendid about some of the words. 'Infinite, eternal and unchangeable.' Isn't that grand ? It has such a roll to it — just like a big organ playing. You couldn't quite call it poetry, I suppose, but it sounds a lot like it, doesn't it ?"

"We're not talking about poetry, Anne — we are talking about saying your prayers. Don't you know it's a terrible wicked thing not to say your prayers every night ? I'm afraid you are a very bad little girl."

"You'd find it easier to be bad than good if you had red hair," said Anne reproachfully. "People who haven't red hair don't know what trouble is. Mrs. Thomas told me that God made my hair red *on purpose,* and I've never cared about Him since. And anyhow I'd always be too tired at night to bother saying prayers. People who have to look after twins can't be expected to say their prayers. Now, do you honestly think they can ?"

Marilla decided that Anne's religious training must be begun at once. Plainly there was no time to be lost.

"You must say your prayers while you are under my roof, Anne."

"Why, of course, if you want me to," assented Anne cheerfully. "I'd do anything to oblige you. But you'll have to tell me what to say for this once. After I get into bed I'll imagine out a real nice prayer to say always. I believe that it will be quite interesting, now that I come to think of it."

"You must kneel down," said Marilla in embarrassment.

Anne knelt at Marilla's knee and looked up gravely.

"Why must people kneel down to pray ? If I really wanted to pray I'll tell you what I'd do. I'd go out into a real big field all alone or into the deep, deep woods, and I'd look up into the sky—up—up—up—

into that lovely blue sky that looks as if there was no end to its blue-
ness. And then I'd just *feel* a prayer. Well, I'm ready. What am I
to say ?"

Marilla felt more embarrassed than ever. She had intended to
teach Anne the childish classic, "Now I lay me down to sleep." But
she had, as I have told you, the glimmerings of a sense of humour —
which is simply another name for a sense of the fitness of things; and
it suddenly occurred to her that that simple little prayer, sacred to a
white-robed childhood lisping at motherly knees, was entirely unsuited
to this freckled witch of a girl who knew and cared nothing about God's
love, since she had never had it translated to her through the medium
of human love.

"You're old enough to pray for yourself, Anne," she said finally.
"Just thank God for your blessings and ask Him humbly for the things
you want."

"Well, I'll do my best," promised Anne, burying her face in
Marilla's lap. "Gracious heavenly Father — that's the way the
ministers say it in church, so I suppose it's all right in a private prayer,
isn't it ?" she interjected, lifting her head for a moment. "Gracious
heavenly Father, I thank Thee for the White Way of Delight and the
Lake of Shining Waters and Bonny and the Snow Queen. I'm really
extremely grateful for them. And that's all the blessings I can think
of just now to thank Thee for. As for the things I want, they're so
numerous that it would take a great deal of time to name them all, so
I will only mention the two most important. Please let me stay at
Green Gables; and please let me be good-looking when I grow up. I
remain.

Yours respectfully, Anne Shirley

"There, did I do it all right ?" she asked eagerly, getting up.
"I could have made it much more flowery if I'd had a little more time
to think it over."

Poor Marilla was only preserved from complete collapse by
remembering that it was not irreverence, but simply spiritual ignorance
on the part of Anne that was responsible for this extraordinary petition.
She tucked the child up in bed, mentally vowing that she should be
taught a prayer the very next day, and was leaving the room with the
light when Anne called her back.

"I've just thought of it now. I should have said 'Amen' in place
of 'yours respectfully,' shouldn't I ? — the way the ministers do. I'd
forgotten it, but I felt a prayer should be finished off in some way, so
I put in the other. Do you suppose it will make any difference ?"

"I — I don't suppose it will," said Marilla. "Go to sleep now
like a good child. Good night."

"I can say good night to-night with a clear conscience," said Anne, cuddling luxuriously down among her pillows.

Marilla retreated to the kitchen, set the candle firmly on the table, and glared at Matthew.

"Matthew Cuthbert, it's about time somebody adopted that child and taught her something. She's next door to a perfect heathen. Will you believe that she never said a prayer in her life till to-night? I'll send to the manse to-morrow and borrow the Peep of Day series, that's what I'll do. And she shall go to Sunday-school just as soon as I can get some suitable clothes for her. I foresee that I shall have my hands full. Well, well, we can't get through this world without our share of trouble. I've had a pretty easy life of it so far, but my time has come at last and I suppose I'll just have to make the best of it."

(Anne of Green Gables)

Sir Cecil E. Denny (1850-1928)

Denny joined the North-West Mounted Police in 1874 and later became an inspector. His most important work, *Riders of the* *Plains,* was published in 1905. The following is from Colonel French's Report of the NWMP March West, 1874.

THE LAW MARCHES WEST

We were at last at our journey's end, the Bow and Belly rivers. Three deserted log huts without roofs were the only forts visible. Here we were supposed to find luxuriant pasturage, a perfect garden of Eden, climate milder than Toronto, etc. As far as our experience goes, that vicinity for sixty or seventy miles in every direction is little better than a desert; not a tree to be seen anywhere, ground parched and poor, and wherever there was a little swamp it had been destroyed by buffalo. A reference to my diary will show what a very serious position we were now in. We had come a distance of seven hundred and eighty-one miles from the Red River, and after the first eighteen had not seen a human habitation except a few Indian wigwams. It was now the middle of September, and the appalling fact was ever pressing on my mind that on the 20th of September last year the whole country from the Cypress Hills to the Old Wives' Lakes was covered with a foot of snow, several oxen and horses having been frozen to death. All over the country there is very little wood, and snow would hide the buffalo chips available. From what I heard of the fertility of the soil on the Bow and Belly rivers I had hoped that the horses and oxen with a few weeks' rest in the vicinity would have pulled up greatly in condition, but in reality the force had to leave there as quickly as possible to prevent their actually being starved to death. In fact several of the oxen did die of starvation, but the mistake is readily accounted for. Those who travelled along the base of the Rocky Mountains reported on the fertility of the soil in the headwaters of the Bow and Belly Rivers, and somehow their reports came to be applied to the whole course of the rivers.

On the 11th the force moved up the Belly River but could find no ford at first, the water being either too deep or too rapid. Pushing on sixteen or eighteen miles we found a ford. I sent out two reconnoitering parties from this point, one up the Belly River, and the other up the Bow River, and made arrangements to send Inspector Walsh and seventy men and fifty-seven horses through to Edmonton. The Edmonton party forded the river on the 14th; on the 13th the Belly River party returned, having travelled about thirty miles west without finding road, trail, or grass, but buffalo moving south in thousands. Inspector Denny's party did not return until late in the afternoon of the 14th. They had been up the Bow River for eighty miles, and gave a dreadful account of the country; neither wood nor grass, country very rough and bad hills ahead. Mr. Levaillee (who was in charge of the party of half-breeds selected by His Honour the Lieutenant-Governor to accompany or precede the force with Indian presents) was with Mr. Denny and placing great reliance on his judgment I asked him if the party could get through to Edmonton. He stated it would be almost impossible to take the horses through, and that we would certainly lose most of them if we tried. With much reluctance I had to counter-order the Edmonton party, and instructed Inspector Walsh to follow the main party south to the Three Buttes.

I feel, sir, that in the foregoing report I have but very inadequately represented the doings of the force. The broad fact is, however, apparent — a Canadian force hastily raised, armed, and equipped, and not under martial law, in a few months marched two thousand miles through a country for the most part as unknown as it proved bare of pasture and scanty in the supply of water. Of such a march under such adverse conditions, all true Canadians may well be proud . . . .

(The Law Marches West)

P. T. Bone (1859-1945)

The book from which this was taken was started when Bone was 84. He also wrote treatises on French pronunciation, and on proportional representation in voting.

WHEN THE STEEL WENT THROUGH

As soon as the bridge at the 3rd crossing of the Kicking Horse was finished — and also the small one over Porcupine Creek — I at once moved camp, to keep out of the way of the track-layers. I moved to a site between the 4th and 5th crossings, past Earle's camp and near to Keefer's on the next section . . . .

Coincident with this increase in the size of my camp, there was a change of cooks. The first cook I had unfortunately became sick and had to leave. I have already stated that I did not remember his name; but in trying to recall it since, the name Harry Nash comes to my mind. As for the name of the cook I got in his place, I doubt if I ever knew it ; for he was known by the nickname of "Montana Pete." Any man who had a nickname like that must have had a history. Be that as it may, he was a good cook, and proved to be quite a hustler when it came to moving camp.

When moving camp on this occasion, we had an exciting experience. As the team with our outfit was nearing the spot where I intended to pitch camp, the mules got balky, and ended by backing the wagon over the edge of the cliff. The wagon pulled the mules over with it, but by a lucky chance, it stuck against a large tree growing on the steep slope, some 40 or 50 feet below. But for this, it would in all likelihood have rolled on down to the river; and that would have been the end of the mules. The teamster, however, managed to get them unhitched from the wagon; badly skinned, but otherwise none the worse for their escapade.

But our camp outfit was scattered all over the slope. "Montana Pete," however, rose to the occasion. He promptly set about searching among the wreckage for some cooking utensils and food, and had an open fire lit and a good meal served to all of us in record time.

After this meal we hunted up our blankets and, as it was getting dark, we rolled up in them and went to sleep for the night on any fairly level spot we could find on the slope. We were astir early in the morning, gathering up our belongings and soon had the tents set up and the camp established at the only level spot we could find close to the tote-road.

The tote-road at this point followed closely along the route of the old pack trail known as the Golden Stairs, which the surveyors had used. In some places, it was just this pack trail widened to make it a wagon road. It wound in and out along the face of the slope which tops the almost sheer cliff, at the foot of which the waters of the Kicking Horse tumble in rapids over rocks and boulders, on their way to swell the less turbulent waters of the Columbia.

To avoid much heavy work along the face of this cliff, the railway crossed to the other side of the river at the 6th crossing. The bridge at this crossing was at the mouth of a tunnel, known as Muir's tunnel, built by Muir Brothers, the contractors.

Our camp was almost directly above this tunnel — some hundreds of feet — so we had some fairly stiff climbs to make in connection with the bridge building which we looked after from this camp. Besides the 6th crossing there were a number of fairly large trestle and pile bridges, over tributaries of the Kicking Horse, between the 5th and 6th crossings. And we had also the 7th crossing, where the railway crossed back again to the right bank of the river . . . .

The bridge to be built across the Columbia was the principal one which engaged my attention at this camp. It was a two-truss bridge and the piles for the pier connecting these trusses were driven from a scow, which was attached to a cable stretched across the river.

One day while I was watching the piles being driven I saw, approaching the cable, a raft floating downstream, with a man and a camp outfit on it. It was quite evident that this raft would get entangled with the cable, which hung low close to the water. The pile-driver crew shouted to the man on the raft to look out. Too late ! The raft swept under the cable, and passed on, but minus the passenger and cargo. For the cable caught the camp outfit and sheered it right off the raft. It caught the man too, but he hung on to it. With both hands gripping the cable, and one leg over it, he gave an exhibition of some rather odd gymnastics as he bobbed up and down in his struggles, half immersed in the water.

When finally rescued from his plight by the men on the scow, he turned out to be Greer, one of the subcontractors whom I had already met and knew quite well. Having finished a contract, he was moving his outfit to the mouth of the Beaver River where he expected to get another job. He thought that floating by raft would be the cheapest way to get there. But he hadn't calculated on the hazard of encountering a cable on the way.

Some of his outfit was salvaged, but how much I cannot say. One thing, however, was certain. He got a cold dip, for the season was well advanced and there was ice floating down the Columbia at the time . . . .

When the time came to move camp from Quartz Creek, winter had definitely set in. Two teams with sleighs arrived at camp one evening, and stayed the night to be ready to move the camp in the morning. It was a very cold night, and the temperature — according to current talk the next day — dropped to 40 degrees below zero. I had no thermometer, so cannot say whether that was, or was not, the right temperature. At any rate, it was cold enough to believe it was 40 below.

I offered to make room in the camp, for the night, for the two teamsters. But they said there was no need to do that; they were accustomed to sleeping out. So they passed the night in their sleighs, rolled up in their blankets.

The taking down of the cook's tent in the morning was no simple job. For the steam from the cooking had frozen the canvas into stiff sheets of ice. However, we got the tent packed up somehow; and we moved camp to a site on the left bank of the Beaver River a few miles from its month, that is to say, from its junction with the Columbia. This junction point later became known as Beavermouth.

Before setting up the tents at this new camping ground, we had first to clear from the site for each tent some two feet of snow; like excavating the cellar for a house before starting to build it. When the tents were set up, we packed this snow round the sides. This was quite a help in keeping out the cold . . .

At some time during the winter, the community at Donald was considerably stirred by an escapade in which some members of the headquarters staff located there had, unwittingly, got themselves involved.

As the story goes, paymaster Lukes and others of the different staffs, among whom was G.H. Duggan, were tobogganing one moonlit evening on the banks of the Columbia, which by that time was frozen over. When so disporting themselves they saw some men moving kegs across the river — whisky pedlars, evidently. Lukes was wearing a buffalo overcoat, similar to the coats worn by the North-West Mounted Police; and the idea, it would seem, occurred to him to play a joke on these men and give them a good scare, by pretending to be a policeman. So he bore down on them, ordering them in the name of the law to stop. They evidently did take him for a policeman, for they fled, leaving their kegs on the ice.

What was done with these kegs is not clear. But the joke turned out to be on Lukes and the other members of the party. For, a few days later, a charge of stealing whisky was laid against them, and they were summoned to appear at court at Beavermouth, to answer to the charge.

Sara Jeannette Duncan (1861-1922)

This writer was born in England but grew up in Brantford where she later taught school. She frequetly wrote for the *Toronto Globe,* was once on the editorial staff of the *Washington Post* and in 1888 became parliamentary correspondent for the *Montreal Star.*

A SOCIAL DEPARTURE

It was Orthodocia's first experience of a Pullman sleeper, and I dare say she found it exciting. I know I did. For economy's sake we had taken a lower berth together instead of luxuriating in a whole section; and as we sat in a vacant place across the car she watched the transformation of our own seat into a bed with disfavour from the beginning. "Extremely stuffy!" she said, "Extremely stuffy!" When the upper berth was shut down and the curtains drawn she thought it time to interfere. "Please put the top bed up," she said to the Negro porter, "we can't possibly sleep that way!"

"Sawry not tuh be able tuh 'commodate yuh, Miss; but dat berth's took by a gen'leman in de smokin' car at present, Miss."

"I suppose there is some mistake," said Orthodocia to me, whereupon I was obliged to tell her that the proceeding was perfectly regular, and that the gentleman in the smoking car would probably be a large oleomarginous person who would snore hideously, diffuse an odour of stale tobacco, and drop his boots at intervals during the night into our berth. Orthodocia then stated her intention of sitting up all night, a course from which she was dissuaded by the appearance of claimants for the only two seats that were left. Then the gentleman came in from the smoking car, and turned out to be a perfectly inoffensive little English curate, as new to the customs of the aborigines as Orthodocia, and quite as deeply distressed. "Perhaps — perhaps you would prefer my sitting up?" he said unhappily. "Oh no," said Orthodocia, *"I'll* sit up." "But really —" protested the curate. "It's not of the slightest consequence," Orthodocia interrupted frigidly, and sat down on the edge of our berth, while the frightened little man scrambled up to his with the aid of a stepladder. Orthodocia told me next morning that she sat there a long time waiting for the boots, but as nothing appeared she concluded that he must have slept in them. The curtains that screen the berths are buttoned loosely together, and the usual method of reconnoitring before making a sortie in the direction of the toilet-room is to thrust one's head out between the buttons. It was very early in the morning when Orthodocia did this : no sound was to be heard but the rattling of the train, and she did it very deliberately and very stealthily. She looked carefully in all directions, and was just about to depart, when an upward glance made her withdraw precipitately. For there above her was the anxious countenance and dishevelled locks of the curate, also scanning the situation and looking for the stepladder. I suppose, if I had not been willing, after performing my own toilet, to hold the top curtains together while Orthodocia made her exit, both she and the curate might have been there still.

We entered after that, the little curate and Orthodocia and I, into the most amicable relations, for it took us two days to get to Winnipeg, which was our first stopping-place, and nobody can sit within three feet of a small thin pale Ritualist, an alien in the Canadian Northwest, for two days, without feeling sorry for him and wishing to mitigate his lot in every possible way. So we fed him with chicken sandwiches from our hamper and made him cups of tea with our spirit lamp, and he in return gave us each three throat lozenges and some excellent spiritual nourishment in the form of tracts. He was going, he said, to labour in Assiniboia among the Indians, and hoped it would not be long before he could expostulate with them in their own tongue. In fact, he had quite expected to have picked up something of the language by this time. Possibly I could speak a little Cree ? He was disappointed, I think, to find that the aboriginal dialects did not survive more widely.

The country for the first day was very grim and barren and dreary. We rushed along through a wilderness of rocks and stunted shrubs, juniper chiefly. The great boulders thrust themselves through the scanty grasses like gaunt shoulders through a ragged gown. Now and then a spray of yellowing maple or of reddening oak broke the grey monotony, or the rocks blossomed into lichens, but this only gave an accent to the general desolation. And steadily travelling with us all along the sky-line went a fringe of blackened firs, martyred memorials of forest fires. That alliterative expression belongs properly to the curate, whose depression was frightful about this time, and whom I saw write it down in his note-book. I hope that any of the curate's English relations, who may read this chapter and be able to identify the phrase by one of his letters, will charitably refrain from communicating the plagiarism to the public. It is a very little one.

But next day we hurried along the north shore of Lake Superior, and the country grew in colour and boldness and significance. We could almost touch the great wet masses of stone the railway pierced, and there were tangled forest depths to look into, and always some glimpse of the majesty of the lake. It had many moods, sometimes blue and still and tender over headlands far away, sometimes deep and darkling in great inlets that gave back the tamarack and the pine clinging to their sheer rocky sides, sometimes sending long white waves dashing among broken boulders within a few feet of the road. I think when the world grew orthodox they exiled Pan to the north shore of Lake Superior, its beauty is so conscious, so strong, so eternal.

Arthur Buies (1840-1901)

Après des études agitées au Canada, à Dublin et à Paris, il participa à la campagne de Sicile dans l'armée de Garibaldi, puis rentra au Canada, fit du journalisme, fonda *La Lanterne* (1868-9), et fut un des chefs du mouvement libéral et anti-religieux dont le siège était l'Institut canadien de Montréal. Plus tard, il travailla à la colonisation sous la direction du curé Labelle et écrivit plusieurs monographies géographiques.

DESPERANZA

Je suis né il y a trente ans passés, et depuis lors je suis orphelin. De ma mère je ne connus que son tombeau, seize ans plus tard, dans un cimetière abandonné, à mille lieues de l'endroit où je vis le jour. Ce tombeau était une petite pierre déjà noire, presque cachée sous la mousse, loin des regards, sans doute oubliée depuis longtemps. Peut-être seul dans le monde y suis-je venu pleurer et prier.

Je fus longtemps sans pouvoir retracer son nom gravé dans la pierre; une inscription presque illisible disait qu'elle était morte à vingt-six ans, mais rien ne disait qu'elle avait été pleurée.

Le ciel était brûlant, et, cependant, le sol autour de cette pierre solitaire était humide. Sans doute l'ange de la mort vient de temps en temps verser des larmes sur les tombes inconnues et y secouer son aile pleine de la rosée de l'éternité.

Mon père avait amené ma mère dans une lointaine contrée de l'Amérique du Sud en me laissant aux soins de quelques bons parents qui m'ont recueilli. Aussi, mon berceau fut désert; je n'eus pas une caresse à cet âge même où le premier regard de l'enfant est un sourire; je puisai le lait au sein d'une inconnue, et, depuis, j'ai grandi, isolé au milieu des hommes, fatigué d'avance du temps que j'avais à vivre, déclassé toujours, ne trouvant rien qui pût m'attacher, ou qui valût quelque souci, de toutes les choses que l'homme convoite.

J'ai rencontré cependant quelques affections, mais un destin impitoyable les brisait à peine formées. Je ne suis pas fait pour rien de ce qui dure; j'ai été jeté dans la vie comme une feuille arrachée au palmier du désert et que le vent emporte, sans jamais lui laisser un coin de terre où se trouve l'abri ou le repos. Ainsi j'ai parcouru le monde et nulle part je n'ai pu reposer mon âme accablée d'amertume; j'ai laissé dans tous les lieux une partie de moi-même, mais en conservant intact le poids qui pèse sur ma vie comme la terre sur un cercueil.

Mes amours ont été des orages; il n'est jamais sorti de mon coeur que des flammes brûlantes qui ravageaient tout ce qu'elles pouvaient atteindre. Jamais aucune lèvre n'approcha la mienne pour y souffler l'amour saint et dévoué qui fait l'épouse et la mère.

Pourtant, un jour, j'ai cru, j'ai voulu aimer. J'engageai avec le destin une lutte horrible, qui dura tant que j'eus la force et la volonté de combattre. Pour trouver un coeur qui répondît au mien, j'ai fouillé des mondes, j'ai déchiré les voiles du mystère. Maintenant, vaincu, abattu pour toujours, sorti sanglant de cette tempête, je me demande si j'ai seulement aimé ! Peut-être que j'aimais, je ne sais trop; mon âme est un abîme où je n'ose plus regarder; il y a dans les natures profondes une vie mystérieuse qui ne se révèle jamais, semblable à ces mondes qui gisent au fond de l'océan, dans un éternel et sinistre repos. O mon Dieu ! cet amour était mon salut peut-être, et j'aurais vécu pour une petite part de ce bonheur commun à tous les hommes. Mais non; la pluie généreuse ruisselle en vain sur le front de l'arbre frappé par la foudre; il ne peut renaître ... Bientôt, abandonnant les rameaux flétris, elle retombe goutte à goutte, silencieuse, désolée, comme les pleurs qu'on verse dans l'abandon.

Seul désormais, et pour toujours rejeté dans la nuit du coeur avec l'amertume de la félicité rêvée et perdue, je ne veux, ni ne désire, ni n'attends plus rien, si ce n'est le repos que la mort seule donne. Le trouverai-je ? Peut-être; parce que, déjà, j'ai la quiétude de l'accablement, la tranquillité de l'impuissance reconnue contre laquelle on ne peut se débattre. Mon âme n'est plus qu'un désert sans écho où le vent seul du désespoir souffle, sans même y réveiller une plainte.

Et de quoi me plaindrais-je ? Quel cri la douleur peut-elle encore m'arracher ? Oh ! si je pouvais pleurer seulement un jour, ce serait un jour de bonheur et de joie. Les larmes sont une consolation et la douleur qui s'épanche se soulage. Mais la mienne n'a pas de cours; j'ai en moi une fontaine amère et n'en puis exprimer une goutte, je garde mon supplice pour le nourrir, je vis avec un poison dans le coeur, un mal que je ne puis nommer, et je n'ai plus une larme pour l'adoucir, pas même celle d'un ami pour m'en consoler.

Maintenant tout est fini pour moi; j'ai épuisé la somme de volonté et d'espérance que le ciel m'avait donnée. Otez au soleil sa lumière, au ciel ses astres, que restera-t-il ? L'immensité dans la nuit; voilà le désespoir. Mes souvenirs ressemblent à ces fleurs qu'aucune rosée ne peut plus rafraîchir, à ces tiges nues dont le vent a arraché les feuilles. Je dis adieu au soleil de mes jeunes années comme on salue au réveil les songes brillants qui s'enfuient. Chaque matin de ma vie a vu s'évanouir un rêve, et maintenant je me demande si j'ai vécu. Je compte les années qui ont fui : elles m'apparaissent comme des songes brisés qu'on cherche en vain à ressaisir, comme la vague jetée sur l'écueil rend au loin un son déchiré, longtemps après être retombée dans le sombre océan.

J'ai mesuré au pas de course le néant des choses humaines, de tout ce qui fait palpiter le coeur de l'homme, l'ambition, l'amour . . . L'ambition ! j'en ai eu deux ou trois ans à peine : cette fleur amère que les larmes de toute une vie ne suffisent pas à arroser, s'est épanouie pour moi tout à coup et s'est flétrie de même.

En trente ans j'ai souffert ce qu'on souffre en soixante; j'ai vidé bien au-delà de ma coupe de fiel; à peine au milieu de la vie, je suis déjà au déclin de ma force, de mon énergie, de mes espérances. Pour moi il n'y a plus de patrie, plus d'avenir ! . . .

L'avenir ! eh ! que m'importe ! Quand on a perdu l'illusion, il ne reste plus rien devant soi. J'ai souffert la plus belle moitié de la vie, que pourrais-je faire de l'autre, et pourquoi disputer au néant quelques restes de moi-même ? Sur le retour de la vie, quand les belles années ont disparu, l'homme ne peut plus songer qu'au passé, car il voit la mort de trop près; il ne désire plus, il regrette, et ce qu'il aime est déjà loin de lui. Pour cette nouvelle et dernière lutte, j'arriverai sans force, épuisé d'avance, certain d'être vaincu, tout prêt pour la mort qui attend, certaine, inévitable, pour tout enfouir et tout effacer.

Non, non, je ne veux plus . . . je m'efface maintenant que je ne laisse ni un regret ni une pensée. Si, plus tard, quelqu'un me cherche, il ne me trouvera pas; mais, peut-être qu'en passant un jour près d'une de ces fosses isolées où aucun nom n'arrête le regard, où nulle voix n'invite au souvenir, il sentira un peu de poussière emportée par le souffle de l'air s'arrêter sur son front humide . . . cette poussière sera peut-être moi . . .

8 juin 1874.

(*Chroniques, Voyages, II,* 1875)

Laure Conan (1845-1924)

Félicité Angers vécut à La Malbaie et a écrit quelques biographies, des romans historiques et le premier roman d'analyse canadien-français, *Angéline de Montbrun* (1884), dont l'héroïne trouve dans la méditation le remède à la solitude désespérante de sa vie. Elle fut la première femme de lettres du Canada français.

L'AMOUR DU PÈRE

7 juillet.

La consolation, c'est d'accepter la volonté de Dieu, c'est de songer à la joie du revoir, c'est de savoir que je l'ai aimé autant que je pouvais aimer.

Dans quelle délicieuse union nous vivions ensemble. Rien ne me coûtait pour lui plaire; mais je savais que les froissements involontaires sont inévitables, et pour en effacer toute trace, rarement je le quittais le soir sans lui demander pardon. Chère et douce habitude, qui me ramena vers lui la veille de sa mort. Quand je pense à cette journée du 17 ! Quelles heureuses folles nous étions, Mina et moi ! Jamais jour si triste eut-il une veille si gaie ? Combien j'ai béni Dieu, ensuite, d'avoir suivi l'inspiration qui me portait vers mon père. Ce dernier entretien restera l'une des forces de ma vie.

Je le trouvai qui lisait tranquillement. Nox dormait à ses pieds devant la cheminée où le feu allait s'éteindre. Je me souviens qu'à la porte, je m'arrêtai un instant pour jouir de l'aspect charmant de la salle. Il aimait passionnément la verdure et les fleurs et j'en mettais partout. Par la fenêtre ouverte, à travers le feuillage j'apercevais la mer tranquille, le ciel radieux. Sans lever les yeux de son livre, mon père me demanda ce qu'il y avait. Je m'approchai, et m'agenouillant comme j'aimais à le faire devant lui, je lui dis que je ne pourrais m'endormir sans la certitude qu'aucune ombre de froideur ne s'était glissée entre nous, sans lui demander pardon si j'avais eu le malheur de lui déplaire en quelque chose. Je vois encore son air moitié amusé, moitié attendri. Il m'embrassa sur les cheveux en m'appelant sa chère folle, et me fit asseoir pour causer. Il était dans ses heures d'enjouement, et alors sa parole ondoyante et légère avait un singulier charme. Je n'ai connu personne dont la gaieté se prît si vite. Mais ce soir-là quelque chose de solennel m'oppressait. Je me sentais émue sans savoir pourquoi. Tout ce que je lui devais me revenait à l'esprit. Il me semblait que je n'avais jamais apprécié son admirable tendresse. J'éprouvais un immense besoin de le remercier, de le chérir. Minuit sonna, et avec ce son, qui me parut lugubre, une crainte vague et terrible entra en moi. Cette chambre si jolie, si riante me fit soudain l'effet d'un tombeau. Je me levai pour cacher mon trouble et m'approchai de la fenêtre. La mer s'était retirée au large, mais le faible bruit des flots m'arrivait par intervalles. J'essayais résolument de raffermir mon coeur, car je ne voulais pas attrister mon père. Lui commença dans l'appartement un de ces va-et-vient qui étaient dans ses habitudes. En passant, son regard tomba sur la *fille du Tintoret* et une ombre douloureuse couvrit son visage. Il s'arrêta et resta sombre et rêveur à la considérer. Je l'observais sans oser suivre sa pensée. Nos yeux se rencontrèrent, et ses larmes jaillirent. Il me tendit les bras et sanglota : O mon bien suprême ! ô ma Tintorella !

Je fondis en larmes. Cette soudaine et extraordinaire émotion répondant à ma secrète angoisse m'épouvantait, et je m'écriai : Mon Dieu, mon Dieu, que va-t-il donc arriver ?

Il se remit à l'instant, et essaya de me rassurer, mais je sentais les violents battements de son coeur, pendant qu'il répétait de sa voix la plus calme : Ce n'est rien, ce n'est rien, c'est la sympathie pour le pauvre Jacques Robusti.

Et comme je pleurais toujours et frissonnais entre ses bras, il me porta sur le sofa au coin du feu; puis il alla fermer la fenêtre et jeta ensuite quelques morceaux de bois sur les tisons. La flamme s'éleva bientôt vive et brillante. Alors revenant à moi, il me demanda pourquoi j'étais si bouleversée. Je lui avouai mes terreurs.

Bah ! dit-il légèrement, des nerfs. Et comme j'insistais, en disant que lui aussi avait senti l'approche du malheur, il me dit :

— J'ai eu un moment d'émotion, mais tu sais que Mina assure que j'ai une nature d'artiste.

Il me badinait, me raisonnait, me câlinait, et comme je restais toute troublée, il me prit dans ses bras, et me demanda gravement : Mon enfant, si moi ton père j'avais l'entière disposition de ton avenir serais-tu bien terrifiée ?

Alors, partant de là, il m'entretint avec une adorable tendresse de la folie, de l'absurdité de la défiance de Dieu; *plus père que tous les pères ensemble.*

Sa foi entrait en moi comme une vigueur. La vague, l'horrible crainte disparut, et étroitement pressée contre son coeur, je ne pleurais plus que sur ces bornes douloureuses où s'arrête, avec la puissance de l'union, la puissance de l'amour. Jamais, non jamais je ne m'étais sentie si profondément, si passionnément aimée. Pourtant je comprenais (et avec quelle lumineuse clarté) que rien dans les tendresses humaines ne peut faire soupçonner ce qu'est l'amour de Dieu pour ses créatures.

(*Angéline de Montbrun*, 1884)

Thomas Chapais (1859-1946)

Avocat, journaliste, conseiller législatif, ministre et sénateur, président de la Société royale du Canada (1923), créé chevalier (Knight) en 1925, personnage considérable de son temps, il a professé à l'Université Laval un Cours d'histoire du Canada qui fut publié et qui porte surtout sur l'évolution constitutionnelle et l'histoire politique de 1760 à 1867. Il est aussi l'auteur de biographies de Talon et de Montcalm.

LE CARNAVAL QUÉBECQUOIS DE 1758

La fin du carnaval québecquois de 1758 fut étourdissante. L'intendant donna trois bals coup sur coup. Et le jeu prit des proportions fantastiques. « Il y a, notait Montcalm dans ses chroniques épistolaires, des acteurs qui perdent ou gagnent cent ou cent cinquante livres; mais pour qu'on parle de vous, il faut être homme à perdre trois ou quatre cents livres... L'intendant perd quatre-vingt mille francs, et, entre nous, en est très piqué... Toujours le plus effroyable jeu. L'intendant a perdu cette nuit quinze cents livres en trois quarts d'heure. Il est à cinquante mille écus de pertes, au moyen de quoi toute la ville, le militaire gagne peu ou prou, et ses valets qui jouent gros contre lui. Peu de militaires perdent heureusement. Johanne et Lestang du leur; mais les petits pontes gras à pleine peau ». A ce moment une lettre du ministre, expédiée par Louisbourg, apporta une ordonnance du Roi pour défendre les jeux de hasard. « Ce qui est arrivé à propos, écrit Montcalm dans son journal, vu l'excès où la fureur du jeu s'était portée, par l'exemple de M. Bigot et la tolérance du marquis de Vaudreuil. Cet intendant a perdu deux cent quatre mille livres, ce qui n'a pas empêché que plusieurs officiers ne se soient encore dérangés. Cette somme n'est rien pour un intendant du Canada qui n'est pas scrupuleux sur les moyens ». L'ordonnance royale produisit momentanément son effet. Et le 9 février Montcalm en donnait à Lévis la nouvelle : « Le jeu fini d'hier : Johanne, de Selles, Bougainville, Baros (?), les Berry vainqueurs, surtout Cadillac qui gagne quarante ou cinquante mille francs; l'intendant perdit encore hier six cents livres; je le crois bien fou du jeu ». Cependant Bigot crut devoir déclarer qu'il consentait à ce « qu'on le regardât comme un misérable si on jouait des jeux de hasard l'année prochaine chez lui ». On verra que promesse de joueur ne vaut guère mieux que promesse de buveur.

Ce qui était surtout de nature à indigner les bons citoyens, dans les folies criminelles dont nous venons de donner une esquisse, c'était leur contraste avec la détresse générale. La misère régnait partout; le peuple de Québec continuait à n'avoir pas de pain; le blé était rare à la campagne. On avait rendu une ordonnance pour faire sceller les moulins afin, disait-on, d'empêcher les habitants de faire moudre le grain nécessaire aux semences. La ration des troupes avait été réduite, le 19 octobre, à une livre de pain, un quart de lard et quatre onces de pois. Et le 1er novembre elle avait été réduite encore à une demi-livre de pain, trois quarts de boeuf, un quart de morue et un quart de pain, avec une demi-livre de pain payée en argent. Enfin, depuis le mois de décembre les troupes et la population mangeaient du cheval. A Montréal la seconde diminution de la ration fit regimber les troupes de la marine, qui refusèrent de prendre leurs vivres à la distribution. M. de Lévis se porta à leurs quartiers et les fit rentrer dans l'ordre. Lorsqu'au mois de décembre on substitua pour partie le cheval au boeuf, les femmes de Montréal s'attroupèrent tumultueusement à la porte du marquis de Vaudreuil. Il en fit entrer quatre et leur demanda ce qu'elles voulaient. Elles répondirent qu'elles venaient lui demander du pain. Il leur déclara qu'il n'en avait pas à leur faire donner, que les troupes mêmes étaient à la ration, mais qu'il avait fait tuer des boeufs et des chevaux pour assister les pauvres dans ce temps de misère. Elles répliquèrent que la viande de cheval leur répugnait, que le cheval était ami de l'homme, que la religion défendait de le tuer et qu'elles aimeraient mieux mourir que d'en manger. Le gouverneur leur dit alors que c'était là des chimères, que la viande de cheval était bonne, et il les congédia en leur affirmant que si elles s'ameutaient encore, il les ferait toutes mettre en prison et en ferait pendre la moitié.

Lorsqu'arriva le moment de la première distribution de cheval aux troupes, on s'aperçut qu'il y avait de la fermentation parmi elles, et qu'elles étaient excitées par le peuple à la résistance. Averti que les soldats refusaient leur ration de cheval et se retiraient de la distribution, M. de Lévis accourut, ordonna de rassembler les compagnies, et en leur présence fit couper du cheval pour lui-même et commanda aux grenadiers d'en prendre. Ils voulurent faire quelques représentations, mais il les arrêta en leur enjoignant d'obéir, et en leur déclarant qu'il ferait pendre le premier qui broncherait, ajoutant qu'il les entendrait après la distribution. Les grenadiers, matés, prirent leur cheval, exemple qui fut suivi par toutes les compagnies. Alors ils eurent la liberté de faire leurs observations. Après avoir écouté leurs griefs, M. de Lévis les harangua et fit bonne justice du préjugé populaire qu'on avait essayé de leur faire partager. Il leur représenta que la viande de cheval était saine, qu'on en avait souvent mangé dans les villes assiégées, qu'il aurait l'oeil à ce que les chevaux abattus fussent en bonne condition, que lui-même en mangeait tous les jours, que les troupes de terre devaient donner l'exemple, etc. Ce ferme langage les fit rentrer dans le devoir, et il n'y eut plus de difficultés à ce sujet.

(*Le marquis de Montcalm,* 1911)

Lionel Groulx (1878-1967)

Professeur d'histoire à l'Université de Montréal de 1915 à 1948, il fonda l'Institut d'histoire de l'Amérique française en 1946 et, en 1947, la *Revue d'histoire de l'Amérique française.* Il fut membre de la Société royale du Canada et membre de l'Académie canadienne-française. Son oeuvre très abondante couvre presque toutes les périodes de notre histoire. Ses discours et essais en ont fait un chef de file du nationalisme. Il est aussi l'auteur de deux romans.

LE CANADA DE 1713

Aspect social : les classes.

Où l'histoire du Canada prend, en ce temps-là, son plus vif intérêt, c'est bien plutôt dans son aspect social. L'histoire d'un peuple colonial, faut-il y insister, n'est pas l'histoire d'un peuple fait; c'est l'histoire attachante d'un peuple qui se fait. Sous l'influence des institutions, d'un nouveau mode de vie, du milieu géographique, des classes naissent, se transforment, accentuent leurs traits, leur originalité. Où en sont quelques-unes de ces classes ?

Au bas de l'échelle où il s'est mis lui-même, voici *le coureur de bois.* Il se distingue nettement du « voyageur », voiturier par eau, homme d'un métier nécessaire dans un pays à vastes étendues où la route fluviale gardera longtemps sa suprématie; homme aussi d'un métier autorisé, aux gages des marchands « équipeurs », des missionnaires, des commandants des postes, pour le transport des marchandises dans l'ouest ou ailleurs, aux gages aussi parfois des gouvernants pour le transport des présents aux sauvages, courrier, ambassadeur vers les postes ou les nations alliées des Pays d'en haut. Tout autre le coureur de bois, qui se définit par deux traits principaux : ceux d'un vagabond professionnel et d'un hors la loi. Au début, l'on ne se faisait coureur que pour un temps, pour s'amasser quelque pécule, hâter, améliorer son établissement. Vers 1690, la course des bois est devenue un métier, la fonction unique et permanente d'une classe d'hommes. Et cette fonction, on l'exerce en rupture avec le cadre civilisé, en dépit des lois et châtiments, se refusant même aux amnisties du roi. Le coureur de bois, c'est désormais le converti sans retour au mode de vie indienne, qui s'agrège même parfois aux nations indiennes pour n'en plus sortir. Non seulement il forme une classe sociale, mais il a l'orgueil de sa classe. Ce vagabond aux moeurs dissolues peut être aussi bien un fils de seigneur qu'un fils d'habitant. Au dire même de de Meulles et de bien d'autres, la passion de la course sévirait surtout parmi les fils des seigneurs. Quelle que soit son origine, le coureur de bois affiche une insolente fierté de son métier; et il pousse cette fierté fanfaronne jusqu'au mépris de l'existence routinière du sédentaire. La course des bois, renchérit Denonville, « en fait des nobles portant l'espée, la dentelle... » Et le gouverneur d'appuyer encore : « L'air de noble qu'ils prennent à leur retour par leurs ajustements et par leurs débauches au cabaret, fait que meprisans les peisans ils tiennent au dessous d'eus d'epouser leurs filles... et outre cela ne se veulent plus abesser à cultiver la terre et ne veulent plus entendre qu'à retourner dans les bois continuer le mesme metier... » Type social assez complexe. Premier prolétaire de la colonie, il sera pour elle une maladie, un chancre, et il ne laissera pas de lui rendre quelques services. Il dirigera trop volontiers la fourrure vers les comptoirs anglais; il se fera même le fourrier des Anglais vers l'hinterland américain; il assemblera aussi la fourrure pour le compte des siens; il restera l'un des agents des grandes explorations, parmi les premiers avant 1700 à sonder l'ouest américain, à se jeter à la découverte du Missouri et des mines du Nouveau-Mexique. Course des bois : gaspillage de la plus virile jeunesse, de celle des champs et de celle des manoirs; mais aussi passion presque fatale d'une jeunesse victime des sortilèges de son pays et plus ou moins en révolte contre une économie trop fermée, à carrières trop limitées. Métier qui a produit un type humain quand même séduisant par sa vigueur physique, son audace, son esprit d'aventure, sa contribution au folklore et voire sa fanfaronnade. Assez original et prenant pour inspirer toute une littérature et s'ouvrir les portes de la légende et de l'art.

Un autre type social achève de prendre ses traits définitifs : l'habitant. La guerre lui a été dure. Elle lui a infligé des dévastations et dérangements sur dérangements. Il a souffert de la misère généralisée, des dévaluations de la monnaie de carte, de la course des bois qui lui a pris trop de ses fils. La merveille est que son ascension vers l'aisance ne s'est ralentie que temporairement. Dans son enquête de 1712 sur les seigneuries, Gédéon de Catalogne a trouvé en maints endroits des colons « aisés » et même « fort aisés » et « riches » : « C'est icy le meilleur pays du monde pour le laboureur », ne se retient pas d'écrire Catalogne. Les missionnaires et curés, bien placés pour voir, ne parlent pas autrement. Pour les « commodités de la vie », tous le mettent au-dessus du paysan de France. De cette condition lui viennent peut-être sa qualité d'âme, sa psychologie. L'habitant canadien, qui est-il en définitive sinon un prolétaire, un engagé d'hier en voie d'exhaussement social et qui prend conscience de cette élévation ? Sur son grand rectangle de sol dont il se sait le propriétaire et le maître, il sait aussi qu'il fait oeuvre solide, féconde, la plus féconde de son pays. Il le sait par la sorte de fascination qu'il exerce sur le troupier des compagnies du roi trop enclin, au gré des autorités, à sortir des rangs pour prendre terre. Il le sait par le cas que font de son travail et de son rôle les gouvernants de la colonie, les Raudot par exemple, qui regardaient les habitants comme les vrais bâtisseurs de la colonie. « Il est certain, écrivaient ces intendants, que ce sera toujours les habitants qui feront la fortune de cette colonie. » L'habitant est fier, nous dit-on. Et comment ne le serait-il pas ? On nous apprend qu'il refuse d'exercer les petits métiers, celui de ramoneur de cheminées par exemple, qu'il faut faire venir de la Savoie. Quoi de plus explicable ? Les habitants « font de mauvais valets », reprend Charlevoix, parce qu'« ils ont le coeur trop haut ». Et pourquoi, nous disent d'autres contemporains, se feraient-ils valets quand il leur est si facile d'être leur propre maître ? Ils n'aiment pas non plus qu'on les appelle « paysans ». Rappelons-nous le texte tant de fois cité de Lahontan : « Quand je dis Païsans, je me trompe, il faut dire habitans, car ce titre de Païsan n'est non plus reçu ici qu'en Espagne, soit parce qu'ils ne payent ni sel ni taille, et qu'ils ont la liberté de la chasse et de la pêche, ou qu'enfin leur vie aisée les met en parallèle avec les Nobles ». L'habitant de la fin du dix-septième siècle a lui aussi, et dès ce temps-là, sa fierté de classe : fierté de l'homme adonné à l'exploitation autonome, fierté de patron, de chef d'entreprise.

Le type du *seigneur* est peut-être celui qui a le moins bougé, le moins évolué. Les seigneurs canadiens se partagent toujours en deux catégories : les seigneurs actifs, terriens, occupés à la mise en valeur de leurs terres; les seigneurs en disponibilité, oserais-je dire, presque solitaires dans leur seigneurie, tentés par la course des bois, l'aventure, à l'affût de quelque emploi dans le service, dans la magistrature, dans les postes ou garnisons des Pays d'en haut. Les premiers vivent généralement à l'aise; les seconds forment la classe des grands indigents. Prisonniers des us et coutumes des gentilshommes de France, comme dit l'intendant Duchesneau, ceux-ci font « leur plus grande occupation de la chasse et de la pesche, négligent leurs terres, s'endettent, excittent leurs jeunes habitants de courir les bois et y envoient leurs enfants afin de traitter des pelleteries ... » Ou bien, entrés dans le service, sans rien d'autre pour vivre que les appointements d'une administration lésineuse, ils laissent à leur mort, après avoir vécu petitement, une famille sans ressources. Deux arrêts, l'un du Conseil d'Etat du 10 mars 1685, l'autre, l'Arrêt royal de Marly (6 juillet 1711), qu'on pourrait appeler la charte des seigneurs canadiens, auraient pu grandement influer sur leur type social. Le premier autorisait « nobles et gentilshommes habituez dans la Nouvelle-France » à commercer sans encourir la dérogeance. Rien de plus propre assurément à secouer l'indolence des gentilshommes fainéants. Les mêler, comme en Angleterre, à la vie économique de la colonie, c'était les y enraciner tout de bon. Mais encore leur fallait-il des capitaux pour l'organisation technique de la moindre entreprise ? N'en trouvant point, ils se tourneront vers le commerce le moins exigeant en mise de fonds : celui de la fourrure. Seigneurs d'aventure et ceux-là mêmes qui, d'après Duchesneau, se sont jetés dans la course des bois et y ont poussé leurs fils. Quelques-uns pourtant ont profité de l'arrêt ou ne l'ont pas attendu pour se libérer du préjugé aristocratique. Un Courtemanche fonde un établissement de conséquence sur la baie Phélipeaux au Labrador. Un François Hazeur, seigneur de la Malbaie, donne l'impression de toucher à tout, d'essayer de tout : pelleteries, pêche, exploitation forestière. On en pourrait dire autant d'un Aubert de la Chesnaye et de quelques autres.

L'Arrêt de Marly réitérait au seigneur, et sous les peines les plus sévères, l'obligation de concéder gratuitement de la terre au défricheur. On saisit l'importance du document. En somme, que faisait le roi sinon maintenir le régime seigneurial dans sa bienfaisance sociale ? Entre la classe des grands et des petits propriétaires, il empêchait le fossé de se creuser et les distances de s'élargir. Le seigneur resterait un aristocrate; il ne deviendrait pas un hobereau. Toute la santé de la colonie, tout son équilibre social, peut-on dire, étaient enfermés dans cette formule. D'ailleurs l'heure semble aussi approcher où le seigneur pourra pourvoir avec plus d'aise au placement de ses fils. Denonville a préconisé la fondation d'une école de marine. Le même Denonville et Frontenac ont insisté pour que place fût faite à l'élite de la jeunesse coloniale dans les grades supérieurs des troupes ou encore qu'on formât pour elle des compagnies militaires de gens du pays. Par privilège spécial du roi, quelques jeunes Canadiens commencent à prendre rang dans l'armée coloniale. On se défend mal toutefois de quelque inquiétude pour cette haute classe de la colonie. Trop de familles paraissent mal acclimatées, mal enracinées. Peu liées au destin du pays il semble qu'elles préfigurent déjà leur avenir.

Aspect social : la vie coloniale.

Veut-on élargir cet aspect social de l'histoire, pousser jusqu'aux façons de vivre, jusqu'aux sentiments de fond de cette génération du traité d'Utrecht ? On connaît les textes généralement cités pour décrire le Canadien de l'ancien régime, textes en quelque sorte classiques de Lahontan, de Chrestien Le Clercq, de la Potherie, des intendants de Meulles, Raudot, de Ruette d'Auteuil, de Charlevoix dans son *Journal historique*. Mais a-t-on assez remarqué que ces textes, même ceux de Charlevoix, datent des environs de 1713 et s'appliquent par conséquent aux Canadiens de l'époque où nous sommes ?

Un premier fait paraît avoir frappé tous ces observateurs : l'évolution déjà avancée de ce type de Français du nouveau monde, évolution psychologique et sociale. Les 18,000 colons du Canada forment déjà « un corps de peuple » original et d'une singulière unité. Le milieu naturel, les conditions de vie, de travail, le régime de propriété ont différencié le type colonial du type métropolitain, en même temps que la même langue, le même droit, la même foi, de longues et lourdes épreuves subies en commun ont profondément unifié la petite collectivité. Le Canadien de 1713 exprime, par tout son être, la fusion rapide et complète de tous les sangs de France, de tous les types provinciaux du vieux pays. Entendons ce que nous en dit Chrestien Le Clercq : « J'avais peine à concevoir qu'une peuplade formée de personnes de toutes les provinces de France, de moeurs, de nation, de conditions, d'intérêts, de génie si différents, et d'une manière de vie, coutumes, éducation si contraires, fût si accomplie qu'on me le représentait ... » Au besoin l'unité de langage témoignerait de cette assimilation : « Quoi qu'il y ait un mélange de presque toutes les provinces de France, on ne saurait distinguer le parler d'aucune dans les Canadiennes », remarque la Potherie. Dans le brassage des types ethniques et des parlers divers de France, quelques formes dialectales, celles qui ressortissent à un métier, à une technique, ont pu survivre en quelques régions. Selon les lois usuelles, les dialectes ont cédé devant la langue la plus robuste, la plus organique, la plus chargée de civilisation, langue au surplus de l'enseignement, de l'Eglise, de l'administration. Dès la première génération, semble-t-il, les colons entendent et parlent le français. Et ce français parlé s'attire des éloges qu'on a peine à ne pas croire excessifs. « On parle ici parfaitement bien, sans mauvais accent », veut bien accorder La Potherie. « Nulle part on ne parle plus purement notre langue. On ne remarque même ici aucun accent », confirme Charlevoix.

Serions-nous déjà en présence d'une variété du type ethnique français, d'un particularisme national en voie de formation ? Les colons les premiers s'en persuaderaient volontiers. Depuis longtemps déjà leur groupe collectif s'entend désigner par un terme distinct : celui de *Canadien*. En 1695, le Père Jean de Lamberville, pour les distinguer, à ce qu'il semble, de l'espèce de « Canadiens » que sont, pour les missionnaires, les Indiens des réductions, applique au groupe de colons le terme « Canadiens français ». Ce particularisme, nous le voulons bien, ne s'affirme pas encore avec cette pointe d'animosité qui, sur la fin du régime, fera écrire à Bougainville, avec beaucoup d'excès : « Il semble que nous soyons d'une nation différente, ennemie même ». Mais voyez comme les gentilshommes et leurs fils trouvent à souffrir de la différence de traitement accordé dans les troupes, aux métropolitains et aux coloniaux. Les altercations sont promptes entre Canadiens et Français. Et il arrive déjà aux Canadiens de parler du Canada comme de leur « patrie ». Que de plaintes aussi, de la part des administrateurs coloniaux, sur l'esprit d'indépendance du colon, sur son caractère revêche à la discipline, à l'obéissance. Dans le journal de son expédition de 1686 à la Baie d'Hudson, le chevalier de Troyes se plaint d'avoir eu toutes les peines du monde à contenir les Canadiens qui « ne veulent obéir qu'à eus mesmes ». L'opposition de ces coloniaux à toute taxe ou impôt, même aux corvées royales, opposition qui se manifeste dans toutes les classes de la population, même du clergé, cause les pires embarras aux gouvernants qui, parfois, se plaignent de céder « faute de troupes », pour faire exécuter les ordres du roi. Sans doute, ne faut-il parler de fossé entre Français et Canadiens; mais d'un cadet qui supporte déjà malaisément la tutelle de son aîné.

Est-ce à dire qu'il faille se représenter ces fiers coloniaux comme des demi-rustres, des demi-sauvages, étrangers aux goûts et aux finesses des civilisés ? De cette époque datent aussi les textes de la Potherie, de Charlevoix et d'autres qui célèbrent les charmes, les manières policées de la société canadienne. Encore là-dessus, chacun s'est plu à marquer la distance qui sépare l'habitant du Canada du paysan de France. « Les manières douces et polies sont communes à tous, et la rusticité, soit dans le langage, soit dans les façons, n'est pas même connue dans les campagnes les plus reculées », veut bien nous assurer Charlevoix. Et l'historien jésuite n'est pas seul à vanter, dans la société bourgeoise et seigneuriale, « ces cercles aussi brillants » que partout ailleurs, où « on politique sur le passé », « conjecture sur l'avenir », où « les sciences et les beaux arts ont leur tour », et où « la conversation ne tombe point ». La Potherie estime que le beau sexe, au Canada, « est aussi poli qu'en aucun lieu du Royaume », que « la Marchande tient de la femme de qualité » et que « celle d'Officier imite en tout le bon goût qu'on trouve en France ». On connaît déjà au Canada ce qu'on pourrait appeler les amusements et le bon ton de la haute société.

On parle politique, dit Charlevoix; de politique européenne, sans doute, l'été, après l'arrivée du courrier de France. On doit parler aussi de politique indienne, celle-ci tout aussi importante pour la colonie; elle a son personnel d'interprètes et de diplomates qui pratiquent une forme d'éloquence assez originale, éloquence en « stile sauvage » où ils se montrent habiles à manier le parler et la gesticulation imagés des plus grands orateurs des tribus. Dans le Canada de 1713 on sait aussi s'habiller, on le sait même trop. Des gentilshommes, leurs femmes et filles s'appauvrissent, se retranchent sur le nécessaire pour se bien vêtir. On festoie, on festoie encore trop, un grand nombre vivant au-dessus de leurs moyens. On aime le théâtre, et toujours encore trop, au gré des autorités religieuses.

Quelques-uns cultivent les sciences. Quelques missionnaires, tel le Père Lafitau, se livrent à l'indianologie. L'on a commencé de cueillir et d'expédier des plantes rares pour les jardins du roi. On ne disserte pas seulement autour des beaux-arts. Qui ne connaît les fins travaux de Jeanne Le Ber, « la sainte artisane » ? Et elle n'est pas la seule artiste de son temps. On goûte la musique. L'annaliste de l'Hôtel-Dieu de Québec a gardé si bon souvenir de l'intendant Raudot, le père, pour les concerts qu'il offrait chez lui à la jeunesse de Québec, « concert mêlé de voix et d'instruments, qui faisoient une charmante harmonie », et qu'il allait faire entendre parfois, soit à la maison des religieuses, soit à leur église. On sait aussi chansonner, au Canada, et telle chanson satirique de M. d'Esgly, chantée dans les rues de Québec par les gamins, se voit frappée d'interdiction par ordonnance de l'intendant; ce qui fait qu'on chansonne naturellement M. l'intendant et que Mme la Gouvernante elle-même se serait mêlée de chansonner. Telles de ces chansons obtiendront si grande vogue qu'on les chantera dans les côtes et jusqu'au fort de Frontenac et jusqu'à Détroit. Enfin, il fait si bon vivre en Nouvelle-France, que beaucoup de prisonniers anglais, nous assure-t-on, libres de s'en retourner chez eux, ont souvent choisi de rester.

(*Histoire du Canada français, I*, 1950)

Gustave Lanctot (Né en 1883)

Archiviste et diplomate, il fut conservateur en chef des Archives à Ottawa et président de la Société royale | du Canada (1948). Son oeuvre abondante porte surtout sur le régime français et sur nos relations avec les États-Unis.

LE CLIMAT SOCIAL EN 1663

Si l'on veut connaître à fond le caractère de l'émigration féminine en Nouvelle-France, il importe de s'informer du climat social, où elle s'opère, et des directives, qui la conditionnent. En 1663, la colonie continuait d'être une « mission », où cherchait à s'exercer l'emprise théocratique de Mgr de Laval et des jésuites, qui l'avaient fait choisir, affirme Louis XIV, « comme estans dans leur entière dépendance ».[1] Les départs d'Argenson et d'Avaugour et la nomination de Mésy établissent la puissance de « l'union de l'évêque et des pères ».[2] Cette union se donnait pour premier objectif la conversion des indigènes, qui devait à leurs yeux s'appuyer plutôt sur « peu de bons chrétiens » que sur « un plus grand nombre » d'émigrants quelconques.[3] Pour faire « régner la religion et la piété » le clergé avait institué, à Québec, une Congrégation de la Sainte-Famille, où les hommes sont conduits par les pères, les femmes par des Dames de piété et les filles par les Ursulines.[4] A Montréal, un grand nombre d'hommes et de femmes assistaient à la messe sur semaine.[5] L'ambiance religieuse prévalait à ce point qu'à l'arrivée des troupes pour la guerre contre les Iroquois, « on leur a fait comprendre que c'est une guerre sainte, où il ne s'agit que de la gloire de Dieu et du salut des âmes. Il y a bien cinq cents soldats qui ont pris le scapulaire de la Sainte-Vierge. »[6]

Dans ce climat, avec une minuscule population de trois mille à six mille âmes,[7] et un seul port de débarquement, il s'avère impossible que des convois de filles galantes se soient succédé, sans laisser la plus imperceptible trace ni dans les pièces administratives, ni dans la

---

[1] *Rapport de l'archiviste*, 1930-1931, Mémoire du Roi à Talon, 27 mars 1665, p. 11; *Arch. Col. B¹*, Colbert à Courcelles, 15 mai 1669, fol. 144; *Rapport*, 1930-1931, Mémoire du Roi à Talon, 27 mars 1665, p. 6.
[2] *Lettres de la Révérende Mère Marie de l'Incarnation*, II, 30 septembre 1165, p. 345.
[3] *Id.*, II, octobre 1669, p. 436.
[4] *Id.*, II, 19 août 1664, p. 285.
[5] Morin, Soeur Marie, *Annales de l'Hôtel-Dieu de Montréal*, Montréal, 1931, p. 114.
[6] *Id.*, II, 30 septembre 1665, p. 309.
[7] *Recensements du Canada*, IV, p. XVI.

correspondance, ni dans les journaux privés, pendant les onze ans que dure l'émigration féminine. Et pourtant, ces écrits notent, au jour le jour, l'arrivée des navires et souvent le nombre et la qualité des passagers.[8] Il serait non moins extraordinaire que Mgr de Laval et les jésuites, qui veillaient exagérément, au dire de Talon et de Frontenac, jusqu'à l'intérieur des foyers, à la bonne conduite des familles,[9] eussent assisté, sans mot dire, au déversement annuel de femmes dévergondées dans leur colonie-mission, eux qui se dressèrent contre le sagace Talon,[10] l'impérieux Frontenac[11] et même le tout-puissant Colbert,[12] au sujet, entre autres, de la vente des boissons aux Sauvages.

Mais, en cette matière de l'émigration féminine, ce qu'il importe fondamentalement de connaître, ce sont les intentions du roi, et surtout, les mesures prises et les instructions émises en vue d'en assurer efficacement la réalisation. Avec la suppression des guérillas iroquoises, Louis XIV se propose, avant tout, le peuplement rapide de cette vaste Nouvelle-France, qu'il vient de placer sous l'administration royale. Dès 1662, chaque année un convoi de colons se met en route pour Québec.[13] Chargé de refonder la colonie, Talon recevra cette consigne : « une augmentation considérable de lad. colonie, qui est la fin principale où Sa Majesté désire parvenir. »[14] Aux émigrants recrutés avec soin, on joindra dès que disponibles, « les soldats tant du regiment de Carignan que des quatre compagnies », en campagne contre les Iroquois.[15]

« Comme la multiplication des peuples dépend de la fréquence des mariages », selon ses termes,[16] Colbert organise l'envoi de filles à marier avec les célibataires. En France, le ministre veille à ce qu'on apporte « toutes les précautions qui seront possibles », dans le choix des colons et « particulièrement dans celuy des filles »,[17] pendant qu'à Québec, l'intendant passe en revue chaque groupe d'émigrantes.[17a] Le premier convoi fut levé dans la région de La Rochelle, comprenant

---

8 *Journal des Jésuites,* p. 45, 357 et 120 & 319.
9 *Rapport,* 1926-27, Frontenac à Colbert, 13 novembre 1673, p. 31. *Rapport,* 1930-31, Mémoire de Talon, 1667, p. 64.
10 *Rapport,* 1930-31, Talon à Colbert, 13 novembre 1666, p. 61.
11 *Rapport,* 1926-27, Colbert à Frontenac, 18 mai 1677, p. 92; Delanglez, P., *Frontenac & les jésuites . . .*
12 *Rapport sur les Archives du Canada,* Ottawa, 1885, M. Dudonyt à Mgr de Laval, 1677, p. XCVII-CXIII.
13 *Jugts et Del.,* I, p. 31; Lettres, I, 1663, p. 268; 18 août 1664, p. 274; 28 juillet 1665, p. 289, et *passim.*
14 *Rapport,* 1930-31, Mémoire du roi à Talon, 27 mars 1665, p. 5.
15 *Id.,* Mémoire du roi à Talon, 27 mars 1665, p. 9.
16 *Id.,* Colbert à Talon, 5 avril 1667, p. 71.
17 *Id.,* Colbert à Talon, 5 janvier 1666, p. 45.
17a *Id.,* Observations faites par Talon, 1669, p. 103-8.

trente-huit épouseuses. Elles devaient être de bonne qualité, car Colbert s'en déclare satisfait.[18] Aussitôt « recherchées », elles trouvèrent mari sans tarder, malgré les efforts de plusieurs habitants de les garder à leur service. Elles ne font l'objet d'aucune critique du Conseil souverain, qui, d'autre part, se plaint fortement des émigrants masculins.[19] Autre note favorable, les dix-sept d'entre elles, qui passèrent à Montréal, furent logées par Soeur Marguerite Bourgeoys, dans « la maison de la Sainte-Vierge » comme « c'était pour former des familles ».[20]

Malgré cet excellent départ, le Conseil souverain, en liaison avec l'évêque et les jésuites,[21] voulut prendre ses sûretés contre toute émigration indésirable.

(Filles de joie ou filles du Roi, 1952)

Alain Grandbois (Né en 1900)

Le poète est aussi un de nos meilleurs prosateurs, comme en fait foi	sa biographie de Jolliet, *Né à Québec, dont voici* les dernières pages.

DERNIÈRES ANNÉES

Et d'autres années passèrent encore. Jolliet vivait dans son île. Elle lui avait coûté trop de luttes et d'efforts pour qu'il ne lui fût point entièrement attaché. Et elle cachait trop de mystères pour qu'elle risquât de lui paraître monotone. Ses côtes ingrates, les sapins tordus de ses falaises, ses brouillards sournois lui étaient devenus nécessaires.

Il songeait encore au pays des Illinois. Mais sans regrets, et avec cette sorte de douceur nostalgique que crée le souvenir d'une femme autrefois chérie, dont la vie nous a séparés, et que d'autres amours nous ont rendue étrangère.

Ses fils étaient devenus des hommes. Ils vivaient dans ses établissements. Parfois, l'hiver, celui de Mingan venait à Anticosti, traînant à sa suite une bande de Papinachois hilares et muets. Alors, la nuit,

---

[18] *Id.,* Colbert à Talon, 5 avril 1667, p. 69.
[19] *Jugts. et Del.,* I, 18 et 25 juin 1664, p. 18 et 201-2.
[20] *Histoire de la Congrégation de Notre Dame de Montréal,* II, p. 302.
[21] *Rapport,* 1930-31, Mémoire de Talon, 1667, p. 64.

farouches, grondeurs, les chiens du nord, enfouis dans des trous de neige, montaient la garde autour de l'habitation. Et les ours disparaissaient pour des jours.

L'âge ne semblait toucher Jolliet que pour augmenter sa puissance et sa force. Hâlé par le soleil, les vents, la neige, son visage avait pris la teinte du cuir. Il était plus grand qu'aucun de ses fils. Il comptait parmi les notables de la colonie.

Il avait reçu le brevet de pilote royal lors d'un dernier voyage en France. Il était titulaire d'une chaire d'hydrographie. Frontenac lui avait octroyé une petite seigneurie, du côté de Lauzon, sur la rivière des Etchemins.

Deux ans après son voyage à la baie d'Hudson, des Canadiens, sur les indications de Jolliet, avaient formé la *Compagnie du Nord,* dans le but de faire concurrence aux associés de Londres. Radisson et Des Groseillers firent échouer l'entreprise. Plus tard, Le Moyne d'Iberville s'était emparé des postes anglais de la baie. Le drapeau français flottait maintenant du grand Nord blanc aux savanes fiévreuses de la Louisiane.

Jolliet avait bien servi. Il en avait conscience, regardait ses fils, souriait.

Frontenac se faisait vieux. Sa petite taille s'était ramassée davantage. Il portait toujours ses moustaches à la mousquetaire, mais elles avaient blanchi. Il évitait la colère pour ménager son coeur. Il ne tenait plus l'indulgence pour le signe de la faiblesse. Il avait près de soixante-quinze ans.

Dans les années qui précédèrent sa mort, il rencontrait parfois un long vieillard maigre et courbé qui s'appuyait en marchant sur une canne. Alors ils se saluaient comme les vieillards se saluent, précautionneusement, avec, au fond des prunelles, cette lueur humide et vive.

M. de Laval et Frontenac se dégageaient peu à peu du monde des vivants.

Mais rien ne ressemblait moins à Jolliet qu'un homme désigné par la mort. Il avait atteint l'âge où la course du sang s'établit sur un rythme définitif, où la vie prend des apparences éternelles.

Il fréta un jour sa barque pour rejoindre ses établissements de Mingan. C'était au printemps de 1700. On ne le revit plus. Plus tard, certains prétendirent que ses restes reposaient sur l'île Megatina; d'autres, sur une des îles Mingan; d'autres encore, à Anticosti même. Rien n'est moins certain.

(*Né à Québec,* 1933)

Léon Gérin (1863-1951)

Avocat, puis traducteur à la Chambre des Communes, Gérin consacra ses loisirs à l'étude de la sociologie dont il fut le pionnier au Canada français. Il fut président de la Société royale du Canada en 1933. Le texte qui suit est le début d'un de ses essais.

L'INTÉRÊT SOCIOLOGIQUE DE NOTRE HISTOIRE AU LENDEMAIN DE LA CONQUÊTE

Le siècle qui a suivi la cession du Canada à l'Angleterre forme la période la moins étudiée peut-être de notre histoire. C'est pourtant celle dont l'intérêt, sinon humain du moins sociologique, est de beaucoup le plus grand. Plus nettement qu'à aucune autre époque, on y observe l'action et la réaction les uns sur les autres de groupements sociaux très divers. Au sein de la Race et de la Religion, grands groupements amorphes, du type le plus ancien et le moins spécialisé, et dont l'influence reste la moins changeante et toujours sourdement impérative, on voit poindre des groupements moins compréhensifs, mieux adaptés aux besoins actuels, et aussi plus dépendants de la volonté et de l'intelligence humaines, ceux, par exemple, qui se rattachent à l'organisation économique ou politique du pays.

Trois éléments figurent invariablement dans la composition de toute société, de tout type social; et suivant qu'ils s'y combinent en telle ou telle proportion, ou s'y manifestent sous telle ou telle forme, permettent de les distinguer facilement : conditions physiques (ou géographiques, ou anthropologiques); traditions, contraintes, pratiques plus ou moins communautaires du groupe; action plus ou moins importante, plus ou moins énergique, des individus. Nous avons ainsi, dans l'ordre de complexité croissante, des sociétés procédant surtout de la Nature, des sociétés s'inspirant surtout de la Coutume, et des sociétés caractérisées surtout par l'initiative particulière.

Les Indiens du Canada nous fournissent un bon exemple du premier de ces trois types de sociétés. Ils n'ont qu'un petit nombre de groupements spécifiques : la Famille y est en même temps Atelier de travail et, avec le Clan et la Tribu, pourvoit à tous les besoins de la vie publique ou de la vie privée. Et ces groupements, dont l'origine se perd dans la nuit des temps, sont en correspondance étroite, d'une part avec la nature du lieu, d'autre part avec la conformation physique de la race. A la fois l'homme et l'organisation sociale y paraissent dominés par l'ordre naturel ambiant. La structure anatomique tant de l'homme que des institutions n'est en quelque sorte qu'une simple transposition des caractères du milieu physique. Le Peau-Rouge ne réagit que faiblement contre les influences du Lieu; il se contente pour sa nourriture des productions que ce lieu lui offre spontanément; il ne se protège guère, par le vêtement et l'habitation, contre les agents atmosphériques. Il est lui-même comme une dernière production spontanée du pays, et dès qu'on l'en déracine, ou qu'on l'isole de la grande nature, il dépérit et il meurt. Aussi bien, d'institution sociale il ne connaît que les groupements fondés sur la consanguinité, qu'elle soit réelle, ou qu'elle soit fictive.

On observe, d'autre part, des sociétés dans lesquelles les impulsions de la Nature, pour n'être pas absentes, sont fortement encadrées par les croyances, les usages, les contraintes émanant de la vie sociale elle-même. Régies par des coutumes fort anciennes et respectées, ces sociétés ne donnent pas, comme les groupes de primitifs, l'impression d'une étroite communion avec la Nature, mais elles produisent l'illusion de la fixité, de l'immobilité. Telles furent ces sociétés du Moyen Age, formées par les progéniteurs directs des colons du Nouveau Monde; et même tels étaient au début, à beaucoup d'égards, les groupes de population rurale de la Nouvelle-France et de la Nouvelle-Angleterre, épris de tradition plutôt que de nouveauté.

Il est un troisième type de sociétés où le facteur dominant n'est plus la Nature, n'est plus la tradition communautaire, mais bien plutôt la personnalité humaine, et c'est là un caractère qui distingue particulièrement les sociétés modernes. Il n'y a pas ici le mystère, la fatalité, qui se dégagent de l'étude des sociétés primitives antiques : des groupements nouveaux se constituent sous nos yeux. Il n'y a plus l'imposante immobilité des sociétés fondées sur la coutume : les groupements s'adaptent avec célérité aux exigences nouvelles, et se modifient en vue de multiples besoins, au gré de multiples caprices. En revanche, si la société nouvelle a perdu l'attrait du mystérieux et le prestige de l'immuable, elle a l'intérêt dramatique qu'inspirent toujours le mouvement, la vie, l'action consciente et ordonnée de grands organismes.

A la suite de son occupation par les Anglais, la Nouvelle-France présente le spectacle d'une société encore toute pénétrée de traditions et d'usages séculaires qui, presque à son insu, est entraînée dans la voie du changement et de l'imprévu; de groupes de population qui, avant même d'avoir perdu le souvenir de leurs origines ethniques diverses, sont mis en concurrence sur le même sol, bien plus, sont appelés à coopérer en vue de la constitution de groupements d'un ordre nouveau, que les ancêtres n'avaient pas connu, et n'avaient pu prévoir : les institutions d'une colonie à gouvernement libre et autonome.

Français et Franco-canadiens, d'une part, Anglais et Anglo-américains, de l'autre, avaient alors entre eux plus d'un point de ressemblance. Par exemple, chez les uns comme chez les autres, on observait, allié à certains caractères physiques définis et persistants, ainsi qu'à des survivances de traditions et de coutumes très anciennes, un notable développement de l'initiative privée, quoique pour des objets et dans des sens divers. Tous, au dire des historiens, avaient des origines ethniques communes, les divergences à partir de la souche première étant de date assez récente. Tous résultaient de la rencontre et de la combinaison d'influences surtout celtiques, romaines, germaines et normandes. Le Breton des îles britanniques est le congénère du Gaulois, comme le Saxon est le congénère du Franc, et les uns comme les autres ont connu la domination romaine et subi le joug normand. Enfin, tous, classe pour classe, étaient à peu près au même degré de culture et de civilisation.

Mais aussi chacun de ces quatre types avait acquis et retenait certains traits distinctifs. Dans l'Ancienne France, l'initiative se donnait carrière surtout dans l'ordre militaire et administratif. Déjà César, dès avant l'ère chrétienne, signalait l'existence dans les Gaules d'un régime bien tranché de classes et de factions. La paysannerie, qui formait la masse de la nation, n'y jouissait d'aucune considération, et n'avait point part à la direction des affaires publiques, que se réservaient les chevaliers et les druides. La période suivante, celle du Franc et du Féodal, fut féconde en merveilleux progrès. Elle fixa au sol cette population jusque-là flottante; elle vit s'opérer le défrichement de la France, et le développement d'une vie locale intense. Mais dans une troisième période ce beau mouvement fut enrayé, et on assista à la constitution, aux envahissements graduels, puis à l'irrémédiable décadence de la grande monarchie militaire et centralisée des Capétiens, des Valois et des Bourbons.

La France, grandie par les efforts persévérants de nombreuses générations de travailleurs est alors relativement populaire et riche, mais son organisation sociale est médiocre. Sa classe de paysans, repliée sur elle-même, ne cherche pas à s'élever, et dès lors n'exerce aucun contrôle effectif sur sa classe dirigeante, et ne comble pas les vides qui se produisent dans ses rangs. Celle-ci d'autre part, s'est détachée de la vie rurale, a renoncé à la direction des arts usuels, applique et gaspille de plus en plus son énergie à l'accaparement, et parfois à l'exercice, des charges de l'Etat, comme à la recherche des plaisirs de la Cour.

Les distinctions s'accentuent entre classes de dirigeants et classes de dirigés, et aussi les défiances. Il se produit une recrudescence du régime en vogue chez les Gallo-romains, sorte de régime de clans rivaux et très instables, parce qu'ils reposent entièrement sur des rapports de personne à personne, que le Féodal avait remplacés par des rapports de domaine à domaine. Or ce régime de classes et de factions, fâcheux pour la Gaule, l'est infiniment plus pour la France de Louis XIV et de Louis XV, à cause de l'agglomération des habitants, de la complexité et de l'importance des intérêts à régir.

La Nouvelle-France était, à beaucoup d'égards, un duplicata de l'Ancienne. Comme celle-ci elle se composait essentiellement d'une population de paysans, gouvernée de haut par une noblesse et par un clergé. Dans la colonie, comme dans sa métropole, la classe dirigeante vivait en très grande partie des subventions, des faveurs, des privilèges accordés par l'Etat, au gré des factions qui assiègent le pouvoir. Sans doute, dans ce pays neuf, le paysan s'était quelque peu émancipé, il était devenu coureur de bois, et de son côté, le gentilhomme s'était parfois frotté d'aventures, était devenu chef d'expéditions de traite ou de découvertes lointaines. Mais ni l'un ni l'autre, sous le régime de réglementation administrative institué par Richelieu et Louis XIV, n'avait perdu sa formation ancienne. C'était souvent un paysan avisé et débrouillard que l'Habitant canadien, mais ce n'était que très exceptionnellement qu'il s'élevait au-dessus de cette condition, du moins sans sortir de la culture; et, dans l'administration des affaires du pays, son rôle était purement passif. C'était souvent un soldat et un navigateur admirable que le gentilhomme canadien, mais sans fortune, et sans les aptitudes pratiques pour s'en amasser.

Toute la colonie vivait directement ou indirectement du commerce des fourrures, organisé administrativement. Dans ces conditions, le trait le plus marquant de l'ordre social, c'était l'enchevêtrement des intérêts et des attributions en matière politique, religieuse, économique. Le Conseil supérieur, où siégeaient, à côté du gouverneur, de l'intendant et de plusieurs conseillers laïques, l'évêque de Québec et le supérieur des Jésuites, se chargeait, — sauf le contrôle éloigné, l'intervention intermittente, de la métropole, — de tout régenter, de tout réglementer : la justice et la police, l'agriculture et l'industrie, et aussi la religion. On sait assez quelle place tiennent dans l'histoire de la colonie française les conflits d'autorité entre le gouverneur et l'intendant ou les conseillers, entre les fonctionnaires civils ou militaires et les dignitaires ecclésiastiques, et souvent à propos de puériles questions de préséance.

La société anglaise, séparée de la société française par un simple bras de mer, composée d'éléments ethniques assez semblables, ayant subi à peu près les mêmes influences, n'en a pas moins de très bonne heure évolué dans un tout autre sens. Tandis qu'en France la masse gallo-romaine, sous l'impulsion du dominateur franc et du seigneur féodal, ne s'est transformée qu'à demi, et a conservé beaucoup de traits de communautaire et d'instable, en Angleterre, le particulariste saxon a refoulé ou asservi le communautaire breton, premier occupant du sol, a supplanté le communautaire germain (angle ou mercien), et finalement a évincé l'envahisseur danois. Déjà au temps d'Alfred le Grand et d'Edouard le Confesseur s'affirme la supériorité du Saxon et se dessinent les grandes lignes de la constitution sociale du peuple anglais, fondée sur le libre jeu de l'initiative particulière dans la vie privée comme dans la vie publique, et que plusieurs siècles de domination normande ne parviendront pas à déformer. Le beau livre d'Henri de Tourville, *l'Histoire de la formation particulariste,* jette une vive lumière sur toutes les phases de cette épopée sociale.

Ce double souci de la liberté individuelle et de la liberté politique, de l'indépendance de la vie privée et du contrôle effectif des pouvoirs publics, se manifeste à toutes les époques de l'histoire d'Angleterre, mais jamais plus énergiquement qu'au sortir du Moyen Age, à la suite de l'émancipation des serfs, de l'éclosion de l'industrie, de la navigation et du commerce international, des grandes découvertes d'outre-mer, de l'invention de l'imprimerie, du mouvement de la Réforme. On vit alors apparaître en Angleterre (il n'est ici question ni du pays de Galles, ni de l'Ecosse, ni de l'Irlande) une société où les liens fondés sur la nature ou la tradition étaient faibles, relâchés en comparaison de ceux noués de date récente par l'initiative particulière, en vue de nécessités actuelles et pratiques.

Tandis que le clergé catholique et le clergé anglican, son spoliateur, se voient désertés par leurs ouailles, qui multiplient les sectes comme à plaisir, les grands propriétaires accapareurs de champs, destructeurs de villages, ne trouvent plus pour cultiver leurs réserves, pour tirer parti de leurs domaines, que des journaliers de passage, que des fermiers qu'aucun lien durable ne rattache à eux. Le bordier, le petit paysan, ont émigré pour la plupart : les uns vont recruter la population industrielle des villes, les autres sont allés fonder des domaines indépendants en Amérique ou ailleurs. Entre-temps, le commerce, la fabrication, les transports s'organisent de toute part, donnent naissance à de grandes villes, accumulent d'énormes richesses. Toute l'ancienne société s'est effondrée, remplacée par une efflorescence de groupements nouveaux.

C'est partout une sourde mais intense fermentation sociale. Dans tous les ordres de la vie publique ou de la vie privée, les dirigeants, dès qu'ils faiblissent ou dégénèrent, sont dépossédés au profit des sujets d'élite de la classe sous-jacente. A la Cour, au Parlement, à l'armée, aux affaires, mais aussi dans l'agriculture, l'industrie et le commerce, c'est une lutte constante, une active concurrence, entre particuliers, où de nouvelles couches se font jour périodiquement, pendant qu'au sommet de l'échelle, la classe politique dominante s'applique sans relâche à restreindre les prérogatives de la Couronne et de la Chambre haute, au profit des attributions de la Chambre des communes.

Or, même dans ces conditions, l'Angleterre reste une société de type aristocratique, où l'indépendance de la vie privée et la liberté de la vie publique existent et sont maintenues surtout par l'entremise et au profit d'une classe privilégiée. Par contre, les colonies anglaises de l'Amérique, peuplées au début en forte proportion de groupes d'émigrants qui avaient quitté la métropole en révolte contre la situation de faveur et l'autorité reconnues au souverain et aux grands, appliquèrent sous une forme nettement démocratique les principes du self-help et du self-government.

Les colonies esclavagistes du Sud, il est vrai, s'organisèrent suivant un type rappelant celui de l'Angleterre, avec le grand propriétaire rural comme agent directeur de l'activité économique, et le comté comme maîtresse pièce de l'organisme public local. Mais dans le Nord, dans la Nouvelle-Angleterre surtout, la clé de tout le système fut le « farmer », petit propriétaire exploitant de ses mains, mais en général plus entreprenant et mieux renseigné que le paysan; de plus, très apte à l'administration du township, circonscription en général moins étendue que le comté, mais plus vaste que la paroisse. Et n'a-t-on pas prétendu que c'est grâce à l'activité administrative des townships de la Nouvelle-Angleterre que le Yankee a pu triompher de la bureaucratie anglaise ? Mais il ne faudrait pas perdre de vue le caractère urbain de beaucoup de ces townships, et le rôle prépondérant joué dès le début par l'élément commerçant et industriel.

En somme, nous avons trois types en présence. La société française (dont la société franco-canadienne n'est qu'un décalque, avec en plus les rivalités entre Français et Canadiens), est saine, excellente sous bien des rapports; mais la liberté individuelle y est plus ou moins gênée, et la liberté politique n'y existe pas. La société anglaise est encore quelque peu férue des traditions du régime autocratique des Tudors et des Stuarts; elle se complaît dans le faste du souverain et des grands; elle souffre de distinctions et de rivalités de classes. Mais de longue date déjà l'initiative individuelle s'y donne librement carrière dans l'agriculture, le commerce et l'industrie, et on y jouit d'une large mesure de liberté politique, en dépit des privilèges que les moeurs, plutôt que les lois, reconnaissent aux nobles et aux bourgeois. Quant au type américain ou yankee, il est précisément très occupé, au point où nous sommes rendus, à préparer les voies pour une transformation radicale dans le sens de ses propres habitudes et de sa propre mentalité, de la constitution politique et sociale importée de sa métropole.

Rien n'est intéressant comme de noter, dans les documents contemporains, comment s'est opéré le premier contact de nos trois types en pays canadien. Les deux forts volumes de pièces, de mémoires et de lettres sur l'histoire constitutionnelle du Canada, publiés ces années dernières par le bureau des archives du Dominion, grâce à l'initiative de MM. Shortt et Doughty, nous renseignent abondamment sur les faits de cette période.

Ce qui frappe de prime abord chez les officiers anglais que la capitulation de Québec (1759), la capitulation de Montréal (1760) et le traité de Paris (1763) laissent maîtres de la Nouvelle-France, c'est leur ferme volonté de se concilier les nouveaux sujets du roi d'Angleterre, en leur témoignant une entière confiance, en les invitant à coopérer à l'administration de la colonie et en se garant des fautes commises et des gênes imposées inutilement par leurs prédécesseurs. Le placard d'Amherst, publié quinze jours après la capitulation de Montréal, est particulièrement instructif à cet égard. Il autorise les gouverneurs des trois villes principales à nommer aux emplois vacants dans la milice, entre tous autres, ceux qui jouissaient de tels honneurs sous Sa Majesté Très Chrétienne. Il charge l'officier de milice commandant dans chaque paroisse de connaître les différends et d'en juger en première instance. Il est ordonné aux troupes « de payer tout ce qu'elles achètent de l'Habitant argent comptant et espèces sonnantes ». Le commerce est déclaré « libre et sans impôt à un chacun ». Pareille proclamation devait avoir un prodigieux effet sur le colon de la Nouvelle-France, qui n'avait pas été habitué à tant d'égards et de considération de la part de ses propres gouvernants.

Le rapport de Murray, gouverneur de Québec, en date du 5 juin 1762, est aussi très éclairant. Sans doute, il faut faire la part de ses préventions d'Anglais et de protestant; mais à côté de cela, comme les intentions sont bienveillantes, comme les vues sont larges et s'inspirent en général d'une juste et saine appréciation des conditions de la prospérité sociale ! S'il se méfie de la classe seigneuriale, et du haut clergé, s'il se montre assez mal disposé envers les Jésuites et les Récollets, comme il sait reconnaître les qualités de l'Habitant, la vigueur physique de la race, sa moralité, sa sobriété. C'est dans cette classe de paisibles campagnards que les gouvernants anglais, suivant lui, devront chercher leur principal appui. Qu'ils se l'attachent au moyen d'un traitement équitable et généreux, qu'ils encouragent le séminaire de Québec, parce qu'il dotera le pays d'un clergé canadien. Qu'ils habituent cette population à se suffire à elle-même et en toutes choses à se passer des Français et des Américains.

Il n'y a pas lieu de trop s'étonner si les militaires anglais, chargés d'organiser le pays immédiatement après la conquête, font preuve de préoccupations d'intérêt public et d'un réel souci du bien-être des classes populaires. On sait que les règnes des deux premiers souverains de la maison de Hanovre, Georges Ier (1714-1727) et Georges II (1727-1760), furent une époque de grand relâchement de l'autorité royale et d'accroissement des attributions de la Chambre des communes et de l'influence des masses. On sait que William Pitt, devenu premier ministre en 1757, et qui, en 1759, chargeait Wolfe de la conduite des opérations contre Québec, s'était en quelque sorte imposé à Georges II en exploitant les défiances du populaire anglais à l'endroit de cette dynastie étrangère. Il avait désigné Wolfe pour commander l'expédition, au mépris des droits de l'ancienneté et des préjugés aristocratiques. De même pour obtenir que Guy Carleton fît partie de l'état-major de Wolfe, il dut forcer la main au souverain, auprès de qui Carleton n'était pas en faveur, pour avoir dénigré les troupes hanovriennes.

Si les chefs militaires anglais dépêchés vers les bords du Saint-Laurent dans les dernières années du règne de Georges II, surent, grâce surtout à la justesse et à la liberté de leur conception politique, — puisée dans le milieu social anglais de leurs jeunes années, et quelque peu aussi au contact du milieu américain, — s'imposer au respect et même gagner les coeurs de beaucoup de Canadiens, il en fut tout autrement, au début, d'une autre classe de gens de langue anglaise, qui vinrent à leur suite s'abattre sur la colonie. Sortis, pour la plupart, des villes de la Nouvelle-Angleterre et de la Nouvelle-York, se recrutant presque tous dans les classes commerciales et ouvrières, ils représentaient assez bien le type anglo-américain d'alors, avec ses qualités et ses défauts, excellent au fond, mais qui, à ce moment particulier de son histoire, violemment tendu vers la conquête de la liberté politique complète, était d'un abord rude, désagréable, et se montrait intolérant pour tout ce qui pouvait l'empêcher d'atteindre son but.

Bien qu'ils ne fussent qu'une poignée au Canada, ces Yankees avaient la prétention d'y tout mener. Ils manifestaient en toute occasion leur antipathie pour les croyances des catholiques, pour les coutumes françaises, pour le régime seigneurial des terres et le mode de transmission des biens. Avec la courte vue de petites gens qui n'ont l'habitude de la conduite que de leurs intérêts particuliers, sans avoir à tenir compte des autres, ils auraient voulu supprimer tout cela du

jour au lendemain, et réclamaient hautement pour eux seuls, à l'exclu-
sion de la population française et catholique et même des fonctionnaires
anglais, l'administration de la chose publique. Leur action allait avant
longtemps se faire sentir de plus énergique manière.

(*Revue trimestrielle canadienne,* vol. I, no 1, mai 1915)

Errol Bouchette (1863-1912)

Avocat, fonctionnaire,
bibliothécaire à la Bibliothèque
du Parlement,
membre de la Société royale
du Canada, il a préconisé
l'émancipation économique des
Canadiens français dans des essais
et un court roman qui en font
un pionnier de l'économie politique
au Canada français. Suit un extrait
d'un de ses essais en ce domaine.

APTITUDE DES CANADIENS FRANÇAIS
POUR L'INDUSTRIE

Avant d'aller plus loin, il ne sera peut-être pas inutile d'examiner
brièvement cette question : Les Canadiens-français sont-ils aptes au
haut commerce et à la grande industrie ? Non pas que la réponse soit
douteuse pour ceux qui connaissent bien nos compatriotes d'origine
française. Mais beaucoup de gens ont dit et répété que nous sommes
inaptes aux choses commerciales et industrielles (*unfit for business*); et
cette opinion, bien qu'inavouée, s'est accréditée dans plusieurs de nos
collèges classiques, chose bien malheureuse. Nous comparant aux hommes d'affaires d'autres origines, dont la vieille prospérité faisait paraître
encore plus pitoyables nos pénibles débuts, trop d'entre nous se sont dit :
Eh ! bien, renonçons-y, ce n'est évidemment pas notre vocation. Nous
avons nous-mêmes entendu des hommes qui auraient dû être éclairés
raisonner ainsi et cela tout récemment.

Les circonstances ont voulu que même la science semblât être de
complot pour accréditer cette fausse idée. Parkman, en fournissant des
matériaux aux amateurs de *folklore,* est devenu la source, peut-être
involontaire, de contes de plus en plus étonnants, si bien que nous ne
sommes plus, aux yeux de beaucoup d'Américains, qu'un phénomène
intéressant de fossilisation. *Parkman discovered French Canada,* s'écrie-
t-on, et là-dessus on brode des romans, absolument comme on pourrait
le faire sur les ruines de Pompeï ou de Babylone. D'autres font à notre

sujet des découvertes en fait d'économie sociale. Vous êtes Français, disent-ils, d'origine celtique et latine, de formation communautaire; n'allez pas vous imaginer que vous pouvez faire ce que nous faisons; il se passera encore de longues années avant que vous soyez capables de grandes entreprises industrielles. Cela est d'autant plus grave que la science sociale, qui est nouvelle, a ébloui le monde par de brillantes théories basées sur des observations justes, mais évidemment encore incomplètes. L'éminent fondateur de l'école déclarait lui-même qu'il n'avait pu compléter son étude des phénomènes sociaux contemporains. Ses continuateurs pas davantage. C'est une oeuvre longue, lente, souvent à recommencer. Cette science est certainement appelée à rendre d'importants services, surtout lorsque les observations qui en forment la base seront complètes. Mais en attendant, nous pouvons voir par ce qui se passe sous nos yeux, sur notre continent, que certaines études auraient besoin d'être révisées; celles qui regardent la race celtique en Amérique, par exemple. Certains écrivains pourraient constater que les montagnards celtes purs que nous décrit sir Walter Scott, vivant par clans, réfractaires au travail, méprisant le commerce et l'industrie, n'estimant que les professions de soldat et de brigand, sont devenus, tout à coup, dans les pays nouveaux où les poussait la destruction de leur antique organisation sociale, de vaillants combattants dans l'arène industrielle et commerciale. Comme le Celte d'Ecosse, son congénère d'Irlande, émigrant prolétaire et naïf, a subi en touchant le sol d'Amérique une transformation étonnante. Qui a voyagé aux Etats-Unis s'en aperçoit sans peine. Et cependant, si nous voulons bien y réfléchir, nous devrons conclure que la transformation du Celte d'Irlande et d'Ecosse est moins étonnante que celle de cette poignée de paysans français si casaniers, si routiniers dans leur pays d'origine, qui surent ouvrir aux autres peuples la voie du nouveau continent, se tailler isolément, la hache à la main, dans la forêt vierge, des établissement durables, protéger leurs libertés, et s'assimiler la constitution britannique en contribuant à son perfectionnement.

L'explication n'est pas difficile. C'est qu'en fait d'anthropologie, il est un facteur qu'on ne trouve pas dans les autres sciences. Les lois physiques sont ici dominées par une autre loi. En étudiant l'homme et les aptitudes humaines, on ne saurait procéder comme dans l'étude des habitudes et des instincts des animaux. Chez l'homme existent sans doute les caractères physiques et l'instinct, mais ce ne sont que des accessoires. Sous les haillons d'un chanteur ambulant brille la splendeur d'Homère. Ce corps d'ivrogne, mendiant, voleur, abject, contient la pensée de Maimon. Chaque homme a une âme immortelle. Donnez-lui la lumière, elle peut atteindre des hauteurs incalculables. Donc, en étudiant l'humanité, pas de règle absolue possible, si ce n'est celle-ci, que l'homme est essentiellement perfectible. Si certaines races caucasiennes semblent rester inférieures, ce n'est pas à cause de leur infériorité inhérente, mais par suite des circonstances défavorables qui les entourent et que leur plus ou moins d'ignorance ou de faiblesse les empêche de dominer. Et c'est ici que l'utilité de la science sociale apparaît. En signalant les vraies causes de l'infériorité de certains groupes d'hommes, elle indique en même temps comment on peut les combattre et les faire disparaître.

La science sociale ainsi comprise viendra appuyer notre thèse. Elle constatera que l'arbuste transplanté dans un sol nouveau a amélioré ses fruits : que nous avons conservé les qualités de nos ancêtres tout en en acquérant d'autres qui nous sont propres; que nous sommes un peuple primitif enfin, un peu comme ceux qui sortirent jadis des forêts de la Germanie, pour se substituer à la puissance romaine. Nous avons leur intelligence, leur indépendance, leur audace. Nous avons déjà accompli beaucoup. En matière commerciale notamment, malgré notre infériorité apparente, l'histoire dira que nous avons remporté un succès réel en nous assurant même notre faible part, entravés et découragés que nous étions par un groupe d'hommes qui désiraient conserver pour eux seuls un monopole lucratif; et qui y ont réussi pendant quelque temps, grâce aux influences puissantes dont ils disposaient en Angleterre, longtemps notre seul, aujourd'hui encore notre principal marché. Si ces faits étaient connus on les tenait dans l'ombre. C'était le raisonnement du renard de la fable que le suivant, que nous faisait un vieux professeur. Le commerce, l'industrie, disait-il, sont des occupations matérielles; nous, Canadiens-français, sommes faits pour quelque chose de plus noble; soyons cultivateurs comme Cincinnatus, orateurs comme Cicéron et Bossuet; la charrue, la tribune, la chaire nous appellent; laissons le gain matériel aux natures plus grossières. Peut-être fut-il un temps où ce sophisme pouvait servir, mais ce temps est passé. Les idées et les circonstances ont bien changé. Il est essentiel maintenant de faire connaître les causes véritables de l'apparente infériorité industrielle et commerciale de nos compatriotes. Ce sera là un des travaux de l'avenir, travail nécessitant beaucoup de recherches et d'analyse, mais travail utile puisqu'il fera justice de certaines erreurs populaires. On comprendra alors qu'aucune race n'est plus apte que nous le sommes à la production de la richesse industrielle. Une race agricole dans un pays possédant des ressources industrielles naturelles, est celle qui peut développer ces ressources avec le plus d'avantage pour le pays et le plus d'intelligence. L'agriculture produit la richesse du premier degré, et l'industrie, du second. Des gradations insensibles rapprochent ces deux professions, surtout de nos jours. Les économistes signalent à l'appui de cette proposition la transformation de la Hongrie, qui, il y a peu d'années, était exclusivement agricole, et qui maintenant possède une population industrielle considérable. On y dépense annuellement plus d'un demi-million de dollars pour l'enseignement industriel, à part les encouragements prodigués aux industries. (Voir l'*Economiste français*.) Quant à la noblesse du but, elle est sans égale, puisque travailler aujourd'hui au développement industriel des Canadiens-français c'est travailler au salut de tout un peuple, c'est continuer la mission de nos devanciers, c'est faire oeuvre non seulement utile, mais tellement essentielle et obligatoire qu'y manquer serait antipatriotique.

Les limites imposées à ce travail ne nous permettent pas de faire une longue étude de la question. C'est tout au plus si nous pouvons en indiquer le canevas; dire en quelques mots pourquoi nous croyons que nos compatriotes de la province de Québec ont tout ce qu'il faut pour réussir dans toute entreprise industrielle raisonnable et sagement conçue. Les circonstances ont voulu que jusqu'à présent la plus grande somme de leur énergie fût dirigée vers d'autres voies. Aujourd'hui que l'évolution économique les pousse vers la carrière de la grande industrie, pourquoi y seraient-ils moins aptes que les Anglo-saxons, les Ecossais, les Irlandais ? L'histoire nous enseigne que c'est en France que la grande industrie a pris naissance et qu'elle s'est d'abord développée, pour se répandre ensuite en Europe par des essaims français sortis de leur pays.[1] Les Français les premiers, croyons-nous, conçurent l'idée des grandes compagnies de commerce colonial, laquelle, en Angleterre, contribua si puissamment à la grandeur de l'empire colonial britannique. Car, comme les Romains, les Anglais ont su comprendre et s'approprier les grandes idées qui transforment le monde. Ce sont les lois françaises qui, aujourd'hui encore, forment la base du code commercial de l'univers, nous disent les économistes. « Le génie de Colbert, dit Luigi Cossa,[2] conçut une oeuvre grandiose, et il eut la volonté ferme de l'atteindre. Il ne s'en tint pas aux expédients mesquins de ses prédécesseurs. . . . Il est facile de comprendre pourquoi Walpole et Pitt (aîné) en Angleterre, Frédéric-Guillaume 1er et Frédéric II de Prusse, Joseph II d'Autriche et Pierre le Grand, en Russie, ont essayé, rarement avec la même habileté et par suite avec un succès varié, de suivre les traces de Colbert. » Et au siècle dernier, malgré la Révolution, des guerres et des convulsions politiques incessantes, la France industrielle affaiblie n'a cependant pas succombé. Elle tend au contraire à se relever, malgré des causes de faiblesse nationale que nous connaissons tous et qui n'existent pas chez les Canadiens-français.

Nous avons en germe les qualités maîtresses de deux grands peuples, de celui dont nous sortons et de celui sous le drapeau duquel

---

[1] *Histoire de Jacquard,* par Lamartine.
[2] *Histoire des Doctrines économiques,* traduction A. Deschamps, p. 224.

nous avons grandi. Nous sommes quelquefois routiniers dans nos campagnes, tout comme les cultivateurs d'Angleterre, du reste. Mais lorsqu'on nous a montré comment nous pouvions améliorer nos cultures, nous nous sommes lancés avec audace dans la voie nouvelle qu'on nous indiquait. Nous avons longtemps manifesté une tendance trop prononcée vers les professions libérales et la politique. Cela tient à une habitude contractée au cours de nos longues luttes constitutionnelles, alors que le titre d'avocat et de tribun n'étaient point une vaine parure, mais supposaient une vraie mission patriotique. Aujourd'hui cela n'est plus qu'un préjugé qui tend à disparaître, et « l'avocat » n'est plus le demi-dieu d'autrefois. Nous semblons présentement trop portés vers les positions inférieures, le travail à gages. Il n'y a rien là qui doive surprendre, si nous tenons compte des nombreux obstacles apportés à la colonisation et de l'absence presque absolue d'instruction technique dans notre pays. « L'absence d'écoles professionnelles ou d'application scientifique, dit le regretté Arthur Buies dans son ouvrage *La Province de Québec,* a longtemps empêché les Canadiens-français de connaître et d'apprécier à leur valeur véritable les ressources étonnantes de leur pays; qu'ils réussissent enfin à avoir des écoles de cette nature, qu'ils puissent enfin ouvrir le grand livre des sciences appliquées, eux qui sont si singulièrement bien doués et si ingénieux en ce qui concerne l'intelligence et l'emploi des forces et des inventions mécaniques, et l'on peut assurer qu'ils se feront et garderont une large place dans les conditions futures des populations nord-américaines. » Ceux qui ont pu observer nos compatriotes dans les centres industriels savent combien ces paroles sont vraies. Recueillir en un faisceau une multitude des faits tendant à prouver combien nos compatriotes sont aptes à la grande industrie, voilà encore un travail nécessaire à faire; travail relativement facile, car ces faits abondent, mais qui fera ouvrir de grands yeux à bien des gens.

Déjà ce jour qu'appelait Buies commence à poindre. Ouvrez les journaux, ces photographies de l'esprit public, vous y trouverez la claire manifestation d'une ambition réveillée, d'une force nouvelle qu'il faut sans retard canaliser et diriger. Vers quel but ? Ici nous trouvons un terrain tout préparé où il ne s'agit que de jeter la semence. Depuis bien des générations, ces hommes défrichent dans la forêt, ils connaissent mieux que qui que ce soit toutes les essences forestières et les conditions de la vie des bois. C'est donc vers les industries des bois et vers les industries accessoires qu'il faut surtout les diriger. Ces industries leur sont en partie connues. Mettons-les en mesure de les exploiter scientifiquement, de les transformer en grandes industries et nous ne forcerons pas la nature, nous ne ferons qu'aider à compléter l'évolution. Cette évolution se produirait peut-être d'elle-même par la force des choses, mais elle serait relativement lente. Malheureusement, à notre époque et situés comme nous le sommes, nous n'avons guère le temps d'attendre. Il faut nous hâter si nous ne voulons pas qu'on nous devance. Or, nous savons qu'il nous reste beaucoup à faire pour compléter l'évolution.

Mais nous touchons ici à une autre partie de notre sujet. Contentons-nous pour le moment d'examiner ces considérations à la lumière du sens commun. Nous croyons qu'une conclusion s'impose, c'est que nos compatriotes de la province de Québec ne sont pas moins aptes à l'industrie que les autres races du continent et que, bien instruits et dirigés, ils obtiendront des résultats qui étonneront tout le monde et eux-mêmes les premiers.

(L'Evolution économique du Québec, in Mémoires de la Société royale du Canada, (1901)

Olivar Asselin (1874-1937)

Journaliste, polémiste redouté, ce chef du mouvement nationaliste participa avec Bourassa à la fondation du *Devoir.* Plus tard, il fonda l'*Ordre,* puis *La Renaissance.* On a recueilli quelques-uns de ses articles dans *Pensée française* (1938), dont est tiré le texte qui suit.

NOTRE DEVOIR LE PLUS URGENT

Tout d'abord, posons en principe que jamais peuple de vie économique et politique inférieure n'eut le moindre prestige ni n'exerça la moindre influence intellectuelle hors de ses frontières. La Grèce de l'époque romaine ne fait exception à cette règle qu'en apparence : à Rome comme ailleurs, le rôle qu'elle avait joué sur la scène politique était encore présent à toutes les mémoires; et elle avait gardé dans sa défaite une splendeur matérielle que les rapaces proconsuls romains ne savaient que trop apprécier. Le rayonnement extraordinaire de la pensée juive en Asie mineure, à Alexandrie et jusqu'en Grèce vers la même époque ne surprend de même qu'au premier coup d'oeil; sous tous ses maîtres le Juif avait conservé l'unité et la continuité de pensée qui sont le principe le plus actif de vie politique; les missionnaires qui étaient en train de conquérir le monde au monothéisme judaïque quand parut le Christ, et après lui saint Paul, étaient soutenus dans leur prosélytisme par une foi inébranlable à la résurrection prochaine de la nation juive. A l'époque moderne, on a vu des nationalités méprisées naguère forcer en quelques années l'attention puis l'admiration du monde par leurs oeuvres intellectuelles; pour n'en nommer qu'une, citons les Tchèques, dont la situation, longtemps analogue à la nôtre, comporterait pour nous de si salutaires leçons si notre suffisance nous permettait de chercher des enseignements quelque part. Mais le relèvement économique et politique, qui avait été pour ces nationalités une des conditions essentielles de la renaissance intellectuelle, a été la condition non moins essentielle de leur réhabilitation intellectuelle aux yeux de l'étranger. Les Américains qui ont étudié à Paris admirent passionnément la littérature et l'art français; ils se font une gloire d'aller entendre et applaudir les conférenciers de l'Alliance française en tournée dans leur pays; mais leur sympathie intellectuelle pour les populations d'ouvriers et de manoeuvres franco-américains qui peinent dans les chantiers et les usines des Etats-Unis n'en est pas accrue d'un iota; à tort ou à raison, ils continuent de croire que ces populations, si admirable que d'autres jugent et que puisse être leur pieux attachement au souvenir de la France, ne vivent pas assez intensément de la vie française pour arrêter, même passagèrement, leur attention. Eussions-nous dans le Québec les écoles les plus parfaites du monde, nos compatriotes anglais des autres provinces seraient excusables de ne s'en pas douter tant que, avec une politique économique dirigée au profit de la haute finance anglaise et une presse d'« action sociale catholique » tout occupée à faire de la casuistique religieuse au profit de partis politiques, nous serons dans notre propre maison des « porteurs d'eau » et des « scieurs de bois ». Eussions-nous la plus belle littérature et la plus haute culture scientifique du monde, que nous ne pourrions pas faire un crime à l'Ontario de l'ignorer tant que nos journalistes et nos hommes politiques, effrayés de leur ombre, incapables d'une idée personnelle, apporteront dans la délibération des problèmes nationaux des âmes de castrats et des intelligences de concierges. Le praticien romain prenait des leçons de ses affranchis, quand ils étaient grecs et qu'ils les savait venus directement des écoles d'Athènes : il n'en prenait point de ses esclaves. Montréal, à ce qu'on m'assure, est plein de docteurs ès-lettres italiens, russes, polonais et juifs qui ont beaucoup plus de distinction intellectuelle que la plupart des membres de notre Société Royale et qui, en attendant d'avoir pu se familiariser avec les langues et les coutumes du pays, gagnent leur vie à malaxer du béton ou à porter l'oiseau : qui de nous les connaît, qui de nous se donne la peine de les découvrir ?

Pour inspirer aux Canadiens anglais le respect de notre langue, nous avons encore d'autres conditions à remplir. Pour l'instant je n'en indiquerai que trois.

La première, c'est de leur prouver que le français tel que nous le vivons, si je puis m'exprimer ainsi, ne nuit pas à notre formation intellectuelle. En d'autres termes, c'est d'abord de faire en sorte que nos écoles existent.

Et je n'entends pas ici parler de l'école primaire. Certes, malgré toute la joie que doivent nous causer la fréquence de plus en plus grande des congrès de « commissaires », l'augmentation graduelle du traitement des institutrices à $150 par année, et quelques autres progrès d'égale importance, il y aurait de dures vérités à dire sur ce rouage de notre enseignement et l'ineptie de ceux qui le dirigent. J'ai en ce moment à l'esprit un livre de lecture adopté par presque tous nos corps enseignants pour sa prétendue supériorité et dont la bonne fortune, réalisée sous le régime du laisser-faire, est précisément un des arguments les plus chers aux adversaires de l'uniformité obligatoire des livres de classe : on y lit entre autres choses que le siège de l'industrie du fer au Canada est aux Forges du Saint-Maurice. Publié pour la première fois il y a cinquante ans, on n'y a apparemment pas changé une virgule depuis; il a gardé jusqu'à ses coquilles typographiques. Il m'a été donné récemment de lire toutes les lettres reçues des institutrices laïques de l'école primaire par certain comité patriotique; autant elles réconfortaient par la noblesse des sentiments, autant elles attristaient par la pauvreté invariable — oui, *invariable* — de la composition et de la syntaxe. Je ne crois pas que même ceux qui, pour employer le mot consacré, « font métier de dénigrer notre enseignement », aient jamais soupçonné un dénuement pareil. C'est à faire pleurer. Je souhaiterais que pour son édification personnelle un homme loyal comme mon ami Héroux, du *Devoir*, se donnât la peine d'examiner cette littérature. N'exagérons toutefois pas la part de l'école primaire dans la création des hautes valeurs intellectuelles par quoi se juge une civilisation. N'hésitons pas même à reconnaître que son action morale — comme il semble que le prouve à l'évidence l'état d'âme actuel de cette nation française où on disait que l'école neutre avait tué pour toujours l'idée religieuse — n'est pas comparable à celle de l'église ou du foyer. Bornons-nous, si on le veut, aux enseignements secondaire et supérieur.

Pour ce qui est de notre enseignement secondaire, quelque progrès qu'un homme d'âge mûr y constate en causant avec les écoliers d'aujourd'hui, il suffirait, pour en apprécier la valeur, de faire observer que tous les professeurs qui se sont succédé à la chaire de littérature de l'Université Laval à Montréal étaient en France simples professeurs de lycées, c'est-à-dire de collèges classiques. Bien plus, et même en classant séparément un tout petit nombre de maisons placées dans ces conditions exceptionnelles, on ne voit pas que cet enseignement puisse jamais sortir de la médiocrité tant qu'il n'y aura pas d'école normale supérieure pour la formation du personnel enseignant, et tant que, les « collèges » étant avant tout des petits séminaires, le recrutement du personnel enseignant sera subordonné aux exigences du ministère ecclésiastique.

C'est surtout par notre enseignement supérieur que nous pourrions espérer nous révéler un jour comme force intellectuelle. Quand les plus célèbres universités américaines ou anglaises viennent chercher des professeurs au McGill's — comme cela s'est vu cinq ou six fois depuis quinze ans — ou qu'un ancien professeur du McGill's, encore lié de très près à cette maison, reçoit le prix Nobel pour des découvertes scientifiques, nous n'avons pas besoin d'en savoir plus long pour conclure que le Canada anglais commence à compter dans le mouvement intellectuel universel. De même est-il à présumer que si, une fois tous les dix ou vingt ans, les travaux d'un professeur de Laval étaient couronnés par une Académie de réputation mondiale, M. Hocken lui-même attacherait peut-être une moindre signification au fait que nous rétribuons plus mal que nos servantes les institutrices de nos écoles primaires. Or, ne craignons pas de le demander à quiconque ne s'est pas crétinisé en passant par là, l'Université Laval comme *université,* c'est-à-dire comme préparation à l'intelligence de toute chose, cela existe-t-il ? Quel est l'enseignement qui se donne là et qu'un bon homme d'affaires comme M. Leblond de Brumath ou M. de Kerméno ne pût faire donner tout aussi bien par des « nègres » à quarante sous de l'heure ? Quelle espérance au moins avons-nous que l'institution sera jamais autre chose que ce qu'elle a toujours été, savoir : une école qui, en donnant à ses élèves — pour la plupart jeunes hommes très contents d'eux-mêmes — ce qu'il leur faut pour gagner leur vie, les pénètre juste assez du sentiment de son utilité pour, hélas ! les empêcher de voir tout ce qui lui manque ? Quant à moi, lorsque je cherche à mesurer aussi exactement que possible le degré de culture de notre personnel universitaire, j'évoque malgré moi la délicieuse histoire de ces nombreux chefs-d'oeuvre de peinture accrochés aux murs de l'Université québecquoise pendant un demi-siècle sans que personne en soupçonnât l'existence, et qui, découverts en 1910 par un vague peintre américain du nom de Purvis Carter, font maintenant la gloire de ce foyer intellectuel, gloire lui-même d'une ville qui s'intitule modestement l'Athènes de l'Amérique.

La deuxième condition, c'est de faciliter l'étude du français à nos compatriotes anglo-protestants. Il va de soi, en effet, que nous ne pouvons blâmer ceux-ci d'ignorer notre langue s'ils sont virtuellement dans l'impossibilité de l'apprendre. Or, de la plus humble de nos écoles primaires jusqu'à notre soi-disant université, quelle est celle de nos institutions scolaires qui ne soit avant tout une institution religieuse et qu'un protestant — abstraction faite de la valeur intellectuelle ou professionnelle de l'enseignement — pût fréquenter sans se manquer de respect ? Et si l'on prétend que les Anglais peuvent apprendre le français comme nous apprenons l'anglais, je réponds tout simplement que pour des raisons évidentes ce n'est pas là parler sérieusement.

La troisième condition, c'est que dans nos mouvements de protestations nous fassions un état plus considérable de la valeur du français considéré en soi, comme instrument de culture intellectuelle. Depuis le commencement de la présente guerre, la preuve est faite, semble-t-il, et pour toujours, que pour être bon Français il n'est pas indispensable d'appartenir à telle ou telle religion — non plus, bien entendu, qu'à telle ou telle secte antireligieuse. Au fond, il n'y a probablement pas plus de raison d'établir une corrélation entre le patriotisme canadien-français et la foi catholique. Parmi les Canadiens-Français anglicisés, j'en ai connu beaucoup qui avaient renié le catholicisme, mais j'en ai aussi connu un grand nombre qui étaient restés foncièrement, dévotement catholiques. D'autre part, je crois bien ne rien apprendre à personne en disant qu'aux Etats-Unis comme au Canada on trouverait nombre de Canadiens français indifférents en matière religieuse et cependant résolus à rester français. Mais si l'on tient mordicus à lier la langue à la foi, il faut à tout le moins prendre garde que ce ne soit pas parfois au détriment de la langue. La Société du Parler Français eût pu faire beaucoup pour la propagation du français dans le Canada anglais : on sait sous quelles influences elle s'est changée en Société du parler catholique et français. Pour complaire aux visées étroites de Mgr Roy et de quelques autres, elle s'est aliéné non seulement les Canadiens protestants qui auraient pu seconder son effort, mais l'armée innombrable des catholiques canadiens-français qui ne se sentent pas de vocation pour la propagande religieuse, et qui du reste sentent confusément que dans ce mariage de la langue et de la foi, décrétée par raison d'Etat, je veux dire par raison d'Eglise, ce n'est pas la foi qui a le plus à perdre. Comment peut-on sincèrement s'imaginer servir la cause du français dans l'Ontario protestant en ne cessant de proclamer que pour nous le français est d'abord un instrument de conservation et de propagande catholique ? Et comment espérer en même temps faire croire à la Province de Québec que l'on n'est mû que par l'amour du français, quand, au coeur même de cette province, le français se meurt dans les arts et métiers, la procédure judiciaire, les administrations publiques et privées et vingt autres sphères; que de toute évidence un commerce intellectuel plus intime avec la France pourrait seul nous rendre, avec l'esprit français, la force d'expansion et de rayonnement qui nous manque; que néanmoins, par crainte de « l'irréligion »,

et en dépit de leurs beaux discours, ceux qui pourraient nous rapprocher de la France agissent au fond comme s'ils étaient enchantés de
nous en tenir éloignés. Le jour où le clergé canadien-français ne mettra plus de conditions à sa défense du français, il conquerra le cœur
de ceux pour qui le français aussi est une religion, et c'est-à-dire que
ce jour-là il y aura peut-être encore des indifférents en matière religieuse, voire des incroyants, dans le Canada français, mais qu'il n'y
aura plus d'anticléricaux. Au contraire, la plus grande maladresse dont
il soit capable, et pour la religion et pour le français, c'est de continuer
à se mettre en travers de tout mouvement d'action française qu'il n'a
pas conçu et qu'il ne dirige pas, et qui ne s'affiche pas d'abord comme
un mouvement catholique.

(*L'Action,* 30 janvier 1915; reproduit in *Pensée française,* 1937)

Edouard Montpetit (1881-1954)

Avocat, économiste, professeur
de droit et d'économie,
il fut longtemps secrétaire
général de l'Université de Montréal
et a exercé une grande influence
tant par la parole que par la plume.

Il fut membre de la Société royale
du Canada. Plus humaniste
que technologue, son oeuvre
s'adresse plus au grand public
qu'aux économistes, comme
on en jugera par le texte qui suit.

LA CONQUÊTE ÉCONOMIQUE

Qu'est-ce qui nous a retenus loin des préoccupations économiques ? Deux objections, fondées sur les droits de l'intelligence et de la
morale, et qui exigent l'entente d'une définition.

L'économie politique étudie l'ensemble de l'activité humaine qui
produit et distribue les richesses. Ce dernier mot, d'où vient tout le
mal, fut ramassé dans la langue populaire par les fondateurs qui lui
donnèrent un sens nouveau. Les richesses sont-elles uniquement l'or
et l'argent ? Pas un économiste qui le prétende, fût-ce le libéral le plus
pur. Seule l'école des bullionnistes, qui touche au moyen âge, l'a cru;
et déjà les mercantilistes le niaient. On admet depuis longtemps que
l'argent et l'or, s'ils possèdent une valeur propre, ne sont qu'un signe,
une mesure. Les richesses sont les *utilités* qui satisfont les besoins
de l'homme. Ces besoins déclenchent l'initiative; ils ne sont pas tous
de première nécessité et l'économique rêve de satisfaire des besoins

intellectuels ou moraux. Pour l'économiste, ce sont des truismes. Un livre, une oeuvre d'art, une bibliothèque, un musée, sont, aussi bien qu'une denrée, un combustible, un vêtement ou une habitation, des richesses parce que ce sont des utilités, c'est-à-dire, à des degrés divers, des moyens de satisfaction. Je l'entends ainsi avec bien d'autres. Dès lors, l'accord paraît facile à ceux que n'aveugle pas le parti pris.

On ne sacrifiera pas l'intelligence à la matière. Les richesses, dans un ensemble ordonné, ne sont qu'un acheminement, une amorce, un moyen. La construction d'une université ou d'un hôpital est une question d'argent. L'oeuvre d'enseignement ou l'oeuvre d'assistance s'érigent sur la matière. Certes, le sacrifice a fait beaucoup autrefois pour entasser des matériaux, dresser des murs, déployer des toits, lancer des flèches; mais nous vivons dans notre siècle. Le mal est fait.

Placé au sortir de l'enseignement français en face d'une tâche, j'écrivais en 1910 : « Le sens pratique a créé des peuples comme l'idéal, jadis, en a formé; mais les nations qui ont connu d'abord la vie économique éprouvent, une fois grandies, le désir, le besoin, de chercher dans la culture intellectuelle un élément qui les complète, fussent-elles nées dans une époque d'égoïsme et eussent-elles fondé sur les affaires un empire dont la grandeur bientôt ne leur a plus suffi. Ce sera le mérite de l'industrialisme d'avoir permis à l'homme de vivre un peu plus la vie de l'esprit et du coeur en assurant un peu mieux chaque jour la vie du corps. A côté du sillon, nos usines ont grandi. Nous avons fait de merveilleux progrès et nous sommes devenus une nation productrice qui compte et qui prend place dans les préoccupations politiques et économiques du monde contemporain. L'heure de l'idée est donc venue pour nous. Qu'une vie intellectuelle plus intense naisse de notre existence matérielle assurée. On disait autrefois : *Emparons-nous du sol;* on a écrit hier : *Emparons-nous de l'industrie;* disons à notre tour : *Emparons-nous de la science et de l'art.* Illuminons de ce rayon notre histoire, où, suivant la belle expression de M. Hector Fabre, « pas un recul ne se trouve ».

On me pardonnera de rappeler ces paroles, inspirées par le retour au pays et par la création d'une école supérieure. Bien souvent je les ai répétées et je les reprends aujourd'hui sans y rien changer. La richesse accumulée a pour fin la civilisation. La France, notre patrie d'origine, y a dès longtemps consenti. Elle ne s'est pas désintéressée de la fortune qui est une des raisons de son succès dans la pensée et dans l'art. Les Croisades et la Renaissance ont, par l'industrie et le commerce qu'elles ont fait fleurir, préparé l'ensoleillement des grands siècles. Henri IV et Sully ont regardé au delà de l'économie nationale qu'ils fondaient sur l'agriculture; Louis XIV et Colbert, en créant la manufacture royale, en animant les métiers, en inaugurant une politique industrielle encore maladroite, ont voulu asseoir sur une base solide la supériorité française. Les Flandres opulentes ont produit l'école d'art la plus belle. L'Angleterre, livrée aux puissances d'argent, doit tout de même une part de sa renommée à ses poètes et à ses savants. Les Etats-Unis, encore enlisés dans les sables d'or, construisent des monuments, multiplient des enseignements où, parmi des naïvetés de parvenu, on perçoit la recherche de satisfactions intellectuelles.

L'intelligence créatrice garde ainsi ses droits sur la richesse dont elle se sert pour aller vers des fécondités nouvelles. Le chercheur, l'inventeur, le penseur, l'artiste, vivent et agissent. Le peuple, qui apprécie ses loisirs, proclame ses véritables chefs et les suit. Vision trop optimiste ? Sans doute, et irréalisable. Est-ce une raison pour ne pas l'indiquer ? On craindra encore que la richesse ne se tourne contre l'intelligence. Il se peut, si l'histoire des décadences le démontre. Le peuple qui s'enrichit est perdu s'il ne prend de la fortune que son culte. La modération est le point difficile. Est-ce une raison pour ne pas le prévoir ni le fixer, pour s'abandonner aux forces aveugles ? Pour éloigner le danger, nous userons d'une surveillance constante sur nous-mêmes, nous repousserons le matérialisme, nous nous rappellerons la pondération de notre génie, nous instruirons le riche, qui ne sait jamais trop ses devoirs et toujours assez ses droits, nous ne sacrifierons au sens pratique que juste ce qu'il faut pour révéler nos qualités, nous vivrons et nous progresserons par nous-mêmes et nous nous refuserons à servir les autres. Il y aura des victimes ? Combien y en aura-t-il sans cela ?

Ne faisons pas céder la préoccupation morale devant la poursuite des avantages pécuniaires. La moralité est un élément de la science économique. En veut-on des exemples ? Sur quoi repose la production ? Sur l'ordre. Que demande-t-on aux pays producteurs ? Des hommes; et le principe de population est un principe moral. Qu'est-ce que l'homme même, moteur initial de l'activité économique ? — Un être raisonnable. Que réclame-t-on de l'ouvrier, outre l'habileté ? — La conscience. Pourquoi supprime-t-on les industries novices ? Sur quoi se fonde la lutte contre le monopole, sinon sur la déloyauté d'une concurrence ? Qu'est-ce qu'un juste salaire, un bénéfice raisonnable, des intérêts sans usure, un prix maximum ? Et si les producteurs oublient volontiers toutes ces choses, cela démontre-t-il que le bon fonctionnement de l'ensemble économique n'en exige pas le respect ? La circulation ordonne d'assainir la monnaie. Le protectionnisme est la mise en oeuvre d'un sentiment puissant sur les foules. Il n'est pas jusqu'au prix de vente qu'une moralité de la consommation ne se charge de ramener dans des limites normales. Le luxe exagéré n'est qu'une brillante inutilité, une perte condamnée par les économistes.

C'est un aspect seulement de la question. La richesse, ai-je dit, n'est qu'un moyen; la satisfaction morale dans la paix et le bien-être est le but suprême. Que ce ne soit pas pour demain ne légitime pas la reculade devant le reproche d'utopie. L'intérêt guide le monde économique. Sans aucun doute, mais est-ce une raison pour n'y rien faire ? Piètre science, qui, établissant la nécessité de l'ordre, ne reconnaîtrait pas que les abus engendrent la révolution. La législation a précisément pour objet d'opposer le bien de tous à la volonté de chacun. Les lois supérieures de la moralité contraignent à de justes limites les lois économiques.

Jamais les économistes n'ont dit cela ? Il y a d'abord économistes et économistes, et, chez nous, on a tendance à l'ignorer. Des ouvrages honnissent les *orthodoxes,* qui sont confondus avec les économistes, sans qualificatif; et cela suffit pour que l'étiquette serve à tous. Ici, l'Ecole libérale engouffre tous ceux qui s'efforcent d'écrire sur l'économique avec quelque indépendance et, comme elle effraie — on oublie qu'il y a une école libérale catholique — on y a vite ramené tous les suspects. Les libéraux nous ont donné d'excellentes leçons et des arguments; mais, en matière de répartition des richesses, ils ont formulé la doctrine déplorable du *laisser faire* qui, d'ailleurs, les a tués. Partout la réaction est vive. Il n'est plus d'*inhumains,* s'il est encore des économistes qui croient à la liberté.

L'effort vers la moralisation vaut qu'on le tente. Les besoins humains sont à la base de l'économie; plus ils se développent, plus les complexités de la vie économique s'accentuent. Nous subirons la loi de l'extensibilité des besoins, n'étant pas autrement faits que le reste des hommes. Nous la subissons déjà : nos villes attirent chaque jour davantage l'homme que la terre ne satisfait plus, et ce qu'on appelle le *centre urbain* se modifie à vue d'oeil dans un sens qui n'est pas toujours heureux. La misère monte à côté de la fortune. Richesse ou dénuement, il arrive que l'on ait à choisir. Nous touchons au problème individuel dont l'angoisse est souvent la source des pires faiblesses. Les forces agissent. Il est temps que l'on accepte le mouvement économique pour le diriger en respectant les principes sains de la production. Ce qui ne se fera pas avec nous se fera sûrement sans nous et, peut-être, contre nous.

(*La Conquête économique,* I, 1938)

Jules Fournier (1884-1918)

Journaliste lié à Bourassa et à Asselin, il fut directeur du *Nationaliste,* rédacteur au *Devoir* et fonda *L'Action* (1911-1916) avant de devenir traducteur au Sénat en 1917.

Satiriste de talent, il fut un polémiste vigoureux et, poursuivi et condamné pour libelle, il fut emprisonné trois mois en 1909 et écrivit des *Souvenirs de prison* dont est tiré le portrait qui suit.

LE MÉDECIN MALGRÉ MOI

Le docteur Robitaille était en ce temps-là médecin de la prison de Québec. Il est mort depuis; Dieu ait son âme !

A l'époque dont je parle, il n'avait pas moins de soixante-dix ans bien comptés. Il était sourd comme plusieurs pots et, malgré un cornet acoustique plus gros que sa tête, ne comprenait jamais un traître mot de tout ce qu'on lui disait.

Il restait aux détenus, pour communiquer avec lui, la suprême ressource de lui exposer par écrit leurs besoins. Mais encore cela n'était pas toujours facile. Jamais je n'ai tant regretté, quant à moi, de n'avoir pas de style.

A peu près tous les jours, entre dix heures et midi, il faisait son apparition dans les corridors du 17. La première fois que je le vis, son aspect m'étonna. Figurez-vous un petit vieux, perdu dans une ample redingote, et qui s'avançait à pas peureux et hésitants ... Son nez épaté, ses yeux bridés, sa figure grimaçante et barbue, lui donnaient tout à fait l'air d'une chauve-souris clouée sur un contre-vent. Sa bouche toujours entrouverte laissait apercevoir ses dents et un sourire égaré errait continuellement sur ses lèvres ...

De toute évidence, cet homme-là était tombé depuis longtemps dans le gâtisme. Pourquoi l'on laissait tout de même entre ses mains les vies de tant d'infortunés, c'est ce que je ne pus comprendre tout d'abord. Un garde se chargea de me l'expliquer.

— Voyez-vous, me dit-il, le *docteur* est ici depuis vingt-cinq ans : le renvoyer, ce serait sa mort.

Pour cette profonde raison, le docteur Robitaille restait donc — avec le docteur LeBel — l'un des deux médecins de la prison. Un mois sur deux, il avait toute liberté de prodiguer ses soins aux détenus.

Son cornet acoustique d'une main, de l'autre un thermomètre, — toujours le même, — il faisait régulièrement le tour de la prison chaque matin. Il prenait la température aux malades, leur tâtait le pouls, leur faisait tirer la langue ... Tout cela avec conscience et lenteur.

Mais où il brillait principalement, c'était dans l'auscultation. Le docteur Robitaille avait cette passion-là : l'auscultation. Vingt fois par jour on le trouvait penché sur la poitrine d'un malade. Peu lui importait la nature du mal, et qu'il s'agît d'une inflammation de poumons, d'une indigestion ou d'une écorchure au genou, ce lui était tout un ... L'auscultation rentrait pour lui dans la thérapeutique proprement dite, et volontiers il eût dit : Je l'auscultai, Dieu le guérit.

Chose remarquable, ce besoin d'ausculter, loin de s'apaiser, grandissait avec la surdité du docteur. Les jours où il n'entendait absolument rien, pas même avec son cornet, de véritables rages d'auscultation le prenaient. Un matin qu'il était plus sourd encore que la veille, je le vis ausculter l'Italien, qui souffrait, comme je vous l'ai conté, d'un bobo à la lèvre supérieure. Une autre fois (mais à cela je n'ose croire), on assure qu'il ausculta un détenu qui se plaignait de durillons au pied gauche. — Toujours sans l'aide d'aucun instrument, je crois vous l'avoir dit ...

Serez-vous bien étonné si j'ajoute qu'il trouvait rarement à ses patients les maux dont ils se croyaient atteints ? — En revanche, et c'est là la merveille ! il leur découvrait continuellement toutes sortes de maladies effroyables dont ils prétendaient n'avoir jamais souffert. C'est ainsi qu'il vous déclarait sans plus de cérémonie, si vous l'alliez consulter pour un mal de tête : « Vous, mon ami, j'ai votre affaire ... J'ai vu cela tout de suite : vous êtes atteint d'une maladie de coeur qui vous emportera promptement. » C'est ainsi que certain jour il disait à un dyspeptique : « Ce soir vous vous mettrez des mouches noires ... Vous avez une congestion : ça pourrait devenir dangereux. »

.   .   .   .
.   .   .   .

Au moment que j'entrai en prison, je souffrais d'une dépression qui inspirait de vives craintes à mon médecin. Les nuits blanches du *Nationaliste* m'avaient complètement épuisé et ma santé, paraît-il, était aussi compromise que possible.

Je me hâte d'ajouter, pour rassurer mes nombreux ennemis, que j'ai eu le temps, depuis, de me remettre. A l'heure où j'écris ces lignes, je ne suis pas loin de peser le poids d'un député ordinaire; mes muscles s'affermissent chaque jour, on dit même que je prends du ventre, et si je continue je serai bientôt aussi épais qu'un numéro de *La Presse*.

Mais en 1909 j'étais loin de pouvoir en dire autant. Mon médecin m'abreuvait sans relâche de toniques, et je me rappelle fort bien que durant les deux mois — notamment — qui précédèrent ma condamnation, je ne pus me tenir debout qu'à force de suralimentation.

Je voulus savoir du docteur Robitaille s'il faisait, au point de vue de ma santé, une différence quelconque entre les viandes saignantes et le skelley. Il m'assura qu'il n'en voyait aucune.

Ayant mis à exécution ce projet :

— Je vois, dit-il en me regardant au blanc des yeux, ce que vous avez. C'est des apéritifs qu'il vous faut. Je m'en vais vous envoyer des amers.

Durant la semaine qui suivit, il ne manqua pas un seul jour de me venir ausculter, ni de m'envoyer des amers.

Oh ! ces amers... Régulièrement à tous les repas, on me les apportait dans ma cellule. Je n'ai pas souvenir qu'on y ait manqué une seule fois.

Le malheur, c'est que plus on me donnait envie de manger, moins on me donnait de quoi manger. J'en étais toujours réduit au skelley matin et soir, à la soupe aux légumes ou à la *jambe de botte* le midi.

Vous pouvez penser si j'avais là de quoi *faire,* comme disait mon médecin, de la suralimentation !

En six jours, — grâce aux amers, je suppose, — j'avais bien pu prendre de huit à dix bouchées à la table pénitentiaire. Je n'exagère pas.

Joignez à cela le repos bien mérité de la cellule (de cinq heures et demie du soir à six heures du matin), dans l'atmosphère parfumée par le voisinage de l'Italien; les insomnies et les nausées... et dites si je n'aurais pas eu mauvaise grâce à me plaindre !

Le jour même de mon arrivée, j'entendais un garde faire en ma présence cette constatation encourageante, que je n'avais que la peau et les os. Une semaine plus tard, j'avais maigri de quinze livres.

Et le *docteur* continuait à m'envoyer des amers...

Il est mort depuis; Dieu ait son âme !

(*Souvenirs de prison,* 1910)

R. D. Symons (Born in 1898)

This writer was born in England and came to the prairies in 1914. Subsequently he was a soldier, rancher, homesteader, game warden, naturalist and finally an artist-writer.

His artwork may be seen in the Museum of Natural History in Regina. The selection presented here is a chapter from his story of the early west, *Many Trails*.

MA PARSONS

Mrs. Parsons is about ninety if she is still alive — and I bet she is. She was young at eighty-six when I saw her last. I used to ride with her son Allen, who was older than I, and a thoroughly good cow hand. Sometimes I used to ride over to their ranch of a Sunday, and have a good feed — Allen always said his ma was a first-rate hand at pies.

I knew the family had come from the East years before, over the plains by wagon; and between yarning with Allen and asking questions of the old lady I pieced together the story, which is a remarkable epic of pioneering not so much for the adventures encountered as for the lack of them.

She was born Rowena Webb, at Horning's Mill in old Ontario, in the days when it was Upper Canada and the third concession was 'way back in the bush. She was seventeen when she married Amos Parsons who had been her father's hired man; and like most young folks of those days they planned for a farm of their own. So they went to Manitoba. "Manitoba was turrible far in them days."

Amos was from what they call pioneer stock, which means he wasn't afraid to work. If he had been he would never have been able to work for Tom Webb, let alone marry his daughter. Tom's own father had hewn out a farm from the hardwood bush. And this is almost precisely what his son-in-law did, for he chose a homestead in the wooded valley of Swan River in sight of the blue heights of the Riding Mountain; and, granted that soft white poplar and bunchy willow fall to the axe more easily than maple and ash, still it took a worker to prove-up and get title.

But I won't go into details of grubbing willow crowns and urging the ox-drawn breaker plow through the heavy sod; of the building of the log shack; of the first crop of Red Fife wheat. Nor of Rowena's long winter evenings knitting for her growing family or the equally long summer days of housekeeping, chicken rearing, and gardening. Neither shall I more than mention the many anxious nights when her man was late coming from "town," as they called the little settlement where the trading was done — nights when she sat up, keeping the kettle hot;

straining her ears for the creak and whine of sleigh runners, but hearing only the hiss of the wind-driven snow as it banked against the cabin; hoping he would see the guiding rays of the lantern she had hung at the gate.

I want to tell you of Rowena's crowning triumph — The Trip, as she called it.

Well, after many years on the homestead they made good; but as the farm became well established more settlers came, and then the railroad; and presently, to use Rowena's words, "a person didn't have room to swing a cat any more."

Amos got restless first.

"They say there's first-class cattle country 'way west; good grass and lots of room." A bit too dry for wheat; but he preferred cattle anyway. And he wanted to take a look at it.

So they talked it over. Amos wanted to take a look and perhaps get work with one of the ranchers, and he figured Rowena could run the farm for a bit. Allen was thirteen now and could handle the plowing and cutting, and the littler 'uns could stook the grain and do chores. If he settled on a place she could come out later and bring the family and the stock.

Rowena, at sight of his glowing face, knew her man had already made up his mind. She belonged to a breed of wise women who know that there is a type of man who has to follow a star; and she had the loyalty as well as the love which goes with that breed. So she never for a moment even considered that there was anything else she could do but stick it out and leave him to go his way.

And so it was arranged. Amos went to Swift Current, the jumping-off place for the cattle country of what was then Assiniboia Territory. A year later found him herding cattle on Battle Creek, just south of the rolling Cypress Hills, where Canada touches the State of Montana among broken hills and scented sage flats. To the south, sixty miles away, rose the jagged peaks of the Bear Paws; to the south-west the triple buttes of the Sweetgrass Hills; to the north the timbered coulees and level high benches of the Cypress. Towns? Havre, Montana, a wild cow town, forty-five miles to the south on Milk River. To the northeast on the Canadian Pacific's transcontinental line, Maple Creek, a booming cattle town with its neat Mounted Police barracks. Neighbours? A few ranchers — Texans, down-East Canadians, English and Scotch; a few Mounted Policemen and some half-breed horse breakers; plenty of half-wild range cattle, mustangs, antelope and other animals of the plains. Roads? Prairie trails — twin grooves a few feet apart, worn by freight wagons in the grassy sod, winding snake-like between the low hills and over the gentle swells.

A big land of immense blue distances and great horizons. A dry land where grass is green only briefly in May and June, scorched to tawny and yellow and pinkish-grey in fall. A land of high plateaus and clear crisp air; of balmy spring breezes and January blizzards. But, as Amos had been told, a good cattle country — the very drying of the grass on the stem being a curing process which retained in the blade all the nourishment that stock required for winter grazing.

Amos had filed on a quarter by the creek, and had a small log shack sheltered against a cut bank, a few good saddle horses and a Cripple Creek saddle. With grazing plentiful, he had a few dollars coming in and could see his way, as he would have said, to running a "spread."

So he sent for Rowena. He didn't bother her with details and instructions as to what to sell and what to bring, or how to do it. He knew Rowena; so he simply wrote :

Dear Rowena :

I have started a ranch on Battle Crick. Sell the Farm or tell Lawyer Robson to sell it if you can't right away. Bring the cows and oxen and wagons and whatever you think we need. Allen better herd the cattle along. If you start the first grass you'll get here before freeze-up. When you get to Maple Crick go to Trueman's barn and he will put you on the Havre trail. Cross through the Cypress Gap and you will come to the Police post at Ten Mile, and the fellow there will show you the trail to our place, it's only a few miles further. Take care of yourself and take it easy, and tell the kids to be good.

Hoping this finds you and the kids fine as it leaves me, I sign myself as usual,

Your loving husband.

P.S. I should of said theys plenty of good spring water and some reel pretty flowers here, and you will like the place.

So Rowena sold the farm — there were plenty of buyers in those days, what with the new railroad and all — and set about the business of packing. This was April, and new grass meant about the end of May — plenty of time to get ready.

First to the bank, where she was told that a branch had been opened at Swift Current. So she had most of the money from the sale put through to Amos's credit there, carefully keeping enough for incidental expenses on the way. Pioneer women are good at business, even if they seem to handle it in a funny way sometimes — as when she parcelled up the notes and asked the bank manager to send them by registered mail to the branch out West. He smiled and said "Sure"; and Ma Parsons still swears that the identical notes of "my money" made the long trip!

Finances being shipshape, her next concern was what to take and what to leave. The big oval daguerreotypes of Pa and Ma, in their gilt frames, simply had to be taken; and great was her concern over the packing of this evidence of her good Ontario parentage. She dusted Ma's photo with great care, remembering the old lady's injunction about not packing dirty things. Then there were the big cookstove, the heater and the most substantial pieces of furniture; the chinaware, to be packed in barrels with the spare bedding; the kitchen utensils; and the special household treasures — especially the Good Book in which were recorded her wedding day and the children's birthdays. All the miscellaneous things, cleaned and sorted and packed, soon stood ready. The cookstove, the kitchen things and the "using" bedding would be needed to the last minute, and had to be the last things loaded; and they would continue to be used on the way.

The two wagons were got ready. Tires had to be reset by the blacksmith, the wheels had to be well greased and the woodwork repaired. Two canvas tops had to be made, of heavy rough canvas that her sewing machine could not take; so she sewed them by hand, using an old sail-maker's palm that a sea-going uncle had given her for a souvenir when she was a little girl. Funny how things always come in handy if you keep them long enough!

Came a month of methodical work — taking it easy as Amos had said — during which she was helped by thirteen-year-old Allen, who was coming into his growth; and rather hindered by the four smaller fry, two girls and two boys. A month of packing, figuring and planning, and all was ready. The caravan — not an uncommon one in those days — left Swan River, Manitoba, on a May morning of bright sunshine that made the poplar leaves as yellow as the breasts of the meadow larks which fluttered and whistled before them.

Rowena drove the first white-canopied wagon, perched high on the spring seat and handling the heavy leather ox reins with ease — for they drive oxen like horses in Manitoba, with bridles and bits. At the rear of the wagon she had set up her cookstove, its black pipe projecting through a neatly bound opening in the canvas, her flour barrel on one side of the stove and her pork barrel on the other; and here she cooked for six, three times a day. Rowena had wanted to bring at least one brood sow, but figuring it out she realized that the beast could hardly make it on foot with the cattle, and would take up too much room crated alive; and, as she said, "I like my pigs best in the pork barrel anyways." So that settled the problems of both transportation and of meat supply on the way.

Her utensils hung close to hand in friendly company, frying-pan and kettles clanking against each other with every jolt of the wheels. In this wagon, too, she kept the rolled-up bedding by day. At night it was spread on the wagon floor for her and the girls, and on the prairie grass under the wagon for the three boys.

The second wagon had the big hayrack on it, and was packed tight with furniture and hand tools. It also carried the cutting bar of the mower, the wheel part of which was slung underneath. Here was a glorious miscellany of chattels, from the protesting hens in the crate at the back to the baby's cradle wedged in the middle, its interior crammed with winter clothing. The quietest and oldest oxen were hitched to this wagon; and there being no one to drive them, they were simply fastened to the front wagon by strong halter shanks, which meant careful driving to prevent a sudden speed-up breaking the ropes.

Behind the second wagon, and drawn by the simple expedient of having its shafts lashed to the wagon axle, came the shiny family buggy. Not for anything would Rowena have parted with that buggy. It was a symbol of prosperity and horsepower, marking the transition from the homesteader's oxen to the farmer's driving horses. The one horse, a Standardbred driver, free of the shafts, carried young Allen as he brought up the rear with the driven cattle — eight or nine milch cows and a scattering of yearlings, heifers soon to be cows, and steers for the family beef.

The party travelled southwest for about two weeks, following the old Fort Ellice trail and crossing the Qu'Appelle River near Spy Hill. Then they proceeded westward parallel to the Canadian Pacific Railway, built only a few years before and still the only railroad in the whole Northwest. Sometimes they were near it, sometimes far away, according to the trail; sometimes they came close enough to one of the string of mushroom towns to camp on the outskirts and do a little small shopping or have minor repairs made to the vehicles. Some days they travelled only seven or eight miles, on others ten or even fifteen; but not once did they move on a Sunday.

On the fine mornings all but the two youngest children — three-year-old Jessie and the baby, born after her father had left Manitoba — walked beside the wagons or else behind, helping Allen with the stock; sometimes running off the trail to look at a bird's nest in the grass, or pick the lovely harebells that nodded their blue heads all day. Their hard little feet, accustomed to being unshod in summer, scuffed the dust of the trail or scampered over prickly bull thistles with equal disregard. On the rainy days, or when the strong west wind whipped the grasses low and sent dust devils whirling from horizon to horizon, Rowena made them stay under cover. Rain on a bare head, she averred, never did any good and too much wind took the breath away.

And all the way across the plains this woman attended to her housework and chores in the same steady, orderly fashion that she had learnt as a girl. With one exception — wash-day was not Monday but Saturday. I have already indicated that Rowena was no "Sabbath breaker" (as she would have said), and under no circumstances would she travel on the first day of the week. But she soon found that washing hung out to dry on and about the moving wagons picked up plenty of fine black dust, and that it would be necessary to stop and camp in order to dry the weekly wash properly; so she wisely altered the old family routine and washed at Saturday night's camp, hanging the clothes on a line between the wagons. And there they stayed all day Sunday, to be gathered clean and fresh as prairie herbs early on Monday morning.

She bathed the children first and washed the clothes afterwards, reheating the water in the big pot, as the children called the rotund and heavy cauldron which had started life boiling maple sap in the far-off bush days. Sunday morning saw neat, clean children in a neat camp, gathered round their mother as she read from the Bible — stories of wanderings in strange lands, of hunger and thirst and deliverance — while the row of small garments flapped bravely on the line and the oxen lay down with contented grunts to chew their morning cud.

"It didn't hardly look right," says Rowena, "to be reading from Scripture with the kids' underwear a-flapping ; but anyhow I knew them clothes hadn't been washed on a Sunda, and I weren't going to take them down on a Sunda."

After three weeks or more of travelling over the park-like prairies to the Qu'Appelle, they began to leave the poplar and willow groves behind and come into more level and open plains. They missed the friendliness of the groves and they missed the hundreds of shining sloughs with their throngs of wild-fowl — green-headed mallard, graceful pintails, broad-billed shovellers, various small teal and the black-and-white scaup ducks. The grass began to get shorter and finer — real prairie wool — and they began to see birds which were strange to them — small black ones with white wing patches, which the children called at once "white-wings," not knowing that they were lark buntings.

Rowena somehow always had a bright fire in her stove and water in the barrel lashed to the wagon's creaking side. Word always seemed to go ahead that a woman and kids were on their way west, so that sometimes when Rowena asked at a homesteader's sod shack or a constructor's camp as to the best place for water or grass she found that she was already expected, and so had leave to camp by someone's well; or she might be directed to a creek or spring.

When the scanty waterside willows permitted, the smaller children were set to work gathering dry twigs and branches; but otherwise their fuel was dried dung picked up on the prairie — "cow chips" as they called them, and mighty good fuel as every old-timer knows.

In the evening the cows had to be milked and the warm milk set in pans overnight for the cream to rise. In the morning she skimmed it off and gave what was left to the calves — two of which had been dropped on the way, and were now crammed somehow into the second wagon. In addition, the morning's milk went directly to them — or at least as much as they could take. What the children and the calves could not drink had to be thrown away, as the cream would not rise during the daytime travelling. Her faithful barrel churn hung at the wagon's back, and twice a week the cream was put in it and turned to yellow butter by the ceaseless jolting and swaying of the wagon as it followed the uneven trail; so that at the evening camp it could be worked in the wooden bowl, salted and pressed away in the big stone crocks.

As the July heat ripened the wild strawberries and saskatoons, there was many a feast of fresh fruit and cream to vary the monotony of salt pork, bread, porridge and prunes. To smell that home-made bread and see that firm butter was almost as good as eating it; and what with a few eggs from the hens and plenty of thick cream on the breakfast oats Queen Victoria herself fared no better.

Not that things always ran smoothly. The cows drifted off one stormy night and Rowena and Allen had to thrash about in the wet till daybreak rounding them up — only to find that in their absence Jessie had walked in her sleep, upsetting the sponge for the next day's bread and putting the whole camp in an uproar. And there was the loneliness to fight, for a grown woman yearns for somebody more "talkable" than a thirteen-year-old, and a boy at that; and some of the nights were very dark, and the coyotes' howling didn't make them any better.

Some nights she would wake with a feeling that something was wrong, and reaching out her hand would touch the rough side of the wagon box and suddenly remember that she was out on the lone prairie with her small children dependent on her. But remembering Allen, almost a man, heartened her and she would sometimes call out, "Are you awake, son ?" and Allen would sleepily answer that he was. "Go to sleep, Ma, everything is all right, and I'm keeping Jim covered."

Mosquitoes were a plague. On still evenings they appeared in grey clouds in the long grass around the sloughs and drove the stock almost frantic at times, as well as attacking the humans. The children's legs looked quite "measly," as they laughingly told one another. But as the drier weather and the party's arrival into the shorter grass of the cattle country thinned the humming ranks of these insects, the party got respite and were gradually able to discontinue the smudge-pot of cow chips and green grass, and the children could stop scratching their legs.

They rose early and breakfasted early. But by the time the cows were gathered and the milking done and everything packed, it was usually about eight o'clock before they were off. Oxen are no good in the heat of the day so they made noon camp about eleven o'clock, and while the oxen rested and grazed Rowena would iron or mend or sometimes take a nap, while the elder children looked for berries. At three in the afternoon they would be on the trail again till six, when it would be time to make the night camp.

So they travelled on as spring gradually turned to summer and the prairie became bright with sunflowers; and summer itself began to age, and the grasses ripened with the smell of new-mown hay; and the young gophers could be seen almost as big as their parents as they peeped and whistled from their holes.

Suns rose like molten discs from behind the horizon's rim. Day breezes freshened and swept the grass into waves and ripples, and blew the brown pipits before the wagons like autumn leaves. After a morning's run the children loved to lie back in the buggy and watch the procession of great fleecy clouds with turreted tops like castles, slowly and steadily moving overhead. Suns set slowly, gloriously, as only on the plains they can; cool nights followed burning days and sage-scented twilights.

And this woman, with her little world for which she was responsible, went on to where her man waited. Cook, housekeeper, teamster, stockman; doctor, nurse, preacher, dairymaid — such was Ma Parsons. And she did all this in a perfectly natural, contented and efficient manner that left no room for stupid anxieties or useless grumbling. She knew that she could hurry along and make the trip in little more than half the time. But she also knew the cost to the cattle, the vehicles and her own nerves (though she wouldn't have understood that word !) of hurrying and bustling and being impatient. And she reckoned to arrive with the "hull kit an' boodle" safe and sound.

So it was well into August before they got to Maple Creek, nearly 700 miles from their starting point. There Trueman took care of their animals for a day or two, while his missus took care of Rowena's youngest children so that Rowena herself could do a little shopping at Dixon's store and generally freshen up before starting on the last lap. And since one of the young policemen was making a patrol to Ten Mile, Trueman — who was well acquainted with the police through supplying fodder for their horses — asked him to let Amos Parsons know that his wife and kids had arrived from Manitoba.

So it came to pass that, having been duly put on the Havre trail by their friend, they were making noon camp at Fish Creek when Amos himself rode up.

The baby was frightened of her father, but they all finally got settled down; and in the evening, talking more quietly as the children slept, Rowena may have told Amos about the nights she was a bit scared. And she was proud to show him that she had made enough butter to do them all winter in case the cows dried up with the cold weather, and knitted a full supply of winter socks and mitts and scarfs.

She did like the ranch and soon set about making the cabin more homelike. And they prospered as they deserved, in cattle and land; but better than that they had three more children, making eight in all.

Mrs. Parsons became Ma to most of the bachelors for miles around, though she was no older than most of them, and could trip it at the cowboy dances with the best — yes, and make the finest coffee afterwards while they all waited till daylight to go home.

When I last saw Ma Parsons, not so long ago, she sat in her big rocking-chair on the ranch porch, as happy and hearty and as full of fun as ever. Allen, a great hulking chap with rough red whiskers, himself the father of four or five, had stopped in as he was riding by and clanked through the kitchen and had to be spoken to by his mother who "never could abide spurs in my house."

I would hardly dare call Mrs. Parsons a heroine. She wouldn't like it. She thinks a "heroeen" is some woman who does something extraordinarily brave and marvellous.

(Many Trails)

Frederick Philip Grove (1871-1948)

Novelist and essayist, Grove was born in Russia of a Swedish father and a Scottish mother. He grew up in an aristocratic Swedish home and was touring Canada in 1892 when he received news of his father's death and bankruptcy. He went to work as a farm hand on the prairies and was later a school teacher in Manitoba. His novels of life in the Canadian west have earned him the reputation of being Canada's first realistic novelist. This is a chapter from his novel of homesteading called *Fruits of the Earth*.

THE CROP

Throughout that summer of 1912 Abe never ceased worrying about his crop. Things going well, he was apt to feel that some disaster was preparing itself. Never did the grain suffer from excessive moisture or lack of it. Never a blade turned yellow before the second week in August; and then a golden spell brought the very weather for ripening wheat. The straw was of good height but did not lodge. The stand was remarkably thick and even; and not on Abe's place only but throughout the district and even south of the Somerville Line and in the river valley to the east. Unless some major disaster intervened, a late hailstorm or a prairie fire, unheard-of wealth would be garnered that fall throughout the southern part of the province. Even though, with such a crop, the price of wheat was bound to fall, there would be plenty. Abe estimated his yield at forty bushels per acre. The grade could hardly be less than Number One Northern, coveted by every grower of wheat. Unless some major disaster interfered, this crop would place him at the goal of his ambitions. But could it be that no disaster was to come? He felt as though a sacrifice was needed to propitiate the fates. He caught himself casting about for something he might do to hurt himself, so as to lessen the provocation and challenge his prospect of wealth must be to whatever power had taken the place of the gods.

He had read of such crops; he had heard tales told. South of the Big Marsh, a man had bought a farm on credit for ten thousand dollars, with only his equipment and his industry on the asset side of his balance sheet; his first crop was said to have paid for the farm. Such cases were used by the great transportation companies to advertise the West. They were on everybody's lips. But Abe knew that against them stood hundreds of cases of failure, of bare livings made by the hardest work. Was his going to be the one case in a thousand?

Yet, no matter how he looked at things, even allowing the price of wheat to fall to an exceptionnally low level, unless some major disaster interfered, he was bound to see his material wishes fulfilled. Twelve hundred acres under wheat ! Forty bushels per acre. At, say, sixty cents a bushel — surely, that was the lowest possible price ? Thirty thousand dollars were growing in his fields — a fortune sufficient for his needs.

This was the harvest for which he had worked through all these years since he had first bought additional land. Slowly, as his holdings increased, the plan had dawned on him to arrange the rotation forced on him by the problem of weeds in such a way as to make it possible once in a decade to put his whole area under crop, staking a decade's work on a throw of the dice : a venture so costly as to make failure seem a catastrophe.

Everywhere the young were elated at the prospect ; everywhere the aged, the old-timers — in the Mennonite Reserve, for instance — shook their heads. Wet years had always come in a three-year succession. This year spring had been normal ; summer, a marvel of favouring conditions : no human intelligence, endowed with the power of determining seasonal events, could have planned things in a more auspicious way. But there was still time for rains to come ; and if they came now, they would come at the one and only time at which they could endanger all Abe's work. He might not be able to cut his wheat ; being cut, the grain might sprout in the stook and be ruined. The fall was his vulnerable point, his only one.

Already, in certain districts, people spoke of a year in the early nineties when, in the settlement to the West, it had been impossible to thresh in the fall. The crops had stood in the fields through the winter, to be threshed in spring. Farmers had considered themselves lucky to save a fraction of their wealth. Could nothing be done to save all ? In August Abe did what he had never done before. He went great distances into the districts to the West ; to Ivy, eleven miles from Morley ; and thence southwest, to Wheatland and Ferney, standing about in stores and listening to the gossip of farmers. Wherever he went, reports were the same : unless something went wrong at the last moment, it would be a bumper crop. One danger was pointed out : before this, an early killing frost had overtaken the West. When Abe reached home, he went into his fields and rubbed a sample of his wheat from ears here and there until he arrived at the conclusion that his crop was safe ; frost might lower the grade ; it could not ruin the whole.

Others who shook their heads in anticipation of what must go wrong were fatalists in spite of misgivings. What must come would come ; no use trying to fight ; no use worrying. Too bad if anything happened ; but if it did, it could not be helped.

But Abe rebelled at that thought. He was changing. His ambitions had been material ones ; but there were other things in life, dimly seen as in a mist. A happiness based on things not material was blindly emerging. Abe was a slave to the soil ; till he had satisfied that soil which he himself had endowed with the power of enslaving him, he must postpone all other things ; only when he had done what he must do, would he have time and energy for anything else. This crop he must have.

And cutting started. Abe began with two binders drawn by horses : the problem of help was acute. Harvest was general. Abe asked Nicoll for his boy Tom, seventeen years old. Nicoll was obstinate.

"I'll hurry things along," he said. "I'll let the girls stook. Loan me a binder and team, and I'll let Tom drive my own outfit ; I'll drive yours. That way I'll get through in half the time. When I finish I'll come with three boys. But I can't afford to let my sixty acres wait. With an additional binder it's a question of two, three days."

Abe went to see Henry Topp and received the same answer. It was late at night when he got home ; he harnessed five horses to one of his binders and drove it over to Nicoll's Corner. It was after midnight.

People had heard him for miles around ; sounds carry far over the prairie. Next morning Stanley came to Abe's asking for a repair part for his binder. He spoke in a peculiar vein. "You know, Spalding, I can drive a team ; but I can't stook with one arm. When such an affliction comes, you learn patience. When I look at you, I see myself as I used to be. I thought I could force things. I've learned to trust in the Lord. That's what's wrong with us all ; we have lost our faith. You are going to have that crop or to lose it ; and if you're to lose it, nothing that you can do will save it for you."

Abe looked at the man who had spoken with an insistence unusual between people who are not intimate. "That may be," he said. "But it may also be that God helps them that help themselves."

He could not afford to sit back and look on. A few days later, the weather remaining incredibly golden, Abe's harvest got into its stride. He paid his stookers three dollars a dap : wages unheard of except in threshing, and they drew every hand. Even Stanley sent Bill ; and Harry Sotbarn came from a distance of ten miles — a man who was to play a part in Abe's destinies two years later.

On Sunday Abe went to Somerville to fetch a fifth binder : what was the cost of a binder when such a crop was at stake ? Three acres of wheat would pay for the machine. Abe was still financing on last year's crop ; not a cent did he owe at the bank.

Twice, during the first day, there was trouble with the two oldest binders. Abe sent to town ; the assistant to one of the grain buyers was a binder expert ; henceforth this man, drawing five dollars a day, remained in the field, driving the bronchos hitched to a buggy, available wherever a binder stopped. A supply of repair parts lay in the box.

At noon, the whole crew was fed at Horanski's where the woman seemed glad of this overflow of harvest joy lapping about the door. At five, a lunch was served to the men, with beer or coffee to drink as they preferred. The binder expert brought baskets full of sandwiches and jugs full of coffee and beer to the field. Abe's driving power told ; for two weeks, work in the fields became an orgy.

Then, just before the end, a slight rain fell like a warning. It was after dinner ; by night they would have finished. The rain ceased almost as soon as it had begun ; but work had to be suspended. Abe was in a panic. When, three days later, on 3rd September, the last sheaf was stooked, some of the binders and the tractor were at the northern line of the Hudson's Bay section ; the stooks stood so close together that it was impossible to take the machines across the field. In a buoyancy of exultation, Abe took a pair of pliers from the tool-box of the nearest binder and went to the fence to pull the staples holding the wires to the posts. The whole caravan crossed over to the wild land in the west and circled the farm in the dusk.

Two days later a heavy rain fell. But dry weather followed imme-diately and continued for several days. Yet signs began to multiply that more rain was to follow. Abe lived in a frenzy of worry. If all went well, there were forty thousand dollars' worth of wheat in the stooks. Abe, full of forebodings, began to wish for an early frost.

On 11th September Abe was up at four in the morning, feeding the horses himself from sheer nervousness ; for more than a year now he had left such chores entirely to Horanski who seemed famished for work ; but Abe felt as though, by keeping himself even uselessly busy, he was doing his share to avert a disaster ; nobody would be able to say that he had been sitting idly while his crops were being ruined.

Always he had thought fastest and to the best effect when at work. He could never grasp all the bearings of a problem sitting down ; at work, difficulties seemed to solve themselves as by magic.

Thus having done the chores at the barn, all but the milking, he climbed into the loft, taking a lantern, to throw down hay for the day; and, happening to look into the grain bin, he saw there were little oats left near the chute. He climbed in and, with a half-bushel scoop, sho-velled the grain over from the talus-slopes of the margin.

Suddenly he straightened under the impact of a thought.

Yes, he would stack his crop !

Nobody throughout the length and breadth of the river valley had to his knowledge stacked his grain. In thirteen years he had not seen conditions which might make it necessary or desirable to do so. It would cost hundreds of dollars ; he would have to pay threshing wages. Yet, since threshermen would not come into the district till the work in more densely settled parts was done, his crop would be safe.

He dropped the scoop, climbed out of the bin and down the ladder. That moment Horanski entered the barn.

"Quick," Abe said. "I've done the feeding. Take Pride. Make the round south of the ditch. Four dollars a day. Let the Topp brothers and Hilmer bring a hayrack each. Start at six. Hurry up now."

Horanski was jumping. "Ya, ya. But what ?"

"Never mind. Hurry. We stack."

Abe had four ordinary wagons ; only two of them were still fitted with hayracks ; in threshing, boxes were needed. By almost superhuman exertion he managed to tilt the boxes of the other two to the ground and to replace them by flat racks lying near the shed. Having done so, he did not go to the house to light the fire in the kitchen but took Bay, Pride's sister, from her stall, threw a blanket over her back, and in a minute was galloping east to see Nicoll.

Nicoll, harvest being done and threshing far afield, came down in his night-wear when he heard Abe's frantic hammering. When Abe told him what he wanted, he was amazed. "Surely not. Nobody ever stacks here."

"Never mind what others do. Four dollars a day for man or boy. Six for a man with rack and team."

With that he was away. Similar scenes were enacted at Shilloe's, Hartley's, Nawosad's, Stanley's. Back to the farm in the grey of dawn.

Even now he did not go to the house for breakfast. He harnessed eight horses and hitched them to the racks in the yard. Daylight came, and with it the first helpers arrived.

Abe started them at once to gather sheaves, north of the yard. He drew a load of hay to the margin of the field and spread it on the ground. By half-past six the whole crew had arrived ; eleven hayracks were gathering sheaves ; Abe and Nicoll were stacking.

At seven, Charlie appeared beyond the fence. "Daddy, daddy !"

It was several minutes before Abe heard. "What is it ?"

"Aren't you coming in for breakfast ?"

"No. Bring me a cup of coffee and a slice of bread."

The day was white and hazy, a distant, rayless sun lighting the world. At noon, they changed horses rather than give those they had been using time to digest. At night they went on till it was dark. Only then did it strike Abe that this was the night of the council meeting at Somerville. He had never yet missed a meeting. "Can't be helped," he muttered, "I've got to save that crop."

Two stacks had been finished, thirty feet in diameter, twenty high: giant stacks thatched with hay. The third one, just begun, Abe covered with a tarpaulin, working by lantern light.

But it did not rain next day. Hilmer reported that he had seen threshing south of the Line. Surely all was going to be well ; there was no need for this extra expense ? He meant kindly, wishing to save Abe money even though part of it flowed into his own pocket.

Abe knew that not a man in his crew approved of what he was doing. They were glad to take his cash but thought him crazy to spend it.

At ten o'clock Wheeldon appeared in his rattling car. "What the hell . . . " he began.

Abe stared. They called Henry Topp the "runt" ; this man was a pigmy.

"Who's ever heard of such a thing ?" Wheeldon asked. "In a semi-arid country as this claims to be."

"Never mind," Slim Topp shouted. "Come on. Lend a hand."

"Be hanged if I do. What sort of wages are you fellows licking up ?"

"I pay threshing wages," Abe said.

"I'm going south," Wheeldon boasted. "I'll bring a fellow back to thresh me at once."

"Nothing like trying."

Wheeldon returned in the afternoon.

"What luck ?" Horanski asked from where he was pitching sheaves to the fifth great stack that was rising into the air.

"Every doggone fellow laughs at the idea of coming up here." Abe heard what he said. "If you want a job."

"By golly, I believe I do."

"To-morrow morning at six. Bring a rack."

The third day dawned grey and threatening. By eight o'clock Abe moved the scene of operations to a point west of the pasture. With

the menace of a cloudy sky overhead, the men worked feverishly, Horanski setting a frantic pace. In routine work nobody would have
exerted himself ; but this was so quixotic that work seemed sport or
play.

That night, with a high wind from the east, slight drizzles began
to sweep over the prairie like painters' brushes, continuing for more than
a day. Then a dry sunny spell ; but it did not turn warm. As soon as
the stooks dried in the fields, everybody went south, east, west, to in-
duce a thresherman to come, using Abe's huge crop for a bait.
Threshing fees were running high ; there were reports of heavier rains
in the south. Nicoll reported several engines to be stuck on the roads.
Victor Lafontaine tried to get through ; in vain.

Once more Abe sent word around. Four and a half dollars a
day ! Already a few doubted the wisdom of working for wages. Yet,
when the Topp brothers and even Wheeldon came — the latter saying,
"By gosh, four and a half dollars is too good to miss !" — Nicoll and
the others threw their misgivings to the wind.

And things looked brighter again. Soon frost would come. In
freezing weather the crops would be safe. But Abe stacked.

The scene of operations had shifted to the Hudson's Bay section
when one afternoon a large new car appeared on the trail west of the
field. A tall man in city clothes alighted. He climbed the fence and
came to the stack where Abe and Nicoll were working.

"Well, well, well !" said Mr. Rogers, for it was he ; "you must be
anticipating foul weather, Mr. Spalding."

"I am playing safe," Abe replied and slipped to the ground.

"What are you afraid of ?"

"Nothing, nothing at all."

"Threshing is beginning to be general again."

"Some machines are stuck right now."

"They were in too much of a hurry after the rain ; I can understand
a man stacking if he farms in a small way. But you."

There was a pause. Then Abe asked, "Any business you came
for ?"

"Why, yes. Let's step aside. You know Mr. Eastman's term as
reeve expires in December. There is a certain deal pending. Some of
us have been waiting for just what is going on. We want an honest man
for the place. In fact, we want you."

"For reeve ?"

"For reeve. Will you accept nomination ?"

"I don't know." Municipal honours were far from Abe's mind just now.

"It won't take more of your time than you are already giving to the public business. You are the only man from a north ward who can swing the south wards as well."

"I wouldn't canvass."

"One of the assets which we are counting on. The position you take on that point is known. It will win us more votes than anything else. One joint meeting, adroitly managed. You say a few words."

"I am not a speaker."

"Again, all the better."

"I'll think it over." Abe's eyes were on the horizon.

"I'd like to take over your answer back."

"All right," Abe decided, "I'll run."

"Good !" And, picking up a sheaf, "There's weight in that. Well, so long. I see why you were absent from the last meeting."

On 25th September Abe finished stacking his crop. Next day it began to rain ; and, with low welts of cloud driven over the prairie by dismal winds, ever shifting, it went on raining, with few let-ups, till 20th October. The ditches ran full ; water began to stand in the fields.

This fall of 1912, when farmers throughout the south of the province could not thresh, is still being used to date certain events. "You remember," people will say, "that was the year before — or the year after — the fall when we could not thresh." The stooks stood in water. Everywhere people prayed for frost. Ordinarily an early freeze-up is undesirable; even if the crops escape, it interferes with plowing; which means that work will be late next spring. But that year it rained and rained ; and when the rains began, it turned warm again.

Abe might have exulted. Instead, he felt like a man who has, without knowing it, crossed a lake covered with thin ice. The fact that he had been very near to losing the greatest crop he had ever raised drove home to him how much uncertainty there is even in the most fundamental industry of man. If he had not stacked !

Day after day, clad in glistening slicker, he went into his drenched fields and, with the rain descending fitfully about him, reached into his stacks, extending a long arm, and made sure that no moisture was penetrating the sheaves. He had an old book on farming, printed in England, and reread the chapters that treated of stacking. A good deal was said of the sweating of grain which improves its quality. He watched that process, rubbing a handful of grain from the ears, to look at the kernels and to compare them with the pictures in the book.

With nothing to do in field or yard, he took once more to going to town. The village was always crowded now; for everybody was, as to leisure, in the same position as Abe ; what was the use of sitting at home and worrying ? In town, they had at least company. Abe heard people describing what was happening to their crops : the grain sprouting in the stooks, the roots weaving the sheaves into a solid, co-hering mass.

Of his own wheat Abe took handfuls to the elevators. Number One Northern. "Have you threshed ?" the buyers asked. "I have stacked." And the buyers whistled through their teeth. Abe's crop became famous.

Threshermen sought him out. The general disaster hit them as hard as anyone else. "Say, Abe," one would say ; "Say, Spalding," others ; a few went as far as, "Say, Mr. Spalding ... have you made arrangements for threshing yet ?" "No." And the men would under-bid each other, coming down from sixteen cents a bushel, which had been the peak, to fifteen, twelve, ten cents. Abe listened ; but suddenly without giving an answer, he walked away. "Getting queer," some said. "His good luck's affecting his mind." A man who had spoken to him before drew him aside. "Abe, there's no chance of moving my outfit till after the freeze-up. But you've stacked. Good crop, they say. I wouldn't want this known. But I'll thresh you for six and a half." And when Abe made a motion to leave him, he detained him by a finger on his arm. "Abe, listen. I'll knock another quarter of a cent off." But Abe turned away, the thresherman staring after him. On forty thousand bushels a quarter of a cent meant a saving of a hundred dollars.

Mr. Diamond surpassed himself in smiles. "Some weather, Abe. But you can laugh. You were wise. How about a new fur coat for the winter ?"

"We'll see."

"Want to buy this store, Abe ?" — with a broad laugh.

Abe was restless ; it seemed incredible that he should have es-caped.

On 21st October, a grey, chilly day, but without rain at last, Abe saw Nicoll at his stable as he drove past. Anxious for company, he turned into the yard, cutting a deep, sharp rut into the ground which looked like the bottom of a freshly drained pool.

Nicoll came dejectedly and stood between the wheels of the buggy.

"How's your wheat ?"

"Bad. Think the rain's over ?"

"Hard to tell. I hope so."

"Not that it matters."

"Is it as bad as that ?"

"It's as bad as can be."

"I'm sorry. Thought I'd ask. So long."

"So long, Abe."

From the culvert bridging the ditch Abe looked down on the slow, yellow flood which ran even with the banks. He had done it ! Next year he would build. But never again would he allow himself to be caught without a threshing outfit of his own !

In town he met Eastham, the reeve.

"Hello, Spalding," the latter said. "Running against me ?"

"I ?" For in his preoccupation he had not thought of it again.

"So they say," the squarely built man with the big, red moustache said ironically and grimly.

"Come to think of it, they did ask me."

"When you ran for the council, you got in by the skin of your teeth."

"That's a fact," Abe said. "You know I don't do any campaigning. You'll have it all your own way. I won't stir a finger."

"Well-l-l" Mr Eastham said and raised a hand to the edge of his expensive hat of soft grey felt . . . .

In the district people were more excited over the fact that Abe had saved his crop than that they were losing theirs.

"What I'd like to know," said Henry Topp, "is how he could tell."

"He's a wise one," Hartley replied. "If he hadn't stacked, we'd have threshed, I bet."

"Nonsense !" Stanley exclaimed. "You'd have worked on a threshing crew while threshing lasted. But no outfit would have come in here. We're out of the way. He had the luck."

"He has the luck every time !" Henry said.

But it was left to Mrs. Grappentin to find the true solution of the problem : Abe was in league with the devil, or he would never have thought of stacking. And Hartley and Henry laughed enough to split their sides.

On 25th October it rained again ; but the rain turned into snow, and it froze up. The crops, half ruined by sprouting, froze to the ground; the fields looked like skating rinks. Not one of the farmers threshed that fall ; and when they did, next spring, the yield was low ; the grade was "no grade" ; the grain was sold for feed.

(Fruits of the Earth)

Laura Goodman Salverson (Born in 1890)

Mrs. Salverson is of Icelandic descent and much of her writing deals with the struggles of immigrants in the Canadian west.

A native of Manitoba, Mrs. Salverson has twice won the Governor-General's Award.

I DISCOVER MY BIRTHPLACE

I have no further recollection of that journey to Winnipeg, nor any clear memory of our arrival in that muddy village. I do remember, however, that we went to live in a row of houses, all built alike, all having bay windows ; floors where the frost gathered around the doors and baseboards ; and facing upon a street where two planks represented the last word in civic improvement.

In wet weather, the road, like an angry sea-serpent looping along, dripped a red, gummy spume, through which horses and men slithered and slipped, and often enough, to my vast amusement, sank half-way to their knees. Rubbers were sucked off with a hungry, smacking sound, and the feet of the horses glug-glug-glugged endlessly. In winter patches of ice formed in the low spots, and the little ridges of dirty snow made the sleighs jolt and screech as they flew by to the sound of singing bells.

Winter, I discovered, had compensations. It was bad to have your feet always cold, and disagreeable to run into the kitchen only to find every chair spread with frozen clothes off the line, but it was pleasant to make a clear spot on the snowy window-pane and watch the hurrying world go by. No one ever got stuck in the winter time. Horses were never beaten to make them strain and struggle in a sickening manner. No angry shouts and rumble of ugly words rent the air. In the winter, all sorts of queer contraptions and funny people came to see papa. There was a sleigh, with a top like a house, where a stove-pipe gave off feathers of smoke, and out of which men and women tumbled like the animals out of the Ark. They came from Icelandic River, and sometimes they brought a gift of fish, deer meat, or mutton, and now and then a bag of wool. Most of the men had whiskers and smoked short pipes, which made me think they were all grandfathers. For papa neither smoked nor wore a beard, but only now and then dipped snuff from a pretty silver box; and his moustache was short and carefully trimmed. His hair, too, was sleek and black as the fur on my new tomcat, whereas these visiting grandfathers, for the most part, were thatched with sandy-coloured straw.

The women either brought babies, or, when they left after a stay in Winnipeg, took babies back with them. It was a little tiresome, to be sure, and yet there was a certain thrill in seeing the door fly open, and bundles of people rolling in, with whiffs of frosty air circling them in clouds. There was always a lot of laughter, mysterious head-shakes, and once the visit got under way, pots and pots of coffee, with plates of mamma's famous pancakes. Sometimes, too, there was singing, and a queer kind of chanting, which papa called *Kveda,* and told me I should listen, for the verses were full of ancient wisdom. It was a dignified sort of noise, so I usually listened willingly enough, especially if papa let me sip from his saucer when mamma was not looking.

There came a time, however, when papa failed to come home. He had been taken sick, and carried to the hospital. It was a little colder in the house thereafter and the pancakes had a flat taste, and mamma drank her coffee black.

Not long after that, mother dressed me in my little coat, and said we must make a visit to Great-Uncle Jonathan. She had work to do, she said, and I must be a good child and stay with uncle until she fetched me. It was fun following the crack in the plank sidewalk, and speculating upon where we were going. When we got there I saw before us a small white house, with two trees in front of the low veranda. There was a little hall, where mother took off my coat and hung it on a nail. It was queer, I thought, that no one met us. But a moment later, when we stepped into the room giving off the hall, I understood, and was struck dumb.

In the middle of the room was a strange sort of chair, with big yellow wheels and a high yellow back. In the chair sat a man dressed in a purple gown, his legs covered with a plaid shawl. His eyes, deep, brown, and luminous, turned on us out of a serious face that looked parchment pale in contrast with the long, flowing, curly brown beard that rippled down his bosom.

It was an awesome moment ! Made doubly so when I heard my mother say, quite calmly: "Kondu saell godi min."

I clutched her skirt. Surely even a mother ought not to say to the Lord, careless-like, "How do you do, my dear !" But no thunderclap followed. Just a very human rumble, replying, "So-so-so-so — what have you got there behind your skirts ?"

I decided to risk a peep. The bearded monarch was smiling — actually smiling. Oh, thought I, with boundless relief. It was not the Lord God Almighty after all. God was not the smiling sort. It must be Moses.

Even that was not quite accurate, I learned to my astonishment. The venerable gentleman was very like a patriarch, and, as I was many years later to see, actually resembled Michelangelo's Moses, but he was just my Great-uncle Jonathan, an old, old sea captain, many years home from the sea.

That was the beginning of the happiest months of my entire child-hood. Great-uncle was confined to an invalid's chair, having suffered a stroke which left his legs paralyzed. It was a secret between us that I took care of uncle, and not uncle of me. He was a beautiful old man of impressive dignity, and full of quiet humour. His little, plainly fur-nished room, which we very shortly turned into a lively universe, round which we shipped from port to port, lives unspoiled in my memory.

(Confessions of An Immigrant's Daughter)

Will R. Bird (Born in 1891)

A very prolific writer, he has published short stories in a wide variety of Canadian, American and British magazines. Bird is a veteran of World War I, a past president of the Canadian Authors' Association, and is currently Chairman of the Historic Sites Advisory Council of Nova Scotia.

SUNRISE FOR PETER

The Newfoundlanders were moving to the Somme. Three days "D" Company had marched through a sun-bathed, picturesque part of France, fragrant with flowers and fruit trees, pleasing to the eye. Peasant women in the fields had smiled at them, and children had clapped their hands and shouted *Bonne chance*. The soldiers had feasted their eyes on homely, chalk-walled cottages nestled in a background of deep verdure, grassy, gay with buttercups and poppies, rich with clover in bloom. And now they were falling in for a night move, which meant they were nearing the line.

A ceaseless, far-away, throaty grumble of gunfire was as impres-sive as the low-spoken comment of the veterans, and Private Peter Teale spoke quietly to the white-faced youth beside him.

"It'll take us th' night t' get there, and we won't be for it then."

The boy-like soldier looked up at him quickly, as if seeking a hope.

"But they'll shell us bad up there, won't they ?" he asked, and his voice was unsteady.

"It won't be cushy, that's sure," returned Peter, "but it'll not be too bad. There may be dugouts for the day."

The sergeant-major barked an order and the men stood stiffly at attention as their company commander took over. The latter was a tall man, slightly stooped and his voice was kind though tense as he proceeded, after telling them to stand at ease, to read an order. It dealt with a contemplated attack. The battalion would take over a part of the line near Bus and the company would be in Pineapple Trench. The enemy would be shelled for two hours previous to the assault, and there would be an abundance of artillery support afterward. During the actual attack each man was to do his utmost to reach the objective — the German second trench — and no one was to pause to assist a wounded comrade. Every moment would count toward success or disaster.

Men shuffled uneasily, hitching at their equipment, and a coarse whisper was audible. "What a bloody hope we got."

The company moved out on the road and swung into rhythmical step. Just outside their billeting area an old curé stood by his church, peering at them as they passed, his head uncovered and bowed, a beautiful but ominous gesture. Peter felt melancholy, and a sort of homesickness banished all the thrill that had stirred him as they fell in; he felt incoherently sympathetic for all the blurred figures about him.

They marched into open country, and as the night deepened he watched the colour drain out of the landscape, leaving all contours vague and grey beneath a pallid starlight.

"Oh, madamoiselle from Armentières, parley-vous . . ."

The soldiers sang riotously, without attempts at harmony, seizing the song as an outlet for pent emotions. Peter did not join in. His melancholy muzzled him, and anyway he disliked the words. The doggerel ended and for a time there was only the thudding shuffle of hobnailed boots, the creak of equipment, and then someone started a sentimental ditty that drew mixed comment.

". . . and another poor mother has lost her son."

It finished like a ribald defiance to the future.

They passed through another village. A door opened and a light gleamed, then a voice asked where they were going.

"The Somme, the Somme !" The challenge was unmistakable.

"Somme, Ah, no bon." The voice sounded hollow, hushed, seemed to drift in the damp air, ghostlike. "Ah, no bon."

It was disturbing, that sighing comment, but the marching men sang louder until they were exhausted. Then came a halt, and they fell out by the roadside and cigarettes glowed like fireflies. Peter sat by the youngster, and watched him loosen his belt and twist irritably at his haversack.

"It's cooler at nights," he offered, "and there's no marching to attention."

The youth twitched again. "My shoulders are raw," he complained. "I'll be glad when we're there."

Peter was carrying the boy's rifle and extra bandolier long before they reached the dark abyss of a communication trench that led to the front line, and in helping him he forgot for a time a worry that gnawed at his heart. He had not, however, slumped on a chicken-wire bunk in the dugout to which they were assigned, before he remembered, and stirred about until he saw the sergeant.

"Has no mail come up?" he asked.

The non-com grunted wearily. "I'll see," he said. "The limbers came behind us."

By the flickering light of a few candles the dugout looked a grisly cavern. Its roof timbers and jutting bunks made gloomy, shadow-ridden corners, and the sleeping men sprawled about as if they had been so stricken. Peter gazed at them with a return of his melancholy, and watched for the sergeant. Would there be a letter for him?

He glanced at the white, upturned face of Telfer, the youth, and realized that if there were a letter he must wake the lad. He could not wait till morning to have its message read. If only there had been one the previous night, when they had been rested and had had a good supper of stew and bread and hot tea. Then he would have had time to ponder each line, each phrase, like a tasty morsel, until he had imbibed the whole so thoroughly that it would have become a part of his memory.

It had been a snug billet, that overnight stopping place, very cooling and restful after marching over the hard, hot pavé. The big, stone-built barn held fresh clean straw, and in the rear were pollarded willows overhanging a little river of bright water. The splashings of many bathers and the murmur of the men's voices had but added to the soothing qualities of the scene. Telfer had rested and slept like a child.

Peter wondered how many of the men would go that way again. He wondered if he would. Such thinking was a recent thing for him and, in a way, had gripped him. Before their last "trip" in the line there had been Simon Teale, his cousin, to talk to, to ask advice, but now he was alone save for young Telfer, and there were so many things that such a young lad could not understand. For instance, he would not know about dreams, and dreams were guides if one understood them as Simon had done.

And Simon was a home man. He had lived at Old Bear Bay just down along from Peter, and they had fished and hunted and trapped together through many lean years. Simon was clever with tools, and he could read and was versed in many "outside" matters. Peter was more of a hunter and trapper. He knew every pond and barren and drogue all the way to Old Woman Tickle; could sense his way in the winter through dense stunted spruce where the windfalls of ages made countless pitfalls hidden under light snow coverings.

He and Simon had come to France together, and their intimacy had been a great thing for Peter. They could talk of home, and the fishing and sealing, the old folks and the young folks, and Simon could read their letters to him. He also wrote to Peter's wife. It was a huge help, that letter writing, for Simon could put things in words so easily and Peter could not. He had less to write about, too, for Simon had a family, three husky sons and two daughters; Peter and his wife were childless.

Strangely, it was Simon, the family man, who had first mentioned enlisting. Peter had heard vague rumours about a war over in Europe, but his meagre geography had never caused him to think it had anything to do with Newfoundland, and he was astounded when Simon said so. His amazement increased when within the week his partner gravely informed him that it was their duty to go to St. John's and "sign up."

"But who'll do the hunting and fishing and get the firewood?" asked Peter. Simon had upset his world.

"There'll be money from the government," Simon explained. "Wages like, that the wife will get, enough to buy 'lasses and flour. It's our duty to go, man, a wonderful chanc't, and the Good Book says so."

That settled it. Peter hated to leave home but he was a pious man, a believer. He had not the religion of some of the outport Newfoundlanders, who were subject to "glory fits" and loud repentances, but he had a faith of his own, partly the result of hearing Simon read the Bible on stormy days and Sundays, and partly due to his own thinking.

Out in the vast whiteness of winter, with the glitter on the trees and an awesome silence over all, he would think and think as he visited his snares and traps, and when a perfect pelt rewarded him he would stand and gaze about him in a peculiarly reverent fashion. On summer nights when the huskies howled and the Northern Lights rustled with the changing of a million tints, he had the same sensations, and would go up on the hills and rocky crags above the little bay and sit for hours alone. Mary, his wife, did not like such moods, and so he never told her about them.

"All right, Simon," he had said. "I'll go soon as I fix for a winter's diet, but I know I"ll hate the killing. It don't seem right to me."

"There was killing in Bible times," Simon asserted, "so it must have been right, and Samson slew the Philistines. 'Tis likely these Germans be the same."

So the two men had gone down to St. John's and there had become soldiers of the English King who needed them. Peter had hated it all, the bayonet fighting and bomb throwing and especially the heartless jesting. And he hated leaving Mary.

In France a discerning sergeant had noticed their silent cat-footed ways in the dark and had made them his platoon scouts, which pleased Peter as much as anything could in that war-defiled country. Out in no-man's-land, lying in the stealthy quiet of a listening post, he could watch the endless flares and imagine himself back on the hills behind Old Bear Bay. Such dreamings had been easy in the sector where Simon was killed. It was a rough-cratered territory in a mining region and there had been a lovely crescent moon afloat, an enchanting moon that changed the lines into soft contours until reminiscence teased his memory, for even the sombre slag heaps, huge against the luminous sky, became the dark rocky spurs that guarded his home harbour. And there had been a stillness he liked, a quiet in which he could bathe his soul as in a deep, cool pool. He had said so to Simon.

A shuddering sigh had been his comrade's first response, and there came a whisper, hoarse with emotion. "It's my night, Peter. I've had my dream."

Peter had almost blamed himself afterward for letting Simon sleep. He had known, by his easy breathing, that Simon was dozing, and had not roused him, and so the death vision had come. But would it not have come anyway, or would he not have been killed without warning? Peter knew that no man could live beyond his time.

"What was it like?" he had asked, crushing back a first urge toward pity, for it could never help a man. "What were the signs?"

"I saw my door, wonderful clear," whispered Simon, "and Maggie were in it waving good-bye. It were like daylight, all the bay, and the boys were down by the fish wharf. It were my dream."

And then, because he knew nothing else to do, Peter had held out his hand and gripped Simon's with his warmest pressure and assured him he had one consolation — he had lived clean and honest and God-fearing, and that was a comfort to anyone.

When their hour was up they had crawled back toward the trench, and Peter had noticed how the wet weeds that brushed his face were like dead fingers. Then the Germans sent up coloured lights, and he saw that the red ones made the water holes pools of blood, and the green ones gave all the area a ghastly corpselike sheen. It did not surprise him in the least when a sniper's bullet came with the hiss of an evil thing and killed Simon instantly.

Peter had helped carry the dead man back to a little cemetery where all the graves had white crosses, bearing names and numbers. To one of his faith and nature, respectful burial was a mighty thing. When, before they marched to the Somme, he had visited the graves and seen skylarks springing up from them, flooding the earth with melody and soaring to enormous heights before dropping back to the fields, he was certain that Simon was "Resting in Peace" according to the legend above him.

He was thinking of how obligingly young Telfer had written a decent letter to Simon's wife, one that she would feel was a personal message, and how the lad had clung with him since, when the sergeant returned and stared across the dugout, blinking wearily.

"That you, Peter? There was no letter. The mail's slow these times."

"It is," said Peter, "I'm a month without hearing from my woman, and the last one was long coming. I been wonderin' about my Mary."

"She'll be all right," grunted the sergeant drowsily. "The folks back home have lots to do while we're away. You'd better get to sleep. We'll be in the front trench tomorrow night and we might be unlucky."

He had not stopped speaking, it seemed, before he was snoring, and Peter blew out the candle that had been burning beside him, waxed on the top of his steel helmet. Then he lay down and stared into the murk of his corner and listened to rats in the dugout walls while he tried to visualize Mary, his wife, in the tiny garden he had made of good earth scraped from hollows in the hills and carried down in baskets, and fed each spring with decaying small fish, after which he faced again the stern fact that Mary had not written him.

Had she tried the salmon netting herself? He stirred uneasily. He had told her not to try it, for it was a man's work, and there was no need while the government sent her money. Mary! He wanted to speak the name aloud, softly, caressingly, to hear the music of it, and as he stared into the dark he saw her face, smiling, wistful, alluring, daring, gay, whimsical — she could change like spring weather — and he gazed spellbound until a thudding overhead explosion shook the dugout, and the face vanished like reflections in the still water of the bay when a ripple crossed it.

There was another jarring crash, dulled by the heavy gas blankets hung across the stairway but audible enough to rouse several sleepers. "That's big stuff," said one, and another growled assent. They listened and heard the next shells land further away, and went to sleep again. Peter, his mind diverted, also slept.

It was afternoon and the shelling was heavy but Peter stayed in the trench. He wanted to think and he could not do so in the foul, fetid air of the dugout. The men were boiling tea, and frying bully in mess-tin tops, and the odours of their cookers mingled with the stale, saline smell of perspiration. He wanted to inhale fresh air.

The trench was but one in a zigzag warren and had lately been German ground. A coal-scuttle helmet, daubed with camouflage paint, had been tramped into the earth, and stick bombs were piled on what had been the enemy fire-step. He moved around a bay and saw a sand-bagged hollow that had been a machine-gun post. A dead gunner was sprawled over his wrecked weapon and big blue flies buzzed about him. Old boots, bottles, a gas mask, were littered about, and the German's pockets had been turned inside out by some hasty souvenir hunter. Letters, postcards and a photo had been flung down. Peter's face set grimly. He judged it an ungodly thing to rob the dead.

He looked around. There were successive explosions in the area to his right, just where a house had been, and he saw a stretcher party hurrying away with a burden. He mused, sadly. Everyone had said that July, 1916, would be the turning point of war. It had come but nothing great had happened. There certainly was no rout. Soon the line would move on and the ruin would be but another rubbish heap; then a plot of little white crosses would be formed in what had been the garden and a sign-board by the filled-in craters would say "Dangerous Corner." That was the routine of war.

He hated war, abhorred it. Over on the low ground he could see fresh graves in the swampy mud. The cross of the nearest one had been struck by a shell splinter, so that only the name remained. One name. "Karl . . ." And the inscription *Ruht in Gott*. Peter looked at the letters a long time, wondering what they meant, and when a corporal passed by he got him to decipher them and explain.

"The Heinies is all Karls and Ottos," said the non-com as he hurried on. "Nobody"ll ever know who's planted there."

The thought struck Peter forcibly. That was the worst part of war, the desecration of graves, of the dead. He had never dreaded death nearly as much as he dreaded being left as a discard on a battle-field, to be rat-eaten and fly-blown, blackened and shriveled, and at last hastily covered by a careless burial party. He moved down the trench to the dugout. The company was not to go forward until dark, and he would talk with Telfer, try to encourage the lad, and in the doing ease his own mind.

"What's it like up front ?" asked Telfer. He was lying on his bunk and his face was pale and drawn.

"Not so bad," said Peter. "They're shelling all over but no place gets much. It's open ground in front and all trenches and wire and shell holes, same as we came through."

"We're to go up at nine," said Telfer. "The sergeant was here and told us. We stay in Pineapple Trench until five and then go over." Then, as if for something to say, the boy looked up with a feeble grin. "Did you know it'll be Sunday," he said, "and the first day of August ?"

Peter felt as if someone had prodded him. He stared at Telfer.

"The first of August," he repeated. "It's my wedding day, ten years ago. Man, there'll be a letter, sure."

Then he moved over and sat beside Telfer and talked as if he were making explanations.

"It were a Sunday, too, when we were married, though Mary didn't want it. She were a great one for jolly times and there wasn't much for to do that day, but her father had his boats to sea and couldn't come before. I didn't like it because she didn't, but any day would have suited me, lad, for I knew I were the luckiest man in Old Bear Bay in catching Mary. You'd never think, to see her, that she'd have the likes of me."

Peter paused and gazed at his rough hands and wrists, disfigured by sea boils. Then he shook his head in a solemn fashion.

"I don't know what she be doing now for to keep her spirits. There won't be much going on with the men away, and Simon and two others killed, and" — he glanced at Telfer — "there were no children to make her busy. It'll be hard on her, the waiting and bad news, for Mary's not like the others. She were always a gay one, bright and joking with everybody, and there isn't her match in looks on the coast. I hope she isn't tryin' the nets." Peter's voice was lower. "She's not got the strength for it and there isn't the need to do it."

Telfer turned uneasily. "There's not much shelling now," he said. "Let's go and have a look. The sergeant said if it rained we wouldn't go over this time."

But there was no hope. The air was windless and cool and the sun had set with every promise of fine weather. The early dusk revealed a desolation that appalled. The trenches and dugout entrances and tree stubs were all touched with a drab greyness that seemed phantom-laden, and a faint smell, indescribable, from the unburied dead, made Telfer shiver.

"I hate it," he said. "Why don't they bury them Heinies?"

"There's not the time," said Peter, "but there should be. The dead should be respected wherever they are. I hope I have a grave when my time comes."

"Don't talk that way," said Telfer sharply. "You sound as if — if you expected to be killed."

Peter's rugged features remained sombre. "I have a bad feeling," he said moodily. "In Old Bear Bay there's many has a gift of seeing ahead, and they always tell that a man's luck begins on his tenth wedding day. It's in me here" — Peter tapped his broad bony chest — "that somethin's gone wrong with my Mary. She were a warm-lovin' woman, and there's been a sickness or bad luck at the Bay. Simon told her how I keep her letters, and that I had them all.". Peter unbuttoned a tunic pocket and drew forth a closely tied bundle, rather thumbed and dirty, but readable. "Them has been a help when we're in a bad billet and there's not much to do. I know 'em, what's in 'em, every one." Then he clenched a big fist and looked over the dim snaky line of trenches. "Them transport chaps need lookin' after," he growled. "They be careless with the mail bags at times."

"Let's go into the dugout," said Telfer. "I hate this place."

The sergeant-major met them. "I suppose you're thinking of your leave, Peter," he said. "I tried to get you off this trip, but we're short of good men. You'll be away as soon as we're out again."

"Oh, my gosh," gasped Telfer in an undertone, and when the sergeant-major had gone he was vehement. "Beat them out," he cried. "It's a dirty trick, sending a man into the line when his leave's due. Go sick or something. Don't let them fool you that way."

But Peter shook his head. "I don't do them tricks," he said, "and I won't start now. Besides I wouldn't want to go afore I got my letter."

"You've earned two leaves, man," insisted Telfer. "And never mind your mail. Lots of chaps haven't got any since we started to move. Your wife's all right or somebody would have wired you."

Pineapple Trench was swathed in darkness and the lines were fairly quiet. Now and then flares lobbed up and filled the night with an eerie whiteness, and when the machine-guns were not shooting the very atmosphere seemed charged with expectancy. Peter was in a small trench shelter with Telfer huddled beside him, pressed close as if for warmth. The night dragged slowly.

An hour before the barrage was to begin, Peter awoke from a short sleep and roused Telfer excitedly. "I had a dream and it were wonderful," he said. "The sun were coming up on the bald rock back of the Bay and there was a dory going ashore. A sunrise is wonderful good luck. I wish Simon were here. He'd tell you."

"Dreams don't mean nothing," said Telfer, half-pityingly. He shivered. "It's near the time."

"You're too young to know," returned Peter. "Sunrise in a dream is the best there is."

All at once the earth fairly shook as the barrage began. Smashing, pounding explosions almost burst their eardrums, and gradually the reek of high explosives drifted to their trench.

The sergeant came along the trench, assisting an officer to issue a rum ration, and he gave Peter a letter, telling him it had come up in the night.

Peter was wild with thanks. He thrust the letter into Telfer's hands. "Read it quick," he shouted. "We've not long now."

He lighted a candle and held the stub in his fingers.

Telfer tore the envelope open and his fingers were trembling. He peered at the missive and bent over as Peter shielded the candle from any draught, then glanced up at him with the affrighted look of a cornered animal.

Peter put a hand on his shoulder. "Never mind the shelling," he said in a voice for a windy sea. "I'll stay by youse. What's Mary sayin' this time?"

Telfer did not look up but hesitated as if unsure of himself and then read in a high-pitched tremolo:

"My dear Peter. You must remember our wedding day and think of me. The garden has been fine. I have not gone to the salmon nets for there is no need at all. Simon's boys have a net for me. There is plenty of grass for the goat back of the hills and I have got berries preserved for when you come home. The boats are not running so often and my letters will be later. Write me as soon as you can. I love you, Peter, the same as I did ten years ago. Your loving wife. Mary."

For a full moment Peter did not move and then his rugged face broke into a smile startlingly alien to their surroundings. He puffed out the candle.

"Man," he shouted. "That's the best letter I ever had. Don't youse be feared today. Good luck's with me, sure."

"You two come with me," said the sergeant. "The captain wants me to be one flank. You bring bombs, Peter. I'll use you, Telfer, for a runner."

The signal whistle blew and Peter patted the letter in his pocket. "Sunrise is a wonderful sign," he cried cheerfully.

An hour later Peter worked desperately, helping the sergeant establish a trench block. "D" Company had taken its objective, after heavy losses, but the enemy still held a post on the extreme right. Noon found the situation unchanged and three of the flanking garrison added to the inert dead. Peter's bombs were exhausted and he was depending on his rifle. The sergeant decided to send for help. Not too far away, across a bit of open ground, a platoon was entrenched. If Telfer could reach them . . . .

He explained matters to the lad who crouched beside him. "One quick rush and you're across. They'll never get a shot at you. We can't hold out here."

Peter saw Telfer gaze at dried pools of blood beside a dead man and knew that fear was holding him.

"Go on," yelled the sergeant. "We've got to have help."

Telfer gave him a dog-like glance of entreaty, tried to climb to the open and slipped on the mud-greased bags so that the sergeant swore again. Peter, watching, made a sudden resolve. Telfer had helped him with his letters; he must help Telfer. Why not attack the enemy? Only a few remained and they might be routed. Through all the mad fighting he had one phrase singing in his mind. "My dear Peter." Never before had Mary begun a letter so affectionately.

"Wait," he shouted. "Youse follow me." Before the sergeant could stop him he had leaped the trench barrier and was at the German garrison like an avenging fury.

In five minutes the German post was a welter of blood and its owners were the sergeant and Telfer, but the cost was dear. Peter lay on the fire-step with a wound they could not staunch. He was conscious but his thoughts were not clear.

Where was he? The noise that beat on his ears reminded him of the tearing, slamming northeasters at Old Bear Bay. There was a mud wall beside him but when he closed his eyes he could see a tiny harbour and hills that sheltered a cottage on the windward side.

"Telfer!" Peter breathed with labour. "Read — that letter."

Telfer fumbled with Peter's pocket and his voice rose shrill and tremulous. "My dear Peter . . ." As everything was now in hand the sergeant listened, and wondered. Telfer's gaze was not on the writing. And suddenly Peter gave a long restful sigh and lay still.

The sergeant reached for the letter as Telfer started to replace it in Peter's pocket, and read it.

"Dear Peter. Mary died last night. Come three weeks Sunday she were up on the rocks where you used to sit, and fell. Her wouldn't let us write before. The boys will tend the goat and your nets. Last thing her thought of your wedding day. Please God you don't be hurt. I had to send this word. Your cousin, Ann Teale."

The sergeant read the letter a second time, then spoke gruffly to steady his voice. "You did him a grand turn but how did you know what to say ?"

"I knew what he wanted, sarge." Telfer had regained control of himself. "And if you'll let me use some prisoners we'll carry him back and bury him decent, like he wanted."

"Go ahead," said the sergeant. "He deserves it. But what if he'd found out ?"

"I daren't tell him the truth," Telfer said slowly. "He's been mighty good to me, and he thought this was his lucky day."

There was a long silence, and the sergeant looked at the letter again.

"I believe it was," he said softly.

Gwen Lewis

Mrs. Lewis lives in Regina where in addition to being a housewife she studies Indian culture.	Her collection of Indian recipes, *Buckskin Cookery* has now sold over 30,000 copies.

BABICHE LAND

The trail from now on wound tediously through lonely snow-shrouded countryside. We saw no sign of big game at all; only rabbits, countless rabbits. They swarmed over the area, crisscrossing the snow with runways, and staining its whiteness with their droppings. Spruce grouse, disturbed by the passing sleighs, whirred away through the spreading branches. White owls, slipping silently from tree to tree, peered curiously at our strange cavalcade and hooted, querying, to each other.

The mileage on George Dudley's trail signs, which we had been noting ever since we left civilization, decreased in number with a maddening slowness. And then the temperature began to drop, slowly and steadily. At last the cruel cold silenced the singing and the exchange of buffoonery along the sleigh train, and we were each left to our own dour thoughts.

Day after day passed, one much the same as the other. Then suddenly, during one of our noon stops, we were startled to hear a high-pitched chorus of peculiar yapping and sobbing cries.

"It sounds like a string of huskies hauling a heavy load up an incline," Ross said. And just as he spoke, a strange group struggled into view over the brow of the hill on which we were camped.

An Indian, on snowshoes, bending low under a large packsack, was in the lead. At his heels lurched a team of gaunt Huskies, noisily voicing their protest at having to drag up the heavily laden toboggan. A number of Indians at the back of the toboggan were alternately bracing and pushing, until they had worked their craft over the crest of the hill.

When they saw us they seemed to stiffen into a hostile, suspicious stance. Occasionally one would pass a low remark to another. Ross walked over to meet them, but they met his greetings with silence. Eventually he was able to entice them to join our group at the fire.

"Are they friendly Indians?" I asked Ross.

"I don't know," he answered in a low voice. "I don't recognize them. Notice the fancy fur hat their leader is wearing? He's their medicine man, but the white ermine symbols sewn in the dark fur are strange to me. Well, we'll soon see."

He pointed to our lunch, and called to the Indians.

"Come, catchum grub."

They moved slowly forward, staring at each of us in turn, their faces inscrutable. Some wore plaid windbreakers, the rest deerskin jackets. Their high moccasins were ornamented with red tassels and bright beads.

"Where you from?" Ross persisted.

The leader pointed towards the north, but said nothing.

"Wantum trade?" Ross continued. "See sleighs? Gottum lotsa grub, tobacco, knives, bullets, jam."

The Indians remained unaffected. Suddenly one of them caught sight of my face, which was the only unbearded one in the whole goup, for even Bill and Autie were nurturing a downy growth by now. He stared, wide-eyed, and then jabbed a finger in my direction.

"What that one ?" he demanded.

"That white woman," Ross answered.

All the Indians were now staring at me, and I tried to slip out of their sight behind a sleigh.

"What for bringum woman ?" one of them asked.

"To cook grub. Why you no bringum your woman ?" Ross returned, to keep the conversation going.

"No got woman. Got squaw. Squaw stay. Catchum more furs."

With this they lapsed back into silence. Ross called me back into their view.

"Charm the strangers, lady !" Ross growled out the corner of his mouth. "Think of something quick ! I want to see their furs."

I swallowed hard, took a deep breath, and with the greatest solemnity gathered a handful of thawing doughnuts from a branch over the campfire and gravely doled them out to my taciturn guests. Under the talisman touch of these soggy-skinned, icy-hearted peace offerings, the Indians relaxed and in a few minutes were answering questions about their furs.

One of the Indians returned to the toboggan and brought out a large iron pot from beneath the bales. When he removed the cover I saw its contents : a pale-coloured stew, frozen solid. He placed it over the campfire and rejoined the men. Eventually the stew began to steam, and the same Indian solemnly ladled some of it into all our plates. I viewed the half a rabbit that slid around in my dish with misgivings, but dared not show my feelings. I speared the meat with my fork, and started to eat. It was good, and so was the gravy in which it had cooked. I was heartily spooning up the last of my portion when I came upon something at the bottom which made me slowly lay my plate on the snow, and quietly slip away behind a sleigh where I could be sick in privacy. It had been a necklace of clear rabbit bowel, beaded with droppings.

Meanwhile Fred, in endeavouring to ingratiate himself once more, offered to help himself to another serving. He dipped deep with the ladle and started to fill his dish. Then very gently he returned the contents to the pot.

The medicine man, who had been watching the procedure through narrowed eyes, grunted in disgust.

"No scratchum bottom," he said scathingly. "Diggum up pills."

"So I see," Fred said in a strained voice.

When I rejoined the group Ross was examining the furs on the toboggan. At last the trading was finished, and the Indians proceeded on their way. As they passed our sleigh box, they spied the thermometer and crowded around it.

The medicine man pointed to the numbers.

"What cold machine say?" he demanded.

"It says twenty-eight degrees below zero," Fred answered.

"What that?"

"Not big cold. Not little cold. Just some cold."

The Indians nodded sagely, and seemed quite satisfied. They shouted at their dogs and were soon out of sight on our back trail.

We camped that night on Windfall Hill, in the centre of a dense stand of tall, bare-trunked trees, whose top-heavy tips swayed deeply with every gust of the strong wind which had been blowing all day. The trail was simply a passageway slashed through banks of windfall which had been cleared from the roadway. The men started fires right at the edge of the trail and, as the flames ate into the piles, we moved the pots back after them. The tents were erected in the trail ahead, and the horses left standing where they stopped, with their halters tied to the box ahead. It was impossible to move off the trail, so supper was served in front of the first sleigh, from which the horses had been unharnessed so we could use the propped up tongue for a seat.

During the night a weird, unearthly cry awakened me, and I lifted my head with a start. It was the unforgettable cry of a northern timber wolf. Two more voices added their lonely overtures from the opposite side of the valley. The chorus of spine-tingling wails, augmented by the moaning of the night winds, made sleep impossible.

Suddenly the tent flap shot inward, and a dark furry form sprang at my throat. I screamed in terror and threw up my arms to fend it off. Fred staggered up from the bedroll, snapping a match alight.

"Patrick!" he yelled. "You crazy dog! Get out of here!"

I lowered my arms from my head. The collie, completely unnerved by the howling of the wolves, lay on his back beside my bed, with his legs waving helplessly in the air, and his eyes enormous with fear.

I collapsed, shaking with relief and laughter. The dog spent the rest of the night hugging my back, and nervously listening to every sound. Fred muttered and grumbled for a while, but soon lapsed back into his usual deep sleep.

At noon the next day we broke clear of the timber and, from an opening high on a hill, caught a glimpse of a wide cleft in the countryside ahead.

"There is your Conroy River," Ross said.

(Babiche Land)

Bob Edwards (1864-1922)

Born in Edinburgh, Edwards came to Canada as a young man and founded the Wetaskawin (Alta.) *Free Lance.* In 1902 he moved to High River where he began the publication of the famous *Eye Opener,* a periodical which was supposed to be a weekly but which was brought out whenever Edwards felt like it. The humour in this was lusty enough to shock the pious and influential enough to be a power in politics.

The *Eye Opener* was published for 18 years, its editorial office moving with Edwards from High River to Calgary, to Winnipeg, to Fort William, to Toronto and finally back to Calgary. In 1921 Edwards was elected to the Alberta Legislature.

THE EYE OPENER RACE

The *Eye Opener* Race was a famous sporting event. In the *Eye Opener* for December 25, 1920, Bob wrote :

"The *Eye Opener* road race of 1906 was in the nature of a Novelty Race, and afforded intense amusement to the populace. Contestants started from the corner of First Street East and Eighth Avenue, underneath our office in the Cameron block, to the shot from a pistol fired, as now, by Captain Smart of the Fire Department. On this occasion there were fifteen starters, all of whom had agreed to abide by the rather unique conditions. At the crack of the pistol they were off in a bunch, with a contestant from High River slightly in the lead and the Olds entry close up.

"Running west up the avenue, according to the terms of the race, the contestants raced up to the Royal Hotel, where each had to drink a glass of whisky at the bar; thence helter-skelter up the street to the

Alberta, where a snort of dry gin was the next condition laid down; from there they flew round the corner to the Dominion and put away a schooner of beer, speeding on and on from bar to bar the whole length of Ninth Avenue, drinking horn after horn, no two alike. A corps of umpires followed the runners the whole length of the course. Rounding into Eighth Avenue, it was noticed that only three were left in the race, and these just barely managed to make the Queen's Hotel. Only one emerged ten minutes later to finish the race. He had just one block to go, and it was indeed fortunate for him that Eighth Avenue is a narrow thoroughfare, for he came along bumping against the buildings on either side and staggering from one side of the street to the other. This was the only thing that kept him on his feet. He was the Macleod entry, and had been training for just such an event as this for years."

Jack Miner (1865-1944)

A Canadian naturalist, Miner established the first bird sanctuary in America on his farm near Kingsville, Ontario. No other Canadian of his day was so widely known abroad.

NESTING CANADA GEESE

Jack Miner, Canada's famous birdman, was never happier than when studying the wild creatures of the woods, the pond, and the air. On his property near Kingsville, Ontario, on the north shore of Lake Erie, he established a bird sanctuary, where wild ducks, swans, and geese found shelter, food and protection. Since his death, in 1944, arrangements have been made to continue the sanctuary.

In 1907, the third year I had my clipped Canada geese, one pair nested, and every season since I have had from one to three pairs raise young. This is the very time these old ganders especially expose their incomparable, clean, noble ways, which even we human beings might well envy them.

One spring I had a painter from town out here brightening things up a little, so one day I told him to paint the cornice of the bird house, which is about seven feet high. I paid no more attention to him, but went on with my work at the tile factory, about three hundred feet away. All at once I heard a scream that was joined with language too loud to look well in print. I got out just in time to see this scared man come rolling over the brick wall, his legs and arms sticking up like odd sections in a Ferris-wheel! To see and hear him wrinkled my red face into a broad grin; he came towards me with both torn shirt-sleeves fluttering in the wind and white paint dabbled on one leg of his trousers, without hat, paint, pail or pipe. He began to reel it off. Then it all came to me in a flash. I had forgotten to tell him about the goose-nest that was concealed in the weeds near that spot. And now it was too late to give him any explanation, for really he did not know whether he was bitten or stung. While he was not hurt a particle, he was nearly frightened into fits, and he could not, or would not, believe there were only two geese there. I finally went and found his pipe, Christy hat and paint pail, but he never would go back in that enclosure; and worse still, I doubt if he has ever forgiven me, as he thought I had put up a job on him.

One picture would do for all the pairs of Canada geese I ever saw nesting. While the gander takes no part in building the nest or sitting, turn about, on the eggs, as some birds do, yet he is always guarding her and is never over two rods away, seeing all enemies before they do him. He will usually lie flat on the ground, his black neck and snake-like head straight out, and if any creature goes right on by, all is well; but should one note him and stop, then he will suddenly jump on it from an unexpected quarter. His looks and hissing honks will almost frighten any other creature into decline; and while frightening is his chief defence, yet I know from personal experience how he can bite, and hang on like a pup, while he deals unbelievably heavy blows with the first joint of his powerful wings. The worst blow I ever got in my life was from an old gander that I caught to tag; he struck me on the jaw with the first joint of his doubled-up wings and, believe me, I had the mumps for weeks!

While I have seen the goose run at a domestic fowl or so, yet she does not pretend to do much fighting. She usually leaves that strenuous exercise for him, and depends on his protection; and well she may, for he never fails her. He will even leave his family and fight for her.

A pair once nested near the tile kiln, and a collie dog attacked this gander. The goose won out, but the dog bit the end of his backbone right off. I saw the blood running down his legs and in a few days I noticed he was always in the one place, lying down by his sweetheart. I went over and found he was sick and so weak he let me pick him up. I saw what was wrong, so I went and got the turpentine bottle and poured some in this decaying cavity. I then brought the dear old fellow water and food, but it was fully a week before he could stand up. He finally got well, and I still have him, but he was dying at his post. His name is Tom Johnson.

I never saw the wild geese go near where one of these pairs was nesting. So one spring I took fully ten bushels of corn and scattered it around near a nest. And the thousands of geese that came here would not combine their forces and go near, after the corn, or interfere with his preserve, but would prefer flying all over the country to feed, where some of them are continually getting shot. This will explain to you how they respect each others' rights.

(Canada Geese)

John Archer Carter (Born in 1893)

A journalist now living in Charlotte, North Carolina, Mr. Carter has for many years been in charge of radio and television programming for the American Heritage Foundation.

WHEN LEACOCK INTERVIEWED HIMSELF

Dr. Stephen Leacock, Canada's celebrated humorist and for 28 years Professor of Economics and Political Science at McGill University, wrote a unique article — an "interview" with himself — at the Hotel Jefferson in Richmond, Virginia, early one morning some forty years ago.

His "interview" appears in print for the first time today. Last December 30 marked the ninety-sixth anniversary of Dr Leacock's birth.

This is how he came to write the "interview":

The late Dr. D. S. Freeman, then editor of the *Richmond News Leader* and later Pulitzer Prize-winning biographer of General Robert E. Lee, summoned me, his assistant editor, to his office around 9 A.M. to advise me I was to interview Dr. Stephen Leacock.

I telephoned Dr. Leacock, who invited me to come right on up to the hotel.

When I rapped on the door of his suite about an hour later, the door swung open and there stood a very big man, with a large, longish face and a mass of greying hair parted on the side — I write from memory — and he did not look like any humorist I'd ever seen. Political scientist, economist, mortician or chief mourner, maybe, but not a humorist, surely. He was all solemnity when he thrust into my unready hands five sheets of Hotel Jefferson stationery, each sheet cluttered with ascending lines of virtually indecipherable writing.

"How do you do ?" Dr Leacock said from a sad mouth. "That's the interview with me. I've already written it. Wrote it while waiting for you. Save us time and bother, you know. Both of us. You'll wish to read it ? Oh, naturally ! Come in, come in !"

So I went in. He indicated a large upholstered chair, and there I sat down and started reading while Dr. Leacock began pacing up and down the room, apparently thinking deep thoughts.

And this was Dr. Leacock's "interview" with himself :

"Professor Stephen Leacock of Montreal, head of the Department of Economics at McGill University, who is lecturing this week at the University of Richmond, had a brief chat this morning with a representative of this journal.

"Dr. Leacock spoke in his characteristically humorous vein of his increasing difficulty in being interviewed by the press.

" 'I have grown to have so many friends,' he said, 'in so many places and of such different ways of thinking that I can't say anything at all without losing some of them. For example, I hold very strong views on the Volstead act, but I daren't say what they are. I'd like to tell you how beautifully the Quebec system of government control works, but I mustn't. I have strong views on Evolution and Fundamentalism. In fact I truly believe that all the adherents of one side are soft in the head, but I won't say which. I either think that Mussolini is the hope of the world or the death knell of democracy. People who fly across the Atlantic are either damn fools or heroes. In fact, all my opinions are too violent for friendly intercourse.

" 'But I am here on a mission which fortunately is not controversial at all. I am giving three lectures out at the University on the relation of the great humorists of the world to social progress. The lectures are to deal with Charles Dickens, and Mark Twain, and O. Henry, with a hint here and there on the side that I am doing a little good myself.

" 'That's why I don't want to give an interview. Good-bye.' "

I read the entire opus through without cracking a smile, though the effort almost broke a couple of muscles. He was pulling my leg and I knew it. So when I looked up from the manuscript and faced the pacing humorist there in his suite, I was as solemn as he, if not more so, as I said, nodding my head betimes :

"If I may say so, sir, this is magnificent. And so doggoned refreshing to an interviewer. Lots of guys, you know, dodge the issues.

They're slippery as stewed okra. Nothing like that here. You come right out with it. Bluntly and boldly. Five pages of uncompromising stuff. Pardon me, sir, but you've got guts, sir !"

Dr. Leacock had been looking at me. Now he turned to face the window. He seemed to shake as with a touch of palsy. Then came the explosion. It was a roar ! He threw back his head and thundered with laughter. And promptly I joined in. Presently I told him that teams of oxen couldn't drag those five sheets of "interview" away from me. They were mine I told him. Not one word would get into whatever news story I would write for my paper. He nodded his approval. Whereupon we set about assembling a little something that would get me off the hook . . . a few pieces of informative data to make what seemed to be a news story.

And before we realized it we were talking about O. Henry.

"Just about the best story about O. Henry that I ever knew about," Dr. Leacock said, still pacing up and down the room, "was one that he, with his wonderful feeling for humour, couldn't very well have known about. He died, you recall — or maybe you don't — back in 1910, and the funeral was scheduled for a certain hour in the Little Church Around the Corner in New York.

"Well, they had the body of O. Henry in the hearse, one of those large vehicles made of wood painted black, with glass and with black curtains inside and pulled by black horses with black plumes.

"Of course, funerals are motorized, so to speak, today though still far too funereal ! And the day is coming, of course, when people will live to be 125 years old or so, and then there won't be anybody . . . old friends and kinsmen, left . . . to mourn. And the deceased will have had so many years of idleness and tedium that his funeral will be as happy as his birth, or marriage. Hearses then will be convertibles, sports cars probably, and painted gold with zigzags of scarlet and green.

"But about O. Henry. When the hearse and the pall bearers and the mourners got to the church somebody ran out to advise the undertaker that a mistake had been made somewhere, and O. Henry would just have to wait a while. Take his place in line, so to speak. It seems that the minister was in the midst of marrying a couple of young people and simply couldn't be interrupted. How O. Henry would have loved that !"

We both chuckled at the thought. He strolled about the room a while and then resumed his patter about O. Henry :

"You know, because I was something of an authority on O. Henry, I was delegated, you might say, to seek out any of his unpublished material that might be lying around. After he finally got into that Little

Church of course. So I advertised widely. There would be ample payment for any O. Henry material worthy of publication. After that the deluge. And it struck my office exclusively. People from all over the land mailed me what they declared to be O. Henry stories. Within a few weeks manuscripts were cluttering up my desk, and they lay in piles all over my office. Very terrific stuff, believe me. I was disgusted to observe how many."

He paused, seeking a word.

"Phonies? Creeps? Fakes?" I suggested.

"Phonies," he said, "is the word. How many there were in the country! First disgust, then nausea, then anger. Madness, you might say. So one morning I pushed all the manuscripts off the desk and then picked up one, chosen at random. It was atrocious! And some lady had mailed it to me. I shouldn't have written to her as I did, when returning the manuscript. What I said was on the macabre side, and not in the best of taste. I was sorry afterwards but I was very angry.

" 'I wrote something like this :

" 'Thank you, madam, for sending me this story by the late O. Henry, which I am returning because it doesn't quite fill our needs. However it is amazing and astounding and miraculous, and the reason for that is that obviously the story was written by O. Henry after his brain had been removed.'

"No, I shouldn't have written that, but I was angry."

And I was laughing, whether the letter was macabre or not. Presently he was laughing the usual thunderous Leacock roar.

Finally I got my story with the great man. But I've clung to those five pages in his own handwriting ever since.

Mazo de la Roche (1879-1961)

Toronto-born author who, by her winning of the $10,000 *Atlantic Monthly* Prize for her novel *Jalna*, became world-famous. *Jalna* was followed by several other novels using the same locale and central characters, which combined to give Miss de la Roche an international following probably achieved by no other Canadian novelist of her time.

RINGING THE CHANGES

In time *Jalna* was finished and the typed manuscript sent to Macmillans of New York. Hugh Eayrs had already expressed great hopes for it. The New York house agreed and were to publish it in a few months. Preparations were on the way. Then, in a chance copy of the *Atlantic Monthly* I came upon the notice of a competition the editors were holding for "the most interesting novel" by any author from any part of the world. The prize was large. Very much I should have liked to enter *Jalna* in this competition, but there it was — bound by contract to the New York Macmillans !

The more I thought of it, the more I wanted to enter that competition. "I don't see how you possibly can," said Caroline.

Neither could I see how I could but still I mused on the possibility.

Then brightly came the thought that as my chances of winning were slight it would do no harm to anyone and would be a satisfaction to me just to send *Jalna* to the *Atlantic* and discover if it made any impression. I could not resist the temptation. The bulky manuscript (a carbon copy) was posted, and when Caroline returned that evening I confessed what I had done.

"Now," she said, "you may be in for trouble."

Weeks passed and more weeks.

Between the *Atlantic* on the one hand and New York Macmillans on the other I began to get really nervous. Then came a letter from Harold Latham, Fiction Editor of Macmillans, setting the time of publication and speaking of proofs to be corrected. This sort of double life could not go on. I decided that I must retrieve my manuscript from the competition. How terrible it would be, I thought, if I should win the competition during the full tide of preparation for publication by Macmillans. Why, I might end in prison !

I wrote to the editors of the *Atlantic* asking them to return *Jalna* to me, as I had a publisher for it. They replied that my manuscript was being held, with two others, for further consideration. I should hear from them soon.

A flood of excitement shook me, but I was not submerged. I had promised myself that I would be henceforth honourable and above board with publishers, and so must I be. I wrote to Mr. Latham telling him that I had entered a second copy of *Jalna* in the *Atlantic* competition. I asked him if, in the event of my winning, Macmillans would release me from my contract with them. He replied (I suppose that in his wildest imaginings he did not consider this a possibility) that they would release me. There was kindness indeed. I settled down to wait.

Oh, the cruel suspense of that waiting ! Each morning after breakfast I perched on the window seat to watch for the postman. Each morning I flew down the stairs to get the mail. There was nothing from the *Atlantic*. I made up my mind that one of the other manuscripts had been chosen, *Jalna* had been thrust aside and forgotten. Again I wrote demanding the return of the manuscript. "How I wish you never had gone into that dreadful competition," exclaimed Caroline. "You grow paler every day. It is killing you."

Next a telegram came from the *Atlantic*. It was signed T. Fitzpatrick and was to this effect : "Have patience. Happy news awaits you."

But it was difficult to have patience. If I had won — why, in God's name why, did they not tell me so ? As days passed I sank into one of my darkest moods — I was the victim, I told myself, of some ghastly joke. I did not reply to that telegram. Then came a long-distance call from Boston. The voice at that end was the voice of T. Fitzpatrick — not the voice of a man — not the voice of Thomas or Terence, but the voice of Theresa, secretary to Ellery Sedgwick, editor of the *Atlantic*. She was charming but still told me nothing definite. She counselled patience.

It turned out that Mr. Sedgwick was ill in bed at the time — and wanted no one but himself to give me the good news. He and I had had some very friendly correspondence — confidential on my part, warmly sympathetic on his. He had remarked of me to a visitor from Toronto, "She has a far better friend in me than she guesses."
It was he then who wrote to me of the judges' final decision.

When Caroline came home from the office I told her that *Jalna* had won the *Atlantic* competition but she was past rejoicing. Too long had she suffered suspense. She simply said, "Oh," and sat down and looked at me. The fount of our enthusiasm had dried. We sat silent, unable to rejoice.

After a little I said : "It is a large prize I have won."

"Yes, it is large," she agreed.

"Now we can travel."

"We can never leave Bunty," Caroline objected.

Bunty, hearing her name, rose and came to me. She placed her forepaws on my knee and, raising her face to mine, gave a gruff protesting little bark, as though to say, "I will go anywhere you go."

Israël Tarte (1848-1907)

Né à Lanoraie, étudia au Collège de l'Assomption et à l'Université de Montréal; fut notaire, journaliste (*La Patrie*), eut une carrière politique mouvementée, et fut conservateur, puis libéral, puis de nouveau conservateur. Il fut ministre des Travaux publics de 1896 à 1902.

A QUEBEC POLITICIAN REGRETS ENGLISH-CANADIAN IGNORANCE OF FRENCH CANADIANS
Israël Tarte to Willison, November 28, 1900

... The trouble is that the French Canadians are not understood in your province and, I am sorry to say, by yourself. You are evidently under the impression that we are a kind of backward people, of simple-minded fellows, who cannot keep pace with their English fellow citizens. On that point you are altogether astray. The "habitant", as you call him, is a wide awake "boy". He has, in my humble opinion, more political sagacity than many of his fellow citizens of English origin — not because he has more intelligence, but because he has been obliged to conquer his liberty inch by inch.

Do me the pleasure of being my guest in Montreal for a couple of weeks. I will take you to the houses of those "innocent" habitants. You will find their dwellings, their tables, their habits, in a light that would not fail to change your views. I laughed heartily when you spoke of our farmers in the following manner. "With the coming in of the steam navigation, of the cable, of the cheap press, the gulf has narrowed, but the change must have been very slowly realized by the habitant, living a lonely and simple life under the paternal guidance of the church." True, you speak of the French habitants of the past, but you clearly mean to prove, for the benefit of your Ontario fellows, that the French habitants have not gone forward as nicely as they have gone. Again you are greatly mistaken. The French-Canadian population do not belong, if I may speak that way, to the same civilization as their fellow-countrymen of English origin. The French genius is not the same as the Anglo-Saxon genius. We are French, you are English. Would you permit me to add that we are Canadians to the fullest extent of the word while, on many occasions, you are more British than Canadians. If there is any trouble in future, the trouble will come out of that difference.

The reluctance of the French Canadians to taking part in the Transvaal war had for its cause the earnest desire of the French population not to be involved in continental conflicts. Mr. Spender was perfectly right when he wrote that the French Canadians "do not like the war, but they love the British rule." Is it not our right, not to love

that infernal war in South Africa ? And why should we be accused of
disloyalty because we don't like the war ? We think that in minding
our own business we could be a very happy people. The English and
the French of this continent would very soon become close friends if
there was a real, genuine national sentiment.

(Willison Papers)

Emile Nelligan   (1879-1941)

Considéré par plusieurs critiques
comme le plus grand poète canadien,
gloire de l'Ecole littéraire
de Montréal
dont il fut l'enfant précoce,
il a écrit toute son oeuvre avant
de sombrer dans la névrose

à vingt ans. Ses poésies,
publiées par Louis Dantin dès 1903,
plusieurs fois rééditées,
ont fait l'objet d'une édition
critique établie par
Luc Lacourcière (1952).

LE VAISSEAU D'OR

Ce fut un grand vaisseau taillé dans l'or massif :
Ses mâts touchaient l'azur sur des mers inconnues;
La Cyprine d'amour, cheveux épars, chairs nues,
S'étalait à sa proue, au soleil excessif.

Mais il vint une nuit frapper le grand écueil
Dans l'Océan trompeur où chantait la Sirène,
Et le naufrage horrible inclina sa carène
Aux profondeurs du gouffre, immuable cercueil.

Ce fut un Vaisseau d'or, dont les flancs diaphanes
Révélaient des trésors que les marins profanes,
Dégoût, Haine et Névrose, entre eux ont disputé

Que reste-t-il de lui dans la tempête brève ?
Qu'est devenu mon coeur, navire déserté ?
Hélas ! il a sombré dans l'abîme du Rêve !

(Poésies complètes, 1952)

CLAIR DE LUNE INTELLECTUEL

Ma pensée est couleur de lumières lointaines,
Du fond de quelque crypte aux vagues profondeurs.
Elle a l'éclat parfois des subtiles verdeurs
D'un golfe où le soleil abaisse ses antennes.

En un jardin sonore, au soupir des fontaines,
Elle a vécu dans les soirs doux, dans les odeurs;
Ma pensée est couleur de lumières lointaines,
Du fond de quelque crypte aux vagues profondeurs.

Elle court à jamais les blanches prétentaines,
Au pays angélique où montent ses ardeurs,
Et, loin de la matière et des brutes laideurs,
Elle rêve l'essor aux célestes Athènes.

Ma pensée est couleur de lunes d'or lointaines.

(*Poésies complètes,* 1952)

VISION

Or, j'ai la vision d'ombres sanguinolentes
        Et de chevaux fougueux piaffants,
Et c'est comme des cris de gueux, hoquets d'enfants
        Râles d'expirations lentes.
D'où me viennent, dis-moi, tous les ouragans rauques,
        Rages de fifre ou de tambour ?
On dirait des dragons en galopade au bourg,
        Avec des casques flambant glauques . . .

(*Poésies complètes,* 1952)

Albert Lozeau (1878-1924)

Né à Montréal, atteint du mal
de Pott à quinze ans,
il a vécu reclus toute sa vie
et a chanté la nature
entrevue par la fenêtre,
et les sentiments intimes
et souvent douloureux
de son coeur solitaire.
Ses *Poésies complètes* ont paru
en trois volumes (1925-1926).

LA POUSSIÈRE DU JOUR

La poussière de l'heure et la cendre du jour
En un brouillard léger flottent au crépuscule.
Un lambeau de soleil au lointain du ciel brûle,
Et l'on voit s'effacer les clochers d'alentour.

La poussière du jour et la cendre de l'heure
Montent, comme au-dessus d'un invisible feu,
Et dans le clair de lune adorablement bleu
Planent au gré du vent dont l'air frais nous effleure.

La poussière de l'heure et la cendre du jour
Retombent sur nos coeurs comme une pluie amère,
Car dans le jour fuyant et dans l'heure éphémère
Combien n'ont-ils pas mis d'espérance et d'amour !

La poussière du jour et la cendre de l'heure
Contiennent nos soupirs, nos voeux et nos chansons;
À chaque heure envolée, un peu nous périssons,
Et devant cette mort incessante, je pleure

La poussière du jour et la cendre de l'heure . . .

(*Le Miroir des jours*, 1912)

René Chopin (1885-1953)

Notaire à Montréal, musicien, il a aussi consacré ses loisirs à écrire des poèmes originaux, où s'exprime un curieux sentiment de la nature et qu'il a réunis dans *Le Coeur en exil* (1931) et dans *Dominantes* (1933).

OFFRANDE PROPITIATOIRE

Cygnes effarouchés du chaste hiver qui fond,
Votre vol s'éparpille et déserte ma grève;
Je sens mon coeur s'ouvrir comme une digue crève
Et se répandre ainsi que les grands fleuves font.

Avec mes pleurs votre eau secrète se confond,
O sources dans mon âme, ô printanière sève,
Philtre voluptueux de souffrance et de rêve
Qui jaillit et me verse un bonheur trop profond !

Colombe de la Neige à l'aile pure et blanche,
Pour que ma soif d'aimer cette saison j'étanche,
Entre mes doigts émus et d'un geste pieux

Je tordrai ton cou frêle, ô victime immolée,
Et ta chair hiémale et ta plume souillée
Rougiront sur l'autel en offrande à mes dieux.

(*Dominantes,* 1933)

Paul Morin (1889-1963)

Avocat, docteur ès lettres, interprète et traducteur, professeur et dilettante, mort dans la pauvreté, il a écrit surtout des poèmes exotiques inspirés par ses voyages et ses lectures. D'une grande perfection technique, sa poésie savante et sophistiquée fut une réaction contre la littérature régionale et paysanne. On a réuni ses meilleurs recueils dans l'édition en un volume de ses *Oeuvres poétiques* (1961).

HARMONIE POUR UN SOIR GREC

Heure pourpre où fleurit un blanc vol de mouettes,
Et toi dont je rêvais quand je lisais Byron,
Parfumé de laurier, de miel, de violettes,
Vent de Missolonghi qui promets à mon front
    La fraîcheur des nuits violettes,

Vous ayant désirés si fortement, avec
Toute la fièvre de ma chaude adolescence,
Dans l'odeur, sensuelle et vive, du varech
Ce soir, je vous possède enfin, brève puissance
    Du noble crépuscule grec !

Comme un litre, Itiès embrasse les collines
Parmi les oliviers au feuillage changeant;
Des tartanes et des felouques levantines
Heurtent au môle, ourlé de coquilles d'argent,
    Leurs flancs trop lourds d'herbes marines.

Au loin, sur les monts roux, encore soleilleux,
La tour d'une forteresse vénitienne,
Sépulcre triomphal d'un doge audacieux,
Clame inlassablement sa puissance ancienne
    A l'impassible azur des cieux;

Miroitant à mes pieds, la mer Ionienne
(Telle, aux jours fabuleux de l'intrépide Argo,
Sa voix berçait les pleurs d'Andromaque et d'Hélène . . .)
Scande de ses flots bleus les rythmes inégaux
    D'une éternelle ode païenne.

Du rivage sonore et d'écume argenté
Jusqu'à l'horizon rose, où fuit la voile oblique,
Monte traîtreusement du sein d'Aphrodite
Le frisson précurseur, ardent, et magnifique,
    De la nocturne volupté;

Et sur la grève, assis autour d'un feu de joie,
Graves et contemplant les étincelles d'or,
Des pêcheurs, aux profils cruels d'oiseaux de proie,
Chantent l'Amour, la Guerre, et la Gloire, et la Mort,
    Comme aux jours illustres de Troie.

(Poèmes de cendre et d'or, 1922)

ENFIN, C'EST L'AMICALE...

Enfin c'est l'amicale et la trop brève nuit,
L'heure de cendre et d'or, frémissante et charmée,
Où vers celle qui fut, un jour, la bien-aimée,
S'évade, chaque soir, le coeur qu'elle a séduit.

Déjà la coutumière inquiétude fuit...
Oublions tout labeur et toute renommée,
Et que la lampe éteinte et la porte fermée
Me gardent de l'intrus et de l'hostile bruit.

Ainsi, jusqu'au matin, mémoire nostalgique,
Comme un beau fleuve où chaque escale fut magique
Remontons du Passé le cours vertigineux;

Et que les souvenirs, guirlande épanouie
Changeant la chambre obscure en temple lumineux,
Viennent ensorceler ma pensée éblouie.

(Poèmes de cendre et d'or, 1922)

E. Pauline Johnson (1862-1913)

(Tekahionwake) Canada's best known Indian writer, Miss Johnson was born on the Six Nations Reserve near Brantford, Ontario, and achieved tremendous popularity in Canada and abroad through the reading of her poems about her own people.

MARSHLANDS

A thin wet sky, that yellows at the rim,
And meets with sun-lost lip the marsh's brim.

The pools low lying, dank with moss and mould,
Glint through their mildews like large cups of gold.

Among the wild rice in the still lagoon,
In monotone the lizard shrills his tune.

The wild goose, homing, seeks a sheltering,
Where rushes grow, and oozing lichens cling.

Late cranes with heavy wing, and lazy flight,
Sail up the silence with the nearing night.

And like a spirit, swathed in some dark veil,
Steals twilight and its shadows o'er the swale.

Hushed lie the sedges, and the vapours creep,
Thick, grey and humid, while the marshes sleep.

(Flint and Feather)

Robert Service (1874-1958)

Service went to the Yukon during the Gold Rush to take a job in a Dawson bank. His poems of the far north have given him an international reputation.

MY MADONA

I haled me a woman from the street,
Shameless, but, oh so fair !
I bade her sit in the model's seat,
And I painted her sitting there.

    I hid all trace of her heart unclean;
    I painted a babe at her breast;
    I painted her as she might have been
    If the Worst had been the Best.

She laughed at my picture, and went away.
Then came, with a knowing nod,
A connoisseur, and I heard him say :
" 'Tis Mary, the Mother of God."

    So I painted a halo round her hair,
    And I sold her, and took my fee,
    And she hangs in the church of Saint Hilaire,
    Where you and all may see.

(Songs of a Sourdough)

E. J. Pratt (1883-1964)

Born in Newfoundland,
Pratt was the son of a clergyman.
He came to Toronto during
World War I, and at the time
of his death was generally
recognized as being the best known
and best loved Canadian poet.
A very prolific writer,
he is perhaps most successful
in his longer narrative poems.
These frequently have
the sea as background.

NEWFOUNDLAND

Here the tides flow,
And here they ebb;
Not with that dull, unsinewed tread of waters
Held under bonds to move
Around unpeopled shores —
Moon-driven through a timeless circuit
Of invasion and retreat;
But with a lusty stroke of life
Pounding at stubborn gates,
That they might run
Within the sluices of men's hearts,
Leap under throb of pulse and nerve,
And teach the sea's strong voice
To learn the harmonies of new floods,
The peal of cataract,
And the soft wash of currents
Against resilient banks,
Or the broken rhythms from old chords
Along dark passages
That once were pathways of authentic fires.

Red is the sea-kelp on the beach,
Red as the heart's blood,
Nor is there power in tide or sun
To bleach its stain.
It lies there piled thick
Above the gulch-line.
It is rooted in the joints of rocks,
It is tangled around a spar,
It covers a broken rudder,
It is red as the heart's blood,
And salt as tears.

Here the winds blow,
And here they die,
Not with that wild, exotic rage
That vainly sweeps untrodden shores,
But with familiar breath
Holding a partnership with life,
Resonant with the hopes of spring,
Pungent with the airs of harvest.
They call with the silver fifes of the sea,
They breathe with the lungs of men,
They are one with the tides of the sea,
They are one with the tides of the heart,
They blow with the rising octaves of dawn,
They die with the largo of dusk,
Their hands are full to the overflow.
In their right is the bread of life,
In their left are the waters of death.

Scattered on boom
And rudder and weed
Are tangles of shells;
Some with backs of crusted bronze,
And faces of porcelain blue,
Some crushed by the beach stones
To chips of jade;
And some are spiral-cleft
Spreading their tracery on the sand
In the rich veining of an agate's heart;
And others remain unscarred,
To babble in the passing of the winds.

Here the crags
Meet with winds and tides —
Not with that blind interchange
Of blow for blow
That spills the thunder of insentient seas;
But with the mind that reads assault
In crouch and leap and the quick stealth,
Stiffening the muscles of the waves.
Here they flank the harbours,
Keeping watch
On thresholds, altars, and the fires of home,
Or, like mastiffs,
Over-zealous,
Guard too well.

Tide and wind and crag,
Sea-weed and sea-shell
And broken rudder —
And the story is told
Of human veins and pulses,
Of eternal pathways of fire,
Of dreams that survive the night,
Of doors held ajar in storms.

(Collected Poems of E. J. Pratt)

Arthur S. Bourinot (Born in 1893)

An Ottawa lawyer, he is currently editor of *Canadian Poetry*. His *Collected Poems* were published in 1947, and selections from his verse of 1947 to 1966 in *Watcher of Men* (1966).

PAUL BUNYAN

He came,
striding
over the mountain,
the moon slung on his back,
like a pack,
a great pine
stuck on his shoulder
swayed as he walked,
as he talked
to his blue ox
Babe;
a huge, looming shadow
of a man,
clad
in a mackinaw coat,
his logger's shirt
open at the throat
and the great mane of hair
matching,
meeting
the locks of night,
the smoke of his cauldron pipe
a cloud on the moon

and his laugh
rolled through the mountains
like thunder
on a summer night
while the lightning of his smile
split the heavens
asunder.
His blue ox, Babe,
pawed the ground
till the earth
trembled
and shook
and a high cliff
toppled and fell;
and Babe's bellow
was fellow
to the echo
of Bunyan's laughter;
and then
with one step
he was in the next valley
dragging the moon after,
the stars
tangled,
spangled
in the branches of the great pine.
And as he left
he whistled in the dark
like a far-off train
blowing for a crossing
and plainly heard
were the plodding grunts
of Babe, the blue ox,
trying
to keep pace
from hill to hill,
and then, the sounds,
fading,
dying,
were lost
in the churn of night, —
and all was still.

(Ten Narrative Poems)

Raymond Knister (1900-1932)

Novelist, short story writer and poet, Knister grew up in southwestern Ontario and much of his work reflects the influence of the rural life he knew as a boy. His untimely death cut short a literary career that was just beginning to win recognition.

WHITE CAT

I like to go to the stable after supper —
Remembering fried potatoes and tarts of snow-apple jam —
And watch the men curry the horses,
And feed the pigs, and especially give the butting calves their milk.
When my father has finished milking he will say,
"Now Howard, you'll have to help me carry in these pails.
How will your mother be getting along
All this time without her little man ?"
So we go in, and he carries them, but I help.
My father and I don't need the lanterns.
They hang on the wires up high back of the stalls
And we leave them for Ern and Dick.
It seems such a long way to the house in the dark,
But sometimes we talk, and always
There's the White Cat, that has been watching
While my father milked.
In the dark its gallop goes before like air,
Without any noise,
And it thinks we're awfully slow
Coming with the milk.

(Collected Poems of Raymond Knister)

R. Ross Annett (Born in 1890)

Practically all of Annett's short stories are centred around the same characters — Babe and Little Joe and their widowed father. In the days when the *Saturday Evening Post* was the richest market in the English language and a magazine of considerable literary repute as well, Annett and his Albertan characters made its pages on seventy-five different occasions, a record never approached by any other Canadian writer. This is the very first story in his series and appeared in the *Post,* April 9, 1938.

IT'S GOTTA RAIN SOMETIME

In the seventh year of the drought, the tractor that had been buried in the soil-blowing of 1932 came unexpectedly to light.

Babe and Little Joe found it. They came bursting into the kitchen, their eyes snapping with excitement. Their bare hands were blue with cold, for it was a raw March day and they had no stockings either. Bare legs and feet showed here and there through rents in overalls and shoes.

In the five years of her life, Babe had never had anything but boy's clothing — "and damn little of that," as her father put it.

"Pop !" cried eight-year-old Little Joe shrilly. "There's a pipe — a kind of a rusty stovepipe — stickin' outta the side o' that sand pile !"

"On Uncle Pete's place," explained Babe. "A wusty pipe."

"I scraped the sand away," Little Joe continued breathlessly. "An' — it goes down an' down the pipe does."

"It's a gopher's chimney, I bet."

"G'wan ! Gophers don't have chimneys."

"Or a tractor's, Baby," said Big Joe. "A tractor's exhaust pipe."

"Whose tractor, Pop ?"

Big Joe finished peeling the spuds for dinner and set them on the stove. He emptied the peelings into an old pail for Uncle Pete. He would not let Uncle Pete peel the potatoes, because Uncle Pete made the peelings so thick. He used them in his still.

"Whose tractor, Pop ?" Babe persisted.

"Ourn, Baby," said Big Joe, glancing across at Uncle Pete, who sat beside the window, tinkering with a length of copper pipe that had once been the feed pipe of a car.

The swell car Big Joe had bought in 1930. The year he and Emmy and Little Joe had spent the winter in California.

The car still sat where the garage had been, a forlorn reminder of happier days.

Bit by bit, at times when fuel was scarce, Big Joe had dismantled the garage. Uncle Pete had removed from the car any parts that were useful for his still. It was just a wreck now, and the kids used it to play in.

"I never knew we had a tractor," said Babe.

"We've had six tractors, Baby. Bought two in '26," Big Joe reminisced pleasantly, "an' another in '27. Paid cash for 'em too. That's the way we did them days. In the spring of '32 we traded 'em in on three new ones. We never made no payments on them. The company took two of 'em away, but they couldn't find the third one."

"You buried it," piped Little Joe, chuckling at pop's cleverness.

"Nope," Big Joe said. "Wind buried it. An' now the wind's uncoverin' it again, I quess."

"The Lord taketh away an' the Lord giveth," wheezed Uncle Pete facetiously. A faint gleam showed in his bleary eyes. He was recalling the fact that beside the tractor, and buried with it, was a granary with perhaps a hundred bushels of wheat in it.

Big Joe remembered the day the machine-company men came after the tractors that he could not pay for. That was in 1933.

"Where's the other tractor?" they had demanded.

"Buried," said Big Joe.

"Buried!" cried the machine agent. "What the hell for?"

"For eternity, brother," said Big Joe. "'Nless you bring a steam shovel to dig her out."

The men had gone with him across the road to Uncle Pete's half-section. He showed them the big sand dune that had accumulated in one of the worst blows — and grown considerably since — completely burying tractor and granary.

The men had gone away then, and they never came back. They never expected to see that tractor again.

But if the exhaust stack of the tractor was showing, the dune must be moving on. It would not take much digging to uncover both tractor and granary. And, Big Joe ruminated, the granary contained enough wheat to seed a partial crop — a hundred acres or so. He could use the tractor to sow it — if he could get some tractor fuel and some oil.

The trouble was that nobody would advance him seed or fuel anymore. Everybody thought that the country would never come back, that it ought to be abandoned. Most people, indeed, had moved out.

But not Big Joe. He would not abandon the section of land that had brought him more than one ten-thousand-dollar crop of wheat. True, during the past six years his farm had often not produced feed enough for one cow and a scrawny team of horses, let alone a crop. But Big Joe stuck.

"It's gotta rain sometime," he kept saying.

They had had no milk since they ate the cow to keep her from starving to death; no eggs since they ate the hens for the same reason.

Uncle Pete stayed on too. He used to grumble a lot about a man having nothing to live for if he could not buy liquor. But he kept on living. Never amiable or talkative at any time, during the first few years of the drought he grew more and more morose.

Then one autumn when they got their relief potatoes, Uncle Pete conceived the idea of making a still, and life had taken on a new interest for him. From their potato peelings and those he collected from the few remaining neighbours, Uncle Pete distilled a satisfying liquor. He worked steadily, for he had nothing else to do and he had a pessimistic feeling that the drought would last for years. Big Joe was sure Uncle Pete had a lot of liquor cached away.

Very occasionally, when he needed money, he sold a little. He never gave any away. He would not give you a drink, Uncle Pete wouldn't, not to save your soul.

He might just as well have been a hermit, so utterly solitary was his life. Nobody bothered about him or talked to him much. He seemed less human than the mongrel dog that slunk hungrily about the place — just an old soak, with his mottled, shapeless face and his clothes that had been nondescript in their best days and were now mere rags.

Only Babe, who was too young to know better, rated him as humanly individual, and therefore interesting.

Big Joe did not drink. He had promised Emmy.

"Don't get to be an old soak like Uncle Pete," Emmy used to say, "for the kids' sake."

But sometimes in these last years Big Joe caught himself envying Uncle Pete. Life had grown so sour. Whereas, in bad years as in good, Uncle Pete still had his liquor.

Emmy had been lucky too. She had died before drought and poverty took all the fun out of life. If a fellow could die young ... or else a fellow might get a little fun if he could see his kids having some fun.

Dinner would have been a quiet meal but for the excited chatter of Babe and Little Joe. Big Joe's mind was on that tractor and the seed wheat. He ate his dry potatoes without really tasting them. They had potatoes for dinner and oatmeal porridge for breakfast and supper.

If he could get fuel and oil for the tractor and get that wheat sown, why, maybe it might rain this year. It just naturally had to rain sometime.

Apparently Uncle Pete was thinking of the wheat too. Big Joe had to remind him about eating with his knife.

"How the hell can we make Baby a lady if you don't set her an example ?" Big Joe demanded, pointing accusingly with his own knife at the culprit.

Uncle Pete accepted the reprimand meekly. He appeared to realize that Babe had to be brought up right. Sometimes his bleary eyes rested upon Babe with a faint awareness, as though he were thinking : In an otherwise drab world, ain't she somethin' !

After dinner they all went over to Uncle Pete's place to see the tractor. And there she was — or, at least, there her exhaust stack was — sticking out of the sand as perky as a gopher's snout on the first warm day of spring.

"Another good blow of wind from the right direction, or a few hours' work with a shovel, and she'll be in the clear," Big Joe figured. The granary, still invisible under the slope of the dune, would not be hard to reach either.

Uncle Pete's eyes showed a dull wistfulness, and Big Joe knew he was thinking of one hundred bushels of wheat in terms of the liquor it would buy. But Big Joe was thinking of the crop of wheat it would make if seeded, and if it rained. Food and clothing and school and fun for Babe and Little Joe.

"Now," he planned busily, "we got some seed and we got a tractor. If somebody will stake us to fuel and oil —" He was interrupted by a snort of disgust from Uncle Pete, and whirled angrily. "You want that Baby should go on growin' up like she is ? Well, she ain't gonna — not if I can help it."

He fancied he could read a shamefaced look on Uncle Pete's almost unreadable face, and he continued more kindly : "You keep on drinkin' your old spud licker for a while. If we get a crop, Little Joe and Baby and me'll go places. An' you can buy plenty of good licker . . . What d'ya say, kids ?"

"Damn tootin' !" said Little Joe.

"Damn tootin' !" echoed Babe.

"Ladies don't say 'damn,' Baby."

"Why don't they, Pop ?"

"Well, just because they're ladies, see ?"

"I don' wanna be a lady. Whadda I wanna be a lady for ?"

"Why, damnit, because I promised your mom, Baby."

Little Joe was curious. "What'll she do when she's a lady, Pop ?"

"Oh, ride around in cars and look pretty."

"Gee !" gasped Little Joe. "Will we have a car ?"

"Damn tootin' !" Big Joe promised. "If we get a crop."

And Uncle Pete wheezed pessimistically : "If we get some tractor fuel. An' if it rains."

The next day Big Joe drove to town in his rickety old democrat, whereof the front wheels toed in and the back ones wabbled astonishingly. The tires were held on with hay wire and rattled noisily. His horses were a pathetically bony team of greys that had wintered on Russian thistle, and looked it.

"Couldn't rightly call them specimens of horseflesh," Big Joe said. "Bones an' hide is all they got."

Big Joe took the kids with him because even a trip to Benson was an event for them — Benson, which had only been a hamlet in the good times and was now nothing but a huddle of weathered shacks, most of them deserted. But the kids had never been places and seen things like Big Joe and Emmy — at least, Babe had not been places, and Little Joe had been too young to notice.

On the road, Big Joe entertained them with stories of the "good times." It was his favorite topic and the kids loved it. He told how he and Emmy used to get in the car and roll in to Benson — or farther still, to Sanford — and load up with things to wear and things to eat. Oranges, boxes of apples — all they wanted to eat in those days. Babe, of course, did not know about apples and oranges, and Little Joe had only seen them in Hindson's store. But Big Joe made their eyes glisten as he told about them.

Having prodded the horses up a long rise, they caught sight of Benson. Big Joe told them of the six huge grain elevators that had

once been required to handle the big wheat crops of the district. Only
one remained now, and that was closed. Benson was sure dead. It made
Big Joe feel bad to see the "So-this-is-Paris" look in the kids' eyes as
their democrat clattered down the one gravelly street — to think that
they had seen so little that a dump like Benson gave them a thrill !

Ed Hindson's was the only store left. Ed had fallen heir to many
jobs as people moved out. He was storekeeper, postmaster, undertaker,
sold gas and oil, if any; handled express and freight for the one train
per week that the railroad ran over the branch. In fact, Ed did all the
business that was done in Benson. And he had plenty of spare time.
Ed was too old to move when the drought came. He said he was going
to stay on in Benson until he just naturally dried up and blew away
like the Russian thistle.

In court, an accused person is considered innocent until proved
guilty. In Hindson's store a person was considered broke until he
proved otherwise.

You had to tell Ed what you wanted and show him the money to
pay for it before he would get up out of his chair by the potbellied
stove. That is what six years of drought had done to Ed Hindson. He
was glad to see you, though; there were so few people to talk to.

Big Joe approached the matter of tractor fuel nervously. He hated
to ask for favours; he who had always paid cash when he had cash.
Also, he did not want to let on about the tractor, at least until he got
his crop seeded. The machine agent had moved out, leaving Ed as the
company's representative, but the company would seize the tractor fast
enough if they heard about it.

"Look, Ed," he began. "I can get seed wheat and I can get the
use of a tractor to do the seedin'. All I need is fuel and oil for the tractor,
and if — I wondered if you'd stake me to that. If I get a crop . . ."

He began to flounder, because he saw that Ed was not registering
enthusiasm. Ed was drawing hard on a battered pipe, and the smell
of the tobacco made Big Joe faint as with hunger. He had not had any
tobacco himself since God-knows-when.

Ed was rubbing his bald head with one hand and squinting through
the tobacco smoke at Babe, where she stood beside the stove, dimpling
shyly and hanging on to Big Joe's ragged pants leg. Looking down at
her, Big Joe realized all at once that she had a poor colour, pasty
almost. Little Joe was the same. Oatmeal and potatoes did not make
a balanced diet for growing kids.

Ed Hindson spat on the stove and it sizzled. His slitted eyes
glinted angrily.

"Lookit, Joe," he said at last. "You take them kids outta this country and I'll help you all I can to get away. But to put in another crop — My God, you're dumb, Joe ! Won't you ever realize it's quit rainin' ? It ain't ever goin' to rain no more here."

"It's gotta rain sometime," Big Joe insisted.

"Why's it gotta ?"

Eventually, Big Joe abandoned the hopeless argument. But he was bitterly disappointed. It was sure going to be tough if a few dollars' worth of gas and oil was going to stand between him and a crop.

After a while he remembered an errand he had promised to do for Uncle Pete.

"Listen, Ed, could you spare Uncle Pete an empty five-gallon oil can for his — he wants a five-gallon can. He told me to ask you."

"I guess maybe," said Ed. "There's one right behind you . . . Not that one . . . The next one to it."

Big Joe picked up the can and set it down again. He had a sudden desperate idea. He would talk a while and then absent-mindedly pick up the wrong can and walk out with five gallons of tractor oil. That would be a start toward his seeding requirements and Ed might not notice what was happening.

So he sat on the counter and listened to Ed talk about Japan and China. Big Joe could not afford a newspaper, so that, as far as news of the outside world was concerned, he was like a man down a well. He never heard what was going on outside unless someone like Ed Hindson came to the edge and called down to him.

"Well, kids," he said at last, "guess we better be hittin' the trail."

He picked up a full can of oil, trying to handle it as though it were empty.

Babe piped shrilly, "You got the wrong can, Pop !"

Big Joe could almost have slapped her. "Why, damnit, so I have !" he ejaculated.

He exchanged the cans with the elaborately innocent manner of a man caught stealing five gallons of oil. "Well, so long, Ed," he growled.

"Wait."

Ed Hindson hobbled behind the counter and filled a large bag with oranges, which he presented to Babe and Little Joe.

"It's criminal," he muttered to himself, and he was referring to the obvious effects of malnutrition in the kids' faces, not to Big Joe's attempted theft. That was kind of pathetic.

First time he ever tried to pinch anything in his life, Ed thought. An' after six years of drought, he'd steal, if necessary, to get another crop in. Some people never learn.

He watched them cross the street to the democrat — the gaunt and shabby farmer and the ragged boy and girl. He saw the kids dig into the bag of oranges, saw Big Joe refuse an orange and walk down the street. Big Joe had a fondness for oranges, too, Ed remembered. He himself had often seen Big Joe eat three and four at a time when he could afford to buy them.

Suddenly Ed ambled around the counter, picked up two cans of oil and carried them across the street. He put them in the back of the democrat.

"Tell your pop he can have this much oil, but it's all I can afford. He'll have to get gas some place else."

"Just encouragin' him in foolishness, but what the hell !" he growled as he returned to the store.

A big man in a big new car drove in to Big Joe's place a week later. Big Joe guessed that he was a Government man. Guessed likely Ed Hindson sent him. Only Government men could afford cars nowadays. If it were not for Government men, Joe guessed the automobile factories would have to close down. And if everybody got jobs with the Government, who the aitch would raise wheat ?

This man was an "orderin' " kind of a fellow, too, and Big Joe never "ordered" worth a cent. The stranger began by practically ordering Big Joe to let himself and family be moved to somewhere they could raise feed for a cow at least.

"You owe it to your kids," he declared. But he brought that point up too late in the argument, after Joe's mind was set.

Uncle Pete and the kids were admiring the car.

"I know them kind of places you'd move me to," said Big Joe. "Places where you can raise enough vegetables and such to just live on. One crop of wheat and I'll make more money than them folks do in a lifetime. How come you got money to move me and the family, but you won't advance me forty-fifty dollars for gas to put a crop in ?"

"I'm not allowed to," said the stranger, "because you can't get a crop of wheat in this country. It's got to be abandoned."

"Come around at the end of July and maybe I'll talk to you," was all Big Joe would concede, and the man climbed into his shiny car and drove away.

"Likely he'll stop at Benson — he better had," wheezed Uncle Pete at Big Joe's elbow.

"What do you care where he stops ?"

Uncle Pete made asthmatic noises which might have been a chuckle.

"If he don't stop at Benson, he'll find himself outta gas, that's all," he said. "I siphoned 'bout eight gallons outta his gas tank."

Big Joe stared, open-mouthed, at Uncle Pete. Sometimes he wondered if the purple-veined mask that was Uncle Pete's face could ever have been smooth and clear like Babe's. But he was not thinking about that now.

"It's an idea," he muttered. "If we only had enough people come here in cars —"

It was time to get on the land and Big Joe was growing anxious. He and Uncle Pete had dug the tractor out and tinkered it into shape. And they had shoveled a way into the granary. But he had been to Sanford and canvassed everyone he knew, in a vain effort to get gasoline on credit. He had nothing on the place which was worth selling; not even the team of feeble old horses would bring any money.

With the oil Ed Hindson had provided and the gas Uncle Pete had pilfered, they got the tractor running. They hooked the tractor to a disk with the seed drill behind that. They had to disk and seed in one operation, for they could not afford to go over the land twice. Anyway, it was light soil, and wind-blown, so it worked easy.

"You go ahead — as far as eight gallons'll take you," Big Joe told Uncle Pete. "I'll be back tonight with some gas."

He put an old gasoline drum in the back of the democrat, hitched up the team and drove ten miles to Sanford. There were no cars in Benson. This time he did not take the kids. He did not want them to witness what he was about to do. And, besides, he might be arrested.

The meadow larks were whistling cheerfully as he drove along. Big Joe liked meadow larks. He admired them because they could sure take it, whistling cheerful defiance to cold or drought.

Big Joe could take it too. There was enough of the boy in him to delight in bird songs, to thrill to the challenge of wintry winds. The sweep of dawn across the prairie, the far-flung sunsets, moved him as glorious sound symphonies might move some men. And those were things that even poverty could not deprive him of.

But those things did not buy grub for Babe and Little Joe or put colour in their cheeks. They needed more than potatoes and oatmeal, even if he could stand it. So Big Joe was embarked on a career of crime.

He regretted it, though. He knew that he would not get the pleasure from the meadow lark's songs any more.

Court was sitting in Sanford and there were many cars parked all around the courthouse block. Big Joe found an empty space and pulled his team in to the curb between two parked cars.

He had two empty pails hanging from the reach of the democrat, in each pail a sufficient length of rubber tubing. He unscrewed the cap on the gas tank of the nearest car, pushed one end of each tube in and then sucked on the other ends until he got a mouthful of gasoline.

Then he dropped one of the free ends in each pail and stood by while the stuff siphoned, examining the hub of the democrat wheel with such obvious innocence that anyone observing him would have become suspicious at once.

Also, he wrote down the car's license number. When he got a crop he was going to give back to the car owner two pails of gasoline.

When the pails were nearly full, he replaced the cap on the gas tank, backed his team out carefully, so as not to set the pails swinging, and drove to a deserted alley. There, unobserved, he poured the contents of the pails into the drum on the democrat. Then he reslung the pails to the reach and cruised around the block, looking for a new parking place.

It was tedious work. More, it was tense and nerve-wracking. Big Joe had never stolen a nickel in his life, and sometimes when people passed on the sidewalk the perspiration oozed from him, he was sure, faster than the gasoline flowed into the pails beneath the democrat.

Once two men came out of the side door of the courthouse and approached the car next to the one Big Joe had been working on — just as he was backing out from the curb.

"I smell gas," he heard one of the men say. "I wonder is that feed line leaking again."

As Joe drove away, he noticed the fellow with his head under the hood of his car.

He had been late getting to town, and court was over before he had filled the drum. But he got a few more bucketfuls from cars parked in front of restaurants.

As he drove out of town in the dusk of the spring evening he noticed cars parked along the street where the movie theatre was. There was still a movie in Sanford. North of town the drought had not hit so hard. People always got a partial crop there. But the farther you went south the worse it got. Joe lived ten miles south. The sight of the cars by the theatre gave Joe an idea. If he kept mooching around in daylight, somebody was bound to get suspicious. But after dark it ought to be safer.

It was after midnight when he got home, but he was up with the first hint of dawn. When there was work to do, Big Joe never felt fatigue.

"I'll run the tractor this morning," he told Uncle Pete. "This afternoon you can spell me off while I go to town for more gas."

Uncle Pete asked no questions. He did not need to.

Big Joe rode the roaring tractor all morning, round and round Uncle Pete's hundred-acre field. He wished they had enough seed for the rest of Uncle Pete's half-section and his own six hundred and forty acres. But with one hundred acres of crop he would be back in the money again anyway.

The tractor thundered along in a cloud of dust, dragging the disk and the seed drill behind it. In the very center of the dust cloud Big Joe sat at the wheel of the tractor, dreaming dreams of food and clothing and fun for Babe and Little Joe — picturing them with the colour of health in their faces while his own face grew black with dirt until he looked like a blackface comedian in a minstrel show.

In the afternoon Uncle Pete relieved him, so that he could drive to town with another empty drum on the democrat. And the early darkness found him plying his new trade up and down the street where the movie theater was.

It was easier in the dark. Sometimes he did not even bother to drive away, but emptied the pails into the drum right there on the street. Nobody paid any attention to a nondescript old farmer messing about a democrat. His nervousness of the day before decreased until at times he was able to meditate dreamily while the pails filled. How he would bring the kids in to the show sometimes. They had never seen a movie. He pictured them, roundeyed with the wonder of it. There was a lot of fun in the world for kids.

It was late when he pulled in to what he thought would be his final call of the evening. He thought the drum was nearly full. No doubt he had grown careless. He had unscrewed the cap on the gas tank of a car and had just got the siphon tubes working when he was horrified to feel the car lurch on its springs. A door flew open and a man leaped out. He looked big against the glare of lights from the theater.

"What's goin' on here?" a gruff voice demanded.

Big Joe was too dumbfounded even to pull the tubes away, and when the beam of a flashlight fell on him, he stood there gaping with the cap of the gas tank plain to be seen in his hand and the smell of gasoline all about him.

"Well, blow me down !" cried the car owner. "Caught in the act, huh ?" He grabbed Big Joe by the arm. "You picked the wrong car this time, fellow. I'm the town constable."

Big Joe could have broken away, perhaps, but he could never have got his team backed out. And anyway, he was still too surprised to move. Suddenly he felt metal on his wrist and found himself handcuffed. The constable played his flashlight on the tubing, the pails hanging from the reach, the drum on the democrat.

"Well, blow me down !" he growled again. Then he took the tubes out of his gas tank, dropped each in its pail and replaced the cap on his gas tank.

"Get in the rig," he ordered curtly. "And drive me round to the jail."

Two cells in the basement of the courthouse constituted the town jail. Long after he was locked up in one of the cells, Big Joe could hear the booming voice of the constable telling somebody the tale.

"The missus went to the show, see, and 'long about time for her to come out, I drove down to bring her home. I was just settin' there, kind of dozin' in the car with the lights out when I seen this baby drive in beside me. Didn't pay much attention at first. But then I heard somethin' clink at the back of the car. Then I climbs out, an' there he is ! Got nearly a drumful of gas too."

The voice trailed on and on until finally Big Joe stopped listening. He began to think of Babe and Little Joe and the wheat that would not be seeded now. He went to sleep thinking, and dreamed wretchedly of pails and rubber tubing and the smell of gasoline, the taste of gasoline.

On the following morning Big Joe came up before a magistrate — a sour-faced, emaciated old man in an advanced stage of influenza. He looked as though he had wintered on Russian thistle, Big Joe thought.

The constable told his story with frequent interruptions while the magistrate sneezed or performed noisy operations with handkerchiefs. Each sneeze was a tremendous eruption which ended with an exasperated "Damnit !"

"You — ah-h-choo ! Damnit ! — got anything to say ?" he demanded, glaring at Big Joe in a way that could only mean ten years at hard labour.

But Big Joe told his story — a plain, unvarnished story, for it was not in him to plead. He told about the granary and tractor that the wind had uncovered after five years' burial, and about his failure to get tractor fuel on credit. He told about Babe and Little Joe. He mentioned the few merchants in Sanford who knew him.

The constable, at least, seemed impressed, and whispered to the magistrate that a little investigation might be advisable. The magistrate consenting, Joe was led back to his cell with those terrific sneezes ringing in his ears.

He was not surprised when told on the following day that the magistrate had taken to his bed.

But the constable was a good egg. He spent some time consulting the merchants Big Joe had mentioned. They all gave Big Joe a good character. They all had refused him credit — solely because they thought it was folly to seed a crop in that south country.

One of them knew Uncle Pete.

"That old coot's a moonshiner," he said. "You can't really blame him for that. For him to do without liquor is like keepin' milk from a baby. The old so-and-so came in here last winter with a tale about their relief potatoes bein' all froze. Big Joe told me weeks later that that was a lie. But Uncle Pete got more potatoes anyway — and none of them reached home. He must have quite a cache of alcohol some-place, and I hear it's mighty good stuff too. I've been told that Tom Dunke will buy all he can get of it."

Tom Dunke was the local bootlegger, whose business flourished as people became too poor to buy good liquor.

Late on the afternoon of the fourth day, Big Joe was haled once more before the magistrate, who seemed more emaciated than ever, and much less amiable. But, on the earnest recommendation of the constable, he finally agreed to a suspension of sentence. But he insisted obstinately on confiscation of the drum of gas for which Big Joe had risked so much.

"The man's crazy anyway," growled the magistrate. "Anybody's crazy that wants to put in another crop in that country."

"I'd like to have saved that gas for you, Joe", said the constable afterward. "I'd buy you a couple drums myself if I had the money. Anyway, what d'ye want to stay down there for? Government experts say that country's gotta be abandoned."

"Experts hell!" growled Joe. "I'll have maybe forty acres seeded anyway — without no more tractor fuel. If it's a good year I'll have seed for next year and somethin' to help me through the winter. I sure wish I hadn't picked on your car the other night, though."

"So do I, Joe. So do I."

He was a good egg, that constable. He paid the livery bill for Big Joe's team and sent the farmer home with a heartening slap on the back.

It was dark dusk when Joe arrived home — dusk of a cold, raw day with lowering, low-hanging clouds. It was not a cheerful home-coming. The thought of telling the kids that he had been in jail for stealing made Big Joe squirm. The kids thought he was a hero, kind of.

Why, once, the year before, he had heard them talking behind the house.

"What's God like ?" Babe asked her brother.

And Little Joe had answered without hesitation : "He's a great big guy with a black mustache, and he smokes a pipe."

He felt an overwhelming sense of defeat. Likely it would be a wet year. If he could have got that hundred acres sown, it would have given him a new start. But a lousy forty acres —

As he neared home he heard the barking of the tractor's exhaust. Something must have delayed Uncle Pete, so that after four days he had not finished the drum of gas yet. Tractor broke down, likely.

It was too dark to see far. He judged by the sound that the tractor was a few rods beyond the fence on Uncle Pete's place.

All at once the exhaust ceased. He heard voices — Little Joe's and Uncle Pete's.

Big Joe dropped the reins and jumped from the democrat while the tired team pricked up their ears and ambled down the road toward the gate. Big Joe crawled through the barbed-wire fence.

Soon he could see the shadowy outline of the tractor. Little Joe was on the seat and Uncle Pete, in deeper shadow, was messing around in the neighbourhood of the carburetor.

"What's the matter ?" called Big Joe.

"Not a drop left," wheezed Uncle Pete hoarsely.

"Hello, Pop !" shrieked Little Joe with delight. "We got the wheat seeded."

"All we got gas to seed this year," agreed Big Joe despondently "I got pinched," he added in a low voice to Uncle Pete.

"Thought so, when you didn't come home. Next day Tom Dunke came along. He'd heard about you. Heard we needed gas."

"Yeah ?" Joe supposed, wearily, that everybody would hear about him, even the kids.

"He brought two drums of gas with him." Uncle Pete's voice seem-ed unreasonably bitter.

"Two drums of gas ! What for ?"

"For my — dammit — my potato licker !" gargled Uncle Pete angrily. "Wouldn't leave me a spoonful. Knew we had to have gas, see ?"

"Cripes !" gasped Big Joe. "An' you got all the wheat in ?"

"Ain't enough left in the drill for hen feed," Uncle Pete admitted sourly. "We just ran outta gas this minute."

Big Joe was utterly overcome at the thought of Uncle Pete's self-sacrifice. He could not have been more surprised if the horses had turned from their mangers and said : "Look, Joe : You take this Russian thistle and sell it. We'll starve."

"Where's Baby ?" Big Joe inquired harshly.

"She's asleep over by the granary," Little Joe said.

"Wake her up an' bring her home."

It was almost like Uncle Pete turning his own heart's blood into the tractor's feed line. Big Joe found inadequate words.

"God bless you, Uncle Pete," he growled.

Uncle Pete's reply was not gracious, nor yet sufficiently intelligible to call profane.

A sudden clamour arose from the direction of the granary — angry shrieks from Babe, shrill answering cries from Little Joe.

"What's the matter ?" cried Big Joe, racing toward the cries.

He seized Babe in his arms. She was wrapped in Uncle Pete's ragged sheepskin, the sleeves of which hung to her feet. Her grimy little face was white in the gloom.

"What'sa matter, Baby ?"

"He spit on me !" she cried petulantly. "Little Joe did. My face is wet."

"I didn't neither," Little Joe protested.

"Now, now, Baby !"

Suddenly Big Joe held out a hand wonderingly. Then he swept off his battered hat and turned his face up to the skies.

"It ain't spit, Baby," he said. "It's rain !"

As if they had waited for that dramatic moment, the scattered preliminary drops increased on the instant to a downpour, thudding into the soft earth, pattering on the exposed part of the newly resurrected granary. They stood in it, breathless, faces upturned. Big Joe took it as an omen.

The drought was over !

When Uncle Pete slouched up out of the gloom, it was getting wetter by the minute. But for Uncle Pete there was still a dry spell in prospect.

Ed Arrol (Born in 1922)

Arrol is a journalist who left his desk on a daily newspaper to teach in an Indian Village in northern British Columbia. His experiences with the Indians have provided the background for numerous articles, stories and radio talks.

THE CHINESE CAFE

There is one in nearly every town and village in Western Canada, and anybody raised on the prairies has affection for a Chinese café and the gentleman from China who runs it.

Early memories of the "Rex" or "Royal" at Blairmore, Alberta; the "New York" or "Fat's Bum Coffee" at Bassano, where Fat's was recommended by salesmen as serving the best cup of coffee in southern Alberta — brings visions of penny candy and bubble gum, fire crackers and sunflower seeds. When the teens are reached the memories of a Chinese café include strawberry sodas and chocolate milk shakes and, in winter after skating, cups of hot chocolate.

The working youth will call for a slab of Boston cream pie and a cup of coffee and he will play the jukebox for his girl friend when they drop in to the café for a soft drink or an ice cream float after the show is out.

But whatever the name of the café or the occasion, you might find anyone or anything at "The Chinaman's."

There is colour and romance, noise and friendliness in a Chinese café in Western Canada. Its patrons feel at home there, whether they are calling, "Gimme another piece of pie, Charlie," or having a "chin wag" on a Saturday night.

In communities with towns off the main highways the cafés will be older buildings, usually two stories, with ROOMS FOR RENT upstairs. Most Chinese cafés are big — like the proprietor's heart — and the earlier buildings still have Station Agent or Pot Bellied stoves inside the door while heat from the kitchen warms the back area. As natural gas service comes to more and more prairie towns coal scuttles and shovels disappear when a gas ring is fitted into each stove.

A large showcase of heavy glass displays candy and tobacco just inside the double door, its surface worn and scratched with the passage of coins over the years. Near it is a cash register and its spike holds meal chits. Extending to the kitchen is a long counter where patrons step up and onto stools.

Mirrors may reflect shelves of cream pies and doughnuts and cakes, razor blades and pencils. Often the length of the counter prevents the diner from seeing everyone and it is necessary to walk past the stools on one side and the coats hanging along a partition on the other before he can satisfy a curiosity to know "who's in town?"

A visitor from England might think the booths that line both sides of the café, parallel to the counter, are modelled after English railway coaches, for the booths are made long to seat families. Table tops are porcelain (or imitation), in white for easy cleaning. The standard equipment at one is a sugar bowl or shaker, salt and pepper shakers, a bottle each of catsup and sauce, a dispenser of paper napkins, and the inevitable box of salted crackers.

What the menu lacks in imagination is made up in generous servings and the food is piping hot. A glass of cold water is followed by a bowl of steaming soup. Two slices of white and brown bread appear with a pat or two of butter. Next on the menu is something fried with a scoop of mashed potatoes — all smothered in gravy. Dessert with the meal includes a choice of rice pudding, prunes or ice cream. Listed as "extra" are pastries. The call for "apple pie à la mode" or "raisin pie with ice cream" is popular. Tea or coffee or milk follows to complete a meal that is common fare at "The Chinaman's," unless he is requested by discriminating eaters to furnish Chinese food.

Newer Chinese restaurants like the Redwater Café in the oil boom town north of Edmonton glitter like a palace under their multicoloured neon lights. The horseshoe coffee bar wends like a snake with its pearl-grey-topped counter, its red-plush stools, its music box that fascinates in a rainbow of colours and is seldom silent. The café opens at six o'clock and closes the following morning at one o'clock — most Chinese cafés have a long day. Chinese food is a specialty and patrons are invited to meet their friends at the café.

Nowadays a visitor to a Chinese café is likely to see the proprietor, between rush hours, doing his bookkeeping with a small adding machine, or pecking out a menu on a portable typewriter. But it is still possible to surprise the owner when he is casting up his accounts on the ancient abacus or see one of the waitresses writing the menu by hand.

The Chinese in Canada have come a long way from days when they helped as members on labour gangs in construction and as workers on the railroads to open up the West. Succeeding generations have started restaurants, laundries and general stores.

In a community in southern Alberta, the United Church was filled to capacity when a Chinese general merchant, there for twenty-six years, died recently.

"He was highly regarded in the district," the obituary notice read, "where he had helped out many a poor family during the period of the depression in the early thirties."

By kindness, patience and hard work they have endeared themselves to their chosen communities.

John Patrick Gillese (Born in 1920)

One of Alberta's most successful short-story writers, Gillese is particularly adept at describing rural life as he saw it on the prairie during the depression.

A nature writer as well, he is probably best known for his novelette, *Kirby's Gander*, which was filmed by Hollywood.

ESPECIALLY WORTHY

It was something of a sensation in our part of the world the morning we went to Edmonton for my brother Jim's graduation. Jim was the first one from our part of the country ever to go to college — an event that was a thing of both pride and doubt to my father — and that was back in the days when the Depression was at its worst and the Alberta bushland seemed to be the toughest place in the world to make a living.

There was still dew on the June roses as Dad drove to the station. My mother sat stiffly in the front seat of the buggy, and I had the sinking sensation that she was more scared than she'd ever been in her life before. That was saying something, for all her life Mother had been afraid of school teachers and even of refined visitors, and only because Dad refused to leave the last of his seeding did she consent to go to the city at all. My father wore his overalls tucked inside his knee-rubber boots, which were colourfully patched with red strips from an older inner tube. I had on my good cap, with tissue paper in the lining — and in my pocket was a whole dollar to spend on anything I liked.

The night before, Dad had slipped it to me in the barn, unbeknownst to Mother or my kid sisters. All I could do was gawk. "Where'd you get that?"

"I borrowed it from the storekeeper," my father said, "and you don't have to shout it from the rooftops." He looked around, to make sure no one was within hearing. "Nipper, I want you to look after

Mother at the speaking in there.   Take her up where there's a good
seat.   And if Jim gets too rushed to take her to supper — or something
— you remind him, eh ?"

I knew what Dad meant.   Sometimes I figured that was why he
was always making fun of Jim's learning.   Maybe Jim figured he
wasn't one of us any more.   Maybe he was ashamed of us — ashamed
of the farm and all the hard work and the poorness. Sometimes I figured the way he studied maybe he had forgotten that when we were
poorest of all, we had the most fun of all.

"You know tomorrow means a lot to your mother," Dad said. "It
could break her heart, Nipper."

The way he was talking to Mother now, though, you'd never have
thought he was worried.

"Well, old girl," he said, "be sure to take care of yourself in front
of that grandeur."

My mother gave him a look.   She never could tell when he was
teasing.

"You might tell them," my dad went on, "that any brains he has
he got from his old man."

My mother was so nervous she could hardly stand his talk. It was
only a desperate hunger to share in Jim's day of glory that took her to
Edmonton at all.   In that shining world of his, so removed from the
farm, she felt she did not belong and that somehow it was a sin even
to intrude.   Education, as Mother said, is a wonderful thing. But in
her mind, the riches of it belonged only to great people who were especially clever, especially worthy.

"I suppose now," my father muttered, "he'll be too good to pick
up a manure fork . . ."

It was the kind of talk that could have precipitated another bitter
battle between the two of them, and I was relieved, as we went over
Sam Mead's hill, to hear the train blowing as it left the village ten miles
west of us.

Dad seldom used the buggy whip but he flourished it now, and
the surprised team leaped down Mead's hill so fast that I almost fell
backwards out of the buggy and horse hair flew all over my good suit.

At the station cream cans were stacked in the shade of the long
stucco walls and the station agent had his long wagon piled high with
egg crates.   There were a few people clustered on the platform —
neighbours who'd brought in cream or blacksmithing work. They all
lifted their hat to my mother and asked Dad if he was going to the city,
too.

"Nope," said my father, "can't take time off from seeding."   The
way he said it, you'd have thought money was of no consideration.

"What's this I hear about Jim giving some kind of speech?" Charlie Porter, the elevator agent, asked.

"Oh, you mean his "valediction" address?" Father said. (He had spent half of one night trying to find out the meaning of the word.)

"What's he gonna do now he's educated?"

My father looked unconcerned. "Well, that's up to him. I wanted him to be able to do something more than shovel manure all his life."

I could tell my mother was scandalized by such talk from Dad, for in the first place he had been opposed to Jim's going to college at all and his favorite pastime, in winter, was to write letters to agricultural experts commending them on their various ideas for improving the farm and asking if they had any alternative plans, where you used hay-wire instead of cash?

There was no time for further talk, though, for the train was bearing down on us — a black, hissing monster that made the platform tremble as it passed.

It was my first train ride and, for a while, I hoped it would last for days. After a while, however, it grew a bit monotonous. I was tired drinking water in little paper cups, tired staring out of the windows at the sloughs, with their brown musked waters and wild ducks rising off them as the train clattered by. In every little field, carved out of the shining green poplars and the gay scrub willow, farmers were seeding, standing erect behind the levers, the old wooden drills raising dust clouds behind them.

Finally I went back and sat beside Mother. She had a seat by herself, so she wouldn't be obliged to talk to strangers. She was reading the invitation again, the little card with the green-and-gold crest that invited my parents to the graduation exercises in Convocation Hall and announced the valedictory address would be by James Hugh Kelly. That was Jim.

Suddenly it seemed to me a long time since Jim went away. For two years he'd hardly been home at all, except for the odd weekend. The summer before, he'd spent all the holidays freighting on the Mackenzie waterways. I could hardly remember what he looked like.

"Why didn't he help us on the farm, instead of working on a stern-wheeler?" I asked Mother.

"It was to earn the money to put him through," my mother said severely. "If you're ever going to be something, you have to have an education."

Somehow, in the way she said it I could sense her praying that she would conduct herself properly — that now that Jim was somebody, he wouldn't need to be ashamed because of his family.

It took about four hours to get to Edmonton. We went down the platform between dizzying lines of track, and I had never seen so many people in my life before. I was so busy gawking I lost sight of Mother, and a man's suitcase sent me sprawling.

"Watch where you're going!" Mother scolded me. "And look at your suit, we haven't money to be buying you clothes every year."

I was kind of thankful when Jim met us in the station itself. What I noticed most about him was his haircut and his pressed suit. He grabbed me, as if he didn't know whether just to shake hands or swing me up the way he used to in the old days.

"Well, Nipper!" he laughed. "You and your pants sure have a hard time staying the same size!"

Then he looked at Mother; and for a moment, before he kissed her, I thought I saw a worry in his eyes. He was looking at her vividly-coloured print dress that had been washed — by hand — too many times now to look new.

Then he laughed again and took us to a café. We thought he'd have dinner with us, but it turned out he still hadn't got his speech right and he wanted to spend more time on it.

I could see the disappointment in Mother's eyes. Then, surreptitiously she fumbled with the catch of her old purse. "Here, Jim, you'll want a few cents to treat your friends afterwards."

"Aw, Mother — "I could see the bleakness back in Jim's eyes . . . as if, I thought suddenly, her money wasn't as good as other people's. But he took the two dollars she gave him, anyway, his face tight and different.

"I'll pay you back every cent," he said.

I wanted to say to him : "The only time you can ever pay her back, Jim, is right now." I wanted to desperately; but I was just too dumb to say anything. I knew at that minute Mother would have given everything just to have him eat with her for the last time before the mysterious evening ritual when he would pass forever from her hard world and become a man of learning. I could see the tears standing in her tired eyes as he walked away.

Mother and I ate alone. Then, for two hours, we trudged from one store to another, trying to pick a present for Jim. Nothing seemed practical enough for Mother, or else she couldn't afford it with the few dollars she had left. She priced a pair of slippers and turned away because they were too dear. The salesgirl gave a short, brittle laugh, and I felt embarrassed because everybody could tell we were from the country and were either amused or annoyed by us.

Finally we took a street-car for the South Side, and we went back to shopping. Mother bought a twenty-five-cent pipe for Dad, giving it a couple of experimental pulls to make sure the hole wasn't plugged up. She got some cloth to make dresses for the girls. Finally she bought Jim a striped shirt with a stiff collar, which cost more than all the other things together.

Jim told us where we could get the room. It was near the University. It was hot and stuffy, and Mother let me take my coat off. She started fixing her hair with old-fashioned hairpins, all the while talking about how grand Jim had looked and how hard he had worked to be "something." I kicked my heels on the lumpy old bed and knew she was getting more scared, and this talk was only to bolster courage. I was getting scared, too — I didn't know why.

There was a knock at the door that made me jump. The hotel manager told Mother she was wanted on the telephone. Plain as day I could hear Jim's voice at the other end. He was explaining to Mother that his speech still wasn't satisfactory . . . that we were to have supper alone . . . that he'd pick us up in time to get to Convocation Hall.

I don't know when I have ever spent a more miserable afternoon. I didn't even feel like going out and spending the dollar. It was as if I was in a strange land where everybody rushed, nobody knew anyone else — and nobody cared. I wished I was back snaring gophers in the school grounds, or riding on the dusty, screeching old seeder with Dad.

My mother talked over the days since Jim had gone away. "Many a time," she reflected, "I never knew where the money was coming from. But we got him through, thank God. Now he won't need me no more."

To her, I guess, those words were a triumph : they meant that, through her, Jim had got somewhere. But to me, they seemed the saddest words I had ever heard.

Convocation Hall took my breath away. The college colours — green and gold — were everywhere. The place was packed. The men all wore dark suits ; the women had beautiful corsages. The great velvet curtains up on the stage were billowing softly, like something from a story-book. Dignified men — some fat and clean-shaven, some thin with little dark goatees, all of them preoccupied and seemingly oblivious of the soft buzzing of the crowd — disappeared towards the stage, reappeared again, walking soundlessly as if they didn't want to be seen and yet were quite conscious of the scrutiny.

"The profs," Jim said absently, when I asked who they were.

A couple of fellows about Jim's age came by, showing each other graduation gifts from "the folks." One had a gold watch and the other was waving a cheque, and both were laughing.

"I didn't know what to get ye," mother said, in an aside to Jim. "So I brought you a shirt."

"Oh — yeah — thanks, Mother," Jim whispered back. "You should not have bothered."

Somehow I was glad I had made Mother leave the shirt in the hotel room. I told her Jim would have no place to put it while he was making the speech.

Now, as he led us to a seat in the shadows near the back, I wanted to tell him what Dad had said, only Mother would have heard. I was beginning to feel as if I had stolen the dollar.

Jim was a bit pale, smiling vacantly at people who spoke to him. Either he was looking for somebody — or else he didn't want anybody to know we were his people.

Mother was staring at the beautiful gowns and hair-do's of the women next to her. Then she looked at their hands and buried her own below her handbag. Her fingers were twisted and bent from the hard years on the farm.

"Well — I have to go now !" Jim smiled shakily at us. "It'll start in a minute. I'll see you right afterwards."

He was a few feet away, and I hollered at him.

"Jim! Wait a minute !"

Jim stopped, and I felt as if everybody in the hall was staring in our direction.

"Don't be tormenting him now ! And him with his speech to give !" Mother warned angrily. But she wasn't quick enough to get hold of me before I was out of the seat and darting down the aisle.

I didn't say anything more to Jim until we were outside. Even then, it seemed crazy what I was saying and I was scared Jim would be mad at me for the rest of his life. But I had to tell him.

"Jim," I said, "didn't you want us to come ?"

The breath hissed through Jim's teeth. "You're crazy, kid !"

"No, I'm not," I said. "I thought this was going to be fun. Mother looked forward so long for this — but you've forgotten."

"Forgotten what, Nipper ?" Jim said, and his eyes looked as if he had a headache.

"The last time you needed money," I said. "Mother dug senega root in summer to get that. Every minute she wasn't doing her own work, she was out there digging. You've forgotten how hard it is to dig snake-root. The mosquitoes were so bad that when she'd come home, her clothes would be covered with blood."

"What are you trying to say, kid ?" Jim seemed to yell at me, but it was only a whisper.

"She did it so you could have an education," I told him.

And all of a sudden, remembering her pleadings with Dad, remembering her keeping baby lambs in the kitchen all winter, going without eggs so she could sell them, getting headaches in the heat of August from picking berries to peddle to the towsnpeople — all of a sudden I could hardly see.

"I don't even know how Dad rustled the money so we could come," I said. "But I know he did it because he wanted her to have something for all she'd done. Jim, she doesn't know what to do or say —"

But I couldn't tell Jim any more.

I couldn't upset him on the biggest night of his life. That would have broken Mother's heart. The way he looked at me — like somebody who's known all along that what he was hearing was true, but that, maybe, if somebody didn't tell him he wouldn't have to face it — I was scared maybe I'd put his speech right out of his mind. I ran indoors and left him there.

There was a lot I missed, in between "O Canada" and the appearance of a distinguished-looking man, in formal black clothes, who bowed against the backdrop of the brilliantly-lighted stage. He spoke briefly of the events that had gone before, then said he would call on James Hugh Kelly, the University's outstanding honour scholar of the year, to deliver the valedictory address.

Off-stage in the wings, the band began to play softly, the haunting theme song of the college. Then Jim stepped lightly across the stage, to a tiny table with a water pitcher on it. The drums sounded a deep roll and died. Applause came from the packed auditorium. The lights were off, but I could see the tears slipping down my mother's cheeks. She was so proud of him that nothing could spoil that moment for her.

"He's something at last," she was thinking.

Jim opened his address, and I could tell he was nervous. He said none of us gathered there that night would ever forget the memorable occasion. For the students, Jim said, it was both an ending and a beginning. He talked about the student year and the Tuck Shop and there was laughter, and that seemed to relax him.

With a sort of easy confidence now, he talked ; and it didn't seem possible that once he had pitched hay and hauled firewood with Dad through the deep drifts of winter in the bush country.

Then, after more bursts of laughter and words that were just words to me, Jim paused. The smile left his face ; and I think everybody suddenly realized that the next part of Jim's speech was going to be different.

"Ladies and gentlement," Jim said, "when we — your sons and daughters — receive our diplomas tonight, we are supposed to be worthy of them." You could have heard the silence then, thick and fixed and pregnant. "It means," said Jim, "that into our hands you have passed a great trust. When people come to our doctors, they will come, believing that we have not only the skill and knowledge — but the sacred regard for their bodies, to make them well. When you pass your children to our teachers, you will be conferring on us a tremendous — almost a terrible trust." Jim touched a strand of his hair that had fallen across his face. "I once heard a Divinity student say that the greatest prayer was : 'Lord, that I may be worthy.' Now, I know I at least understand."

Somewhere in the student gallery, somebody snickered. But for the rest of that hall, it was as if even breathing had stopped.

"So," Jim went on, "if we are to be worthy, it must mean that we set forth now with a realization of what others have done for us. There should be no room left for false pride. There should be only gratitude for the sacrifices, hidden and open, of all those who have made our education possible . . . who have given us, as it were, to the service of humanity."

Said Jim : "From the bottom of my heart, I want to say to all to-night that whatever I am, I owe to others. To my professors, who have preserved and handed into my keeping the best knowledge of all the generations. To my classmates, who have shown me and shared with me a beautiful friendship. But most of all . . ."

And here Jim paused.

". . . most of all," he said, "I want to thank my mother, who is down there in the audience with you. With her permission, ladies and gentlemen — and yours — I'd like to tell you what she has given over the years, for my sake and, I hope, for mankind."

All of a sudden, listening to Jim's voice, I couldn't see. For Jim was up there, not pretending any longer, telling those people who knew the value of education, what it meant to be so poor in wordly goods that she'd never owned a washing machine or a toaster or one really lovely dress. She was so unlettered herself she was afraid to speak before strangers . . . He went on and on, telling them about the lambs and the mosquitoes, till everywhere I looked, I could see women daubbing at their eyes and men staring so straight ahead that you knew what it was like with them, too.

When Jim was done, the silence followed him off the stage. Then the applause began. It swept in waves through the auditorium, till at last the distinguished-looking man stepped back and lifted his hands for silence.

"This," he said, "is an occasion of which memories are made — a graduation I shall always remember with pride. May I just say how sincerely honoured we are to have the mothers of our students with us. They, it seems, are behind the 'somebodies' of the world." For a moment, the distinguished-looking man seemed caught up in memories of his own. Then he smiled. "Perhaps it is a good thing for all our graduates to remember," he concluded, "that the riches of education are not meant for the educated alone. They should be given generously to all — but especially to all the unknowns who made our education possible."

Mother was lost completely in admiration of him. In him, she saw a reflection of what Jim would be some day.

At that, I guess it turned out to be the most wonderful trip she'd ever had. On the train going home, she wanted to sit and remember. For her, the years of sacrifice were forgotten ; perhaps they had never been. I suppose she thought the only reason Jim's friends and associates had sought her out was because they were so proud of Jim. And when Jim brought up the distinguished-looking man and introduced him as the Dean of his faculty, Mother actually loosened up under his spell. The Dean bowed when he left her, and for years afterwards Mother referred to him with pride, as "a lovely man." It was the one subject she could comment on with a certain assurance, especially when Dad would begin talking to people of the constructive correspondence he used to carry on with some of the best professors in Alberta, in his earlier years on the farm.

Yes, for Mother it was wonderful train ride home. For me, I thought it would never end. Mother was still in such a daze the day after the graduation that I stuffed myself on banana splits, ice cream, green apples and candy. I could hardly remember to tell Dad that Jim was counting on coming back to the farm for at least a couple of months before he decided what to do with his education, now that he'd got it.

Dad said it was good value for a dollar, all the way.

Harry Boyle (Born in 1912)

A prominent CBC official, Boyle remembers his life as a Western Ontario farm boy in his books *Mostly in Clover, With a Pinch of Sin,* and *Homebrew and Patches.*

HOMEBREW AND PATCHES

Nowadays, when the jerky figures appear on the television screen in a programme recalling the 1929 panic, the subsequent breadlines and the resonant voice of President Roosevelt calling for hope in the midst of gloom, a younger generation is inclined to regard the whole affair as a comedy. But watching such a programme, older people may get a slight twinge of nostalgic pain ; and some know that they will never erase from their consciousness the fear which started in those hopeless days.

What was it really like in the bad old days ?

For many those years were the "Hungry Thirties." Yet remembering them and myself as a boy growing up in the country, I can truly say that they were marked by many amusing incidents that took much of the misery out of them.

Obsolescence was a thing we had never heard about in those days. Things just wore out and were patched or repaired into new usefulness until they vanished. Articles intended for one purpose broke or tore and were adapted to something else. Practically everything around the farm could be put to some useful purpose. There was a great deal of merit in the art of "making do."

As a case history, consider Father's moleskin pants. He had a pair for wearing on occasions which he didn't feel warranted getting the good blue serge out of its tissue wrapper in the spare bedroom. He wore the moleskins, with a clean workshirt, the coat left over from an earlier suit, and a felt hat to sales, nomination meetings and the annual meeting of the beef-ring. He wore this ensemble also when applying for a loan at the bank. In time, he wore the moleskin pants under a suit of overalls when the weather got cold. When they wore out at the knees, they were cut down to make short pants for me. And when I had scudded the seat out of them, they were shredded up to make rag rugs.

We bought flour and sugar by the hundredweight and the sacks were bleached and made into work shirts. When the collar wore thin on one side, it was reversed. Their days as shirts done, if there was enough material left, they were cut up and hemmed into dishtowels ;

eventually they became cleaning rags in the house, and later they popped up in the driving shed for the men to wipe their hands on when they were working with grease. Some of them were used for stuffing broken windows in the stable when we didn't feel like sparing cash for new windows.

When a sheet wore thin in the middle it was split, the outside edges brought together in a centre seam and the thin edges tucked in and hemmed. Thus our sheets never actually wore out ; they only shrank to a point where they were cut up and made into pads for ironing on, dusters and sometimes aprons. Pieces were carefully washed and put away to be used to wrap meat on butchering day.

Binder twine was saved at all times and wound into a ball. Next to baling wire, binder twine was probably the most useful thing around the farm. We patched grain bags with it. Bachelors often used it in place of thread in sewing up torn pants or overalls.

Women insisted that their husbands buy overalls with the longest legs possible. The extra length was cut off, the legs were hemmed and the leftover was put away carefully for patches.

Hardwood ashes were put in one pile and sifted. In the spring, when the soap man came around, the pile was uncovered and for every hundredweight of ashes, or bushel basket in some cases, he returned so much soap. The soap came in large cakes and was probably the strongest cleanser in the world, next to lye. It was said that if a boy was beginning to shave, all he had to do was lather up with this soap and the whiskers would vanish of their own accord.

Used stovepipes were flattened out and used to line the bins in the granary.

It was unheard of to buy a child a pair of shoes that fitted him. They had to be big enough to allow him to grow, and the result was that his feet, splaying around in the big boots, soon spread out and filled them. The same thing applied to storebought clothes. I've worn overalls that felt like balloons and I was tempted to try jumping around inside them. Usually by the time I was big enough to fill them the back pockets had been removed to patch the knees, leaving two dark blue stains against the white, bleached seat.

Reading a newspaper was only the first step as far as its use was concerned. It was then carefully folded and put in the old wooden rack which bore in quaint lettering, HOME SWEET HOME. The paper could be used for covering shelves in the fruit cellar and the pantry, and lining dresser drawers. Mother made dress patterns out of it. The newspaper was put down in the box that held the first baby chicks behind the kitchen stove during a cold spell or when a mother hen had deserted her family. It was stuffed in to caulk cracks around loose-fitting windows in the dead of winter. From it was made the neat pile of twisted spills which reposed on the shelf behind the coal-oil lamps and were used only in emergencies. It lined the honey pail I carried with my lunch to school, and that paper was taken out at night and put in the woodbox to be used in case the fire should go out overnight.

Any boy who blew up and exploded a brown paper bag, in a fit of exuberance, was practically an outcast. Paper bags from the store were folded and put behind the clock. Flattened out, they were used by Father for figuring. Mother cut small corners from them to make up shopping lists. I used them to do rough homework on, not daring to waste a page in a scribbler because scribblers cost five cents.

Nothing was wasted in the kitchen. Bread crumbs and crusts were put away for bread pudding. The soup pot bubbled constantly on the back of the stove, and water from the vegetables, meat scraps and even the bone from the roast went into the mixture. Sometimes an extra portion of dried sage had to be tossed in to cover up a predominant taste but in the main the process produced a lusty kind of soup.

Mother patched and sewed and darned every night. By the time there was more patch than original sock, she had knitted a new pair. Just the same, old ones were unravelled and the serviceable yarn would be used over again.

Things didn't wear out; they gave up in exhaustion. Even our patches eventually found their way into quilt patterns. It was fun to look at a quilt and try to identify former prized possessions.

There were patches on patches, and it wasn't considered a mark of poverty if a man wore patched overalls in town, as long as they were clean. Washlines disclosed that a good many women were wearing underwear that still bore traces of the advertising slogans, such as "Purity Flour" and "Let Redpath Sweeten It," from the original material.

We didn't get the brunt of the depression when the stock-brokers were making jumps without parachutes in 1929. Old Mr. Simpson, who played the market, looked unhappy but then he never was a picture of gaiety. We began to notice it when the prices of the produce we had to sell started falling and the prices of what we had to buy stayed firm. After that, it was quite a squeeze.

(Homebrew and Patches)

Albert Laberge (1871-1960)

Journaliste et critique d'art, il a publié à tirage limité tous ses ouvrages dont aucun n'a été mis en vente. On y trouve des recueils de biographies et d'essais critiques, des volumes de nouvelles et un roman naturaliste, *La Scouine* (1918). L'extrait d'une de ses nouvelles reproduit ici donnera une idée de sa manière.

LE NOTAIRE

Jamais monsieur Daigneault n'avait eu le moindre désir coupable à l'égard des deux vieilles filles qui vivaient sous son toit. Sa passion, c'était son jardin, ses fleurs. Si les vers ne rongeaient pas ses rosiers, si ses dahlias produisaient des fleurs rares, quasi inédites, il était enchanté. Mais le notaire resta perplexe. Certes, il avait toujours écouté les recommandations de son ancien curé et il les avait trouvées sages, mais celui-ci voulait l'obliger à se marier. Ça, c'était une autre paire de manches. De quoi allait-il se mêler, ce nouveau curé ? « Ça m'paraît qu'il veut tout révolutionner en arrivant. Mais il n'y a rien qui presse. Attendons », se dit le notaire à lui-même.

Et il attendit. Des semaines s'écoulèrent, puis, un soir, le curé repassa.

— Eh bien, monsieur Daigneault, quand venez-vous mettre les bans à l'église ?

— Vous allez un peu vite, monsieur le curé. Je ne connais pas personne et je ne veux pas m'atteler avec quelqu'un qui va ruer, se mâter et me donner toutes les misères du monde. Faut penser à ça.

— Vous ne connaissez personne ? Mais prenez l'une des deux femmes qui sont dans votre maison ! Vous les connaissez, celles-là.

Le notaire resta abasourdi.

« Mais si je me marie avec l'une des deux vieilles filles, songea-t-il, c'est alors que les gens pourront jaser, supposer des choses, penser à mal, tandis que maintenant » ... Mais le notaire se contenta de se dire ces choses à lui-même, gardant ses réflexions pour lui.

C'est qu'il était un catholique convaincu qui allait à la grand'messe chaque dimanche et à confesse trois ou quatre fois par an. Il n'avait pas de principes arrêtés, mais le curé en avait pour lui et les autres, et ce qu'il disait faisait loi.

— S'il faut se marier, on se mariera, répondit-il simplement.

Tout de même, l'idée d'épouser l'une de ses bonnes lui paraissait plutôt baroque et n'était pas de nature à lui donner des idées réjouissantes.

Cependant, il pensait à ce que lui avait dit le curé.

Pendant plusieurs jours, il fut songeur, taciturne, ce qui fut remarqué de ses employés et des clients qui venaient au magasin.

— Il y a quelque chose qui le tracasse, disait-on.

Aux repas, il regardait longuement Zéphirine et Françoise, ses deux servantes. Des plis barraient son front. Laquelle prendre ?

Les deux femmes avaient constaté son air étrange et en causaient entre elles.

— Il est curieux, il paraît troublé, disait Zéphirine.

— Oui, depuis quelque temps, il est tout chose, répondait Françoise.

A quelque temps de là, alors que Françoise arrosait les plates-bandes de fleurs après souper, le notaire, qui rôdait dans son jardin, s'approcha d'elle et, à brûle pourpoint :

— Qu'est-ce que tu dirais, Françoise, de se marier ?

La grosse fille aux fortes hanches et aux seins puissants dans sa robe d'indienne bleue se redressa stupéfaite. Elle regardait le notaire avec une expression ahurie.

« Bien sûr qu'il a l'esprit dérangé », se dit-elle.

Et, comme elle était devant lui à le regarder sans répondre, monsieur Daigneault reprit :

— Tu n'as jamais pensé à te marier ?

— Ben, j'vas vous dire, personne ne m'a jamais demandée.

— Mais je te demande, moi. Veux-tu te marier ?

Françoise était bien certaine que monsieur Daigneault était devenu fou.

— Je veux bien, répondit-elle quand même.

— C'est bon. Dans ce cas-là, on publiera dans quinze jours. Puis, je te donnerai de l'argent et tu iras en ville t'acheter une belle robe et un chapeau.

Maintenant Françoise se demandait si c'était elle ou le notaire qui avait perdu la boule. Elle rentra à la maison.

— Le notaire a l'esprit dérangé ben sûr, déclara-t-elle naïvement à Zéphirine. Il m'a demandée en mariage.

Zéphirine parut stupéfaite.

— Il n'avait pourtant pas l'air d'un homme qui pense au mariage. Jamais j'aurais cru qu'il était amoureux de toi ni de personne. Et qu'est-ce que tu as dit ?

— Ben, le notaire m'a demandée et j'ai dit oui.

Le lendemain, monsieur Daigneault annonça qu'il partait pour Montréal. Il reviendrait le soir. Là-bas, il alla voir un dentiste pour se faire faire un râtelier. Il fallait bien se meubler la bouche pour se marier.

A quelques jours de là, ce fut Françoise qui prit le train, un matin. Elle revint avec une robe de soie bleue marine, un chapeau, des bottines et un corset... Un corset! Elle n'en avait jamais porté auparavant, mais quand on se marie!...

La publication des bans de monsieur Anthime Daigneault dit Lafleur avec Françoise Marion, sa servante, causa tout un émoi dans la paroisse. Comme bien on pense, les commentaires furent variés.

Le mariage eut lieu. Le notaire étrennait un beau complet gris et son râtelier, et Françoise, sa robe bleue et son corset.

Monsieur Daigneault était l'ami de la paix et du confort, aussi jugea-t-il inutile de se déranger et de se fatiguer pour faire un voyage de noces.

D'ailleurs, pour l'importance du sentiment qui entrait dans cette affaire!...

Le midi, les nouveaux mariés prirent donc le dîner à la maison en compagnie de quelques voisins. Et, pour ne pas froisser Zéphirine en prenant des airs de dame et en se faisant servir, Françoise mit un tablier et l'aida à mettre les couverts. Monsieur Daigneault ne put guère apprécier le repas, car son râtelier lui était plus nuisible qu'utile. Quant à Françoise, elle se sentait horriblement incommodée dans son corset neuf.

La journée se passa, très calme. Dans l'après-midi, monsieur Daigneault voulut aller faire un tour au magasin.

— Ben, j'te dis, j'croyais qu'il avait l'esprit dérangé quand il m'a demandé pour le marier, répétait Françoise à Zéphirine en lui racontant pour la vingtième fois la proposition du notaire dans le jardin.

Le soir, vers les dix heures, les nouveaux mariés montèrent à leur chambre, là où la première Mme Daigneault était morte il y avait vingt ans. Monsieur Daigneault enleva son râtelier, le regarda un moment, l'essuya avec son mouchoir, l'enveloppa dans une feuille de papier de soie et le serra dans un coffret, à côté d'un collier, de boucles d'oreilles et autres reliques ayant appartenu à sa défunte. Françoise dégrafa son corset, respira longuement et se frotta voluptueusement les côtes et les hanches avec ses poings. Elle aperçut à son doigt le large anneau d'or qu'elle avait reçu le matin à l'église et elle sourit en regardant du côté de son mari. Reprenant le corset qu'elle avait déposé sur une chaise, elle le remit soigneusement dans sa boîte et le déposa au fond d'un tiroir de la vieille commode. Et le notaire et son ancienne servante se mirent au lit.

(*Visages de la vie et de la mort*, 1936)

Robert de Roquebrune (Né en 1889)

Longtemps attaché au bureau de Paris des Archives du Canada après avoir fondé *Le Nigog* en 1919, il a publié des études et des romans historiques; son meilleur livre est sans contredit *Testament de mon enfance* (1951), récit autobiographique plein de poésie et de nostalgie dont est extrait le passage qui suit.

LE COUPAGE DE LA GLACE

Beaucoup d'événements traversent la vie et n'y laissent pas de traces. Comment se souvenir de tant d'heures sans importance ?

On se souvient mieux des autres que de soi-même. Un enfant est profondément attentif au monde extérieur, passionné de découvertes et ignore sa propre existence. Si on essaie, plus tard, cinquante ans après l'enfance, de revenir dans ce pays perdu, il arrive que l'on en retrouve la route. Tout est là, tout est resté dans la mémoire comme un paysage immuable. La maison est à sa place au milieu du jardin, les fleurs ont gardé leurs couleurs et leurs parfums, les chiens aboient. On peut entrer dans la salle à manger, le couvert est mis, maman est au bout de la table et Sambo ouvre la porte de la cuisine en tenant dans ses deux mains noires la soupière de faïence bleue. La famille est réunie. On entend des bruits de chaises rapprochées. Mon père, Roquebrune, René et Hervé, mes soeurs, tous sont à leur place. Je reconnais leurs voix, leurs visages sont vivants. Dans la grande salle basse, sous les poutres de bois ciré, aucun meuble n'a changé, les portraits sont au mur et, sur le buffet d'acajou sombre, la théière d'argent reflète une des fenêtres.

Un seul être est absent, et c'est moi.

Se souvenir, c'est rappeler le monde extérieur, c'est recréer des lieux disparus, faire revivre une famille éteinte, animer des morts. Et le seul personnage encore plein de vie est précisément celui qui paraît le moins saisissable : soi-même. On ne se voit pas.

Cette connaissance des gens et des choses, cette possession du monde, nos sens nous y ont conduit. Des visages familiers, des objets vus chaque jour, l'odeur des fleurs, les meubles, des bêtes, des sons, tout cela est entré en moi, dans ce cerveau d'enfant où il n'y avait encore rien. Et tout est resté, intact, clair et vivant. Mais l'enfant que j'étais alors, a disparu. Comme si les miens, ma maison et les choses qui m'entouraient dans ce temps-là, existaient toujours, et que moi seul serais mort.

Une journée de mon enfance est demeurée particulièrement colorée dans mon souvenir. Est-ce parce que je fus frappé par des images vives et neuves, des sensations éprouvées pour la première fois ? J'aurais pu oublier cette journée comme j'en ai oublié tant d'autres. Elle reste en moi pourtant avec la nuance du ciel d'un bleu profond, la campagne blanche de neige, les arbres noirs et dénudés, le grand froid, les chevaux courant sur la route dure et glacée, la musique des grelots de leurs attelages et, dans son gros capot, Godefroy, debout à l'avant du berlot et criant : « Huhau . . . Harié donc ! »

Chaque hiver, en janvier, au moment des grands froids, Godefroy consacrait quelques jours au coupage de la glace. C'était une opération difficile et que lui seul pouvait réussir car il en avait une longue expérience. Il s'agissait de remplir la glacière, derrière les hangars. De gros blocs de glace, recouverts de sciure, s'entasseraient et y fondraient lentement jusqu'au mois de septembre. C'est dans ce réduit, enfoncé dans la terre, que la grosse Sophronie viendrait, pendant les mois chauds, s'approvisionner de glace pour entourer les morceaux de viande gisant sur les tablettes de la dépense.

Cette glace, il fallait aller la chercher sur le fleuve. La petite rivière, devant la maison, était gelée comme toutes les rivières, tous les lacs et tous les fleuves du Canada. Mais on ne s'approvisionnait pas de glace dans la petite rivière, pour une raison qui m'est demeurée inconnue. C'était sur le Saint-Laurent, devant le village de Saint-Sulpice, que Godefroy allait couper ses blocs de glace. Il avait élu cet endroit comme on choisit un coin du jardin pour y cueillir les meilleurs fruits. Et il en rapportait de beaux cubes glauques, tout un chargement miroitant. Quand le berlot traîné par les deux chevaux, apparaissait dans l'avenue du manoir, Godefroy semblait conduire un char féerique plein de matériaux pour un palais translucide.

Jacques prêtait son aide à Godefroy et mes frères les accompagnaient toujours. Il n'était pas question que Sambo se joignît à l'expédition, car le nègre redoutait le grand froid et l'idée de marcher sur le fleuve, au large du quai de Saint-Sulpice, lui faisait une peur terrible. Je ne rêvais au contraire que de faire partie du voyage. Maman avait toujours refusé, redoutant pour moi une randonnée si longue dans le froid. Mais lorsque Hervé rentrait et me racontait les détails de sa journée, je désirais plus que jamais d'être du voyage de glace. J'en obtins enfin la permission.

Pour une telle expédition, on ajouta à mon accoutrement d'hiver un « nuage » de grosse laine rouge qui s'entortillait autour du cou et dont je pouvais me couvrir la figure. Le reste de mon costume était semblable à celui de mes frères, de Jacques et de Godefroy, c'est-à-dire que nous étions enveloppés du gros capot d'étoffe grise et la tête prise dans la tuque rouge que portaient alors tous les Canadiens. Une ceinture fléchée serrait le capot à la taille et nous portions nos mocassins, car nous avions le projet d'aller courir en raquettes sur la neige pendant que les hommes couperaient la glace.

Un froid sec régnait sur la campagne, un froid sans vent. Assis au fond du berlot, sous les peaux d'ours que l'on appelait des peaux de carriole, mes frères et moi étions comme dans une petite maison en marche. Le froid était tout autour de nous, mais nous ne le sentions pas. Il en était autrement pour Godefroy, à l'avant du traîneau. Le siège du cocher, dans un berlot canadien, était une courroie tendue. Etrange siège, mais sur quoi Godefroy paraissait parfaitement à l'aise. Afin d'entasser les blocs de glace dans le traîneau, on avait enlevé le siège-arrière et, ainsi nous avions pu nous établir dans le fond du véhicule. Lorsque je levais la tête, j'apercevais le dos gris du cocher, sa tête de laine rouge et les croupes des chevaux sur quoi dansaient les grelots de l'attelage.

Dans aucun pays du monde la lumière n'est si pure qu'au Canada pendant l'hiver. Les premières maisons du village de Saint-Sulpice me semblaient tout près, alors qu'elles étaient encore loin de nous. Les fermes, les arbres dénudés et perdus dans des plaines de neige, les grands hangars de bois si semblables à l'arche de Noé de la Bible de Sambo, tout cela me paraissait à portée de la main. La transparence inaltérable de l'atmosphère donnait de l'importance à tout ce qui surgissait du sol blanc.

Les patins du traîneau crissaient et ce bruit strident me semblait la voix même de l'hiver, celle du froid. J'ai entendu cela bien souvent depuis ce jour, en traîneau, sur les routes gelées de la province de Québec. Le crissement des patins et la musique des grelots d'attelages, je les ai écoutés pendant bien des hivers, durant toute mon enfance. Symphonie de sons grêles et cassants que j'associe dans mon souvenir à cette journée de grand soleil, de neige éblouissante et de bonheur.

(*Testament de mon enfance*, 1951)

Jean-Charles Harvey (1891-1967)

Journaliste de carrière, romancier, poète et critique, il est surtout connu par ses romans idéologiques et par ses récits dont le suivant est un bon exemple. On y retrouve le sentiments de la nature qui a inspiré à l'auteur ses meilleures pages.

LA MORT DE L'ORIGNAL

*A Archie Grey Owl
et à sa femme, Anahareo.*

Ce vieil orignal était le patriarche de sa tribu. Intelligent, brave et rusé, il évitait depuis douze ans le feu meurtrier des hommes et, chaque automne, il sortait victorieux des combats que lui livraient d'autres mâles pour les conquêtes de l'amour. Il fallait le voir, dans les sentiers de la forêt, alors que son pas pesant faisait trembler la colline voisine. La seule vue de son large sabot inspirait à ses rivaux une crainte respectueuse. Il longeait les bords des lacs, et quand les moustiques le harcelaient il s'enfonçait dans l'eau jusqu'au poitrail. Son panache à treize branches faisait, sur la surface ridée, une ombre large comme celle des arbres.

Il n'avait peur de rien. Il passait à côté des ours noirs, la tête haute, avec un air de défi, et les fauves n'osaient s'approcher de lui, par peur de son pied, meurtrier comme une massue de pierre. Toutes les bêtes l'admiraient pour sa noble attitude, son grand âge, sa sagesse et sa vénérable barbe. Son calme et sa sérénité le faisaient préférer au cerf, que le lièvre trouvait trop nerveux, trop sautillant, trop léger.

Voici qu'une nuit on entendit, venant du nord, un bruit étrange : « Hou ! hou ! hou ! » De minute en minute, le bruit se répétait et se rapprochait. Les cerfs se regardèrent avec stupeur : « C'est une invasion des barbares », dirent-ils en tremblant. Et le vieil orignal, qui avait gagné tant de duels avec ses semblables, pressentit, pour la première fois, le malheur. Les « barbares », c'étaient les loups.

Ces bêtes cruelles et faméliques, chassées de l'Arctique par la famine, descendaient dans nos montagnes fertiles en gibier, comme les Huns avaient envahi les belles campagnes romaines dans l'espoir d'un riche butin. Le patriarche des élans avait été témoin, dans sa jeunesse, d'une invasion de ce genre. Il y avait perdu son père, sa mère, ses frères et ses soeurs, tous dévorés par ces buveurs de sang et mangeurs de chair. Pendant des jours, il s'en souvenait, son père avait échappé à leurs dents, mais, à la fin, affamé et morfondu, il avait succombé. Le spectacle l'avait horrifié : la curée ! Les grandes veines brisées, le sang jaillissant, la peau déchirée, les entrailles répandues...

Toute la nuit, les loups hurlèrent. Un peu avant l'aube, ils étaient si près qu'on entendait craquer les feuilles sèches sous leurs pas. Le vieil élan n'en avait pas dormi : il ne voulait pas être surpris dans le sommeil. Enfin, le soleil se leva et les bruits sinistres se turent. La lumière chassa le cauchemar. Qu'elle était douce et bienvenue la clarté du jour ! Elle vint sans bruit, sans heurt, caressa le flanc de l'orignal, alluma des reflets roses sur ses bois, posa sur chaque buisson ses plaques d'argent, tira des bas-fonds une buée parfumée d'une odeur de terre humide, fit étinceler chaque goutte de rosée à la pointe des herbes sucrées. La bête sentit comme une délivrance; elle descendit vers le lac et se plongea dans l'eau, pour chasser la fièvre de la nuit, puis elle entra sous bois et marcha longtemps.

Pas de trace des loups de toute la journée. L'orignal crut, un moment, que les ennemis de l'herbivore étaient disparus. Peut-être aussi avait-il été victime d'une illusion ? Mais, le soir venu, les hurlements recommencèrent. L'ennemi était à deux pas. Il était toujours invisible et, pourtant, on l'entendait haleter. Le colosse sentait sa présence à gauche, à droite, en avant, en arrière. Il se rendit compte qu'on l'avait suivi mystérieusement depuis le matin. Les loups, le jugeant encore trop fort pour l'attaquer en pleine lumière, avaient attendu l'obscurité pour le poursuivre. Il en est des loups comme de bien des hommes : ils n'attaquent qu'à coup sûr et dans l'ombre. Alors, le patriarche résolut d'aller plus loin, là-haut, vers une montagne où se tenait, pensait-il, un troupeau de sa race. A peine avait-il fait quelques pas dans le sentier, qu'il vit quatre paires d'yeux luire dans le noir. Il rebroussa chemin, il en vit autant de l'autre côté. Que faire ? Peut-être ses longues jambes lui permettraient-elles de distancer les assaillants. Il prit une course folle à travers bois. C'était comme un ouragan, un cyclone, dans les branches déchiquetées qui se tordaient et claquaient sur son passage. Les lièvres dévalaient devant lui, et les perdrix, qu'il dérangeait dans leur sommeil, s'envolaient avec bruit; les renards en maraude le regardaient avec des yeux ironiques.

Enfin, essoufflé, rendu, il s'arrêta et prêta l'oreille. Tout était silence. Je les ai dépistés, pensa-t-il; et il s'allongea pour dormir. A peine était-il couché, qu'il entendit, à quelques pas, un froissement de feuilles, puis un hurlement auquel répondirent, loin en arrière, d'autres hurlements, « hou ! hou ! » et, comme un écho affaibli, dans le lointain tragique, « hou ! hou ! » Il se releva pour avancer de nouveau. Cinq loups au moins l'attendaient. Il lui fallut retourner et refaire le trajet qu'il venait de parcourir au galop. Tout son corps était moite, et ses jambes aux jarrets si puissants, qui ne lui avaient jamais manqué, flageolaient sous lui. Déjà, l'affolement lui enlevait la moitié de sa vigueur.

Il marcha ainsi toute la nuit, serré de plus en plus près par cette troupe maudite qui semblait mesurer d'instinct l'affaiblissement graduel de la bête traquée. Il avait sommeil, faim et soif. Comme il souhaitait la venue du jour ! L'aube ! l'aube ! Le pâle rayon viendrait-il enfin chasser ces démons ! Alors, il pourrait s'étendre de tout son long pour dormir, après avoir brouté en paix des racines sauvages.

Les loups se consultèrent. Eux aussi prévoyaient le jour. Ils convinrent de se relayer à intervalles dans leur course, afin de permettre aux poursuivants de se reposer et de garder assez de force pour l'assaut suprême. Ils feraient en sorte d'obliger le colosse à tourner dans le même cercle. De distance en distance, un loup se tiendrait au guet et, au passage de l'élan prendrait la place de l'autre loup, qui dormirait en attendant l'appel des camarades.

Le soleil parut. L'orignal se trouvait dans un bas-fond riche en herbages. Tout près, brillait un lac sur lequel des « huards » au col blanc lançaient un cri lugubre, cri tremblotant et liquide qu'on dirait composé de flots de larmes. Il baissa vers la terre son long panache, pour prendre quelques bonnes gueulées de nourriture. A peine avait-il ouvert les mâchoires, qu'un loup surgissait devant lui et faisait mine de lui sauter à la gorge. Il était écrit qu'on ne le laisserait pas manger, afin d'affaiblir sa résistance. Il s'éloigna, pénétra dans un épais fourré et, là, se croyant caché à tous les yeux, il se coucha. Ses flancs avaient à peine touché le sol, qu'il sentait aux jarrets une morsure cruelle et entendait à côté de lui un bondissement.

Une idée lui vint. Le lac près duquel il se trouvait était très long; il le traverserait à la nage. Les loups ne pourraient le suivre, cette fois. Et l'élan entra dans l'eau. On ne vit guère plus que sa tête énorme qui glissait avec ses deux bois magnifiques au-dessus du flot. On eût dit un oiseau monstrueux rasant l'eau, ailes déployées. Malgré son affaiblissement, il se hâtait, tant son désir était grand de se délivrer de l'angoisse.

Il arriva exténué à l'autre bord. Il lui sembla que ses jambes suffisaient à peine à le porter. Il marcha néanmoins à grands pas vers une touffe de hautes herbes, au milieu desquelles il se laissa choir. Il fermait les yeux, quand surgit encore d'un buisson voisin la formidable bête, crocs découverts. Mais le loup hurla : « hou ! hou ! hou !» D'autres cris semblables retentirent au loin. Des loups viendraient en plus grand nombre; ils avaient contourné le lac en vitesse.

Dans l'immensité de la forêt, l'orignal était comme entre les quatre murs d'une prison. Il comprit confusément qu'il n'en sortirait jamais. Son cerveau ténébreux ne lui fournissait plus que des images inconsistantes. Il se laissa désormais aller à l'automatisme de l'instinct. La faim l'emportait sur le sentiment du danger. Il se mit résolument à manger. Ses énormes dents coupaient l'herbe avec un bruit sourd, et les loups, qui l'entendirent, se montrèrent à ses yeux vagues et se mirent à gronder. Il n'y fit pas attention et brouta avidement. Qu'elles étaient bonnes les tiges pleines de suc qui répandaient leur jus dans sa gueule ! Elles ne lui avaient jamais paru si réconfortantes.

Ce ne fut pas long. Un loup, plus grand que tous les autres, bondit derrière lui et le mordit à la cuisse. Le sang gicla. Réveillé tout à coup de sa demi-léthargie, l'orignal se retourna vivement et voulut asséner à l'assaillant un coup de sabot. Le carnassier avait disparu avec la vitesse de l'éclair. Comment atteindre de tels ennemis, qui ont la rapidité du vent, la souplesse du chat et la ruse du renard ?

Et la fuite recommença comme la veille, fuite lente, harassante, presque inconsciente. Le vieil élan n'avait plus aucune pensée. Ses sens mêmes ne percevaient les choses que dans un brouillard fantastique. Il allait dans une féerie, et on aurait pu répéter pour lui ce vers des *Châtiments* :

C'était un rêve errant dans la brume, un mystère . . .

Mille images, tantôt joyeuses, tantôt horribles, tournoyaient dans sa tête . . . Un flanc de montagne couvert de grands arbres, sur lesquels d'autres élans aiguisent leurs bois en vue de la saison du rut . . . Un matin, au bord du lac, un compagnon qui s'abat, après un coup de feu, dans une mare de sang . . . Un souvenir très lointain d'une incursion à travers une plaine nue, la rencontre de chevaux, de troupeaux de vaches, la vue des maisons, des granges, le jappement des chiens, l'apparition soudaine d'un chasseur et la fuite éperdue . . . Un « ravage » d'hiver dans l'épaisseur des sapins, de la neige par-dessus les épaules, la famine, la faim . . . La fonte des neiges, le ruissellement universel, les torrents bondissant du haut des rochers, les premières herbes, les festins parmi les fleurs des marécages . . .

Tous ces souvenirs élémentaires remontaient en lui à la fois. Et il poursuivait le songe comme dans un délire. Les loups, il n'y pensait plus. Il était las d'y penser, il ne pouvait plus . . . Ils le suivaient toujours. Sachant bien que leur poursuite tirait à sa fin, ils ne se hâtaient pas. Ils se contentaient de flairer l'odeur de sa chair, de sa sueur, et ils se pourléchaient d'avance les babines. La langue sortie, la tête basse, ils trottinaient en zigzag. La faim les tenaillait, eux aussi, et leur désir les obsédait.

Le soir vient. Dans un brûlé, une ombre gigantesque s'avance en titubant. Puis elle s'arrête aux dernières lueurs du jour. Sur le ciel mauve se découpent les deux bois, la croupe ronde et forte, les longues pattes de l'élan. Doucement, par degrés, le grand panache s'abaisse. On le dirait trop lourd. Plus rien ne le retient, et il suit la loi de la pesanteur. Puis, c'est la masse entière de l'animal qui s'abat sur le sol. Le patriarche a perdu conscience de tout. Une seule image, suscitée par la faim : un champ de nénuphars sur l'eau, des racines douces et tendres, parmi les fleurs, un parfum de végétation, une boustifaille énorme.

Et pendant que sa vision s'alimente de son dernier désir, de sa dernière souffrance, les cris sinistres retentissent : « Hou ! Hou ! Hou ! » On dirait qu'il y a des milliers de carnassiers conviés au festin : « Hou ! Hou ! Hou ! » Dans toute la forêt, c'est une rumeur sensuelle et meurtrière. Le goût du sang qui se répand d'arbre en arbre, de branche en branche.

Ils sont vingt autour de la proie. Le chef de file s'avance, d'abord prudemment, flaire de loin, observe, et, enfin, d'un bond, se jette à la gorge de l'élan. Une grande veine est crevée. Le sang gicle en un jet gros comme le bras. Un dernier frisson secoue la victime, dont les pattes fauchent la terre.

Et c'est la curée. Des lambeaux de peau déchirée traînent sur le sol, des morceaux de chair palpitante pendant au bord de la gueule des fauves. Un loup s'éloigne en déroulant le long boyau du ventre ouvert.

(*Art et combat,* 1937)

Ringuet (1895-1960)

Sous ce pseudonyme, le Dr Philippe Panneton a publié des romans, des nouvelles et des essais historiques. Médecin, il exerça longtemps à Montréal avant de devenir homme de lettres, puis ambassadeur du Canada au Portugal.

Sa renommée repose surtout sur *Trente arpents,* évocation sombre et puissante de la déchéance d'une famille terrienne sombrée dans la misère. Il était membre de l'Académie canadienne-française.

L'EXIL

Les distractions étaient rares. Maintenant surtout qu'il travaillait de nuit, le père Moisan, le vieux Moisan, ne voyait plus grand monde. Tant que ce fut l'été, il arrivait à un ami d'Ephrem de s'arrêter pour lui dire quelques mots. Pendant un certain temps M. Léger vint assez régulièrement, parfois même accompagné de sa femme; on parlait alors du pays.

Mais les soirées raccourcirent avec l'été mourant; et, sauf de temps à autre Ephrem, personne ne vint plus lui tenir compagnie. Aussi bien la crise de plus en plus angoissante semblait-elle caserner les gens au foyer. Faute d'argent, on ne recevait que peu, chacun d'ailleurs tâchant à cacher aux autres sa propre déchéance, s'imaginant être plus touché et craignant de se donner en spectacle. A quoi bon se réunir puisqu'on ne pouvait désormais parler d'affaires mirobolantes, de transactions fructueuses, de cent mille et de millions. Dans la vie de chacun s'introduisait un brouillard de gêne sourde qui tuait la jactance et l'orgueil de vivre en terre « d'Amérique ».

Une buée déprimante s'appesantissait sur tout, comme sur les villes s'écrasait naguère le dais de la suie. Les voix les plus claironnantes s'étaient assourdies. Les conversations n'étaient plus aux contrats roublards et triomphants, aux inventions géniales qui enrichiraient en un an, aux boutiques originales qu'on allait ouvrir et où se rueraient les chalands. Pour la première fois de mémoire d'Américain, on vivait dans l'heure actuelle, l'esprit inquiet des stocks invendus qui crevaient les entrepôts; des machines qui l'une après l'autre cessaient de ronronner; des cheminées d'usine dont une au moins par semaine exhalait sa dernière fumée. Il semblait que tout ce peuple jusque-là si jeune d'esprit et de coeur fût subitement atteint de vieillesse.

Il s'était même trouvé quelqu'un pour dire à Euchariste :

— Vous êtes chanceux, vous, père Moisan, vous avez une bonne *job steady !*

En sorte que cette dépression qui viciait la vie de White-Falls faisait par comparaison plus douce celle d'Euchariste. Lorsque, rarement, le dimanche après-midi, il se trouvait parmi des Canadiens, surtout des vieux, il pouvait parler du pays. Car vue de si loin, loin du caprice du jour et de la saison, la terre apparaissait auréolée de stabilité. Il disait :

— Chez nous, en Canada, ça ferait rien que les manufactures ferment, parce qu'il n'y a pas de manufactures. Ça ferait rien que les compagnies coupent les salaires, parce qu'y a pas de salaires. Quand on sème du foin, on récolte du foin, un peu plus, un peu moins, mais toujours assez pour vivre.

Et il se trouvait des vieux pour dire comme lui :

— C'est vrai, su' la terre, y a pas de dépression. Quant aux jeunes, songeurs, ils se taisaient.

Jusqu'au jour où il reçut une nouvelle lettre d'Etienne; « . . . Les temps sont ben durs, son père . . . » Il connaissait le refrain. Même après les meilleures années, il ne s'était point fait faute de le chanter et de gémir sur l'âpreté des temps.

« . . . Napoléon est toujours chez nous; y peut pas trouver d'ouvrage. Ça fait ben du monde à nourrir, parce qu'i's sont six à c't'heure; sa femme a encore acheté, pi c'était des bessons. J'voudrais qu'i' s'en retourne en ville, parce que les journaux disent qu'en ville, y vont donner de l'argent aux ceusses qu'ont pas d'ouvrage. Pour les pauvres habitants, par exemple, y aura rien.

« Les Touchette vont avoir leur terre vendue parce que y doivent trop dessus. Chez les Gélinas, c'est pareil.

« Mon foin . . . »

C'est vrai, c'est maintenant le foin à Etienne . . .

« . . . Mon foin de l'année dernière est encore dans la grange. J'sais pas ous'qu'on va mettre celui de cette année. On aurait mieux fait de le vendre comme je pensais. Pi les oeufs sont rendus à treize cennes la douzaine que c'est pas croyable. Ça paye plus en toute. Je sais pas ce qui va arriver. Pi y a Marie-Louise qui coûte gros en docteur pi en remèdes. »

Ainsi c'était donc vrai : même la terre manquait à ses enfants. Pourtant, c'est un vague mouvement de joie qu'il avait d'abord cru sentir à l'idée que sans lui les affaires allassent si mal. Mais il lui revint que pour ce qui était du foin, c'était encore sur son conseil obstiné qu'Etienne n'avait pas vendu.

La terre faillait aux siens, la terre éternelle et maternelle ne nourrissait plus ses fils.

Voilà donc ce qui en était du jour d'aujourd'hui. Sûrement la terre produisait bien encore de quoi manger, de quoi s'abriter, de quoi se chauffer; mais on avait voulu améliorer, moderniser et tous ces changements, toutes ces nouveautés ruinaient l'habitant; les machines qu'il fallait alimenter; le bétail de race qu'il fallait rajeunir; les bâtiments trop luxueux qu'il fallait entretenir.

Toute la crise actuelle n'était-elle pas le plus beau démenti à cette fausse et dangereuse idée de « progrès ». Pour lui, Euchariste, la voie était claire : ce qui s'imposait, c'était le retour au mode sain d'autrefois; renoncer aux mécaniques et vivre sur les trente arpents de terre en ne leur demandant que ce qu'ils pouvaient donner.

Voilà ce qu'il ferait quand il retournerait là-bas. Retourner ! Hélas ! il se sentait bien vieux, bien amoindri.

Retourner là-bas ! Quand cela serait-il ? Il ne pouvait en ce moment songer à abandonner Ephrem.

— L'argent est ben rare, son père, se plaignait celui-ci, vous pourriez pas nous aider un petit peu plus ? Je vous rendrai ça aisé quand les affaires reprendront. Vous, vous en avez pas besoin. Vous avez encore de l'argent; vous êtes pas dans le chemin !

Et, une fois de plus, il avait reculé devant l'aveu; le courage lui avait manqué de dénoncer sa propre honte et sa propre faillite.

— Les qué'ques cennes que je pourrais avoir, i'm' semble que c'est mieux des garder. On sait jamais. Mais si ça peut t'aider, j'vas rester à travailler icitte tant que les affaires iront pas. Qué'ques mois, un an si i' faut. J'su' ben prêt à te donner tout mon gagne. T'en as plus besoin qu'Etienne qu'est su' la terre.

Car, il ne lui avait pas montré la lettre d'Etienne.

Et tous les soirs il reprit le chemin du garage où s'enfermer pour la nuit, parmi le fouillis des mécaniques tapies comme des bêtes dans leur cage.

Et voilà que, petit à petit, sans qu'il sût pourquoi ni comment, se mit à s'effriter en lui la confiance. Il lui parut que le pays laurentien s'éloignait chaque jour un peu plus de son atteinte pour devenir une province du domaine de l'impossible. Il lui revint que chacune des heures qu'il avait vécues depuis était un infini, était une éternité qui ne se pouvait point remonter.

Les beaux jours étaient fanés. Survinrent les pluies d'automne, les interminables froides lavasses d'octobre qui marquent la fin d'un autre cycle et le divorce temporaire du soleil et de la terre, pendant lequel l'homme des champs devient inutile.

En juin, il avait dit, savourant les premières chaleurs :

« V'là un beau temps pour faire lever le foin ».

Deux semaines sans pluie en juillet l'avaient fait songer :

« Si y pleut pas d'ici qué'ques jours, l'avoine donnera pas riche. »

Une série d'averses en août :

« Encore une semaine de même, pi les patates vont pourrir certain. »

Mais maintenant que l'automne prenait possession du monde, sa pensée n'était désormais parallèle à rien d'autrefois.

La terre, ses trentes arpents de bonne terre, à quoi bon désormais, puisque de tout cela plus rien n'était à lui. S'il retournait jamais, ce serait pour vivre en dehors d'elle, au-dessus d'elle, avant que d'aller un jour prochain dormir au-dessous.

Pour la première fois de sa vie, il sentit le poids de son corps affaibli, et n'eut plus de révolte intérieure quand il s'entendit appeler « le vieux », « The old man », comme disait Elsie, sa bru.

Conduire la charrue, il ne le pourrait plus. Soulever les bottes de foin à bout de fourche, plus haut, jusqu'au faîte de la charrette débordante, comme on le faisait avant l'invention du chargeur, il ne s'en sentait plus la force. En lui toute vigueur avait disparu maintenant qu'il n'avait plus contact avec la glèbe.

Que lui resterait-il désormais ? Que de vivre inutile : auprès du poêle, en hiver; et l'été sur le perron à fumer sa pipe pendant que les autres partiraient aux champs, aux champs qui avaient été les siens et qui étaient ceux d'un autre; à ruminer l'amertume de sa vie gâchée, à remâcher l'injustice des gens et des choses; de ces gens à qui, en donnant la terre, il avait tout donné de ce qui n'était pas lui; de ces choses à qui, en donnant sa vie et son coeur, il avait tout donné, tout sans réserve.

A quoi bon !

Il allume le petit poêle dans le bureau du garage car les nuits sont froides déjà. Il se blottit tout près. Que ferait-il d'autre, là-bas ?

La neige est venue, une neige qui n'est pas de la vraie neige, blanche et ferme et sèche, mais une neige qui est presque de la pluie, une neige qui sitôt touché terre n'est plus bientôt que flaques d'eau boueuse où se délaye une pâte grise.

C'est donc cela les Etats, les Etats dont le mirage a fasciné tant et tant de fils de paysans ! A commencer par son Ephrem. Des villes aux maisons barbouillées de suie, aux boutiques désormais vides, aux rues sales où se figent des individus hâves qui offrent aux rares passants leur éventaire de pommes à cinq sous.

Et là-bas ? Si Etienne disait vrai, ce n'était guère mieux. Le journal aussi ...

Le cotillon de l'hiver descendit sur la ville avec ses accessoires accoutumés : verglas qui casse les arbres, bise qui cingle les hommes, froid qui durcit les choses.

Il n'y avait qu'à rester là sans effort, à se chauffer au poêle pour lequel on lui fournissait le charbon à discrétion. Dans le garage dormaient les voitures sans que leur berger eût à veiller sur elles.

De grosses bêtes laides et soumises.

Il n'y avait qu'à attendre l'aurore blême et l'heure de s'en retourner à la maison, pour y dormir et manger.

Noël passa. Il eut pour la Nuit Divine une collation soignée : des sandwiches au poulet et une bouteille de bière qui le fit dormir mieux que d'habitude. Insensiblement se rompait le fil de sa vie laurentienne. Le jour même, Ephrem et les siens s'en furent chez le grand-père Phillimore.

En février, une explosion détruisit une boutique en face du garage.

Avril ramena les oiseaux. A l'aube, ils remplissaient de leur musique un frêne oublié dans la cour. Et toutes les nuits, le vieux Moisan gardait ses croûtes de pain pour les leur donner, par petites boulettes qu'ils venaient chercher timidement, à ses pieds.

Il apprit en juin la mort de Marie-Louise, emportée par la consomption. Comme Oguinase...

Les jours raccourcirent et août souffla ses dernières chaleurs.

Un soir :

« J'me demande c'qui peuvent ben faire, à c't'heure, là-bas, chez Etienne.

« I's parlent p'têt' ben de moé ? »

Chez Etienne, là-bas, le père et le fils aîné sont assis dans la cuisine tiède. Dehors coule doucement la nuit fraîchissante.

A petits coups précis, Etienne vide sa pipe dans le crachoir.

— Dites donc, son père, suggère Hormidas, vous avez pas entendu parler d'un Ecossais, dans les Cantons de l'Est, qui fait de l'argent, de la grosse argent, à cultiver des champignons ?

— Des... quoi...? Des... champignons ?

— Ouais ! des champignons. I' aurait p't'êt' ben moyen d'essayer qué'que chose de même par icitte.

— Quiens ! encore une autre affaire ! En as-tu encore ben de même ? ... Ecoute, mon gars, le progrès, moé, j'ai toujours été pour ça. Mais, m'a dire comme on dit, i' a toujours un mosus de bout'. Ma terre, elle a pas besoin d'affaires de même.

— Ah ! vous savez, son père, ce que j'en dis, c'est plutôt comme manière de parler.

Mais imperceptiblement il a haussé les épaules.

Un silence.

— 'Midas, on va faucher le champ d'en bas d'la côte, demain, dit le père.

— Bon.

Dans son garage, à White-Falls, Euchariste Moisan, le vieux Moisan, fume et toussote.

Sa vue se brouille un peu, depuis quelque temps, et il entend moins bien. Les jambes surtout lui font de plus en plus défaut. Si bien qu'il ne rend plus jamais visite au petit bois, tout au bout de la longue rue Jefferson.

Il n'a pas renoncé à retourner là-bas, à Saint-Jacques; renoncer, cela voudrait dire une décision formelle qu'il n'a pas prise, qu'il ne prendra sans doute jamais, qu'il n'aura jamais à prendre.

Ce sont les choses qui ont décidé pour lui, et les gens, conduits par les choses.

Novembre ramena la pluie et ralluma le poêle.

Chaque année, le printemps revint . . .

. . . et chaque année la terre laurentienne, endormie pendant quatre mois sous la neige, offrit aux hommes ses champs à labourer, herser, fumer, semer, moissonner . . .;

. . . à des hommes différents . . .

. . . une terre toujours la même.

(*Trente Arpents,* 1938)

Claude-Henri Grignon   (Né en 1894)

Autodidacte, grand liseur, journaliste et pamphlétaire, auteur d'un roman dont il a tiré des continuités pour la radio et la télévision : *Un homme et son péché,* portrait d'un avare dont le passage qui suit évoque la fin tragique. Membre de la Société royale du Canada, il a aussi publié des nouvelles, des essais critiques et ses *Pamphlets de Valdombre.*

L'INCENDIE

Le temps était calme, et le bruit le plus léger dans la nature, le vol d'un oiseau parmi les pousses tendres, le saut d'un lièvre, une branche qui tombe, parvenait jusqu'à eux avec la plus nette précision.

Tout à coup, ils aperçurent dans le lointain, où la coupole de l'horizon tombe dans l'infini, des paquets de fumée jaune et noire qui se déplaçaient, pareils à des nuages.

— C'est pas des feux d'abatis, ça, fit l'avare. C'est plus pointu que ça.

— Ç'a pas l'air, constata, à son tour, Alexis.

Et ils avancèrent plus vite. La fumée grossissait toujours, et toujours de plus en plus noire, montait, divisée, dans le ciel.

— On dirait que c'est pas loin de chez vous, fit Alexis.

Ils s'arrêtèrent un moment. L'avare, immobile, sec et brun comme un arbre, regardait droit devant lui. Il blêmissait. Puis, soudain, il cria d'une voix atroce :

— C'est moi qui brûle !

Et il partit comme un éclair. Il courait aussi rapidement que tantôt. Deux fois, il tomba. Il se releva aussi vite pour courir plus fort. Alexis, qui avait jeté le câble au loin, le suivait de près.

— Je brûle, répétait Séraphin d'une voix étranglée, et les deux bras devant lui, comme s'il avait voulu saisir quelque chose ou barrer le passage à une catastrophe qui se faisait inévitable.

Une fumée grise et dense sortait par les fenêtres et par la porte de la maison, tandis que d'autres, plus noires, glissaient sur la toiture ou se dressaient vers le ciel en des contractions spasmodiques.

Séraphin approchait toujours, et sur sa figure, jaune et sèche comme l'avarice, il sentait des souffles chargés d'odeurs de chaux et de cuir brûlé.

Avant qu'Alexis n'eût le temps de faire un geste, Poudrier se précipita, affolé, dans la porte de la cuisine, où il disparut, emporté par un nuage noir.

— Séraphin ! Viens-tu fou ! criait Alexis.

Et il essaya de suivre l'avare dans la maison. Il eut juste le temps de l'entendre qui montait l'escalier au fond du haut côté. Essaierait-il de l'atteindre ? Ah ! s'il pouvait l'accrocher par un bras ! Deux fois, il tenta cet effort; deux fois il dut reculer. Il ne distinguait rien au travers de ces nuages opaques comme du sable et qui brûlaient les yeux. Il voulut crier. Une fumée âcre le saisit à la gorge. Il eut la force de marcher encore dans la cuisine. Découvrant tout à coup la chambranle de la porte où filtrait une lumière pâle, il se laissa entraîner de ce côté.

Alexis se retrouvait dehors, chauffé comme dans un four. Il avait perdu complètement la tête, et il se mit à sauter comme un chat pris de haut mal. Il criait, il cherchait des chaudières, il appelait au secours.

La maison n'était plus qu'un nuage de fumée que traversaient, ici et là, des traits rouges et tordus. Puis, elle se mit à flamber. Des millions de flammèches volaient partout. On eût dit que le hangar et l'étable brûlaient en même temps que la maison. Les flammes se faisaient plus nombreuses, plus rouges et plus rapides. Elles sortaient tout à coup d'une fenêtre ou couraient le long de la corniche. Alexis se rendit compte qu'un pan de mur pouvait tomber sur lui. Il recula, épouvanté. De biais, il crut voir passer une ombre dans une fenêtre, entourée de fumée et de flammes.

Etait-ce Séraphin ? Comment en douter ? Il ne l'avait pas vu sortir. C'est certain qu'il mourrait là, brûlé vif.

Et Alexis criait de plus en plus fort, maudissant la fatalité de ne pouvoir porter secours à son cousin. Est-ce qu'il existait en ce moment sur la terre une chose plus effroyable que cette maison en feu, et Séraphin qui brûlait dedans ? Et lui, impuissant à vaincre la mort ?

Le désespoir horrifiait toujours Alexis, lorsqu'il crut reconnaître Ti-Jean Frappier, Siméon Destreilles, Ti-Noir Gladu et le grand Bardeau, qui accouraient à travers les champs.

Ils arrivèrent juste au moment où la toiture s'écroulait avec fracas, en même temps que deux murs, au milieu de la fumée et des flammes qui montaient en spirales dans le bleu du ciel.

— Il n'y a rien à faire, dit Siméon Destreilles.

On entourait maintenant Alexis et on le déchirait de questions.

— Est-ce que Poudrier le sait, demanda le grand Bardeau ?

Alexis le regarda un moment, les yeux rouges et hagards. Puis, montrant de sa main large et tremblante le brasier, il hurla :

— Séraphin ? Mais il est là. Il brûle avec. Il est mort.

— Non ? non ? Ça se peut pas, disaient les colons effrayés, et tournant ainsi que des bêtes dans la cour.

Ils tentèrent de s'approcher du feu, mais la chaleur était trop grande. Ils durent s'en éloigner aussitôt, avec un tel air de découragement que le fort Alexis ne put retenir ses larmes.

— Si sa grange peut pas y passer, toujours, dit niaisement Siméon Destreilles.

— Je pense pas, reprit Alexis, abruti, parce que le vent est de l'autre bord.

Et tous, saisis d'horreur, regardèrent de loin s'écrouler le dernier mur.

Ce qui restait de la maison flamba jusqu'à six heures du soir.

Beaucoup de monde accourut de partout. Des femmes nu-tête, avec des bébés dans les bras, des hommes avec des fanaux, et des bandes d'enfants qui pleuraient ou qui riaient. Une grande curiosité attirait ces gens misérables. Que Poudrier se fût jeté, ni plus ni moins, dans le feu, cela constituait la plus effrayante nouvelle qui eût jamais secoué ce pays de misère. On se demandait si on retrouverait le cadavre et dans quel état il serait.

Il fallut attendre jusqu'à neuf heures du soir avant de se risquer dans les ruines encore fumantes. A la lueur de plusieurs fanaux, et à

l'aide de piques, de pelles et de fourches, on parvint à déblayer lentement l'endroit où se trouvait, il y a quelques heures à peine, la maison
de Séraphin Poudrier, dit *le riche.*

Sous des débris sans nombre, tout au fond de la cave, on le trouva,
à moitié calciné, étendu à plat ventre sous le poêle, la tête prise comme
dans un étau, les bras croisés sous la poitrine, et les deux poings
fermés.

On réussit à dégager le corps. Avec les plus grandes précautions,
et dans la crainte que cette charpente d'homme qui avait été l'avare
ne tombât en poussière, on le tourna sur le dos. Quelle horreur !
Deux trous à la place des yeux, la bouche grande ouverte, les lèvres
coupées, et une dent, une seule dent qui pendait au-dessus de ce trou.
Tout le reste du corps paraissait avoir été roulé dans de la glaise.

Deux fois Alexis se pencha sur le cadavre. Il voulait savoir
quelque chose. Il le sut.

Il ouvrit les mains de Poudrier. Dans la droite il trouva une
pièce d'or et, dans la gauche, un peu d'avoine que le feu n'avait pas
touchée.

(*Un homme et son péché,* 1933)

Léo-Paul Desrosiers (1896-1967)

Avocat, journaliste, il fut aussi
rédacteur du feuilleton de
la Chambre des Communes,
puis conservateur de
la Bibliothèque municipale
de Montréal. Il a été membre de
la Société royale du Canada
et membre de l'Académie
canadienne-française.

Historien à ses heures,
il est surtout connu par
ses romans historiques bien
documentés et vivants.
On lui doit aussi un roman
mystique d'une poésie intense,
L'Ampoule d'or (1951).
Il avait épousé la romancière
Michelle Le Normand.

UN MARIAGE DE RAISON

Les Saulteurs ont apporté quelques fourrures d'été et des vivres
pour acheter de l'alcool. Et ils ont commencé à boire. Leur figure est
large et ronde, leurs yeux sont égrillards, malins, et leur bouche dessine
un rictus cynique.

Dans un baril de neuf gallons, les traiteurs mettent de l'eau et
quatre ou cinq chopines d'alcool pour les Pieds-Noirs; six chopines

pour les Cris et les Assiniboines, sept ou huit enfin pour les Saulteurs. Atteinte la première par les Blancs, cette tribu est plus adonnée que les autres aux boissons alcooliques. Dans les pays d'En-Haut, la durée du contact avec la civilisation se mesure à la dose plus ou moins forte d'alcool qu'un naturel peut absorber.

Toute la bande boit : elle s'est plongée, en effet, dans l'une de ces infernales boissons dont Montour a eu la révélation atténuée au Fort Vermillon. Les nations de Rabaska s'enivrent avec tristesse; celles des plaines avec austérité; mais les orgies des Saulteurs sont diaboliques. Dans la nuit éclatent des clameurs, des hurlements, des cris de bête; les courses luxurieuses se produisent dans une folie de stupre et de sang. Avec toute leur violence se déchaînent les passions de la vengeance et de l'amour. Meurtres et voies de faits se succèdent. « Je n'étais pas responsable, c'était la boisson », excuse commode qui sert toujours aux Indiens.

Jour et nuit, William Henry poste des sentinelles autour du camp. Car si le rhum manque, les sauvages viennent mendier, supplier à genoux et pleurer de désir ; ils embrassent les pieds des bourgeoys. Mais la colère couve toujours derrière l'humilité. Une flambée d'impatience monte dans les yeux. Soudain, les Indiens menacent, ils reviennent avec des gourdins et des pierres; et les voyageurs doivent repousser les assaillants à coups de crosse de fusil ou de haches.

Au matin du troisième jour, le bourgeoys tient bon : plus de boisson. Les Indiens se dégrisent : l'un d'eux se meurt d'un coup de hache sur l'épaule, deux femmes ont le nez arraché par les dents de leurs maris jaloux.

Heure décisive. On allume les calumets des délibérations. William Henry et Montour veulent convaincre cette bande qu'elle doit passer l'hiver avec Montour au lac de la rivière Rouge; elle chassera le castor et la loutre qui foisonnent dans les cours d'eau de ce district, elle ravitaillera le poste.

Mais les Saulteurs ne veulent pas entendre parler de ce projet. Comment vivre en petit nombre, dispersés, dans la forêt, à proximité des Sioux, ennemis héréditaires ? Des partis de guerre traversent continuellement cette région : le massacre serait assuré.

Henry et Montour représentent qu'en hiver les Sioux s'avancent rarement aussi loin; en cas d'attaque, les voyageurs protégeraient aussi les sauvages.

On fume le calumet; on parle, on répète les mêmes arguments, on piétine sur place. Généreux, les Blancs offrent des cadeaux : brasses de tabac, plumes d'autruche, miroirs, habits rouges, rugines, plioirs, pierres à fusil et surtout liqueurs alcooliques. A chaque refus, les promesses redoublent. Mais ces tentations échouent : le danger est vraiment trop grand. Qui de plein gré irait se poster sous le tomahawk de son ennemi ?

Montour échouera-t-il ? Il confère une dernière fois avec William Henry. Celui-ci se montre brutal.

— Concentre tes efforts sur la Barbiche Blanche. Il a beaucoup d'autorité sur sa tribu. Epouserais-tu sa fille s'il le faut ? Tu pourrais trouver pire; c'est une jolie sauvagesse.

Quelques bourgeoys ont en effet épousé par inclination des Indiennes intelligentes qui leur font honneur.

Montour invite la Barbiche Blanche. Il le voit arriver, un petit vieux à la figure rouge sombre, ridée, que de rares poils blancs encadrent. Il le fait asseoir sur un coffre; il lui offre un petit verre de rhum. Ce fusil est-il brisé ? Qu'à cela ne tienne, les hommes de la brigade le répareront gratuitement. La Barbiche Blanche désire cette vieille hachette ébréchée ? Mais oui, oui, il peut la prendre. Le chef Indien aurait-il l'amabilité d'accepter un morceau de sucre ? Et cette vieille paire de pantalons, voudrait-il l'endosser ?

De ses petits yeux rusés, Nicolas Montour suit l'effet de cette diplomatie enfantine. Il voit s'allumer la cupidité, sourdre la vanité; il voit les sourires de contentement, d'aise, de gourmandise. Mais jamais, il ne perd son objet de vue. D'abord, il offre l'appât d'une médaille spéciale du gouvernement britannique et de présents particuliers. Non, ce n'est pas assez. Montour épousera la Prune Rouge; et le père recevra de beaux cadeaux : trois fusils, une hachette, deux sacs de balles, de la poudre, un miroir, deux barils d'eau-de-vie de neuf gallons, des plumes d'autruche à mettre à son chapeau.

La Barbiche Blanche hésite encore. Montour revient à la charge. Chaque fois qu'il le désirera, la Barbiche Blanche jouira des privilèges d'un Blanc : il entrera dans le fort, lorsqu'il le voudra; il entrera dans l'appartement de Montour chaque fois qu'il en aura le désir et partagera ses repas.

Le duel entre les deux hommes dure longtemps. Enfin, la Barbiche Blanche dit oui, et la bande, devant la perspective d'une autre boisson, se dit prête à obéir à son chef.

Alors se déroule la cérémonie du mariage. On dépouille la jeune sauvagesse de ses vêtements de cuir; on lui donne un bain. Elle endosse une chemise de calicot, un jupon vert, une robe de cotonnade bleue, et elle devient la femme du Blanc.

(*Les Engagés du Grand Portage,* 1938)

Félix-Antoine Savard (Né en 1896)

Curé en pays de colonisation avant de devenir professeur de littérature à l'Université Laval, il a été membre de la Société royale du Canada et est membre de l'Académie canadienne-française. Romancier, conteur et dramaturge, il s'est imposé comme un prosateur de qualité dès son premier livre, *Menaud, maître-draveur* (1937). Il a donné le meilleur de lui-même dans les poèmes en prose, chroniques, portraits et récits folkloriques réunis dans *l'Abatis* (1943) et dans *Le Barachois* (1959).

LES OIES SAUVAGES

Au T.R.P. M.-A. Lamarche, O.P.

Il y aurait un beau poème à faire sur ces ailes transcontinentales, sur ce vol ponctuel et rectiligne, sur ce règlement de voyage, sur cette fidélité aux roseaux originels.

A réfléchir aussi sur cette ténacité d'amour qui anime le dur travail des plumes et darde contre vents et brouillards ce front d'oiseau têtu, obstiné, invincible, sur cette chair raidie, impertubable, qui vole, c'est-à-dire l'emporte sur sa propre pesanteur et participe à l'agilité du désir, enfin, sur cette orientation lucide, infaillible à travers les remous de l'inextricable nuit.

Elles nous arrivent le printemps, la nuit, sur le vent du sud, par les hautes routes de l'air.

Par les hautes routes de l'air, par ce grand large aérien d'où, sans autre condescendance que pour l'escale traditionnelle dans quelque prairie marine, sans autre but qu'un nid dans les roseaux de la toundra, superbes, elles dédaignent d'instinct les villes, les champs, les eaux, les bois, et toute nature et toute humanité et tout ce qui n'entre pas dans leur dessein d'amour.

Elles s'avancent par volées angulaires, liées ensemble à l'oie capitale par un fil invisible. Inlassablement, elles entretiennent cette géométrie mystérieuse, toutes indépendantes, chacune tendue droit vers sa propre fin, mais, en même temps, toutes unies, toutes obliques, sans cesse ramenées, par leur instinct social, vers cette fine pointe qui signifie : orientation, solidarité, pénétration unanime dans le dur de l'air et les risques du voyage.

C'est une démocratie qu'il nous serait utile d'étudier pour le droit et ferme vouloir collectif, pour l'obéissance allègre à la discipline de l'alignement, pour cette vertu de l'oie-capitaine qui, son gouvernement épuisé, cède à une autre, reprend tout simplement la file, sans autre préoccupation que sa propre eurythmie, sans autre récompense que le chant de ses ailes derrière d'autres ailes et la victoire de l'espace parcouru.

Alors, après des jours et des jours de transmigration, lorsque, au bout du vent de la nuit, luisent les grèves; et quand apparaît enfin la batture rousse au bas du cap Tourmente — l'escale d'amour avant la grande terre des nids — le triangle ailé se brise, les oies tombent, confuses, tapageuses et s'abattent comme une blanche giboulée parmi l'aube d'avril.

C'est là qu'elles font leurs amours dans le balancement et le juste équilibre, la virevolte et l'épanouissement de toutes plumes, et dans tout ce qu'un coeur transporté peut donner de vif et de joyeux à des ailes avant les longs nids cloîtrés dans les roseaux du nord.

Cette noce débute avec le printemps de grève, avec cette grande purgation marine qui précède, au fleuve, la tiède montée du vert. Ce mouvement, cet amour, cette joie, cette vie ailée en perpétuel battement au-dessus de ce limon, cette espèce de vol incantatoire et fécondant sur la masse inerte des choses à surgir correspondent, vers le milieu de mai, à l'éclosion du printemps total.

Déjà mûres, ovifères, enivrées par cette liqueur où baigne toute chose autour d'elles, les oies attendent, maintenant, le départ. Elles écoutent la grande rumeur qui les pénètre; elles auscultent le son du vent, regardent rouler devant elles l'immense vague bleue qui porte sève, parfums, effluves; elles passent de longues heures sur les battures rocheuses des îles, déjà prêtes, déjà palpitantes, ouvrant leurs plumes, leurs ailes au flot de vie qui soulève leur chair. Enfin, l'heure venue, les volées se reforment. En longues bandes, au-dessus des îles, des champs, des grèves, au-dessus du jardin du printemps, elles se balancent comme une branche de pommier fleuri. Puis, un soir, sur le vent, le grand vent de la mer, le grand vent dans les bois, le vent profond de l'espace, elles disparaissent...

Cette fois, pour la dernière étape du voyage, la plus longue, la plus dure. Têtes au nord, les oies reprennent le méridien de l'amour et, sans fin, sous elles, le végétal, la profusion des eaux, les lacs innombrables entre les rivières branchues passent...

Altières, imperturbables, elles luttent contre elles-mêmes, contre les bourrasques qui sévissent encore, le ciseau de leur bec tenace dans le glacé de l'air; elles lutttent contre la nuit, exaltées par les constellations qui volent au-dessus, charmées par le bruissement de l'espace dans la syrinx de leurs ailes. Elles luttent aveuglément contre tout, fortifiées par ce qu'elles portent : les coques fragiles, le précieux trésor de l'avenir, l'unique destin de la race au long cours.

Elles sont invincibles parce qu'elles aiment héroïquement ce nid familial, sis à l'extrémité du monde, quelque part entre trois quenouilles, dans la patrie de la toundra.

Admirables, admirables, intrépides et fidèles, que vous m'enseignez de choses !

(*L'Abatis,* 1943)

Medjé Vézina (Née en 1896)

Née à Montréal, publiciste au ministère de l'Agriculture de Québec, elle n'a publié qu'un seul recueil, *Chaque heure a son visage* (1934) qui contient quelques-uns des poèmes les plus passionnés de notre romantisme féminin.

TENDRESSES DÉCLOSES

Mon âme, c'est fini d'étouffer vos tendresses,
D'égrener à vos pas de trop frêles chansons;
Fini de chanceler au chemin qui vous blesse.
J'étais l'épi fragile, et je suis la moisson.
Au rouet du passé j'ai dévidé mes peines,
Mes soupirs n'ont plus peur ni du jour ni des nuits;
Des rayons de plaisir vont couler dans mes veines,
Plus chauds que des oiseaux en boules dans leurs nids.
Le silence à mes doigts pesait comme une amphore :
Voici qu'un vin de joie inonde mon coeur nu.
Je suis neuve, je suis une pâque, une aurore,
Je suis un grand délire, et puis je ne sais plus,
Non, je ne sais plus bien les paroles à dire !
Tout recouvre la voix timide de mon coeur.
J'ai si longtemps souffert et je dus tant sourire,
Folle d'orgueil et folle aussi de ma douleur.
Je souffrais ! Je croyais, mon Dieu, que c'était vivre,
Que c'était là ma part, et je ne tremblais pas.
Sans songer à dresser le cri sourd qui délivre,
J'ai de pleurs arrosé le pain de mon repas.

Qu'importe maintenant si je ne dois plus taire
Le rêve qui luttait sous ma tempe le soir !
Tous les renoncements qui font haïr la terre
Vont crever dans mes mains comme des raisins noirs.
O très cher, je serai ton amante immortelle :
D'impérieux destins ont jumelé nos pas,
Et maintenant, tes mains peuvent comme des ailes
Se poser sur ma chair et délier mes bras.

(Chaque heure a son visage, 1934)

Jovette Bernier (Née en 1900)

Institutrice, puis journaliste, elle a ensuite écrit surtout pour la radio. Elle a publié quelques recueils de poésies où se mêlent un sentimentalisme facile et une fantaisie charmante. Mais ce sourire cache mal des plaies intimes.

ILS ÉTAIENT QUATRE...

Ils étaient quatre dans ma vie :
D'abord ce fut le fort qui caressait mes mains,
Il y avait le vieux qui pleurait pour un rien,
Et qui pensait à tout, sauf à son agonie.
Le sage même... un soir il a cru me charmer.
    C'est le fou que j'ai tant aimé.
Ah ! je l'aimais à m'en damner !

Ils étaient quatre âmes en peine,
Mais ils ne pouvaient rien pour apaiser la mienne.
L'un m'offrait bravoure et pain blanc.
L'autre me faisait châtelaine.
Le troisième évoqua la grâce d'un enfant
    Et le dernier que j'aimais tant,
But tous les jours pendant sept ans.

Toujours le même que j'aimais,
Et toujours quatre qu'ils étaient,
    Auprès de ma misère,
    Comme pour la civière,
Quand on porte quelqu'un en terre.

(Mon deuil en rouge, 1945)

Simone Routier (Née en 1900)

Violoniste, dessinatrice et poète, elle fut archiviste, religieuse cloîtrée, puis attachée d'ambassade. Membre de l'Académie canadienne-française, elle est surtout connue comme poétesse; d'abord romantique sa poésie a évolué vers un lyrisme religieux d'une émouvante sincérité.

JE DEMANDE

Je demande qu'on m'oublie; un grand bonheur en
    moi n'a point fini sa chanson.
Un bonheur comme nul ici-bas n'en rêve et qu'on
    tremble de voir entre ses mains déposé.
Un bonheur pour lequel un coeur seul ne suffit plus
    et pour lequel le présent n'est pas assez long.
Un bonheur dont mes bras apprenaient à peine
    l'étreinte et qui cependant m'aura tout donné.

C'était un bonheur éclatant comme un cri de clairon
    et pourtant c'est à voix basse que nous en parlions.
C'était un homme périssable; mais d'une plénitude
    de dons qui était une sorte de défi.
C'était un oubli à la loi d'exil sur terre que cette rencontre,
    c'était une double trop parfaite communion.
C'était un bonheur humain qui anticipait tout désir,
    justifiait toute attente et nous allait tellement ancrer
    dans la vie . . .

Je demande qu'on m'oublie, un grand bonheur en
    moi n'a point fini sa chanson.
C'est un bonheur qui m'apprit et la découverte et
    l'arrachement et dont je reste l'âme à jamais
    enrichie.
Il bat maintenant dans ma poitrine deux coeurs d'un
    même départ traversé : le mien et celui de mon fier
    compagnon.
Le sien fondu déjà à la joie de Dieu, le mien recevant
    l'essence même de l'Amour à sa source infinie.

Je demande qu'on m'oublie; un grand bonheur
    commence à peine en moi sa chanson.

(*Le Long Voyage*, 1947)

Alfred Desrochers (Né en 1901)

Ouvrier, puis journaliste, cet autodidacte est un poète réaliste et un lyrique qui a chanté surtout la nature canadienne en des vers d'une grande virilité. Il n'a publié qu'une mince partie de son oeuvre abondante et inconnue. Le livre qui l'a rendu justement célèbre est *A l'ombre de l'Orford* (1929).

JE SUIS UN FILS DÉCHU

Je suis un fils déchu de race surhumaine,
Race de violents, de forts, de hasardeux,
Et j'ai le mal du pays neuf, que je tiens d'eux,
Quand viennent les jours gris que septembre ramène.

Tout le passé brutal de ces coureurs des bois :
Chasseurs, trappeurs, scieurs de long, flotteurs de cages,
Marchands aventuriers ou travailleurs à gages,
M'ordonne d'émigrer par en haut pour cinq mois.

Et je rêve d'aller comme allaient les ancêtres :
J'entends pleurer en moi les grands espaces blancs,
Qu'ils parcouraient, nimbés de souffles d'ouragans,
Et j'abhorre comme eux la contrainte des maîtres.

Quand s'abattait sur eux l'orage des fléaux,
Ils maudissaient le val, ils maudissaient la plaine,
Ils maudissaient les loups qui les privaient de laine :
Leurs malédictions engourdissaient leurs maux.

Mais quand le souvenir de l'épouse lointaine
Secouait brusquement les sites devant eux,
Du revers de leur manche, ils s'essuyaient les yeux
Et leur bouche entonnait : « A la claire Fontaine » . . .

Ils l'ont si bien redite aux échos des forêts,
Cette chanson naïve où le rossignol chante,
Sur la plus haute branche, une chanson touchante,
Qu'elle se mêle à mes pensers les plus secrets :

Si je courbe le dos sous d'invisibles charges,
Dans l'âcre brouhaha de départs oppressants,
Et si, devant l'obstacle ou le lien, je sens
Le frisson batailleur qui crispait leurs poings larges;

Si d'eux, qui n'ont jamais connu le désespoir,
Qui sont morts en rêvant d'asservir la nature,
Je tiens ce maladif instinct de l'aventure,
Dont je suis quelquefois tout envoûté, le soir;

Par nos ans sans vigueur, je suis comme le hêtre
Dont la sève a tari sans qu'il soit dépouillé,
Et c'est de désirs morts que je suis enfeuillé,
Quand je rêve d'aller comme allait mon ancêtre;

Mais les mots indistincts que profère ma voix
Sont encore : un rosier, une source, un branchage,
Un chêne, un rossignol parmi le clair feuillage,
Et comme au temps de mon aïeul, coureur des bois,

Ma joie ou ma douleur chantent le paysage.

(A l'ombre de l'Orford, 1929)

Alain Grandbois (Né en 1900)

Grand voyageur,
il séjournera longtemps en Europe,
en Afrique et en Extrême-Orient.
Biographe de Louis Jolliet et de
Marco Polo, conteur aussi, il est
communément considéré
comme le poète canadien
qui exerce la plus grande influence
sur la jeune poésie.

Poète de l'amour et de la mort,
son oeuvre, d'un symbolisme nouveau,
a été réunie en un seul volume,
Poèmes (1963).
On y trouve exprimé de cent manières
le regret de ne pouvoir éterniser les
heures de bonheur abolies pour toujours
par le temps qui ne s'arrête jamais.

PARMI LES HEURES...

Parmi les heures mortes et les heures
       présentes
Parmi le jour accompli pareil à demain
Parmi les racines naissantes des lendemains
Parmi les racines défuntes plongeant aux
       mêmes sèves fortes que le pain
       chaud

Parmi ce jour dans le soleil comme une
    chevelure d'or
Ou dans la pluie comme un voile de veuve
    ou vu d'un désert
      ou vu entre les murs d'une rue
      d'hommes
      ou vu seul peut-être le front aux
        mains dans un endroit anonyme

Parmi les détresses neuves et les plus
    vieilles joies
      la foule ou la solitude au choix
      indifférent
Parmi le désir aux dents de loup
Parmi le blême assouvissement dans
    l'éparpillement des membres mous

Parmi toutes les choses possibles de l'instant
    qui ne seront jamais
Parce que nos yeux ne se sont tournés
    ni à droite ni à gauche
Parce que nos mains sont demeurées
    immobiles
Parce que nos pas ne nous ont pas dirigés
    vers les lieux nécessaires

Parce que nos coeurs n'ont pas battu avec
    le rythme exigé
Parmi ce seul geste issu d'un passé mort
Nous guidant vers les routes ne conduisant
    nulle part
Parmi les mille doigts de l'habitude tissant
    en vain les liens invisibles

Parmi les femmes avec des ongles tristes
Et celles avec un sourire rouge
Et les unes portant leur coeur comme une
    bannière
Et les autres lissant leur ventre bombé
Et chacune conservant une larme pour
    chaque détour du chemin

Parmi les hommes joyeux et tièdes ceux
        des nuits obscures et confidentielles
Et ceux que hantent des cathédrales
Et ces dormeurs avec un espoir gisant aux
        carènes des vaisseaux engloutis
Parmi ceux portant le meurtre comme une
        étoile

Et ceux du Chiffre pareils à une horde de
        rats voraces
Parmi ces muets avec une langue de feu
Et parmi ces aveugles chacun dans sa nuit
        creusant son labyrinthe inconnu
Et parmi ces sourds chacun dans son
        feuillage écoutant sa propre musique
Et parmi ces fous qu'une funèbre beauté
        ronge
Et parmi ces sages buvant et mangeant et
        aimant avec aux épaules signes
        identiques

Parmi les hommes tous conservant un geste
        secret pour chaque détour du chemin
Parmi tous et toutes
Dans cette heure implacablement présente
Dans ce jour actuel pareil à demain
Nous tous les hommes seuls ou entourés
Nous tous amis ou ennemis
Nous tous avec la faim ou la soif ou gorgés
        de trésors ridicules
Nous tous avec des coeurs nus comme des
        chambres vides
Dans un même élan fraternel

Parmi ce jour coulant entre les colonnes
        des nuits comme un fleuve clair
Nous lèverons nos bras au-dessus de nos
        têtes
Nous gonflerons nos poitrines avec des
        cris durs
Et nous tournerons nos bras et nos cris
        et nos poitrines vers les points
        cardinaux

Parmi tous et toutes ou seul avec soi-même
Nous lèverons nos bras dans des appels durs
      comme les astres
Cherchant en vain au bout de nos doigts
      crispés
Ce mortel instant d'une fuyante éternité

(Les Iles de la Nuit, 1944)

FERMONS L'ARMOIRE...

Fermons l'armoire aux sortilèges
Il est trop tard pour tous les jeux
Mes mains ne sont plus libres
Et ne peuvent plus viser droit au coeur
Le monde que j'avais créé
Possédait sa propre clarté
Mais de ce soleil
Mes yeux sont aveuglés
Mon univers sera englouti avec moi
Je m'enfoncerai dans les cavernes profondes
La nuit m'habitera et ses pièges tragiques

Les voix d'à côté ne me parviendront plus
Je posséderai la surdité du minéral
Tout sera glacé
Et même mon doute

Je sais qu'il est trop tard
Déjà la colline engloutit le jour
Déjà je marque l'heure de mon fantôme
Mais ces crépuscules dorés je les vois encore
      se penchant sur des douceurs de lilas
Je vois ces adorables voiles nocturnes
      trouées d'étoiles
Je vois ces rivages aux rives inviolées
J'ai trop aimé le regard extraordinairement
      fixe de l'amour pour ne pas regretter
      l'amour
J'ai trop paré mes femmes d'auréoles sans
      rivales
J'ai trop cultivé de trop miraculeux jardins

Mais une fois j'ai vu les trois cyprès parfaits
Devant la blancheur du logis

J'ai vu et je me tais
Et ma détresse est sans égale

Tout cela est trop tard
Fermons l'armoire aux poisons
Et ces lampes qui brûlent dans le vide
    comme des fées mortes
Rien ne remuera plus dans l'ombre
Les nuits n'entraîneront plus les cloches
    du matin
Les mains immaculées ne se lèveront plus
    au seuil de la maison

Mais toi   ô toi   je t'ai pourtant vue
    marcher sur la mer avec ta chevelure
    pleine d'étincelles
Tu marchais toute droite avec ton blanc
    visage levé
Tu marchais avec tout l'horizon comme une
    coupole autour de toi
Tu marchais et tu repoussais lentement la
    prodigieuse frontière des vagues

Avec tes deux mains devant toi comme les
    deux colombes de l'arche
Et tu nous portais au rendez-vous de
    l'archange
Et tu étais pure et triste et belle avec un
    sourire de coeur désemparé

Et les prophètes couchaient leur grand silence
    sur la jalousie des eaux
Et il ne restait plus que le grand calme
    fraternel des sept mers
Comme le plus mortel tombeau

(*Les Iles de la Nuit*, 1944)

Robert Choquette (Né en 1905)

Né à Manchester, N.H., journaliste, bibliothécaire puis auteur de radio-romans, il est aujourd'hui consul général du Canada à Bordeaux après avoir été sous-commissaire de la Commission du Centenaire. Romancier de moeurs, il est surtout connu comme poète. Romantiques de ton et d'inspiration, ses *Oeuvres poétiques* ont été rééditées en 1956. Il est membre de l'Académie canadienne-française. et de l'Académie Ronsard.

VISION DANS LA BRUME

Trois goélands mouillés de brume sont passés ...
De quels cieux venaient-ils, et vers quels paysages
Volaient, en se hâtant, ces fantômes glacés
Dont le brouillard nocturne estompait les visages ?
Fabuleux voyageurs par la brume effacés,
Peut-être qu'ils étaient les âmes vagabondes
De Baudelaire et d'Edgar Poe et de Rimbaud,
Dans un vol fraternel en fuite vers quels mondes,
Quel profond clair de lune au delà du tombeau ? ...

(*Suite marine*, 1953)

LES DUNES

Je t'attendais, amour. Barbare et radieux
Sous ton manteau divin taillé dans une aurore,
Tu devais sur mon coeur frapper d'un poing sonore,
J'allais appartenir à la race des dieux.

Je t'attendais, amour. Et ton sein héroïque
Dont le souffle est égal au grand vent sur la mer
Eût poussé vers mon front son haleine lyrique;
J'allais chanter, chanter de l'âme et de la chair !

Te voilà sur mon seuil. Qu'as-tu fait de tes armes ?
Qu'as-tu fait de ton front plus vaste que le jour ?
Amour, est-ce bien toi qui m'habites, amour ?

Je tremble, je suis humble et tout facile aux larmes,
Et j'ai tout désappris, sinon poser ma main,
Ma faible main devant mon faible coeur humain.

(*Suite marine*, 1953)

François Hertel (Né en 1905)

Jésuite, professeur de lettres, sécularisé, longtemps exilé volontaire en France, il est revenu au Canada en 1966 pour enseigner la littérature française à Queen's University. Membre de l'Académie canadienne-française, il a publié des poèmes, des romans et des essais fort discutés. Ennemi du conformisme il a exercé une grande influence sur les jeunes dans les années 40.

LE CHANT DE L'EXILÉ

Mon malheur est trop grand pour tenir en ce monde,
Il doit gésir quelque part dans une éternité.
Ma damnation est sur place et mon crime est d'être né,
Mais je ne veux pas mourir; j'aime voir le soleil quelquefois
                      [sur la Seine reluire.

Mon coeur est transpercé de glaives infinis.
J'ai perdu tout mon sang sur des routes de feu,
La glace est en moi-même à demeure,
Mon enfer est glacial. Je me meurs congelé.
J'ai tout perdu ce qu'on peut perdre en cette vie
Et j'attends sans hâte et sans joie
Le jour où je coulerai comme un clou
A pic, au fond des mers, un soir, sans aucun bruit.
Je ne sais même plus formuler ma formule
Spéciale de damnation terrestre.
J'ai perdu jusqu'au rythme
Qui me permit jadis de chasser mes épouvantes
En cadence.
Je chante sans chanter, je me livre au hasard.
J'ai fini d'être beau, j'ai fini de crâner.
Je fus presque un poète et presque un philosophe.
Je souffrais de trop de presque.
Je fus presque un homme.
Je suis presque un mort.

A moi les sursauts du cadavre
Et les affres de la pourriture apprise
Au contact des vers de la vie !
Que j'aime ceux des tombeaux,
Comme ils sont propres et nets et luisants,

Comme ils font bien ce qu'ils savent faire,
Tandis que les autres, ceux qu'on appelle hommes et femmes,
Comme ils vous mordent lâchement au talon

Quand d'être trop absent à cette vie trop précise
Ils vous soupçonnent,
Quand ils ont enfin compris que vous aviez un certain don
                                                    [pour l'inutile,
Un certain amour de l'absolu,
Une certaine soif de l'infini,
Ce qu'ils s'acharnent sur vous désemparé et petit
D'avoir tâché d'être grand.
On est frileux toute sa vie et malade,
On est un nourrisson sans mamelle accueillante,
On est un enfant douloureux, abandonné
Sur le Nil de la destinée,
Quand on a cru qu'il fallait jouer le jeu,
Se donner au monde, être bon, croire aux êtres,
Quand on n'a appris, pendant trente années,
Avec application, malgré ses poussées de haine, et ses goûts de
                                                    [mépris,
Qu'on n'a appris qu'à aimer,
Alors on s'est mis à cette tâche d'aimer,
Un peu au hasard, sans discernement.
On a aimé tous ceux qui se sont trouvés sur la route.
On voyait là un devoir, une grande tâche,
Une **grandeur.**
Puis, on se sentait bon : ça faisait chaud au coeur.
On a aimé des enfants qui, devenus des hommes, vous ont renié,
On a aimé des hommes qui, devenus des vieillards, vous ont haï
                         [pour votre jeunesse miraculeusement sauvée.
On a aimé des femmes qui vous ont méprisé parce que vous les
                                   [aviez traitées comme des reines.
On a aimé des vieillards, qui ont eu le temps encore de vous
                         [vomir dans les râles de leur agonie.
Parce que vous persistiez à demeurer jeune odieusement.
On a aimé Dieu avec désespoir, avec horreur, parce qu'aimer
                         [Dieu, c'est renoncer un peu à soi,
Et on a senti un jour Dieu se retirer pour ne jamais revenir
                                                    [peut-être.

On a été humble jusqu'à l'orgueil de s'anéantir,
On a été chaste jusqu'à cesser de se sentir un homme,
On a été pitoyable jusqu'à s'ôter le pain de la bouche pour le
                                        [jeter aux pourceaux,
On a été juste jusqu'à être loyal avec ses ennemis.
On a été un idiot sublime.

Et voici qu'un bon matin on se réveille, porc parmi les porcs,
Et qu'on a cru refoulés en soi,
Avec tous ces instincts luisants comme des fauves léchés,
Déchaînés et dévorants.
On s'était cru béni, on n'était que plus sûrement maudit que
                                        [les autres.
Et ce qu'on a vu surtout, ce sont les regards de joie de tous,
Des enfants, des hommes, des femmes et des vieillards,
De tous ceux qu'on avait aimés,
Pour lesquels on s'était débité
Comme une bûche à brûler dans l'âtre de toutes les bienfaisances,
Et qui sont heureux de se rendre compte qu'un homme
                                        [n'est qu'un homme,
Et qu'ils n'ont pas à rougir plus souvent qu'à leur tour.
Croulons enfin, colonne,
Mur, écroulons-nous.
Cessons d'être l'opprobre de nos frères,
Et de leur faire honte d'avoir été bon.
Devenons ce tigre impardonné,
Soyons le fouet impitoyable emporté par une main sans but
Vers des itinéraires sans pardons.
Claquez donc, fouet de ma vengeance,
Et meurtrissez-moi, haire de ma haine !
Cette humanité tant de fois maudite,
Maudissons-la encore un peu pour la forme
Et pour que Dieu n'ait pas été le seul à se repentir de la
                                        [naissance de l'homme !

(*Mes naufrages,* 1951)

Cécile Chabot (Née en 1907)

Publiciste et scripteur, membre de la Société royale du Canada, elle a publié des contes poétiques et des poèmes. Partie d'un romantisme fervent inspiré par le sentiment de la nature, elle a évolué comme Simone Routier vers le symbolisme religieux.

ON NE M'A JAMAIS DIT

On ne m'a jamais dit, comme à tant d'autres femmes,
Ces mots troublants et chauds qui fascinent les âmes;
On ne m'a pas chanté sur des airs inconnus
Ces poèmes anciens, ces serments convenus,
Aussi furtifs qu'un vent, aussi vieux que le monde.
On n'a pas comparé la nuit triste et profonde
A mes yeux grands ouverts et je n'ai pu savoir
Si le soleil parfois s'en faisait un miroir.
Mes cheveux sont-ils flous sous le feu des lumières ?
Mon teint possède-t-il le rose des bruyères ?
Mon front est-il taillé dans un marbre trop beau ?
Mes sourcils aussi noirs qu'une aile de corbeau ?
Ma bouche est-elle rouge ainsi qu'une cerise ?
Mon nez grec ou latin ? Ai-je un pied de marquise ?
Ai-je le col d'un cygne ? Un velours sur ma main ?
On ne me l'a pas dit. Non, jamais être humain
Pour moi n'a répété ces mensonges habiles
Que l'amour dicte à l'homme et que les coeurs dociles
Se chantent à mi-voix tout en n'y croyant pas.

Aux sauvages qui vont en étouffant leur pas
Se perdre en la forêt âpre et mystérieuse,
Ivres de liberté, de vie aventureuse,
On ne va pas offrir de la soie ou de l'or
Ou confier en paix la garde d'un trésor.
A l'être décevant, au caractère étrange,
A la fois de démon, d'enfant, de femme et d'ange,
A ce coeur indompté, farouche et trop muet
Et qui ne livre pas son intime secret,
Avec des gestes doux et des paroles vaines,
On ne va pas offrir des tendresses humaines.

Et pourtant sans comprendre au seuil de certain jour
Je sens crier en moi le nostalgique amour.

(*Vitrail*, 1940)

F. R. Scott (Born in 1899)

Scott's influence has been great in the presentation of poetry by writers in both of Canada's major languages. His own work — poetry, criticism, articles on literary, legal and political subjects — has been published regularly in Canadian and American periodicals. F. R. Scott was awarded the Lorne Pierce Medal in 1962. *Selected Poems* appeared in 1966

EVE

Adam stood by a sleeping lion
Feeling its fur with his toes.
He did not hear Eve approaching,
Like a shy fawn she crept close.

The stillness deepened. He turned.
She stood there, too solemn for a speech.
He knew that something had happened
Or she never would stay out of reach.

"What is it ? What have you found ?"
He stared as she held out her hand.
The innocent fruit was shining.
The truth burned like a brand.

"It is good to eat," she said,
"And pleasant to the eyes,
And — this is the reason I took it —
It is going to make us wise !"

She was like that, the beauty,
Always simple and strong.
She was leading him into trouble
But he could not say she was wrong.

Anyway, what could he do ?
She'd already eaten it first.
She could not have all the wisdom.
He'd have to eat and be cursed.

So he ate, and their eyes were opened.
In a flash they knew they were nude.
Their ignorant innocence vanished.
Taste began shaping the crude.

This was no Fall, but Creation,
For although the Terrible Voice
Condemned them to sweat and to labour,
They had conquered the power of choice.

Even God was astonished.
"This man is become one of us.
If he eat of the Tree of Life . . . !"
Out they went in a rush.

As the Flaming Sword receded
Eve walked a little ahead.
"If we keep on using this knowledge
I think we'll be back," she said.

(Events and Signals)

Floris MacLaren   (Born in 1904)

Though born in Alaska, Mrs. MacLaren has been regarded as a Canadian. She was associated with Alan Crawley's magazine, *Contemporary Verse,* and has brought out several volumes of her own poetry, the most successful of which was *Frozen Fire* (1937).

NORTHWEST COAST

I

Low in a cloud
The Cannibal God
Is waiting to suck
The traveller's soul
The lonely body
Will die soon
For the god in the cloud
To feast upon.

The Haida knew this for a haunted country
Hearing the spirits crying in the trees
Seeing the ghosts fly seaward

Walked their beaches
Ringed by the supernatural :
Woman-of-the-Woods Animal People
People-under-the-sea
Strong One standing-and-moving-in-the-earthquake
A jealous hierarchy.

Carved their cedar masks
Turned to the shaman
To make a spell
With birdbone whistle and apron of twisted bearclaws
To cure a sickness or kill an enemy's soul.

While the women lay asleep in the grass
The evil mice ran down their throats
The Skaggy must dance for a day and a night
To draw the bad souls out again.

> At the Battle of the Leaves
> The transparent salmon
> Comes up the stream
> To meet the shaman's spear
> The shaman's body
> Turns four times in the whirlpool
> It is his own soul
> Threshing on the spear.

II

Hemlock seedlings grow from the carved faces
On wooden eyeballs where the legend lies
Rotting in moss
Whistling shamans cannot raise a myth
Buried in archives, in old men's graves.

Over the brown artifacts the tide
Dissolves the clamshell midden
The Winter Dancers are gone.
No transparent salmon no white bird
Nor benevolent otter comes
To lead us home.

A. M. Klein (Born in 1909)

One of Canada's most honoured poets, Klein's best known collection is *The Rocking Chair* (1948), which won a Governor-General's award. He was awarded the Lorne Pierce Medal in 1957 for outstanding work in Canadian letters.

GRAIN ELEVATOR

Up from the low-roofed dockyard warehouses
it rises blind and babylonian
like something out of legend. Something seen
in a children's coloured book. Leviathan
swamped on our shore ? The cliffs of some other river ?
The blind ark lost and petrified ? A cave
built to look innocent, by pirates ? Or
some eastern tomb a travelled patron here makes local ?

But even when known, it's more than what it is :
for here, as in a Josephdream, bow down
the sheaves, the grains, the scruples of the sun
garnered for darkness; and Saskatchewan
is rolled like a rug of a thick and golden thread.
O prison of prairies, ship in whose galleys roll
sunshines like so many shaven heads,
waiting the bushel burst out of the beached bastille !

Sometimes it makes me think Arabian,
the grain picked up, like tic-tacs out of time :
first one; another; singly; one by one —
to save life. Sometimes, some other races claim
the twinship of my thought — as the river stirs
restless in a white Caucasian sleep,
or, as in the steerage of the elevators,
the grains, Mongolian and crowded, dream.

A box : cement, hugeness, and rightangles —
merely the sight of it leaning in my eyes
mixes up continents and makes a montage
of inconsequent time and uncontiguous space.
It's because it's bread. It's because
bread is its theme, an absolute. Because
always this great box flowers over us
with all the coloured faces of mankind . . . .

(The Rocking Chair)

A. J. M. Smith (Born in 1902)

Smith, whose *Collected Poems* was published in 1962, is the leading anthologist of Canadian poetry. Internationally known as poet and critic, he was been awarded an LL. D. by Queen's University, and the Lorne Pierce Medal by the Royal Society of Canada. He is Professor of English at Dalhousie University.

FIELD OF LONG GRASS

When she walks in the field of long grass
The delicate little hands of the grass
Lean forward a little to touch her.

Light is like the waving of the long grass.
Light is the faint to and fro of her dress.
Light rests for a while in her bosom.

When it is all gone from her bosom's hollow
And out of the field of long grass,
She walks in the dark by the edge of the fallow land.

Then she begins to walk in my heart.
Then she walks in me, swaying in my veins.

My wrists are a field of long grass
A little wind is kissing.

(A.J.M. Smith Collected Poems)

Robert Finch (Born in 1900)

Finch has won the Governor-General's award for poetry twice, for *Poems* (1946), and *Acis in Oxford* (1960). His most recent volume is *Silverthorn Bush and Other Poems*.

SURVIVORS

Aslant the window and the wind
The almond and the hawthorn sway,
Inside the window from the sill
Blue bell and fuchsia blend the sound
Of fuchsia and of blue blue bell
Against the gusty August day.

There is no weather any more,
They say, the springtime never comes,
The summer cannot smile again,
The world of yore is out of gear,
The stars are turning into rain,
The rain is turning into bombs.

And yet in March the almond sprang
Its rosy discourse on the sky,
All May the hawthorn burned with fire
Where like a thrush the phoenix sang,
And still, outdoors and brave as here,
Blue bell and fuchsia bell swing high.

(Acis in Oxford)

Muriel Millen

A writer who now lives in Victoria, Muriel Millen grew up in Alberta. Her poem is based upon an incident she witnessed while a school teacher in that province.

HAIL

Into the afternoon the hail swept hard,
a cold sheet of white ruin.
It tattered the corn.
It beat the wheat heads down so that they would not again
stand tall in gold-green ripple.
It flailed ripe kernels from the oats.

The farmer watched from an open door.
He stood silent as the depths
of the empty barn behind him, and when
he faced his wife, he neither lifted nor bowed his head.
"The threshers have been and gone without
    even staying for supper,"
Was all he said.

Louis Ginsberg (Born in 1896)

Ginsberg now lives in Paterson, New Jersey, and is widely known in American literary circles. His work has been included in more than ninety anthologies.

AGE-OLD WISDOM

Though newscasters warn us
    We must take heed in
Times that ripen
    Not as in Eden;

Though diplomats' pouches
    Are bulging with headlines,
And jet-planes hurry
    Crises to deadlines,

Lovers and babies
   Come unfraid,
Into a world
   They never made.

Life is ever,
   Since man was born,
Licking honey
   From a thorn.

(The Fiddlehead)

Fred Swayze (1907-1967)

Swayze was with the Ontario Dept. of Education. He has written | textbooks, children's stories, historical juveniles and several books of verse.

THE NORTH WIND DOTH BLOW

Left on a lonely island to die
The old woman does not hear the angry
Slap of driven waves on the stones
Or the moan of the pines torn by the wind
Although she holds the worn blanket
Shawl-like close against the cold
And stares blindly over the grey lake
Her eyes filmed with the milky iridescence
Of great age, blind with the tears of weakness.
After the pain will come resignation.
After the bitterness and crying
Will come the quiet. Old, old
And at last a burden to her people,
Left to die in a hungry year
When the tribe moved to the winter camp.

Hidden in a shabby genteel home
For the aged, a Victorian mansion crumbling
With dry rot on a pseudo-respectable street
Convenient to street car and subway

Reasonable rates five dollars a day
The old ladies stay meekly in their rooms
Reasonably cold, reasonably starved
Apathetic to the dullness and dust
The dirt and the musty smell of weakness.
Out of sight and out of mind, their world
A chair, a bed and a bureau drawer
They sit quietly, decently dying.

The thin bitter wind that rattles
The black branches of the respectable maples
Is all that is left of a northern blast
That swept over forests, mountains and grey lakes
And roared in the pines of lonely islands.

(The Fiddlehead)

Dorothy Livesay (Born in 1909)

Dorothy Livesay's latest book of poems is *The Unquiet Bed*. She has won two Governor-General's awards for poetry.

In 1959 she went to Zambia as an English specialist for Unesco. Now she is writer-in-residence at University of New Brunswick.

ON LOOKING INTO HENRY MOORE

I

Sun, stun me, sustain me
Turn me to stone :
Stone, goad me and gall me
Urge me to run.

When I have found
Passivity in fire
And fire in stone
Female and male
I'll rise alone
Self-extending and self-known.

II

The message of the tree is this :
Aloneness is the only bliss

Self-adoration is not in it
(Narcissus tried, but could not win it)

Rather, to extend the root
Tombwards, be at home with death

But in the upper branches know
A green eternity of fire and snow.

III
The fire in the farthest hills
Is where I'd burn myself to bone :
Clad in the armour of the sun
I'd stand anew, alone.

Take off this flesh, this hasty dress
Prepare my half-self for myself :
One unit, as a tree or stone
Woman in man, and man in womb.

(Selected Poems of Dorothy Livesay)

John Glassco (Born in 1909)

Mr. Glassco has translated several major works from the French, including *The Journal of Saint-Denys-Garneau*. Winner of the Quebec Literary Prize in 1962, his best known books of poems are *The Deficit Made Flesh* and *A Point of Sky*.

THE DEATH OF DON QUIXOTE

I
So this is what it is,
The world of things arrested.
The music in my brain has stopped.
The armies are simply sheep, the giants windmills,
Dulcinea a cow-girl,
Mambrinus' helmet a barber's basin —
And the priest is delighted,
Fussing over me as I lie here
After my marvellous interminable journeys,

Shorn of my armour, extenuated,
Now in my five wits, restored,
Ready to make a good death.
— Rosinante and Dapple are dead too
Where are their bones ?

Are we all as dead as my Amadis
Who slew so many giants, indomitable ?
I who modelled my endeavour. who tried . . .

Yes, this is what it is to be alive,
To die, to cease
To force a folly on the world.

II

The trees beyond this window are blowing green
The long road white in the distance, the sunshine,
There are flowers at my window
What do I know ?

Well, that nothing partakes of reality,
And I too am simply Alonso Quixano the Good,
The wise gentleman, the restored,
Lying in my bed, tended
By my loving people, ready
To make a good death . . .

I appear to have killed myself
By believing in some other God :
Or perhaps it was the drubbings did for me,
The horseplay, the jokes
Wore out my silly casing of flesh.
In any event, as I lie here,
The withdrawal of the vision,
The removal of the madness,
The supplanting of a world of beauty
By God's sticks and stones and smells
Are afflictions, I find, of something more absurd
Than any book of chivalry.

III

O my God
I have lost everything
In the calm of my sanity

Like a tree that regards itself
In still water
Seeing only another tree,
Not as when the crazy winds of heaven blew
Turning it to a perpetual fountain
Of shaken leaves,
The image of an endless waltz of being,
A thing so close to my heart I was always asking
Why should we not dance so for ever, be always
Trees tossed against the sky ?
Why are we men at all if not to defy
This painted quietude of God's world ?

Well, everything must have an end.
I have had my day
I have come home
I see things as they are.
My ingenious creator has abandoned me
With the insouciance of a nobleman
The fickleness of an author
The phlegm of an alguazil —

Only Sancho is faithful unto death
But in his eyes I discern the terrible dismay
For he sees that mine are at last a mirror of his own.

(A Point of Sky)

Anne Wilkinson (1910-1961)

One of the founding editors of *The Tamarack Review*, Mrs. Wilkinson's two books of poems are *Counterpoint to Sleep* (1951), and *The Hangman Ties the Holly* (1955). Her collected poems have been edited by A.J.M. Smith.

NOEL

She sought a blessing in the snow,
Cool of pity clean,
In rose, and in a bed of straw
Where the lamb had lain.

She hunted God by the light of the moon,
She wore a hedge for shirt;
The holy river ran off with her sin,
And she ate a leper's dirt.

But leper died, and the hedge was torn,
And homeward ran her sin.
Frost and thorn, and mice in the barn,
And God in a tiger skin.

A bright star led to a palace of gin
Where all the queens were tarts,
And kings were toads, and crowned each queen
With coronet of warts.

The barman there was quick to tell —
You'll here ? no grace discover,
For toad and tart embrace one hell,
The heaven in each other.

She entered, and she saw instead,
Rose cuddle with the toad,
And lamb and tart in a bed of straw
Asleep beneath the snow.

(Pan. No. 2)

Don W. Thomson (Born in 1906)

A writer for the Department of Mines and Technical Surveys, | Thomson is the author of *Men and Meridians,* as well as a book of verse.

PERSONAL INCOME TAX
(With apologies to Abe Lincoln)

Two score and several years ago
our fathers brought forth
within this nation
a new tax,

conceived in desperation
and dedicated to the proposition
that all men,
though created equal,
gradually grow to earn
incomes that are unequal.
Now all are engaged
in a great mass of computations
testing whether this taxpayer
or any taxpayer,
so beset and so impoverished,
can long endure.

Our creditors will little note
nor long remember
what we pay now.
But National Revenue,
Income Tax Division,
can never forget
what we report now.

It is not for us,
the taxpayers,
to question the heavy tax
which thus far
has been so boldly spent.
It is for us, the victims
rather, to be here dedicated
to the few bucks remaining
that from our disappearing funds
we take increased devotion
to the great task before us —
so that this tax,
imposed by Parliament
upon the people
for the government,
shall not cause
our few dependents
through sheer hunger
to perish from the earth.

Wilfred Watson (Born in 1911)

Watson was born in England but has spent most of his life in British Columbia and Alberta. A playwright and poet, his *Friday's Child* won the Governor-General's award in 1955 and the Arts Council of Britain award.

GRAVEYARD ON A CLIFF OF WHITE SAND

By the unwashed beach
Of the falling lake
There were three dead fish
Collapsed in the belly;
And they were the walk
Of ant and fly
Who walked out of the cast and throw
Of the mouldy wreath
When the gravedigger
Hurried in the yellow
Blow of the aspen leaf
And the tear shrank
Into the mourner's eye

O mother grieving
The grief that is common and human
O woman wonderful
In your small miracle
Of faith and loving —
Quiet you, that another miracle
Must come and the wind blow
Into the troubles of the sky
The dust you place
On the upraised hand
Of this high cliff — quiet you
That fence of rust
Cannot keep, that ring
Of cement cannot contain
When the gravedigger
Spends his pay
And the wreaths moulder away

O love this world
If you can
Where juniper

Burns blue its cones
Of seed and the whispering
Weed candles and the moth
Reshapes its figure
And the owl
Owls it in the gully
And the hawk
Hawks it and the cougar
Pads out love's melancholy
This world, where
The bones shrink into
The grave and the cliff
Whitens with birth
And the dead wave
Is pierced by the living
Reed, and love weeps
To fill the earth

(Friday's Child)

Irving Layton (Born in 1912)

Layton's strong opinions, the frankness of his language and of his attitude to sex, have made him the most controversial of Canadian poets. Well known are *A Red Carpet for the Sun* and *The Swinging Flesh*. His *Collected Poems* appeared in 1965.

SONG FOR NAOMI

Who is that in the tall grasses singing
By herself, near the water?
I can see her
But can it be her
Than whom the grasses so tall
Are taller,
My daughter,
My lovely daughter?

Who is that in the tall grasses running
Beside her, near the water?

She can not see there
Time that pursued her
In the deep grasses so fast
And faster
And caught her,
My foolish daughter.

What is the wind in the fair grasses saying
Like a verse, near the water ?
Saviours that over
All things have power
Make Time himself grow kind
And kinder
That sought her
My little daughter.

Who is that in the close of the summer
Near the deep lake ? Who wrought her
Comely and slender ?
Time but attends and befriends her
Than whom the grasses though tall
Are not taller,
My daughter,
My gentle daughter.

(Collected Poems of Irving Layton)

Ralph Gustafson (Born in 1909)

Gustafson is well regarded as poet, critic and anthologist. Editor of *The Penguin Book of Canadian Verse,* his own work is found in *Rivers* *Among Rocks, Rocky Mountain Poems,* and most recently *Sift in an Hourglass.*

IN THE YUKON

In Europe, you can't move without going down into history.
Here, all is a beginning. I saw a salmon jump,
Again and again, against the current,
The timbered hills a background, wooded green

Unpushed through; the salmon jumped, silver.
This was news, was commerce, at the end of the summer
The leap for dying. Moose came down to the water edge
To drink and the salmon turned silver arcs.
At night, the northern lights played, great over country
Without tapestry and coronations, kings crowned
With weights of gold. They were green,
Green hangings and great grandeur, over the north
Going to what no man can hold hard in mind,
The dredge of that gravity, being without experience.

(Rocky Mountain Poems)

THE FIRST ARMISTICE

Violet Lang

This poem, which appeared in the *Canadian Forum* in 1946, will be best appreciated by those of us old enough to recall the grief and disillusionment that sobered the nation after the victory hysteria had died away. Nothing is known of the author.

We said to each other, standing at the sidelines,
Muffled by the crowds where the flags went past us
Asymmetrically riotous, colours gaily clashing
While people cheered and excited small children
Dodged policemen, spectacularly dashing
Through soldiers breaking file :
Let there be no more of this, no marching, no colours,
No grandeur, nobility, no more applauding.
Let the men be dirty, no music playing;
Let the women cry with no one to hear them;
Let them think about the crying. Let there be
No noise at all. Only dying.
Only then will war stop.

But the child said : it was like this,
The music very loud and the people running after,
Everybody happy and cheering in the sun,
The band in many colours and so loud, so loud

That the music bursts inside you with the drum
In your stomach and the tuba in your feet
The horns in your ears, the beating in your head
And the flag, the flag at the head of it all,
And the wonder of it all, the terrible wonder
Of the flying thing and the people cheering
Till you wanted to cry; and you burst out crying
With your mouth wide open and your face all over
With tears and dirt on your hands
Till you mother had to take you away.

The years will go by, weeping in brass buttons
Held shining to a large, unearthly light. Children
Grow slowly, their faces backward-looking,
Debating the good of it, remembering might
When men were noble and men died grandly,
Died proudly with eyes turned sightless to light
While bands played, women wept. This was their reward.
Child, small child, let there be misery,
Dirt and bleeding reflected in your eyes.
You in the march past, running so proudly,
Are reading lies.

Ralph Allen (1913-1966)

Managing Editor of the *Toronto Star* at the time of his death, Allen had been a correspondent during World War II. This piece is from his wartime novel, *Home Made Banners,* and the theme is suggested by the way in which men were often forced to "volunteer" for service overseas.

HUT SCENE

Mike put one hand on the hut floor and pivoted his body halfway out of bed into the slab of light from the washroom door, holding his head and his free hand close together in the light. His wrist watch said a quarter to one. He swung his head back to the bunk and half sat up, searching the other bunks in the semiopaque gloom.

They were all there. That was Sumner on the third bed down, across the room. And Drayton two more beds away. He could hear Forsee breathing in the bunk above and see the light bulge of his body through the mattress. They didn't even have guts enough to go loose. They were just lying there, pretending to be asleep and listening to the minutes drag by.

Maybe they knew going loose would be no use either. Maybe they knew they could either take it or give up, and there was no third alternative. They knew how far Miczawicz got. Miczawicz knew his rights. He went running to the major, with his black eye and his two loose teeth, and the major threw him out. And Miczawicz walked back into the cubicle and said: "All right, I'll go active." Barton, Judson, Crowther and Denman — they knew when they were licked too ... *"Eight little zombies, scared as they could be. One got his kisser smacked, then there were three"* ... That Lister was a riot.

Three more. If they'd go active, the whole platoon would get leave.

It would be worse tonight. Last night the corporal was in, and they had to be quiet enough that the corporal could pretend he didn't hear. But the corporal wouldn't be in at all tonight. He'd made a point of telling them. There was no bed check and no roll call tonight. The sentry was still on the gate, but they all knew the way over the fence anyway. They should be coming any time. And they'd be drunk tonight. Some of them anyway. That was the idea. That was what the corporal meant. Or the lieutenant, or the sergeant. Or the major. All of them, probably. They'd played it the same way right from the first day, now that you looked back.

Mike wanted to say something to Forsee, but what could he say?

He could at least ask Forsee for a match, and perhaps asking him for a match would tell Forsee something that he could not tell him in any other way. It might tell him, at least, that the matter which was about to begin would not really be a matter of personalities, however much it must seem to be. It might tell him that the matter had been ordained by forces far beyond the control of anyone in the hut, and that it would be as ridiculous to take it as a personal matter as to take the war itself as personal.

He lifted his body with one elbow and slapped his free hand softly against the mattress above his head. "You got a light, Forsee?" he said.

The clothing hanging behind the bed rustled, and a grey arm sheathed in a woollen undershirt reached down over the sill.

"Thanks."

"If you're short of cigarettes, you'll find some in my half of the kit box," Forsee said.

Mike stopped in the act of striking a match ... They were coming now ...

Their feet were scuffling in the frozen gravel outside the hut. The door creaked open and their boots rang hollowly through the vestibule. They wouldn't all come together. Three or four, or half a dozen at a time.

"Not so much noise !" the voice at the end of the room was thick.

It was answered by a high giggle, and then two tearful voices were singing low from the black corner bunk beside the vestibule :

"If I had my way, dear,

You'd never grow old —

A garden —"

A shadow lurched down the hut. The washroom doors shuttered back on the sudden flare of light. The bed creaked thinly, and Mike felt Forsee's body relax against the upper bunk.

A babel of noisy whispers broke out at the far end of the hut, and a bottle rang a hollow High C against the iron rail of a bedstead. The whispering stopped. A swaying file of shadows moved down the hut through the slab of light from the washroom door, past the glowing stove, and merged in an uncertain knot near the middle of the corridor between the beds. Mike swung his legs to the floor and padded on his bare feet to the fringe of the knot. He recognized the bulky form of Lister at its center.

The knot dissolved away from him and he followed it. A bed creaked heavily in the darkness ahead. Mike looked down at the bed. There were three men sitting on each side of it, hunched together in the darkness like merging black mounds. The covers between them stirred blackly and then were still.

A glaring beam of light stabbed through the darkness, played whitely on the white corner and pillow for a moment and then moved across the pillow and focused on a face. The eyes in the dark were a single clash of copper, like the eyes of a cat caught in headlights at night. The face was pale and flabby.

"Shut up, Sumner !" The words shivered roughly through the silence.

"Shut up, Davis ! I'll handle this." Mike could make out Lister's heavy features now, thrust close behind a flashlight, close to the white face of Sumner on the pillow.

"It's me, Lew. Al Lister."

"Hello, Al." Sumner's eyes were closed tight now against the light. His voice tried to duplicate the casual warmth of the other. It failed; it sounded scared.

"Good old Lew." Lister leaned forward with a torch. His own body and the other bodies on the bed pressed hard against each other, wedging tightly into the shapeless contours of the blankets. Lister's free hand reached down and patted the right cheek of the face on the pillow. And then, lightly but sharply, it slapped each check three times. There was no sound of protest.

"Want a drink, Lew ?"

"No, thanks, Al."

"Sure he does. Give him a drink. Who's got the jug of goof ?"

Another hand thrust the neck of a bottle into the beam of the torch. It glinted purple in the light as it probed for the lips of the man imprisoned under the blankets, and the wine spilled over the lips and rolled down Sumner's flabby chin in a red smear. Sumner tried to rub it off with his shoulder, but the six men holding him in the vise of their bodies leared forward again, pinioning him closer than before. Lister curled a loose fringe of blanket into this free hand and swabbed the chin dry with delicate, oversolicitous stabs.

"All right, Lew ?"

"All right, Al."

"That's not the first drink we've had, Al." Lister turned his head away from Sumner, but still held the flashlight close to Sumner's face. "Me and Lew used to kick around a lot when we first come here," he said. "Me and Lew are pals. Ain't we, Lew ?"

Sumner didn't answer.

"Ain't we, Lew ?"

"Ain't we what ?" For the first time Sumner spoke with a hint of spirit.

"Pals."

"Sure."

"Sure what, Lew ?"

"Pals."

"Pals, who ?"

"What do you mean, Al ?" Sumner no longer spoke with spirit.

"That's what I mean. Al. Al. Just Al. You remember my name, Lew. You just said it. It's Al. Tell them what we are, Lew. Tell the boys right."

"We're pals, Al."

Lister patted one of the cheeks and then slapped both cheeks again, three times on each side, as he had done before.

"Well, Lew," Lister said, "I guess you know what the boys have been saying." He moved the flashlight closer, so close it was almost touching Sumner's nose. "The boys have been saying you're yellow, Lew," Lister said. "That hurt. The boys say you're not only yellow, but you don't wanta play ball with the rest of us. The boys say you don't care if we get our leave tomorrow or not. The boys say you'd do us out of it.

"I don't like that kind of talk, Lew," Lister went on. "And that's not all, Lew. The boys were real mad at you. They wanted to toss your stuff outside in the snow. And then they wanted to throw you in the shower. I said, 'You can't do that, fellahs. You can't throw a man in the showers at this time of night. It's too cold. The water's just like ice. You can't do that to my pal Lew.' That's what I said to the boys, Lew."

Lister said : "And that's not all, Lew. The boys said if that wasn't enough, they'd get rough. Real rough, Lew. I said they couldn't do that either. I said it was all right to have a little fun between friends, but rough stuff don't go. I said it was all right to do like this."

Lister's foot scraped against the floor as he bent his body forward on the bed. He removed the flashlight a little way from Sumner's face and drew his free hand back to the level of his shoulder and then slapped Sumner hard across the mouth, twenty times or more. Each slap made its own sick crash.

"That's all right, Lew," Lister said when he was done. "That's between pals. I told the boys you wouldn't mind that."

The man pinioned in the bed tried to twist his face toward the pillow. His tongue ferreted across his swollen lips but there was no moisture on it.

"I told the boys you'd go active in a minute, Lew," Lister said. "I told the boys if we'd put it up to you man to man there wouldn't be any argument. And there wouldn't either. Would there, Lew ?"

Sumner tried to open his eyes, but the harsh light from the torch ground them shut again.

"Would there, Lew ?"

Lister waited for a minute. They all waited. Their waiting ceased to be an abstract thing. It was physical and it possessed the whole room; you could hear it and you could smell it. The six soldiers sitting on the bed leaned forward to look at Sumner's face, and the

springs of the bed drew together under their shifting weight with a con-
stricted, half-throttled twang. The sound was like an unfinished sigh.
A man standing behind the bed coughed primly. The only breathing
that could be heard was Sumner's; it was heavy but even, like the
breathing of a man taking ether. The unheard breathing of the others
soaked and deadened the air with the stale sick fumes of cheap wine.
The men were sweating, and the sweet musty smell of their sweat
mingled with the smell of the wine, drenching the room with the heavy
odour of climax.

Under the flashlight Sumner's loose face was relaxed and bland,
like a weathered marble statue seen by moonlight. The harsh light
cleansed his face of all line and expression. He had ceased screwing
his eyebrows toward the little jowls of fat beneath his eyes to shut
out the glare of the torch, and his closed eyelids were smooth and
round. You could not have told by any of the conventional yardsticks
whether he was afraid or not, and yet every inch of his face spoke of
fear. If you could hear the waiting in his breathing and smell the
waiting in the air, you could see it still more clearly in Sumner's face.

"Lew!" Lister said at last, "The boys are tired of waiting."

"All right," Sumner said lifelessly. "All right. I'll do it. I'll
go."

The torch snapped out and the room was black again. There was
a congestion of bumping shadows and the smothered ring of clothed
bodies lurching against metal bed frames.

A new voice said: "How do we know he'll go through with it?
How do we know he won't double-cross us?"

"He won't. Because if he double-crosses us, we don't get our
leave. And we'll all be here together for three more nice long days."

Drayton was sitting erect in his upper bunk, waiting for them.
When Lister sprayed the torch on him, he looked for all the world like
a juvenile and highly Nordic Gandhi, sitting cross-legged under his
blankets with his absurdly large issue undershirt billowing away from
his skinny neck to lose his skinny chest under its glazed white folds,
and his shortsighted eyes blinking nakedly in the bleached sacs of flesh
that had been pinched out under them by a lifetime of wearing glasses.

"Go ahead," Drayton said, shrilling out the words in a fractured
parody of resolution and defiance. "Do whatever you want. It doesn't
matter what you do. I still won't."

"All right," Lister commanded, "let's have a look at his stuff."

Drayton watched unmoving while they emptied his kit bags on the
floor, swept the clothing behind the bed into a bundle and rolled it into

a pile on the floor with their feet, and methodically dumped the contents of his brushes box into a smaller pile beside the bed.

Davis rummaged through the debris but found nothing that seemed of interest. Dubiously, he held a white envelope up to the beam of the flashlight.

"Let's have that," Lister said.

"Give it back!" Drayton said fiercely. "You can't take that." He squirmed free of the blankets and made a grab at the letter across the edge of the bed, but another man threw him back on the bed and three others ringed themselves around him, pinning his skinny body against the mattress with their arms. Drayton kicked for a while and then lay still, panting malevolently.

"*Dear Ernest,*" Lister read. And then he repeated prissily: *"Dear Ernest."*

The others chorused: "Dear Ernest."

"We received your letters 64 and 65 today. It hardly seems like 65 days, even though we have seen you since, but in some ways it seems longer."

A high sniggering voice interrupted, with mock approbation: "Ernest writes every day!"

"I am glad you are not finding the life too hard," Lister read, *"or at least that you think you are not finding it too hard. But you were always inclined to take things too robustly."*

Another interruption: "Just look at that robust ole hunk of man!"

"Lister!" Drayton panted desperately, "Stop! Please stop, Lister!"

"I am sending another bottle of milk of magnesia along with the cod-liver oil, the cake and the woollen scarf. I know it will do you good, and if the other boys tease you about taking it, all I have to say is they ought to be ashamed of themselves."

A sharp smack interrupted Lister again as one man hidden in the darkness slapped another's wrist and squealed: "There! That will teach you not to tease Ernest again."

Drayton was crying. "For God's sake, Lister, don't. Please, Lister. It's from my mother."

"I think it's wonderful about you passing all your T.O.E.T.'s. They sound terribly hard and complicated. How did the other boys make out with them? I'll bet not many of them finished ahead of you."

"Ernest finished ahead of everybody," a man behind Lister said triumphantly. "That is, if you read from the bottom up."

"It's nice that you get on with the other boys so well," Lister read. *"I know that somewhere deep down in your secret self you have always considered yourself a little bit backward, especially in sports. But there are other things besides sports, and I'm sure that when the other boys get to know you better you'll be still more popular with them."*

"Boy, is Ernest popular!" the man behind Lister said. "We're going to make him Queen of the May."

"Jesus!" Drayton was crying softly and hopelessly. "Oh, Jesus!"

"Your last letter worried me just a little," Lister read. *"Now I know most of the other boys are going overseas, Ernest, and I can understand why you want to go with them. I don't want to hold you to your promise against your will, but I know it's for the best. You're not as strong as the others. I shudder to think what might happen if you got over to England, all that damp, and eating that terrible food; not to mention the other things."*

"Ernest might get hurted, Ernest might get hurted," the man behind Lister chanted.

"There are plently of important jobs to be done right here in Canada," Lister read, *"and goodness knows, if everybody was needed over there we'd have had conscription long ago."*

The man behind Lister beat time with his hand on the bed and uttered a nasal, "Ta-ra-ra-ra-ra-ra-ra," aping the playing of a fanfare by a band.

Lister read on : *"Dr. Purvis was out today with a specialist from Toronto to see your father. The pain has become worse in the last few days, and I think your father knows now too, although he will give no hint of it. It is no worse and no better than Dr. Purvis feared. At the most your father still has six months left. We must still try to pretend —"*

Lister's voice died away emptily. The man behind him tittered nervously but afterward, for a while, nothing could be heard but the naked sobbing of the boy on the bed. Lister's hand dropped to his side and the letter slipped out of his fingers to the floor. You could not see his face, but a pale hint of light reflected back on it from the wall, from the flashlight, and it was enough to show the sudden sagging droop of his mouth, a dead sag and yet as live as pain. The light was not enough to show his eyes, but it was enough to show the shamed narrowing at their corners; his whole face was a silhouette of shame. The light could not have been crueller to Lister if it had been turned away from the wall and focused full on him.

"Let go of him," Lister said.

The men standing beside the bed obeyed, and Lister said to Drayton : "We'll leave you alone now. You don't have to go active."

Drayton's sobbing had stopped. He sat up in the bed again and held his arm over his face like a garment thrown across his unclothed hurt.

Drayton said : "It's too late. I want to do it now."

Lister said doggedly : "No. Forget it. It doesn't matter."

"I'm going to," Drayton said. "Whether anybody wants me to or not. I thought nobody could make me, and now nobody can stop me."

"No," Lister said, "forget it."

"It's no use telling you what you've done," Drayton said. "You wouldn't understand. But you've done what you set out to do. I'm going active. We don't have to talk about it any more."

Lister turned and shuffled stupidly away from the bed, into the dark aisle of the hut. The others followed him. They knew he would not stop at Forsee's bed now, and the wish to stop there had drained out of them as it had drained out of Lister. But two of them, Davis and another, paused uncertainly.

"There's only Forsee left," Davis whispered. "It's all wasted if we let him go."

Forsee heard them, and they heard Forsee drawing his body in on the bed, and the uneasy dregs of ferment that were left in them by the dispersing mob began to stir again. Davis and the other man moved close to the bed and two more men came up and stood beside them.

Mike found himself still on the outskirts of these uncertain figures, standing barefooted in the middle of the floor, almost exactly where he had been when he first stopped beside Sumner's bed. For the first time he felt thoughts taking shape in his head again. He wondered what had rooted him like this so long, rooted not only his body but the workings of his mind, and more acutely still, he wondered what he would really have thought of the things he had heard and seen if his mind had been less deadened by them. The answer would not come, but he found a part of it. This was the way he had felt, one night years before, when he left a stag party with some other men and went to a house where they featured something called an "Exhibition." The mechanical, a-thousand-times-rehearsed eroticism of the exhibition had left him horrified and physically sick. Yet, while the grisly burlesque was on, he had been unable to tear his eyes away from it. He had sat through it all, fascinated and sick, and then gone outside and vomited.

This night was much the same. Standing barefooted in the middle of the floor, he wondered abstractly, without putting his wonder in words, whether there was such a thing as having carnal knowledge of a man's soul. He wondered if it was less right that men should look with too much detail at women's bodies than that they should look with too much detail at the hearts of men. The shame and revulsion of the night struck and engulfed him in one swift overpowering wave; his body trembled with it.

For the first time since the others had come into the hut, he spoke aloud. His voice was tired, but it rang out loudly through the black room.

"That's enough!" Mike said.

He walked back to his bed and shoved his way through the gathering knot of men to the top of the bed. He felt in the darkness for Forsee's shoulder, and when he found it, he sank his fingers into it and dragged it up from the pillow until Forsee's face was close to his.

"We've all had enough, Forsee," he said. "We're not going to have any more arguments and we're not going to have any more trouble. You're the only R man left in this whole hut and you're going active in the morning. There's no use talking about it, Forsee. That's what you're going to do."

Forsee's body tautened and tried to pull away from him. But Forsee said: "You don't have to do anything. I'm going active. I was going anyway.

The platoon went on leave at noon. In the officers' mess, the colonel stood the company commander a double whisky, and the company commander stood the platoon commander a beer. A few days later a tiny set of fresh statistics passed across a chain of desks at Ottawa, and the owners of the desks observed that the recruiting policy was continuing to work very well.

(Home Made Banners)

Donald Pearce (Born in 1915)

An infantry platoon commander in World War II, Pearce ignored army regulations by keeping a day by day account of his battle experiences. After V E Day he burned most of his journal. Some 18 years later however, at the insistence of his son, he collected the remainder and it eventually became a very successful book.

TO MY SON, WHEN HE IS OLD ENOUGH TO WONDER

March 4, 1945. When will it all end? The idiocy and the tension, the dying of young men, the destruction of homes, of cities, starvation, exhaustion, disease, children parentless and lost, cages full of shivering, starving prisoners, long lines of hopeless civilians plodding through mud, the endless pounding of the battle line. I can scarcely remember what it is like to be where explosions are not going off around me, some hostile, some friendly, all horrible; an exploding shell is a terrible sound. What keeps this war going, now that its end is so clear? What do the Germans think of us, and we of them? I do not think we think of them at all, or much. Do they think of us? I can think of their weapons, their shells, their machine guns, but not of the men behind them. I do not feel as if I were fighting against men, but against machines.

There are times when I feel that every bit of fighting is defensive. Self-defense. If a machine-gun nest is attacked and wiped out by us. by my own platoon, I do not feel very aggressive, as if I had attacked somebody. It is always that I have defended myself against something that was attacking me. Will there come a time when hundreds of miles separate the warring fronts? When long-range weapons and the ghastly impersonality of air attacks are the means of war? It is already a very impersonal thing. When a soldier is killed or wounded, his buddies, shaking their heads, merely say, "Poor old Joe. He got it. Just as he was going up that hill, he got it." As if to imply that he was merely in the wrong place at the wrong time, and that life and death are only matters of luck and do not depend on the calculations of human beings at the other end of a self-propelled gun. When we were in our static positions around Wyler Meer and Nijmegen, the enemy became real to me for the first time. I watched him for weeks, saw him dig, run, hide, fire, walk. And when I went on patrols into his territory, there was meaning in that, too, for I knew where he was. I knew his habits. So that while we were probing the cuticle of the enemy, so to speak, he was real; but now when we are ripping into his body, he has disappeared and has turned into something read about in the papers. But the guns remain, manned by soldiers who are so meaningless to us that when they shoot a fellow, all we can say is, "He got it."

Once I used to get quite a thrill out of seeing a city destroyed and left an ash heap from end to end. It gave me a vicarious sense of power. I felt the romantic and histrionic emotion produced by seeing "retribution" done; and an esthetic emotion produced by beholding ruins; and the childish emotion that comes from destroying man-made things. But it is not that way any more. All I experience is revulsion. Dozen upon dozens of gun crews stationed some two or three miles away from the city simply place shell after shell into hundreds of guns and fire away for a few hours — the simplest and most elementary physical and mental work — and then presently the firing stops, the city has been demolished, has become an ash heap, and great praise is bestowed on the army for the capture.

I am not suggesting that cities shouldn't be captured in this way; actually it saves lives. But it fills me with disgust because it is all so abysmally foolish, so lunatic. Perhaps everyone should be required to spend a couple of hours examining a single smashed home, looking at the fragmentation of every little thing, especially the tiniest things, from kitchen to attic, if he could find an attic; be required, in fact, to list the ruined contents of just one home; something would be served, a little sobriety perhaps honoured.

It is disgusting (that it should be necessary, is what galls me to the bones) that a towering cathedral, built by ages of care and effort, a sweet labour of centuries, should be shot down by laughing artillerymen, mere boys, because somebody with a machine gun is hiding in a belfry tower.

A job has been done on Europe, on the world, and the resulting trauma will be generations long in its effects. It is not just the shock of widespread destruction, of whole cities destroyed, nor the shock which the defeated and the homeless must have suffered, that I am thinking of : it is even more the conqueror's trauma, the habit of violence, the explosion of values, the distortion of relations, the ascending significance of the purely material, the sense of power, and the pride of the two I am not sure that a crass superiority complex is the more quite as long a time as the other things will afflict the victims; and of the two I am not sure that a crass superiority complex is the more desirable. Perhaps I underestimate our ability to return to normal again.

(Front Line Letters to My Son)

Gregory Clark (Born in 1891)

Clark is known to millions of Canadians for his Packsack pieces and stories in *Weekend,* of which he is an associate editor. Author of *Gregory Clark War Stories,* which won him the Leacock Medal, he was decorated for heroism in World War I, and in the second war was Canada's first correspondent in the field.

LA MER

It was several days after the Americans captured Cherbourg that I was able to find anybody on the Canadian front, down in front of Caen, who could think up any excuse for getting a jeep and going north to see the famous port.

And then some RCAF pilots of my acquaintance learned that there were lobsters to be had at Cherbourg.

That, of course, is ample excuse for pilots aged nineteen to twenty-four, flying Spit Nines and Mustangs; so they came to *me* to invite me to come along.

"Pop," they said, for I was in my fifties, "how would you like to run up to Cherbourg with us ?"

"Why, gentlemen !" I exclaimed, as if I hadn't been hinting around about Cherbourg for days.

They figured there might be less difficulty with British and American control posts along the highways north if, in a jeepload of young pilots, they had an old, white-sideburned war correspondent in the front seat who looked, at first glance, to be somebody of importance, if not a bishop in the Chaplain Service.

So away we went, through the incredible sand hummocks and lumps of nothing that had been Saint-Lô, on up through the almost undamaged peninsula, showing us how the Americans fight : smashing one place to stupendous ruin, and then galloping like the wind through mile upon mile, with hardly a shot fired at the bewildered and fleeing enemy.

And we found Cherbourg silent in the sunlight, still dazed by the liberation; all its mighty port facilities, its derricks and cranes and wonderful piers wrecked and ruined by the furious Germans who, up until a couple of weeks before, had imagined themselves to be the masters of the whole world whose hour of destiny, like a Wagner prelude, had sounded.

We parked our jeep in the square. Puzzled American military police smiled us welcome and waved us on to the town.

The square, the streets, were deserted. From windows, eager, cautious faces peered out at us.

My young comrades, lobsters in mind, figured that a tavern would be the likeliest place to find out about lobsters.

We had not far to go. Up the empty main street out of the square we walked only a little way until we heard the sound of music. As we proceeded, the sound turned out to be stentorian singing. And as we neared the source of the music, we realized that it was not only men, many men, but women, singing.

We descended the stairs into a cellar tavern.

There must have been three hundred men and women jammed into that big smoky room.

And from a radio turned on full blast, from a broadcasting station belonging somewhere to the Free French Underground, Charles Trenet, the famous French singer, was singing "La Mer," a song he had himself composed — "The Sea."

And with him, tears pouring down their faces, their arms around one another's shoulders, embracing, sobbing, the whole quivering assemblage was singing in a kind of agony of joy.

Taverns, of course, were out of bounds to the Americans. But when I explained to the protester in the din that we were Canadians, we were uproariously welcomed, and even through the splendor of "La Mer" as Trenet recorded it, the word spread that Canadians were in the room.

Ah, well, it was a fine hilarious lobster hunt. A man of my own age, in sailor's toque and blue-and-white striped jersey, took possession of me, and after about an hour, when my comrades went in quest of lobsters with a dozen young sailors as escort, he took me to see the town. We visited the docks, quays, crushed port facilities. We called at several houses so that I might be introduced to friends of his.

In one small street, a knot of people was gathered outside a cottage, idly waiting at the closed door and apparently trying to see in the windows.

My old sailor explained, quietly, as we passed, that a girl who lived in the cottage had been a sweetheart of a German soldier of the recent garrison. And, the day of liberation, a posse of Cherbourgers had cut off her hair. She was inside, with her parents.

Of course, as a war correspondent, I had already heard of several instances of this mob action against those who were called "collaborators."

To this day I have never been able to figure out whether it was sheer curiosity on my part, or perhaps journalistic inquiry, or perhaps, above all, Trenet's "La Mer" ringing in my ears (for it is still my favourite of all small songs); but I turned to my old sailor and said:

"Do you think I could see her?"

We went into a neighbouring house. A woman of that house went around the back of the houses, by the walls.

And in a few minutes, I was ushered secretly, by the back way, to the door of the besieged cottage.

A pallid, grey man, moving slowly as if in deep shock, took my hand when the sailor introduced me.

He listened as my old sailor explained that I was a chaplain. You see, my appearance suggested this even to tavern acquaintances!

The man, still holding my hand, led me along the small dark hall, with its florid purple wallpaper. Softly he opened a door and nodded me in to the little darkened room.

On the bed lay what I thought at first was a child, the blankets pulled up to her chin.

Her head was small, round, white, like the head of a china doll that has lost its wig.

Her eyes were closed.

Of all the things I have seen in my life, this is the one I am sorriest I saw.

The round small naked head, the ears so grotesquely bared, the large shadowed eye sockets, the mouth composed, like a tiny figurine of utter despair.

My sailor in the hall coughed briefly.

The girl opened her eyes. She stared blankly at me.

Then slowly, like curtains falling at the end of a tragic play, her eyes closed.

We backed out. I hurried to rejoin my young comrades at the jeep in the square. They had lobsters. I hummed "La Mer" all the way home to the Canadian front so as to remember it, never to forget it.

Man! That was fourteen years ago!

Last week, A.G. Green came home from a holiday in England. He came back on a French boat.

"Hey," he said to me on the phone, "I met a friend of yours on the boat."

"Oh ?"

"My cabin steward," he said. "A little chunky old guy, who had been a sailor. He told me how he had met a middle-aged Canadian war correspondent right after Cherbourg was liberated . . ."

"Oh, no !" I cried.

"He told me about taking you around the town . . ."

"About the girl ?"

"Yes. When he described you, and I said I knew you, he asked me to be sure and tell you what happened to the girl.' '

"Go ahead ! Go ahead !"

I could hear "La Mer" starting to orchestrate in my head.

"The German boy came back and married her. They went away. Her hair had all grown back in, beautiful."

Do you know what I said ?

"God, I thank You."

That is what I said.

War is so small, so sad, so inexcusable.

Blair Fraser (Born in 1909)

Fraser has had a long, distinguished career as journalist. Ottawa Editor of *Maclean's,* he is particularly concerned with Canadian politics.

THE SECRET LIFE OF MACKENZIE KING, SPIRITUALIST

For twenty-five years Canada's famous Prime Minister was a practicing spiritualist. He believed that, through mediums, he had communicated with his mother, Franklin D. Roosevelt and even his dog Pat, after they had died. Here, for the first time, is revealed the best-kept secret of Mr. King's amazing career.

One wet Saturday afternoon in October, 1948, William Lyon Mackenzie King lay ill at the Dorchester Hotel in Park Lane. His visitors were few and uniquely eminent — King George VI, Winston Churchill, Prime Minister Nehru of India — so the London press was keeping a close watch on the hotel lobby.

Reporters were amazed when two plainly dressed women came in, asked for Mr. King's suite and were shown up immediately. The two women did not reappear. They were ushered out by a side door (they couldn't understand why at the time) and the reporters never did find out who they were — Geraldine Cummins, well-known medium and author of many books on spiritualism, and her friend and collaborator, Beatrice Gibbes.

That was as close as any outsider ever came, in Mackenzie King's lifetime, to the best-kept secret of his career — the fact that the Prime Minister of Canada had been for more than twenty-five years a convinced and practicing spiritualist.

Actually the word is somewhat ambiguous. Mr. King was not a member of the Spiritualist Church and spiritualism was not a religion to him : he remained to the end of his days a good Presbyterian. But he did believe in the life after death, not as a matter of faith but as a proven fact. He did believe it possible to communicate with the departed, and that he himself had talked beyond the grave many times with his mother, his brother and sister, and such friends as Franklin D. Roosevelt and Sir Wilfrid Laurier. He did repeatedly attend seances and have sittings with mediums here in London and elsewhere.

To his real intimates he made no secret of these beliefs. Some of them joined him many times in sessions with the ouija board at Ottawa. They knew from his own lips what comfort he got from his "communion with the dead." Members of his personal staff knew it too — in some cases Mr. King didn't know they knew, but they all did.

Everybody kept the secret, for an obvious reason : If the facts were publicly known, people might have thought the affairs of Canada were being conducted on advice from the spirit world.

Indeed, Mr. King had not been dead a fortnight before a statement to that effect was published in the spiritualist weekly, *Psychic News*. His old friend, the late Duchess of Hamilton, in an interview, said Mr. King had always sought spirit guidance in affairs of state.

This was untrue — on Mr. King's own testimony and on the evidence of those who knew him best. He sought contact with his dead mother and brother and friends not to consult them but simply to talk to them.

Mrs. Helen Hughes, a pleasant Glasgow housewife who is one of the best-known of present-day mediums and who sat with Mr. King often over a period of many years, explained it to me over a cup of tea in the Psychic College, Edinburgh :

"It was as if he had his mother living over here in Britain — what would any son do, if he came here on business? He'd look her up; he'd want to see her and talk to her. He didn't want her advice about public affairs, for he knew more about them than she did. He wanted to know how she was. He wanted to talk to her about family matters."

Mrs. Hughes cannot recall a single instance, in all her sittings with Mr. King, when there was any mention of public affairs. The only exception, if you can call it an exception, was the question of Mr. King's own retirement from public life.

"He was warned," she said. "At least three years before he died his mother told him he was doing too much, his heart wouldn't stand it. He took her advice in the end, but not soon enough."

Perhaps one reason he delayed was that he got opposite advice from President Roosevelt. He asked F.D.R.'s counsel at a sitting with Miss Cummins; the answer came back "Don't retire, stay on the job. Your country needs you there."

After Mr. King had gone back to Canada Miss Cummins got another message; the President had changed his mind. He now thought Mr. King's health too precarious for the load he was carrying, and urged him to retire at once. Miss Cummins passed the word along to Ottawa.

(Perhaps I'd better say at this point that I myself am not a spiritualist and do not believe in these alleged communications from the next world. For the sake of brevity and clarity, I haven't bothered to use words like "alleged" and "purported" in every other sentence. Whether or not you or I believe these messages were real, the point is that Mackenzie King did believe it.)

At a later sitting with Miss Cummins he got a message from F.D.R. which did concern public affairs. The President told Mr. King to watch Asia — that's where the war danger lay. The Berlin airlift which was a focus of attention then was a side issue, a Soviet bluff. There was no mention of Korea by name, but F.D.R. did say he thought there'd be war in the Far East within two years.

Miss Cummins recalls that the Prime Minister "seemed puzzled and a little shaken by this part of the communication. He said he made it a rule to ignore advice thus given, and trusted solely to his own and his advisers' judgment."

What he wanted from a medium, and what he normally got, was intimate converse with his own family. Like so many others, Mackenzie King became interested in spiritualism because he was a lonely and a sorely bereaved man.

The mother to whom he was and remained devoted; his beloved brother Macdougall King, the doctor; his favorite sister Isabel — all had died in a few years. His bereavement was sharpened by the thought that he had not been at his mother's death-bed. At her insistence he had gone back to his 1917 election campaign in North York, leaving her mortally ill; she was dead when he returned. Mr. King never quite forgave himself for this.

He was introduced to spiritualism by the late Marchioness of Aberdeen, who was herself a believer. Lady Aberdeen told him of Mrs. Etta Wriedt, an American "direct-voice" medium who acquired great fame in her day.

It was Mrs. Wriedt who received, in 1911, the gold watch bequeathed by Queen Victoria to "the most deserving medium" of the time. The Queen had intended the watch for her Highland gillie John Brown, a medium through whom she believed she could talk to her beloved Prince Albert. Mrs. Wriedt in her turn got the watch after having shown, to the satisfaction of British editor W.T. Stead, that she had received a communication from the spirit of Queen Victoria in July 1911.

Mrs. Wriedt decided before her own death that the Queen's watch ought to go back to England. She entrusted it to Mr. King, who brought it here on his next visit and gave it to the London Spiritualist Alliance. There, mounted on a blue velvet cushion, it is still on display.

All that came later. In the early 1920s Mr. King was convinced of the genuineness of Mrs. Wriedt's gift by the experience of a friend of his.

The wife of a Liberal senator, now dead, had lost her father, and the father's will couldn't be found. After futile search she consulted Mrs. Wriedt. The medium told her it was in a chest of drawers in a house in France. She looked, and there it was. That's the story as Mr. King used to tell it.

Mrs. Wriedt used a silver trumpet from which, at her seances, the voice of the departed would proceed. An old friend of Mr. King recalled : "She'd put the trumpet in the middle of the circle and it would roll around and stop in front of the person about to receive a message. I remember the thing rolling up to me and giving me quite a rap on the shin. The voice that came out did sound very like a person I knew who had died.

"However, I was a bit shaken when she got hold of somebody who was supposed to be French. That trumpet spoke very bad French."

Apparently that didn't shake Mr. King, whose own French was rudimentary anyway. He became more and more interested in spiritualism as the years went by. For the last twenty years of his life he found time, on every trip to Britain, for sittings with various mediums.

Mrs. Helen Hughes remembers the first she ever had with him, in the early 1930s : "I had no idea who he was. They don't tell us, you know. All I knew was, a gentleman would be coming for a sitting at 10.30 in the morning. He just came in and sat down without saying anything.

"One of the voices I heard was a man who said he was his brother. Mr. King wanted to be told something about him, and it came through that he was a doctor. After a while I got the name, Mac. He said a lot about the family — he'd say : "Do you remember, Willie, when we were children, do you remember so-and-so ?" After it was over Mr. King said "I know that was my brother. He spoke of things nobody else knew, nobody but the two of us." "

Through Mrs. Hughes and the late Hester Dowden, another medium of considerable fame, Mr. King got in touch not only with the human members of his family but also with his beloved Irish terrier, Pat. Mrs. Hughes once reported to him : "Your sister is here, and she has a beautiful dog with her. The dog doesn't seem to have been very long over there (i.e., very long dead)."

Mr. King was greatly impressed and told Mrs. Hughes a story he had told to many friends in Ottawa. The night before Pat died, Mr. King's watch fell off his bedside table "for no apparent reason" — he found it in the morning, face down on the floor, with the hands stopped at twenty minutes past four.

"I am not psychic," Mr. King said, "but I knew then, as if a voice were speaking to me, that Pat would die before another twenty-four hours went by." Sure enough, that night Pat got out of his basket with a last effort, climbed up on his master's bed, and died there. Mr. King looked at his watch — it was twenty past four.

Mrs. Hughes' method, as a medium, is what they call "clair-audience" — she hears voices and reports what they say to the client. Sometimes, though not always, she can see faces and bodily forms. Sometimes she is in a trance, sometimes fully conscious, but in either case the message comes through in her own Scottish voice. Mrs. Wriedt was a "direct-voice" medium through whom the deceased could speak directly in his or her own earthly accent.

Hester Dowden and Miss Cummins got their communications by "automatic writing." Mrs. Dowden used to be fully conscious and made comments of her own, sometimes rather facetious and irreverent, on the messages coming through. Miss Cummins goes into a trance, she says, and loses consciousness completely before her hand begins to move across the page. She sits down and "goes into the silence," shading her closed eyes with her left hand; after a while her "control," an ancient Greek named Astor, announces his presence and begins to send messages from other departed spirits. Miss Cummins writes all this down in a rapid script with all the words run together, no spaces, and in handwriting that varies markedly as different "communicators" speak.

Mr. King's habit was to take the written messages off the foolscap pad, sheet by sheet as they were completed, and to keep the originals himself. He would send back copies to the mediums, often with comments of his own on the "evidential" material they contained. Of one message from President Roosevelt, reporting that F.D.R. had met Mr. King's mother, the Prime Minister said:

"The phrases he used, the characterization, were exactly what I'd have expected from Franklin Roosevelt if he'd met my mother in life."

These spirit messages, the originals as well as the copies, are still extant in Ottawa and in London, but even now they are treated as closely secret. None of the people associated with Mr. King's spiritualist activities will talk freely or willingly about him. Had it not been for an initial breach of silence just after Mr. King's death, they'd be even less willing to talk.

Most of King's contacts with mediums in Britain were made through Miss Mercy Phillimore, secretary of the London Spiritualist Alliance. Miss Phillimore won't discuss Mr. King's interest in spiritualism, won't reveal to whom she sent him or when or where. But she will talk, very strongly and indignantly, about that unfortunate statement in *Psychic News* that he "always sought spirit guidance in affairs of state."

"Mr. King was an investigator," she said. "He did accept the spirit hypothesis and he had the courage to say so, but he never ceased to be critical in appraising evidence. He was a highly intelligent man with shrewd judgment, and to say he consulted mediums for advice in statecraft is preposterous. It is also outrageous, an insult to his memory."

Actually Mr. King seems to have behaved, in his psychic experiments, with all the caution and circumspection he displayed in other things. The London Spiritualist Alliance, founded under its present name in 1884, is one of the oldest organizations of its kind. It is regarded in spiritualist circles as a pretty careful investigator of mediums' claims, and it also has a reputation for secrecy.

Ordinarily, I was told, the mediums didn't know who Mr. King was. Miss Cummins recalls that at her first sitting with him she thought he was a clergyman from New York. (She says she was so ignorant of

Canada that she thought the capital city was Montreal, yet the messages on that first day included such relatively obscure names as W. S. Fielding, who was Mr. King's rival for the Liberal leadership thirty-two years ago, and Sir Oliver Mowat, a Premier of Ontario in Sir John A. Macdonald's time.)

Mrs. Helen Hughes says she had been giving him sittings over a period of four years, sometimes two in a single week, before she knew his name. She learned his identity for the first time in 1937, at a party given by the Duchess of Hamilton at the London Spiritualist Alliance headquarters in Queensberry Place, South Kensington.

One of the guests at that party was a Scotsman named J. J. Mac-Indoe, and it was he who first revealed that Mackenzie King was a spiritualist. He wrote a letter to the *Psychic News* just after Mr. King's death; the letter was published, and *Psychic News* promptly sent a reporter to interview the Duchess of Hamilton for more details. Both stories were widely reprinted in Canada.

With the secret thus broken, Miss Cummins wrote an appendix to the autobiographical book she was preparing, published in 1951 under the title *Unseen Adventures*. It comprised a partial report of the two sittings she had with Mr. King in 1947 and 1948. Private and personal communications were deleted, but she did reveal that he had got messages from his family and from President Roosevelt.

She sent proofs of the appendix to a friend in Ottawa who showed them to Mackenzie King's executors. One of them, Duncan MacTavish of Ottawa, was flying to England the next day on other business. Leonard W. Brockington, of Toronto, was already in London. Together they called to urge Miss Cummins and her publishers to suppress the story. Reluctantly, and at considerable cost and inconvenience, they agreed to cut out Mr. King's name and a number of identifying details, including the name of President Roosevelt.

In the book as published, the appendix is entitled Reminiscences of a British Commonwealth Statesman; Mr. King appears as Mr. S., F.D.R. as X.Y.Z. Miss Cummins was rather taken aback when I turned up at Miss Gibbes' small house in Chelsea, already able from previous information to identify these pseudonymous characters and fill in a number of the deleted details. She is still worried lest she be accused of breaking faith in consenting to see me at all.

In general, though, people who knew of Mr. King's beliefs are glad the story is coming out.

Mediums differ a lot in their attitude toward their work and their own beliefs concerning it. Mrs. Helen Hughes is a minister of the Spiritualist Church and a professional medium — to her, spiritualism is a religion and sittings an occupation. Miss Cummins, on the other hand, is a devout member of the Church of Ireland, a novelist and playwright by profession. Some of her books are ordinary novels about Ireland, written with her conscious mind. Others she believes to have been dictated to her by writers now dead — many are chronicles of biblical times.

She is not a professional medium, indeed she does not give sittings at all except at the request of personal friends. Like Mackenzie King she regards spiritualism as enquiry and experiment, not worship, and she retains a certain amount of scepticism about the results.

But all spiritualists, the believers and the researchers alike, have an interest in letting the facts be known. They feel that if a man as eminent, as astute, as famous for realistic judgments as Mackenzie King was convinced their conclusions were genuine, they have a right to his testimony before the world. While he lived his secret was kept with absolute fidelity, but they see no point in secrecy now.

Moreover they are absolutely convinced that Mr. King himself would agree with them. He told several people here, in the later years of his life, that it was his firm intention to publish a full account of his psychic experiments and beliefs in the memoirs he then hoped to write. He hadn't quite decided whether this chapter would be published during his lifetime or withheld until after his death, but publish it he would, sooner or later. He wanted to communicate his own unshakable faith in the life after death.

"People who don't believe in survival," he once said to Mrs. Helen Hughes, "haven't yet begun to live."

Therefore they feel that whatever Mr. King's executors may desire, his own wishes are served by publication of the facts. From the little I knew of Mr. King I think they're right. If Mr. King's belief has turned out to be true, and if he is indeed looking over my shoulder from some astral sphere, I don't think he'll mind.

Michael Francis Harrington (Born in 1916)

Editor of the *Evening Telegram,* St. John's, Newfoundland, he has | written many short stories for radio and the magazines.

THE SCHEMER

It was Solomon Weare who first drew the attention of Kettle Cove to Elias Broome's new secret.

Solomon came into Tom Crosse's shop the day the coastal steamer had just sailed for St. John's after her final call for the season at Kettle Cove. The shop, a typical outport one, stocking groceries, drygoods and hardware in orderly disarray was only a few yards from the lane leading to the government wharf, and is was filled with the mid-afternoon group of shoppers and general hangers-on.

"Did ye see what Eli Broome got from St. John's this morning?" he asked them.

"No," they answered in unison, "what was it?"

"Well, now," said Sol, the words stumbling out over a wad of chewing tobacco, "I don't know what it was. Might have been a stove, but 'twas in a bale-box, so I can't rightly say. 'Twas heavy, though!"

"How did he get it home?" queried Tom Crosse, a lanky man with a white mustache stained brown above the middle of the upper lip. To join in the conversation from behind the counter he had to push his head out through several pairs of long rubber boots hanging from hooks in the ceiling.

"Oh, he took it on his horse and longcart. The poor horse had to take more than one spell to get over the Pinch." This was a steep incline where the harbour road went over a ridge above the settlement.

"I wonder what Eli's up to now," mused Pad O'Ragen, a red-faced jolly-looking man, from his seat on a pile of schooner blocks and mooring ropes. "He was always a deep one."

"That he was," echoed Sol. He moved his six feet of bone and hard muscle closer to the hot stove and continued, "I mind the time he bought them two setters, and no one knew a thing about it until Sam Moreton's little dog got into his barn and almost drove them crazy."

"And remember them hens he bought somewhere up the coast?" chuckled Tom Crosse, "Supposed to lay eggs bigger than most hens! I allow Eli thought they were going to lay golden eggs, and they laid nary one at all."

A ripple of laughter, soft and supple, slid through the air —
which was not air at all, but an aroma of oakum and molasses, tobacco
and twines, dried fruits and kerosene that would almost turn the head.

"Aye, Eli was always a deep one," repeated Pad O'Ragen. He got
up to go, picking his way among galvanized water buckets and kegs of
nails underfoot, and women's dresses and men's overalls dangling at
eye level from the ceiling. "Never did him much good, though," he added
philosophically, pausing in the door before going out into the chill
November day.

That brief interchange was the beginning of an interminable discussion in every kitchen in Kettle Cove. Did Eli have a girl in the next
harbour he wasn't telling about, and was he thinking about marriage?
If so, the packing case might hold anything from a new stove to a fancy
chest of drawers. Did he have some scheme to start a business and go
into competition with Tom Crosse and Azariah Redfield, the two
merchant princes of the harbour? Oh, perhaps, it was one of those
new-fangled phonographs — only Father O'Toole and Parson Brown
and Dr. McIntosh had one. It would be just like Eli Broome to try to be
as good as these people!

Eli was a bachelor and unpopular — not because he was a
bachelor, but because he was aloof and secretive. He was also unco-
operative; and in any fishing community on the rough Newfoundland
coast, that was a deadly sin. Community spirit had become an ingredient
of survival through centuries of comparative isolation. But Eli Broome
had long ago become sufficient unto himself. He minded his own
business and Kettle Cove went its way without him.

As winter came and went it was realized that Eli was up to something special. It was apparently so important that he didn't look for
a berth to the ice, and so missed the annual seal hunt for the first time
in twenty springs. First thing he did was build a shed over the water
near his stage, and day and night he'd be sawing and hammering. No
one saw him move the mysterious crate to the shed. Anyway, 'twas
after that metallic noises began to issue from the shed, which were quite
unlike the usual run of sounds familiar to the handymen of Kettle Cove.

Soon the raw northeasters gave way to cool southerlies and warm
southwesters. The icefields drove off the land and the icy conkerbills
trailing from the eaves dripped and dripped away. By the time the
men came back from the seal hunt, some of them making as high as
seventy and eighty dollars for their five weeks out in the steamers, it was
time to prepare for the codfishery.

Boats had to be caulked, twines replaced in nets which were then
barked in the immense barking kettle on the foreshore. 'Tis said that's

how the cove got its name, but that's debatable, as almost every settlement had one. Tree bark was boiled in this pot over a roaring fire and the nets dipped into the concoction to be seasoned and made taut for the months in the sea. Around the barking kettle yarns were told and gossip repeated, observations made and opinions formed.

Eli Broome came there, too, but only when the others were finished. He barked his nets one cold evening in late April when there was no one around to ask questions. Larry Fallon came up from the Gut one night and saw him — a short-legged, thick-set, round-headed man, with a peaked look that sometimes made his angular face look almost savage. Larry tried to make conversation but, receiving no encouragement, went on to Pad O'Ragen's kitchen for the trap-berth discussion.

It was very pleasant in Pad's kitchen, with the open beams painted white against the green plowed-and-tongued board of the low ceiling. Pad used to have an open fireplace high enough for a man to stand up in, but had lately installed a big barrel stove and built a kind of continuous settee on two sides and the back of the chimney. His Missus had padded this bench with horse-hair cushions covered with fancy chintz and the place had become a sort of headquarters, where the regular ritual included the telling of old yarns and the singing of a few "Come-all-ye's" followed by a game of forty-fives. But this night, when Larry entered, the trap berths were the main topic.

"I just saw Eli Broome at the barking pot," Larry volunteered.

"Mark my words, he's up to no good — that omadhaun."

That was enough to change the subject.

"What's he been doing in that shed all winter?" asked Peter Paul Houndshill, a small, wiry man with fiercely blue eyes. "It's something to do with his boat, that's certain sure. He's got her in there now."

Larry said: "I asked him what he was frapeing up in that shed and he got vexed and told me I'd find out soon enough."

An old, grizzled fisherman spoke up. "D'ye know what?" said Martin Canndow, "I votes we all go up there and cross-'ackle him a bit. If we get him mad enough he might tell us."

At this point Pad O'Ragen interrupted. "Come now, that's enough of Eli Broome. We came up here this evening to talk about the trap berths. I understand 'twill follow the same procedure as before — every man to take his chance on the rowing-out, except the Widow Ringwell's boys. They're to get the Red Ledge this year. Is that agreed?"

"Aye, aye," they chorused, "agreed."

Now it's necessary to explain about the business of the trap berths. It goes back to the time when skippers from England who arrived first each season were known as "admirals" of the harbours, and picked out the best fishing grounds, the "prime berths," for themselves. First come, first served was the motto, and the men of Kettle Cove were carrying on a tradition of which few knew the beginning. Some berths, however, had been held continuously by the same families, for their forebears were the first permanent settlers and their descendants claimed their rights like dynasties hold a crown.

Tom Crosse's people possessed the Cobbler until Tom, who was the last of them, turned merchant with some success; the Hadens always fished the Blue Shoal; Nehemiah Kain and his sons had gone to the Gravelly Banks so long 'twas said the fish knew them coming; and no one dared go in Bottle Gulch while there was a Canndow in Kettle Cove. The remainder of the berths were distributed in a free-for-all, with the exception of the Red Ledge. This was the best of the prime berths and was being reserved for Jack and Bob Ringwell, whose father had been lost the previous fall coming from the Labrador. They were being given that ground to help their mother and her big family. The other men would help the Ringwell boys set their traps and haul them.

The row-out mentioned by Pad O'Ragen was as follows: on a fine, calm day, all the boats would line up at a fixed time a few feet from the government wharf. Then Uncle Jake Rokewood climbed to the top of Black Head with his long Poole gun, all seven feet of it, and a carved powder horn on a thong of hide from a caribou, shot when he was a survey guide for the railway company in the 1870s. The crews would watch as he carefully poured out the powder, though the Lord only knows how many fingers he poured in the Long Tom for that eventful day. Then Uncle Jake would raise the old muzzle-loader and there would be a flash and a roar fit to wake the dead in the graveyard under the Head. And at the signal the boats would be off, digging in, back muscles cracking, foam flying.

That's how the trap berths were awarded in Kettle Cove, and the method had always worked out satisfactorily. Men didn't always pick the best berth, but they generally got the berth of their choice, which was sometimes closer to shore and more convenient. Occasionally, as in the case of the Widow Ringwell, a family less fortunate than the rest of the harbour would, by unanimous consent be given one of the "prime berths" — but as a rule everyone took their chance.

Until Elias Broome stole a march on them all.

It was a magnificent May morning when Uncle Jake Rokewood climbed Black Head to start the race for the trap berths. Eli was last to get in line, and despite the excitement, most of the crews were overcome with curiosity at the sight of Broome's big skiff as it came out of the water shed, where he had been tinkering all winter long. Usually Eli raced in a dory; it was easier to row and gave one man a better chance; but here he was now in his skiff, and it had a small box-like affair — a sort of house — in the stern sheets, and he wasn't sitting like the other men on the thwarts with the oars at the ready, but squatting in the well near the house. If they'd had time to think, the wiser ones would have tumbled to it right off, but it wasn't till the starting gun went that they realized the Industrial Revolution had reached Kettle Cove at last.

Almost simultaneously with the roar of the patriarch's sealing gun there came a series of crashing reports from the direction of Elias Broome's trap skiff, and a cloud of blue smoke shot in the air from a black pipe in the house which nobody had noticed until then. As the rowers bent their backs, they saw white water boiling at the skiff's stern, and the next thing she was going out the harbour at twice their speed. They knew at once what they were up against — Eli Broome was the first man in Kettle Cove to bring in and install a gasoline engine, and with his newfangled motorboat had caught them in his sly manner unawares.

That settled it for that year. Eli Broome had the pick of the "prime berths" and in real mean fashion he took the Red Ledge, which the neighbourly and Christian folk of Kettle Cove had already decided was to form the widow's portion. From that time on he was shunned, but being anti-social, that didn't bother him. And he got fish — tons of it. He had to work from daylight till dark, but all the Cove grudgingly admitted that, however mean and sly he was, Eli Broome was a devil to work.

But they were furious.

"That sleveen," snarled Tom Crosse, "to take the bite out of a widow's mouth. I swear he ought never have a day's luck."

"Is there anything we can do about it?" was the practical question from Peter Paul Houndshill.

"Nothing," answered Pad O'Ragen. "The rule is the rule. It's first come, first served, and if Eli got off quicker in a motorboat, that's our hard luck — I mean the Widow's hard luck. We'll have to see about giving her boys one of the other grounds — the White Sail Bank, maybe." Then, adding as an afterthought, "Tis hardly fair, though. He might have given us a hint of what he was up to."

"If he did, he wouldn't be Eli Broome," Larry Fallon declared. "He's that low he could crawl under a dory thwart and never wrinkle his gansey." And that was about the size of it. Everyone abused Eli, what could they do ?

Soon it was June, and then July, and stray icebergs drifted south along the coast, vast and awful, with great seas forever fretting at their base. Icebergs never bothered Kettle Cove till that summer; usually they were too big, so far north, to move close inshore. But that year there was a succession of easterly gales with a long disorderly sea running on the land for days, and one morning the Cove woke earlier than usual to the popping of Eli Broome's engine exhaust. Looking out in the grey dullness before dawn, the fishermen saw something that gave them a momentary glow of satisfaction, soon tinged with alarm. For right on top of the Red Ledge was stranded the biggest iceberg they'd seen inside of Gunner's Island in forty years.

Eli was in luck, though, for the berg hadn't touched his traps. Everybody expected him to move to another ground, for it was tricky fishing in the lun of an ice island half as high as Black Head, with quick tides whirling round it. But not Eli Broome. He had the Red Ledge and he was going to make the most of it. Each day he went out to haul his traps oblivious of the great, gleaming ice-ghost that haunted him and his skiff, so tiny by comparison.

Old-timers got worried as the summer days went by and the hot July sun glared down on the shining berg. But when they offered advice they were told to mind their own business and clean their own fish. This, too, in spite of the fact that Larry Fallon and Sol Weare, whose traps were nearest the Red Ledge, had shifted long ago.

So the iceberg sparkled and towered like a cliff of white marble, seemingly inviolate and everlasting. There was no apparent flaw in it, even after several weeks, no sea-worn caves, no storm-made fissures. The fisherwives of Kettle Cove admired its splendid solidity as they went about their tasks that morning, milking the cows, spreading fish on the flakes, feeding the babies, weeding the kitchen gardens, and marvelled at the tiny boat so near the icy monster with Eli Broome working feverishly to reap his ill-deserved harvest.

Then momentarily, all stood aghast as the massive mountain of ice seemed to explode with a thunderous roar, and an avalanche of ice blocks tumbled into the sea around Eli Broome's trap skiff. Instantly humanity asserted itself, and from all over Kettle Cove the boats hustled to the scene of the anticipated tragedy. The old-timers knew what had happened, even without the evidence — for hadn't they tried to warn him ? The floating fragments revealed that the berg, from long exposure to the sun, had become what the fishermen termed "rotten," honey-combed within while outwardly presenting a reassuring appearance of strength and solidity — till finally it had collapsed.

Now if the story was to end here with a judgment come upon Elias Broome, it might be possible to moralize on the wages of greed and deceit. But Eli wasn't that easy to get rid of. For as the boats entered the welter of the disintegrated berg, expecting the worst, the crews were astonished to find him dazed and bloodied, clinging to a piece of the engine house of his sunken skiff. He was cut and bruised, but other-wise unhurt, and it was none other than Larry Fallon who dragged him out of the water, although he said later it went against the grain.

Eli's fishing gear was ruined, however, and although the Kettle Cove folk, with genuine neighbourliness, scraped together enough of their spare nets and floats and sinkers to fit him out again, he did not resume fishing that summer. But a few days after his narrow escape Eli paid a visit to the Widow Ringwell and turned over his entire catch to her and her family. And, do you know, after that he began calling on her once in a while, and before another trap-berth race came around Eli and the Widow were married ? And they do say there was no more genial man in the settlement thereafter than Elias Broome, who introduced Kettle Cove to the Industrial Revolution.

(Sea Stories from Newfoundland)

William C. Borrett (Born in 1894)

Managing Director of the Maritime Broadcasting Company, Borrett is well known as a radio personality. He has always been interested in the history of Nova Scotia and of his home city, Halifax.

A GREAT CHAMPION

From the slopes of Citadel Hill, by the Old Town Clock of Halifax, Haligonians have watched many famous ships. From the largest to the smallest of ocean-going vessels no ship was more graceful or beau-tiful to the eye, as she moved on the broad expanse of Halifax Harbour on her way to the open sea, than our own Nova Scotian fishing schooner, the *Bluenose*.

It is history now, that the once graceful and triumphant "Queen of the North Atlantic" is no more — that the International Champion racing schooner *Bluenose* went to her doom on January 29, 1946, on the jagged reefs of the Haitian Coast. We can give thanks that none of her crew were lost. Yes, the *Bluenose* is gone — truly a great Champion.

One cannot better express the sentiments of those who have that sense which comprehends the sea, and appreciates the things which make for a country's historic greatness, than by quoting from an editorial which appeared in the *Halifax Herald,* on the day her loss was announced, as follows :

"The *Bluenose* is gone. She had to go sometime : the life of a wooden vessel is limited to a comparatively brief span — but it is sad to see her end her days and career far from her home waters and under an alien flag.

"It is now exactly twenty-five years since the keel of this noble old Champion was laid at Lunenburg. She came into being and did her first fishing and racing in 1921.

"The *Bluenose* was the most authentically Nova Scotian thing we had in this Province. She never should have left Nova Scotia. The nation should have acquired her and kept her here in her home. She could not last forever in a working life. She was bound, sooner or later, to meet her end at sea. Now the end has come. It is a melancholy finish of a grand and glorious career."

The closing years of the career of the great-hearted schooner were ones which might be considered the lot of a drudge; but even then they were useful years. And, when you stop to think of it, practically all the years of the *Bluenose* were years of productive work. Even in the days when her prow forged through the waves, to put her ahead of her rivals in fishermen's races, she was almost then fresh in from the banks. She had to be a bona fide fisherman in order to capture and retain her laurels. But the *Bluenose* was not only a successful fisherman — she was also a high-liner. Thanks for this can go to different things. We like to think that first credit goes to the Roue-designed boat itself. However, Captain Angus Walters, in the days of his command, was a canny skipper and knew all the tricks of his trade. Then, too, Angus always made a point of rounding out a capable crew — and he could pick men. So, all in all, the combination was one to lead to success.

It was in recent years that a plodding type of work fell to the lot of the Atlantic's Queen, for it was in 1942 that she was sold to the West Indies Trading Company. Then came the routine task of carrying merchandise between the Indies and the ports of the United States.

Time passes quickly, and it does not seem much more than a few years ago that the *Bluenose* slid gracefully down the ways of the yard operated by R. W. Smith and G. A. Rhuland at Lunenburg. Yet, when you pause to consider, that was way back in March of 1921.

It is wrong to ever say — or think — that the *Bluenose* was a freak schooner, she was not. She was a true Nova Scotian fisherman, one of a long and illustrious line, and designed by a man with a special flair for this type of work, W. J. Roue, one well qualified to turn out either a craft to meet requirements of the fishing trade or one fitted to show its heels as a racing craft. In the *Bluenose* he combined the two — and without allowing either to lose in the making. Time and again the *Bluenose* proved by her performances on the fishing banks that she was a true Nova Scotian fisherman. Ask Captain Angus Walters about that if you need to be reassured.

Nevertheless there was something — a still mysterious something in her build and design that enabled the graceful *Bluenose* to surge along at speed that excelled. It was that ability to roll off the extra pace, and with the skill of Angus Walters thrown in for good measure, that made it possible for the Nova Scotian boat to set up such an enviable record. In five International Fishermen's Cup contests the *Bluenose* was never defeated, even though she came up against Gloucester's best. In an exhibition series the *Bluenose* saw for one lone occasion that she would have to momentarily hold the position of a loser. During this special exhibition series of 1930, which was not an official cup contest, the *Gertrude L. Thebaud* of Gloucester was credited with nosing out the Nova Scotian vessel in one race.

The last successful bid of the *Bluenose* for the International trophy, which was provided by the *Halifax Herald* and the *Halifax Mail,* was made in 1938, off Boston and Gloucester, and there it was she again proved her superiority over the *Thebaud.*

The *Bluenose* was truly a regal ship — and she had a real link with royalty, too . . . for she sailed for England in 1935 and received a gift from the late King George the Fifth — a set of sails from the royal yacht *Britannia.*

And, it was fitting raiment for a queen to wear — the Queen of the North Atlantic. Her right to that title was spoken of by W. J. Roue, her designer, when he heard the great-hearted vessel was no more. Here is what Bill Roue said — "I don't believe there will ever be another sailing fishing vessel built. The *Bluenose* was the Queen of them all, but the trend today is to powered vessels."

(Tales Retold under the Old Town Clock)

Evelyn Richardson (Born in 1902)

Mrs. Richardson spent most of her life as the wife of a lighthouse keeper on the Nova Scotia coast.

Her book of personal experiences, *We Keep a Light*, won a Governor-General's award in 1945.

A TRYING EXPERIENCE

It was during the February of our second winter on Bon Portage that I put in the most worried hours of our years on the island.

Lem, the hired man, went to Shag Harbour to carry our mail and to get that at the post office, and to buy what few groceries we required. Usually he arrived back at noon or shortly after, but on this day he did not return when expected. His brother was working for my brother, on a neighbouring island, and we had been somewhat annoyed at Lem because he had been seizing every opportunity to stop there for meals and even overnight. Morrill came to the house at half-past three, just as the wind began to spring up, and the first snow squalls drove across the Point. I asked if they had seen any sign of Lem.

"You won't see Lem today; he'd never start over in this storm, so he'll stay at Emerald Isle. I only hope it doesn't blow for two or three days and he's stuck off there."

I said I hoped not, and Morrill went on, "I'm going to take the ox and get another load of wood. I'll be back for supper at five. It looks like a dirty night; keep track of the weather." He was away.

"Keeping track of the weather," by the way, means to notice when snow or fog lessens visibility to five-eighths of a mile or less, and enter this in our records, also the time when visibility increases beyond that limit. Since I am more often where the clock and books are, this duty usually falls to me.

The storm worsened throughout the afternoon, till the snow clung whitely to the windows and the wind moaned in the chimneys and swirled around the corners of the lighthouse in angry gusts. By the time I began to watch for Morrill's return, it was indeed a "dirty" night as he had predicted.

Five o'clock came and no Morrill. That was not greatly out of the ordinary; very often he stopped later than he had planned, to do some extra work, and I never depended upon his being home at any specified time. But I wondered when it became dark enough for the Light to be lit, as he had not asked me to do this and I knew he preferred for me not to have the care of the Light on cold windy nights like this one. I went to the lantern, wound the spring and lit the lamps. While I waited in the cold windy lantern to see that all was functioning smoothly, I kept an anxious eye on the gate through which Morrill and the ox should appear. I was decidedly worried when I still saw no sign of him as I finally descended the three flights of stairs to the kitchen again. I wished Lem were home so that I could send him to find out what was detaining Morrill.

I gave the children their suppers and prepared them for bed, hoping every second to hear the welcome sound of Morrill stamping the snow from his feet as he came through the porch. I tried not to communicate my apprehension to the children, but I had decided I must go look for Morrill if he did not soon return. I felt it unlikely that he had cut himself, since he had taken the ox to *haul,* but I feared a log had rolled or fallen on him, and injured him so that he could not get on the sleds and so reach home. It was not hard to imagine any number of things that could have happened.

Once the children were ready for bed, I put them both in Laurie's crib, which had a side I could fasten securely and so prevent any chance of them getting out of bed and into danger while I should be gone, perhaps for several hours. Anne Gordon took this all very calmly, but two-year-old Laurie sensed something was wrong and began to cry. I took time to talk to him quietly and gently, telling him to "cuddle doon," a little phrase he loved and invariably obeyed, but he would have none of it. He cried and cried, and when I could stay no longer, he pulled himself up by the bars of the crib and clung there, crying broken-heartedly.

Getting ready to set out was like the preparations in a nightmare; my dread of leaving the children and my sense of urgency towards finding Morrill also had a nightmarish quality, and seemed to be pulling me in opposite directions. Both fires must be put out; I had let them down in readiness and the house was already becoming cold. There was the cat — she must go out. I must get and fill the hand-lantern. It might blow out in the wind. Get matches and a piece of sandpaper to scratch them on. Wrap them in a piece of wax-paper and put them in an inside pocket. I must dress warmly since I would be exposed to the sweeping wind much of the way. I knew of nothing I could take for Morrill. My only prayer was to find him, and that the ox had stayed near enough that I could get him on the sleds, and then drive or lead the ox home. I rejected the idea of trying to carry blankets to him through the wind, but at least I could make a fire and prevent his perishing in the cold.

I extinguished all house lamps, since my greatest fear was of the children being trapped by fire. The last thing I heard as I closed the door behind me was Laurie's heart-rending cries, so pitiful in the dark, cold house. I had never before in their short lives left the children alone in the house for more than a few minutes.

When I stepped out into the night, wind and snow closed around me immediately. The easterly wind, cold and evil, sweeps across the Point with ugly force ; that night it brought snow with it, picked up what lay on the field and drove it into my face and through every tiniest opening in my clothes. It howled and shrieked, "What can *you* do on a night like this ? Look. How far can you see ? Turn and face the lighthouse where you have left your babies alone. You can scarcely discern the beam of the Light only a few yards away. See, I can shut it out completely with this effortless swirl. Suppose the lantern catches fire as did the one in the Baccaro Light ? Suppose you fall ? It might well be days and nights before the absence of the light is noticed. What will become of your children fastened in their crib ? Your chance of helping Morrill ? You fool yourself !"

As the snow swirled blindingly between me and the indistinct outline of the lighthouse, I paused. Perhaps my first duty lay with the two little ones, helpless there in the cold wind-battered bedroom. But Morrill — he must need me. So with one more look and a quick prayer to God to guard them and to help me in what I had decided to attempt, I turned again towards where I felt Morrill awaited my coming.

Once up the slight hill and in the shelter of the trees, the force of the wind was less and the snow, though still blinding, no longer cut into my face nor choked my breath as I hurried on. Once I thought I saw sled-marks in the eddying snow before my feet, if so the ox must have returned alone to the barn. But I refused to entertain that thought. All my hopes of helping Morrill lay in the ox having stayed near him, so that I could get him home, since the wood-cutting where he was working was a mile or more from the lighthouse.

A great deal of snow had not yet fallen, or had mostly blown clear, for the drifts were not high enough to impede my way, so that through the more sheltered parts of the path I made good progress; the fear for Morrill's safety that choked me lent speed to my feet. At no time was I sensible of the cold.

"When I reach the boathouse," I thought, "I will be more than half way."

But when I turned out of the woods at the boathouse, my heart stopped for gladness as I heard Morrill's vigorous hail and, as I ran forward, he shouted reassuringly, "O.K., dear."

My first surge of happy relief was followed quickly by bewilderment. What was Morrill doing at the landing this hour of the night? And why? And there was Lem.

There was no time for explanations. Both were safe, and pausing only long enough to put a few things under cover in the boathouse, Morrill and I made all possible haste back to our babies at the lighthouse. Lem followed close behind. The children were both safe. Laurie had fallen exhausted in a huddle, his little hands still clutching the bars of his crib. It was with an overflowing heart that I made up the fires, got dry clothes for Morrill (Lem was not wet), and made a cup of coffee around. Then Morrill had to see that the ox was safe — those *had* been fresh sled-marks I had seen, and Morrill found the ox near the barn with his sleds tangled in a tree.

Finally I heard the story of the night's adventures. How good for Morrill to be safe and sound at home, and to hear the even tones of his voice, after the hours of worry and dread.

Lem had got as far as Emerald Isle on his return trip and then had delayed setting out on the last leg of his journey until the storm was almost upon him. Then he left for Bon Portage, but when he neared the shores of the island he found a band of ice-cakes some two hundred yards through, which the storm had collected and packed against our shore. Looking at the line of ice, blurred and distorted through the snow squalls, he decided it did not look formidable, so he attempted to row through it. Then, when he had worked the boat well into the grip of the ice-cakes, he became afraid he had underestimated their size and extent, so he tried frantically to turn the boat, upon which it jammed in the ice and refused to move either way. Had the bow been left pointing into the ice, the force of the wind astern would have helped to push her bow into the cracks between the cakes and slowly edge her towards the shore. Broadside on, with her deep keel below the ice, she was helpless.

No doubt Lem was frightened; he told us, "I thought my time had come." And well he might be afraid. Everyone along the shore has heard of the cruel strength of the drift ice, and how it sweeps all with it out to sea with the ebb-tide; the cold wind and the driving snow would have made it a terrible night to be adrift in an open boat. He knew the thick snow squalls would prevent our seeing him if he were carried past the lighthouse, or if by a remote chance we caught sight of him, we could neither help him ourselves nor get word to Shag Harbour for aid, since he was in our boat.

I've no doubt that Lem put in a bad half-hour or so, and when Morrill appeared around the boathouse I imagine he was a most welcome sight. It was fortunate for Lem that Morrill had decided to get that last load of wood despite the storm, and that the storm was not then, at four o'clock, thick enough to blot both man and boat out of sight from the shore. It was typical of Lem, that in such dire straits, he was not working with oar and every ounce of energy he could muster to gain an inch or two nearer shore, but was dispiritedly flapping his arms across his chest in a vain effort to keep warm.

Lem had then been sighted, but by no means rescued. He had our boat; the only other craft was a trawl-dory, nineteen feet long, with a beam of about five feet, and sides at least two-and-a-half feet high. This had been put here by the government for use by the light-keeper, and was under cover in the boathouse. Here Broad, the ox, played his part, for he pulled the awkward, heavy dory from the boat-house to the water's edge. Morrill had put into it two pairs of oars with thole-pins, a large sweep, and several coils of pot-lines in hopes of getting a rope to Lem's boat.

Then began a three-hour struggle to work the big dory out through the cakes and against the strong wind to where Lem lay imprisoned in the ice. At first Morrill used the sweep as a pole; placing one end on bottom and the other against his stomach as he stood in the dory, and exerting all his strength he would force the boat forward a foot or less at a time. Soon the water became too deep for this method of progress. It was impossible to row, as oars could not find water between the packed cakes. The trawl-dory, with its broad flat bottom, sat upon the ice-cakes rather than amongst them, so Morrill would get out on a large cake that looked as if it would bear his weight, and push the dory along inch by inch.   A slip would have meant certain death under the ice-cakes, which would have opened to let his body down through their cruel pack, but would never have allowed it to reach the surface again. But the unwieldly weight and height of the trawl-dory, so disadvantageous in many ways, were safeguards in this respect and when an ice-cake broke beneath him, Morrill held to the sides of the boat and clambered back in with nothing worse than wet feet. But soon he began to fear his feet would freeze. Again he would step out, and using his weight at the stern to lift the bow clear and above the ice, would then change his position to the side of the boat and once more inch the dory forward.

It took three hours of this heart-breaking labour to cover the less than two hundred yards that separated him from Lem. The wind fortunately held in the same quarter, else he might have been carried out to sea beyond the Point. The blinding snow squalls, as night began to blacken over the surly water that snarled among the ice-cakes, must have made his task much more difficult, and if he had paused to look about him might well have caused him to give up in despair. But at last he reached the other boat, and Lem stepped into the trawl dory.

Morrill had hoped to save his boat by fastening a line to her, paying it out as he worked his way back to shore, and securing it when he reached there; but in the dark and snow some of the coils of rope had been covered by his discarded oilskins and he failed to locate them, so he was forced to leave his little boat to the mercy of ice and storm.

With two of them to work the dory in and with its high sides almost as serviceable as sails in the east wind, they made much better time on the return trip. They had just landed and pulled up the dory when I made my appearance. (Morrill had caught glimpses of my lantern as I struggled along the path.)

Never were two people more thankful than Morrill and I as we revelled in the warmth and security of fires and home. Morrill's feet, though touched with frost, were not seriously frozen, but he was completely exhausted. The following day he, for once, just *sat*. Several times he pulled himself out of his chair with the idea of attempting some chore, but each time he settled back again, too worn out to move.

The next morning was fine and clear and when the flood tide came in we saw our boat miles away to the southward. The wind was too strong for Morrill to attempt to get her, even if he had felt equal to rowing ; so we watched her drift away with the ebb, and thought sadly that we had seen the last of her, and wondered how we would make out with no boat for a while, and where to find money for a new one. The ebbs here are strong and usually sweep what they clutch out and around Cape Sable and thence to oblivion; but this time the high wind that blew on shore countered the tide and held the boat inside the Cape, so that the next flood brought her in and deposited her safe and sound on near-by Bear Point; from there we recovered her by paying a little to the boy who found her.

(We Keep a Light)

Ernest Buckler (Born in 1908)

Buckler farms near Bridgetown, Nova Scotia. His best-known work is a novel, *The Mountain and the Valley*. He is one of Canada's most engaging short story writers and has published widely in American magazines. He won the President's Medal, University of Western Ontario, for the best Canadian story of the year in both 1957 and 1958.

PENNY IN THE DUST

My sister and I were walking through the old sun-still fields the evening before my father's funeral, recalling this memory or that — trying, after the fashion of families who gather again in the place where they were born, to identify ourselves with the strange children we must have been.

"Do you remember the afternoon we thought you were lost ?" my sister said. I did. That was as long ago as the day I was seven, but I'd had occasion to remember it only yesterday.

"We searched everywhere," she said. "Up in the meeting-house, back in the blueberry barrens — we even looked in the well. I think it's the only time I ever saw Father really upset. He didn't even stop to take the oxen off the wagon tongue when they told him. He raced right through the chopping where Tom Reeve was burning brush, looking for you — right through the flames almost ; they couldn't do a thing with him. And you up in your bed, sound asleep !"

"It was all over losing a penny or something, wasn't it ?" she went on, when I didn't answer. It was. She laughed indulgently. "You were a crazy kid, weren't you."

I was. But there was more to it than that. I had never seen a shining new penny before that day. I'd thought they were all black. This one was bright as gold. And my father had given it to me.

You would have to understand about my father, and that is the hard thing to tell. If I say that he worked all day long but never once had I seen him hurry, that would make him sound like a stupid man. If I say that he never held me on his knee when I was a child and that I never heard him laugh out loud in his life, it would make him sound humourless and severe. If I said that whenever I'd be reeling off some of my fanciful plans and he'd come into the kitchen and I'd stop short, you'd think that he was distant and that in some kind of way I was afraid of him. None of that would be true.

There's no way you can tell it to make it sound like anything more than an inarticulate man a little at sea with an imaginative child.

You'll have to take my word for it that there was more to it than that. It was as if his sure-footed way in the fields forsook him the moment he came near the door of my child's world and that he could never intrude on it without feeling awkward and conscious of trespass; and that I, sensing that but not understanding it, felt at the sound of his solid step outside, the child-world's foolish fragility. He would fix the small spot where I planted beans and other quick-sprouting seeds before he prepared the big garden, even if the spring was late; but he wouldn't ask me how many rows I wanted and if he made three rows and I wanted four, I couldn't ask him to change them. If I walked behind the load of hay, longing to ride, and he walked ahead of the oxen, I couldn't ask him to put me up and he wouldn't make any move to do so until he saw me trying to grasp the binder.

He, my father, had just given me a new penny, bright as gold.

He'd taken it from his pocket several times, pretending to examine the date on it, waiting for me to notice it. He couldn't offer me *anything* until I had shown some sign that the gift would be welcome.

"You can have it if you want it, Pete," he said at last.

"Oh, thanks," I said. Nothing more. I couldn't expose any of my eagerness either.

I started with it, to the store. For a penny you could buy the magic cylinder of "Long Tom" popcorn with Heaven knows what glittering bauble inside. But the more I thought of my bright penny disappearing forever into the black drawstring pouch the storekeeper kept his money in, the slower my steps lagged as the store came nearer and nearer. I sat down in the road.

It was that time of magic suspension in an August afternoon. The lifting smells of leaves and cut clover hung still in the sun. The sun drowsed, like a kitten curled up on my shoulder. The deep flour-fine dust in the road puffed about my bare ankles, warm and soft as sleep. The sound of the cowbells came sharp and hollow from the cool swamp.

I began to play with the penny, putting off the decision. I would close my eyes and bury it deep in the sand; and then, with my eyes still closed, get up and walk around, and then come back to search for it. Tantalizing myself, each time, with the excitement of discovering afresh its bright shining edge. I did that again and again. Alas, once too often.

It was almost dark when their excited talking in the room awakened me. It was Mother who had found me. I suppose when it came dusk she thought of me in my bed other nights, and I suppose she looked there without any reasonable hope but only as you look in every place where the thing that is lost has ever lain before. And now suddenly she was crying because when she opened the door there, miraculously, I was.

"Peter !" she cried, ignoring the obvious in her sudden relief, *"where* have you been ?"

"I lost my penny," I said.

"You lost your penny . . . ? But what made you come up here and hide ?"

If Father hadn't been there, I might have told her the whole story. But when I looked up at Father, standing there like the shape of everything sound and straight, it was like daylight shredding the memory of a silly dream. How could I bear the shame of repeating before him the childish visions I had built in my head in the magic August afternoon when almost anything could be made to seem real, as I buried the penny and dug it up again ? How could I explain that pit-of-the-stomach sickness which struck through the whole day when I had to believe, at last, that it was really gone ? How could I explain that I wasn't really hiding from *them* ? How, with the words and the understanding I had then, that this was the only possible place to run from that awful feeling of loss ?

"I lost my penny," I said again. I looked at Father and turned my face into the pillow. "I want to go to sleep."

"Peter," Mother said, "it's almost nine o'clock. You haven't had a bite of supper. Do you know you almost scared the *life* out of us ?"

"You better get some supper," Father said. It was the only time he had spoken.

I never dreamed that he would mention the thing again. But the next morning when we had the hay forks in our hands, ready to toss out the clover, he seemed to postpone the moment of actually leaving for the field. He stuck his fork in the ground and brought in another pail of water, though the kettle was chock full. He took out the shingle nail that held a broken yoke strap together and put it back in exactly the same hole. He went into the shed to see if the pigs had cleaned up all their breakfast.

And then he said abruptly : "Ain't you got no idea where you lost your penny ?"

"Yes," I said, "I know just about."

"Let's see if we can't find it," he said.

We walked down the road together, stiff with awareness. He didn't hold my hand.

"It's right here somewhere," I said. "I was playin' with it, in the dust."

He looked at me, but he didn't ask me what game anyone could possibly play with a penny in the dust.

I might have known he would find it. He could tap the alder bark with his jackknife just exactly hard enough so it wouldn't split but so it would twist free from the notched wood, to make a whistle. His great fingers could trace loose the hopeless snarl of a fishing line that I could only succeed in tangling tighter and tighter. If I broke the handle of my wheelbarrow ragged beyond sight of any possible repair, he could take it and bring it back to me so you could hardly see the splice if you weren't looking for it.

He got down on his knees and drew his fingers carefully through the dust, like a harrow; not clawing it frantically into heaps as I had done, covering even as I uncovered. He found the penny almost at once.

He held it in his hand, as if the moment of passing it to me were a deadline for something he dreaded to say, but must. Something that could not be put off any longer, if it were to be spoken at all.

"Pete," he said, "you needn'ta hid. I wouldn'ta beat you."

Beat me ? Oh, Father ! You didn't think that was the reason . . . ? I felt almost sick. I felt as if I had struck *him*.

I had to tell him the truth then. Because only the truth, no matter how ridiculous it was, would have the unmistakable sound truth has, to scatter that awful idea out of his head.

"I wasn't hidin', Father," I said, "honest. I was . . . I was buryin' my penny and makin' out I was diggin' up treasure. I was makin' out I was findin' gold. I didn't know what to *do* when I lost it, I just didn't know where to *go* . . ." His head was bent forward, like mere listening. I had to make it truer still.

"I made out it was gold," I said desperately, "and I — I was makin' out I bought you a mowin' machine so's you could get your work done early every day so's you and I could go in to town in the big automobile I made out I bought you — and everyone'd turn around and look at us drivin' down the streets . . ." His head was perfectly still, as if the were only waiting with patience for me to finish. "*Laughin'* and *talk*in'," I said. Louder, smiling intensely, com*pell*ing him, by the absolute conviction of some true particular, to believe me.

He looked up then. It was the only time I had ever seen tears in his eyes. It was the only time in my seven years that he had ever put his arm around me.

I wondered, though, why he hesitated, and then put the penny back in his own pocket.

Yesterday I knew. I never found any fortune and we never had a car to ride in together. But I think he knew what that would be like, just the same. I found the penny again yesterday, when we were getting out his good suit — in an upper vest pocket where no one ever carries change. It was still shining. He must have kept it polished.

I left it there.

Hugh MacLennan (Born in 1907)

Novelist, essayist and professor, MacLennan is one of the outstanding Canadian authors of our time; his work attracts international attention. Here is the first chapter of his best-known book, *Two Solitudes,* a novel that explores Quebec's uneasiness in an age that threatens its isolation.

TWO SOLITUDES

I

Northwest of Montreal, through a valley always in sight of the low mountains of the Laurentian Shield, the Ottawa River flows out of Protestant Ontario into Catholic Quebec. It comes down broad and ale-coloured and joins the Saint Lawrence, the two streams embrace the pan of Montreal Island, the Ottawa merges and loses itself and the mainstream moves northeastward a thousand miles to the sea.

Nowhere has Nature wasted herself as she has here. There is enough water in the Saint Lawrence alone to irrigate half of Europe, but the river pours right out of the continent into the sea. No amount of water can irrigate stones, and most of Quebec is solid rock. It is as though millions of years back in geologic time a sword had been plunged through the rock from the Atlantic to the Great Lakes and savagely wrenched out again, and the pure water of the continental reservoir, unmuddied and almost useless to farmers, drains untouchably away. In summer the cloud packs pass over it in soft, cumulus, pacific towers, endlessly forming and dissolving to make a welter of movement about the sun. In winter when there is no storm the sky is generally empty, blue and glittering over the ice and snow, and the sun stares out of it like a cyclops' eye.

All the narrow plain between the Saint Lawrence and the hills is worked hard. From the Ontario border down to the beginning of the estuary, the farmland runs in two delicate bands along the shores, with roads like a pair of village main streets a thousand miles long, each parallel to the river. All the good land was broken long ago, occupied and divided among seigneurs and their sons. Bleak wooden fences separate each strip of farm from its neighbour, running straight as rulers set at right angles to the river to form long narrow rectangles pointing inland. The plowed land looks like the course of a gigantic and empty steeplechase where all motion has been frozen. Every inch of it is measured, and brooded over by notaries, and blessed by priests.

You can look north across the plain from the river and see the farms between their fences tilting towards the forest, and beyond them the line of trees crawling shaggily up the slope of the hills. The forest crosses the watershed into an evergreen bush that spreads far to the north, lake-dotted and mostly unknown, until it reaches the tundra. The tundra goes to the lower straits of the Arctic Ocean. Nothing lives on it but a few prospectors and hard-rock miners and Mounted Policemen and animals and the flies that brood over the barrens in summer like haze. Winters make it a universe of snow with a terrible wind keening over it, and beyond its horizons the northern lights flare into walls of shifting electric colours that crack and roar like the gods of a dead planet talking to each other out of the dark.

But down in the angle at Montreal, on the island about which the rwo rivers join, there is little of this sense of new and endless space. Two old races and religions meet here and live their separate legends, side by side. If this sprawling half-continent has a heart, here it is. Its pulse throbs out along the rivers and railroads; slow, reluctant and rarely simple, a double beat, a self-moved reciprocation.

II

Father Emile Beaubien stepped onto the porch of his red brick presbytery and looked at the afternoon. It was the autumn of 1917. The October air was sharp enough to shrink his nostrils. The sky was a deep blue, a fathomless blue going up and up into heaven.

The priest drew in deep breaths of the still air. For his noon dinner he had just eaten roast duck. This good meal, and many other blessings, made him feel content and thankful. He decided he could relax a little from the constant strain under which he had worked since coming to this parish as a rather young priest seven years ago. Last Sunday the new church had been consecrated by the bishop : his church, the largest within many miles. This year also the harvest had been bountiful, and owing to the war farm prices had never been better.

He walked briskly back and forth, one hand on his pendant cross, the skirts of his black soutane swishing as he moved. There was great energy in his steps; energy also in the lines of his face. The cheekbones and nose were very large, the mouth wide and straight, the eyes seemingly magnified by the thick lenses of the glasses he wore. Two deep lines, like a pair of dividers, cut the firm flesh of his face above the flanges of the nose to the corners of the lips. His hair was black and closely cropped, somewhat like a monk's cap. His face was brown; his hands, too, were brown, and big-boned, and his posture gave the suggestion that under the soutane the bones were all big, the shoulders strong as a plowman's.

The motionless air was suddenly cracked by two gunshots, and the priest paused in his walk to look up at the sky above the river. He saw three specks rise in it, and with eager interest he watched them. Two more shots cracked the air. One of the specks stopped, wavered and fell straight down. Frenette, the blacksmith, must be shooting ducks from his blind in the marsh near the river. It was years since the priest had done any duck-shooting himself, and he missed it because it had been the only recreation he had ever known. When he was a boy there had been little time from farm work even to shoot food; nor for that matter enough money to buy cartridges for his uncle's old gun.

He resumed his walking. By long habit his mind was vigilant to the parish about him. He carried the whole of Saint-Marc-des-Erables constantly in his thoughts. Quite literally he believed that God held him accountable for every soul in the place.

On this Saturday afternoon the village which was the core of the parish was deserted even by the dogs. Across the dirt road the brown houses, their steps edging shyly forward into the road, were silent. There was no sign of life in their airless front parlours, concealed behind white lace curtains drawn as close and tight as blinds. The men were out in the fields for the fall plowing, the women in the kitchens, the smaller children asleep, the older children at work. Farther down the road, the priest could see the sun glinting on the metal advertising posters that plastered the front of Polycarpe Drouin's general store with a strange mixture of French and English : La Farine Robin Hood, Black Horse Ale, Magic Baking Powder, Fumez le Tabac Old Chum. The store would be empty now except for Ovide Bissonette, who was getting more feeble-minded every year. Ovide would be asleep on a table piled with overalls, his eyes wide open and his legs dangling over the side. Polycarpe himself would be asleep in his rocking-chair in the back kitchen.

Father Beaubien stepped down from the porch and walked slowly across a stretch of grass fronting the presbytery towards the new church. His feet rustled crisply in the newly fallen leaves. At one corner of his house was a large oak tree, its leaves yellow; at the other corner was a giant rock maple. The maple was a tower of silence, a miraculous upward rush of cool flame, every leaf scarlet and dry and so delicately poised that the first wind would tear the whole tower apart and scatter it on the lawn and over the road.

The priest passed over the rustling leaves onto the brown, packed-gravel area before the church. He stood still with his powerful hands folded under his pendant cross, his eyes lifted to the twin spires. He could not look at his church often enough. Sometimes at night during the past week he had wakened after a few hours' sleep and dressed himself and gone out of the presbytery, to cross to the new building. He entered it by his own door and stood in the darkness, watching the votive candles burning before the images; or wandered through the nave under the great canopy of the roof, with the stone cold as a grave-marker under his feet and the whole church shadow-haunted, and so still he could hear his own blood pulsing in his ears : the sound of God.

Now he stood staring at the solid grey stone mass. After everything critics had said against the size of his church, it had been built. He felt both humble and proud that God had permitted a man like himself to build Him such a monument. It was the largest within forty miles. It was larger even than the largest Protestant church in Montreal where millionaires were among the parishioners. And Saint-Marc numbered less than a hundred and thirty families.

But Father Beaubien was not yet satisfied. The building itself was complete, yet it needed better heating equipment to make it comfortable in winter. The sheet-iron roof and the steeples were covered with bright aluminum paint, making the outside look finished and the whole glitter for miles in the sun. But he also required a new bell. The one he had was adequate when there was no wind, but when the wind blew against the sound the Angelus was almost inaudible at the fringes of the parish. He also wanted more images for the chapel, and he wanted particularly an image for the gravelled area in front of the church. He saw clearly in his mind what it should be : a bronze figure of Christ with outstretched arms, about twenty-five feet high, with a halo of coloured lights above the head.

The priest breathed deeply and touched his cross again. Although the bishop had congratulated him on the church, he also had expressed concern about the size of the debt. At present, war prices were helping considerably, but the war could not last forever, and when it was over prices would fall and the debt remain. The parishioners in Saint-Marc were nearly all farmers. They never had much ready money. And yet the priest had faith. The parish could rest indefinitely on the kness of God.

Thinking about the war, Father Beaubien's dark face set into a heavy frown. So far Saint-Marc had kept fairly clear of it. Only one member of the parish had volunteered, and he was on a spree in Trois-Rivières when the recruiting sergeants got him. He was no good anyway, always missing masses. But this year the English provinces had imposed conscription on the whole country, trying to force their conquest on Quebec a second time. Conscription officers had been in the neighbouring parish of Sainte-Justine and had taken young French Canadians out of their homes like thieves to put them into the army.

The priest's solid jaw set hard. His superiors had ordered him not to preach against the war and he had obeyed them. He did not question their wisdom; they knew more than he did. But at least his parish knew how he stood. He thought of the war and the English with the same bitterness. How could French Canadians — the only real Canadians — feel loyalty to a people who had conquered and humiliated them, and were Protestant anyway ? France herself was no better; she had deserted her Canadians a century and a half ago, had left them in the snow and ice along the Saint Lawrence surrounded by their enemies, had later murdered her anointed king and then turned atheist. Father Beaubien had no fondness for the Germans and no wish for them to win the war; he knew nothing whatever about them. But he certainly knew that if a people deserted God they were punished for it, and France was being punished now.

He turned back towards his presbytery and paused on the lawn to pick up an acorn dropped from his great oak. As he did so the silence was cracked again by a pair of gunshots down in the marsh. The priest held the acorn in his palm, looking at it, then he polished it firmly between his thumb and forefinger. This nut was like his own parish of Saint-Marc-des-Erables. It was perfect. You could not not change or improve it, you could not graft it to anything else. But you put it into the earth, and you left it to God, and through God's miracle it became another oak. His mind moving slowly, cautiously as always, the priest visioned the whole of French Canada as a seed-bed for God, a seminary of French parishes speaking the plain old French of their Norman forefathers, continuing the battle of the Counter-Reformation. Everyone in the parish knew the name of every father and grandfather and uncle and cousin and sister and brother and aunt, remembered the few who had married into neighbouring parishes, and the many young men and women who had married the church itself. Let the rest of the world murder itself through war, cheat itself in business, destroy its peace with new inventions and the frantic American rush after money. Quebec remembered God and her own soul, and these were all she needed . . . .

(Two Solitudes)

S. Morgan - Powell (1867-1962)

Morgan-Powell was for many years editor of the *Montreal Star.* When retired he was appointed the *Star's* literary and drama critic.

THE SILENT MEN OF OKA

The Summer sun lies hot upon Oka, bathing the smiling landscape and the distant spaces of the lake with a welter of silver light. It touches the serried ranks of apple trees in the orchards with its ripening glow; it bakes the white dust of the winding road; it spreads in quivering haze along the steep slopes of Mount Calvary, and it flings into sharp relief the three white chapels that crown the summit of that vast hill, standing yet as they stood when first built by the hands of the Sulpician monks nigh three hundred years ago, a white blazing trinity attestant to the far-flung energy of the Catholic Church.

It filters through the shade of myriads of trees and it falls in gentle shafts on the rugged walls of La Trappe, the home of silence and the refuge of the men of silence. But here are no moulded architraves, no weather-beaten gargoyles, redolent of history and worn by the smoothing hand of Time. Here is nothing but rough-hewn grey stone, severe outlines revealing the suppression of the aesthetic at every angle and in every sharp utilitarian turn.

In the rule of the reformed Cistercian Order of Trappist Monks is no room for aught that savours of the easier ways of life. Those who put on the black and white habit and take its vows are dead to the world they once knew. They pass over its portals into a world that has nothing in common with the strife and turmoil of modern humanity — a world of the spirit, a world of relentless, unceasing labour, a world of deep, unbroken silence.

There is something appalling, something that causes a nameless apprehension to thrill one, in this life of silence. It has a sinister air; a suggestion of suppressive awe surrounds it. Speech — the interchange of ideas, the pleasure of mutual converse, the soothing influence of consoling words, the enjoyment of amicable controversy — all this is forbidden. The black-garbed monk of Oka lives in a world apart, a world peopled only with shadows, a world governed by the rule of unquestioning obedience, swayed only by the grim stillness of the grave.

"Silence, the great empire of silence, higher than the stars," wrote Carlyle. It is here at Oka, that wonderful world brought down to earth, enclosed within forbidding walls of gaunt, grey stone, a place alien, self-contained, inviolate from the intrusion of the hurly-burly men call Life.

You must sleep in this grey monastery to realize its spirit to the full. As you lie on your narrow bed, looking into the purple shadows of the night, that spirit descends upon you, enwraps you, claims you and holds you in its thrall. The silence is astounding. It is the silence that fell upon Egypt of old, the silence that can be felt; an absolute calm, a very vivid and vital stillness, a tense hush that holds in seeming endless suspense all the energies, all the potentialities, all the influences, all the mysteries of living.

It is intensely disquieting — at first. One's senses seem preternaturally acute. Every nerve is responsive to the slightest mental suggestion; but after a while it becomes most extraordinarily soothing; it holds a wondrous power, compelling restfulness.

You will say afterwards that you never remember any night in your life when you experienced such all-pervading, absolute rest. The spirits of the dead brood over the spirits of the living. Here, in the still spaces of the night, one is almost in touch with the mysteries of the Beyond. The curtain hangs between, but one feels that at any moment it may be lifted by an unseen hand. In the great world outside, only the stars and burning hearts are awake. But here, in this serene atmosphere of compelling peace, all passions melt, all small things fade away, and there is left only the brooding gloom of midnight and the unfathomable spirit of silence.

Suddenly, upon this hush, as of graveyards, there breaks the clangour of a deep-toned bell. It snaps the spell and wounds the serenity of the midnight watch. If you rise and stand by your window, you may see a long line of phantom-like figures, looming through the shadows, wending their way in silence to the low door that leads into the monastery church. The Silent Men of Oka have risen from their cells and come forth to worship their God.

For them the night is over and the long, laborious, silent day has begun. Through the measured spaces of the darkness, each in his stall, they remain offering up their meed of adoration. Here they break their silence but to pray; here only do they find speech to testify to the Faith.

In stately simplicity Gregorian chants roll sonorous to the vaulted roof. The same chants that once echoed around the heights of the Cistercian Hill, sung in the same language that rolled in measured accents through the Cistercian chapel in olden Rome, now roll and rise and fall within the narrow confines of this holy place. Then silence once more — silence — silence.

(Memories that Live)

Miriam Chapin (1886-1965)

Miss Chapin wrote *Contemporary Canada* and *Quebec Now*. She also translated *Agaguk* and *The* | *Impertinences of Brother Anonymous* from the French.

QUEBEC NOW

Westmount is a city inside Montreal like a kangaroo's baby. It has its own postal service, police force, regulations, street-cleaning. A woman can live her whole life there and never speak a word of French, come in contact with no French Canadian except janitor, tram conductor, store clerk. She can say, as I overheard one, "Poor Sally, she can't find an apartment. She heard of one down in St. Louis Square, but of course only French people live there." So might a Princess Radziwill have spoken of the ghetto. She can dine at the Ritz, at the height of the conscription crisis, and as the French waiter's steady hand sets her soup before her, say as I heard one woman in 1944, "They ought to come down here from Ontario and just clean out the French, the lot of them. They're all yellow."

Les dames de Westmount, as their charwomen call them, lead busy lives. Their charity boards relieve any itch of discomfort they may feel over the contrast between their circumstances and that of their neighbours in St. Henri, so near below the tracks. They say, "But those people know how to get along on their wages." The Red Cross, the I.O.D.E., the Grenfell Mission, the hairdresser, dinner for the boss and his wife, or for Cousin Jim and that friend of Andy's — all these obligations leave little time to think. The husbands are the bank managers, the engineers, the brokers, down through the hierarchy. They have their clubs, the St. James, Mt. Stephen and the rest, the Royal St. Lawrence Yacht Club, and then for the lower echelons, Rotary, Kiwanis and the like. Summer homes are in the mountains; for the very rich, there is Nassau. The older families, those who have not surrendered and moved to apartments, live on the short streets running up Mont Royal from Sherbrooke Street, though most of the towered monstrosities built by railway millionaires have lapsed into use as schools or even rooming-houses.

Life in the middle-class English community of Montreal goes on much like that of Toronto, or a medium-sized American city, except for a certain sense of beleaguerment. It is the same feeling, in minor degree, that besets Atlanta and Singapore, the feeling of being invisibly hemmed in by an alien and unfriendly kind. There is more emphasis on church attendance than in an American city, more army life, more formal social occasions. The great balls of St. Andrew's and the rest are horrendous bores, mitigated only by the gathering of previously alerted cliques in upstairs rooms where the liquor can flow freely, and by the thought of the Dior gowns to be described in next morning's *Gazette*.

But among the young the routine is breaking down. The skiing weekend elbows aside the family dinner, the big houses are demolished to save taxes. The boys' schools with their "forms" and their Greek, have to prepare for Americanized colleges. Cricket is almost unknown; Canadian football (twelve on a side) draws the crowds. More and more girls go to college as a matter of course, not contenting themselves with the finishing school, though more of them will make a formal debut than in any American city. Most English Montreal girls are good looking, in tweeds and sweaters, with shining hair. They lack, however, that touch of vividness that once in a while makes a French *jeune fille* a thing of exquisite loveliness. Boys and girls grow up hardly knowing they are in a French city, unless they come up against some regulation which surprises them, like the ten-year-old who swam in the Lachine Canal with only trunks, and emerged to find his companions had run away, while a policeman pointed a revolver at his skinny little chest, bawling him out for exposing his lascivious form.

The Molsons and the Dawes (beer), the Gordons (textile), the Muirs and Gardners (banks), the Morgans and the Birks ("in trade"), the Allans, the Drummonds and all their kin make up the leadership of English Montreal. They run the hospitals (and beware lest any socialized medicine raise its head); they run McGill, the turret on the bastion of their fortress; they run the Welfare Council; they run the Museum of Fine Arts, Montreal's art gallery. Sometimes there is rebellion. In 1952 the trustees fired the director of the gallery, over loud protests. There was schism in the ranks. He had, in five years, opened up the place for one evening a week with no admission charge, rejected pictures by their favourite portraitist, even put up as "picture of the week", a sketch by that Communist, Picasso.

(Quebec Now)

Leslie Roberts (Born in 1896)

Radio commentator and versatile writer, Roberts is author of *Canada, the Golden Hinge.* His "Unpopular Editorial" has appeared in *The Montrealer;* the following is one of his articles from the *Montreal Star.*

WHY WOULD A NON-FRENCH CANADIAN REALLY WANT TO LIVE IN QUEBEC?

If Mr. Lesage, Mr. Johnson, the R.I.N., the Rassemblement National and all the other odds and ends who have talked provincial politics at us over the past month have done me one favour, they have at least led me to ask myself: Why have I voluntarily lived in this province throughout my adult life?

There is, of course one very simple answer which would come out "because I like it here," which would at once be perfectly true and simultaneously a gross over-simplification. I am, for example, almost equally fond of Nova Scotia, but have never thought of establishing permanent residence there. So what is it that has kept me here when, for the greater part of my working-years, since economics and personal convenience clearly suggested a change of residence?

A good many reasons exist why an Anglo- or Un-French-Canadian probably should prefer to live somewhere else; a point which friends and colleagues who do, repeatedly bring up in conversation. They tell me Toronto is the mecca of Canadian culture (English-speaking). Maybe so. I have no intention of getting into *that* argument, thank you. They tell me (and it is perfectly true) that the Ontario capital is the centre of book-publishing, magazine production, network television and a number of other things connected with the kind of life I live — the centre of these things in matters in which English is the language. Ergo, that's where I should be living. The hell it is.

I can go them one better than that. There have been lengthy periods during which the chores of this trade have caused me to reside in faraway places. Yet there has never been a time when I have not maintained a base either in Montreal or the Eastern Townships, to which I have always applied the term "home." Until I became involved in daily broadcasting approximately a decade ago and some time later in producing this column, there were periods (in fact most of my adult life) when not one bit of my income was earned either in Montreal or any other part of La Belle Province. Obviously I should have been living in a place more adjacent to my bread and butter. So I stayed right here, contrary curmudgeon that I am.

Nor am I a member of what is sometimes called The Establishement. Au contraire, I consider myself a person devoid of what are generally called "social ambitions." Status doesn't interest me. When the time comes, I ask no more than to be remembered as a fellow who had learned enough about the trade of stringing nouns, verbs and adjectives together to be accepted as a craftsman among craftsmen. For the rest of it, phooey. Well, I don't have to live in Quebec either to achieve or fail to achieve that reasonably humble ambition.

The first person singular keeps repeating itself as I ruminate on this typewriter. This, I assure you, is solely because I know very little about any other human being but the one whose by-line occurs under the title. That is to say I know virtually nothing about what goes on inside any head but my own. The motive power of this piece, in other words, isn't personal ego.

It merely explains why one non-French Quebecker is here, by sheer personal, stubborn choice.

I like the stir of ferment in which one resides here and which bubbles up all around him. The reference is not to Expo '67. At peril of breaking up a number of beautiful friendships, I have a hunch next summer might be a good time to be elsewhere. If the Universal, International, Multilingual Exposition of What Man and His World have contrived to do down the course of the centuries is the success I expect it to be, Montreal is going to resemble a madhouse approximately a year from now. As a guy who is addicted to peace and quiet, once curiosity has been sated by taking one good look, if I can't get away, then my quiet sun-and-shade deck, up among the trees, is going to be enough for me. I figure I have made my small contribution to Expo '67 by trying to keep track, day by day, of the street detours of 1966. Forgive the heresy. But that's the way it is.

But to get back to the main line of our topic, one good reason for living in Montreal and La Belle Province is because the place is alive and bubbling over. I know of no other place in North America where so much is happening in so many areas simultaneously. This is one good reason why this is home, although it is a more or less new reason. This does not mean I like everything that is afoot, even physically, in the town. Some of the new packing-case-Gothic architecture and much of the so-called "high rise" bit, gives me the pip, especially when it has been designed to conceal the view, looking up to, not down from, Mount Royal. But, as the hucksters would say, this "is where the action is." I enjoy watching it, getting mad at it, but also having that feeling of participation in watching Montreal become what the Mayor calls "a great world-city." I only hope it doesn't end up looking like a replica of Omaha.

But when I sort it all out, the real reason for being here at all is because the French-speakers are here, too, whereas if I lived in Vancouver (another town I like) I not only would be forced to read or hear speeches made by Wacky Bennett, but look or listen to words happening always in English — a lot of it not even in good English. I prefer to peruse the editorials in *Le Devoir,* thank you.

It is also possible that, having been born a Welshman, I am strictly a natural-born minority member. I actually enjoy fighting back when something is said by, say, René Levesque (of whom I am extremely fond as a person;) which raises my Anglophobe's hackles. I realized, many years ago, for example, that little if any political future exists hereabouts for a non-French citizen, or at least that he can't expect to strike out for the top. Knowing this, despite the fact that in somewhat earlier times one nurtured thoughts of public life, one pushed them to one side and stayed on (if the meteoric career of Mr. Eric Kierans appears to give the lie to the previous statement, his success is in considerable degree attributable to the fact that he has, in a sense, "gone French").

Anyway, I like it here because the French are here, because a lot of them are among my good friends, because we can argue with each other about all the issues around us — then go to lunch together without either party nursing a grievance against the other. I like it here because some of this Gallic love of argumentation has rubbed off onto me — and I love it in spite of my persistent trouble with French irregular verbs, which are almost as unpredictable as French-speaking women — and, incidentally, men. Anybody who has missed the opportunity to participate in all this inexplicable je-ne-sais-quoi has missed a goodly part of the business of being a Canadian.

I loved the Quebec that was, before the current renaissance, although I cordially disliked the kind of government a man named Duplessis ran for so long, whose name was barely mentioned during the campaign until about Wednesday. But, unlike at least some of mes concitoyens de la langue Anglaise, I am all for the reawakening and for most of what has happened since the sleeping giant began to stir in the late 1950s and came wide awake in 1960. As for myself, it is the finest thing that has happened in and to Canada during my years in the land, which are numerous. Some of it irritates me at times. Some of the silly things that are said can make me plain angry. But, hell's bells, I'm no paragon, either. The Old Quebec was a grand place for an Anglo to live in and the new Quebec is even better (pay no heed to all that nonsense about "exploiters" or "conquerors"). As a breed we non-French aren't and never have been either, if only because to the average Anglo the opportunity hasn't been available.

So, to bring this philosophizing to a conclusion, I live in Quebec not "in spite of", but "because of" what is called the French fact. And if I have one final word of advice to my fellow Anglos hereabouts, it is never to segregate yourselves from the French-speaking majority, but to get in with them, just as my advice to my friends de la langue Fran-çaise, is to jump into the main stream of Canadian life.

(Montreal Star)

Guy Frégault (Né en 1918)

Docteur en histoire, professeur à l'Université de Montréal, puis à l'Université d'Ottawa, il est depuis 1961 sous-ministre des Affaires culturelles de Québec.

Membre de l'Académie canadienne-française, ses ouvrages sont peu nombreux mais tous sont importants. Suit la conclusion de *La Guerre de la conquête.*

LA GUERRE DE LA CONQUÊTE

Au terme de la guerre de la Conquête, c'est un livre qui se ferme. L'histoire ne continue pas, elle recommence. Une évolution s'arrête. Sans doute repart-elle, mais pour épouser une telle courbe qu'elle constituera proprement une autre évolution. Ce retournement des choses n'est pas difficile à constater. Il s'accompagne de déclarations si explicites que l'on admire combien, tout en les retenant, on en a peu tenu compte. Ainsi, quinze ans après la capitulation de Montréal, le chef spirituel des Canadiens, Mgr Briand, écrit à un de ses adminis-trés : « ... On dit de moi, comme on dit de vous, que je suis anglais ...

Je suis Anglais, en effet; vous devez l'être; ils [les Canadiens] le doivent être eux aussi, puisqu'ils en ont fait le serment, et que toutes les lois naturelles, divines et humaines le leur commandent. Mais ni moi, ni vous, ni eux ne doivent [*sic*] être de la religion anglaise. Voilà, les pauvres gens, ce qu'ils n'entendent pas; ils sont sous la domination anglaise, pour le civil » ... Trente ans après le traité de Paris, un chef politique de la province de Québec, Chartier de Lotbinière, trouve cet argument pour défendre le statut constitutionnel de la langue française : elle doit, raisonne-t-il, être « agréable » à Georges III, « puisqu'elle lui rappelle la gloire de son empire et qu'elle lui prouve d'une manière forte et puissante que les peuples de ce vaste continent sont attachés à leur prince, qu'ils lui sont fidèles, et qu'ils sont anglais par le coeur avant même d'en savoir prononcer un seul mot ». Ainsi s'expriment, parmi beaucoup d'autres, deux porte-parole des Canadiens : l'un assimile ses compatriotes à des Anglais catholiques; l'autre, à des Anglais francophones.

Singulier réalisme, mêlé à une singulière illusion. Ces deux esprits représentatifs ont compris qu'il s'est produit quelque chose d'infiniment grave chez les Canadiens. Ceux-ci ne sont plus les mêmes depuis qu'ils sont passés sous une « domination » ou, autrement dit, sous un « empire » anglais. Ils ont été transformés par la transfiguration du pays dans lequel ils survivent. Ce changement, toutefois, les atteint plus encore que leurs chefs ne croient. Deux ou trois coups de sonde en révéleraient la profondeur. Peuple que le commerce avait formé, qui avait vécu du négoce plus que de l'agriculture, qui avait trouvé à la terre si peu de « charme » — le mot est de Talon — qu'il fallut, vers 1750, élaborer une législation rigoureuse pour enrayer l'exode rural, voilà maintenant les Canadiens qui se replient sur le sol et qui, lorsqu'ils rentreront dans les villes, y reviendront comme des immigrants. Après avoir vécu sous un gouvernement de type militaire, avoir fourni des capitaines et des combattants à toute la Nouvelle-France et même à la métropole et s'être fait une réputation de « belliqueux », on verra ce groupe humain, et à plus d'une reprise, unanime sur un seul point, lui toujours si divisé : le refus de porter les armes. Capable, durant un siècle et demi, de donner naissance à de nombreuses équipes d'organisateurs, à la fois explorateurs, diplomates, brasseurs de grandes affaires et soldats, aptes à mettre sur pied l'administration, l'exploitation et la défense de territoires immenses autant que variés, la société canadienne montrera tout à coup un embarras extrêmement pénible à pourvoir même à son organisation intérieure. En vérité, les Canadiens ont changé.

Serait-il vrai que « les lois naturelles, divines et humaines » ont fait d'eux des Anglais ou qu'ils le sont devenus « par le coeur » ? Là apparaît l'illusion. En fait, un monde anglais s'est refermé sur les Canadiens, sans pourtant qu'ils se fondent en lui, car il s'est créé contre eux et il se développe sans eux. Leurs générations se succèdent désormais dans un empire, dans un continent et dans un Etat britanniques. Britanniques, les institutions politiques et les réalités économiques au milieu desquelles leur existence s'écoule. Fatalement étrangères, les armatures sociales qui se forgent autour d'eux et au-dessus d'eux. Et leur propre armature sociale ayant été tronquée en même temps que secouée sur ses bases, ils ne forment plus qu'un résidu humain, dépouillé de la direction et des moyens sans lesquels ils ne sont pas à même de concevoir et de mettre en oeuvre la politique et l'économie qu'il leur faut. Les consolations qu'ils cherchent ne leur donnent pas ce qu'ils n'ont plus. Leur condition ne résulte pas d'un choix qu'ils auraient fait : il n'ont guère eu de choix; elle est la conséquence directe de la conquête qui a disloqué leur société, supprimé leurs cadres et affaibli leur dynamisme interne, si bien qu'elle s'achève en eux.

Nous avons mis du temps à comprendre le véritable caractère du conflit qui entraîna, voici bientôt deux siècles, l'écroulement du Canada. Ce retard tient à deux causes principales. En premier lieu, nous nous sommes fait une image à la fois merveilleuse, édifiante et sommaire du régime français. C'était l'époque où la société canadienne avait un développement complet et, surtout, normal; nous nous sommes plu, la nostalgie, la vanité et la littérature aidant, à y voir un milieu historique créé par des hommes extraordinaires et dans des circonstances exceptionnelles. A nous entendre, cette société aurait été fondée à rendre grâces au Ciel de ce qu'elle n'était pas comme le reste des sociétés humaines, où l'esprit s'incarne dans la matière et où la qualité ne va pas toute seule, sans la quantité; nous nous la représentions volontiers toute spiritualiste et qualitative. Dans cette perspective, comment attacher de l'importance à l'effondrement, survenu dans les années 1760, des fondements matériels de la civilisation canadienne ? Des fondements matériels, elle s'en passerait ! En avait-elle jamais eus ? Le « miracle canadien » continuerait, comme toujours, à s'opérer régulièrement.

En second lieu, nous avons été lents à mesurer les répercussions de la défaite parce que, sans nous interdire de nous raconter les épisodes de la guerre qui l'amena, nous ne fûmes pas curieux d'en dégager les causes, de la replacer dans les cadres du conflit mondial où elle se déroula et, moins encore, de connaître les mobiles de ceux à qui le sort des armes donna la victoire. On eût dit qu'il nous suffisait de savoir qu'ils étaient méchants. Les historiens, il convient de l'avouer, ne nous aidaient guère. Canadiens ou français, ils dépouillaient les sources françaises; américains ou anglais, ils consultaient les collections britanniques; et les érudits chicanaient. Sans doute Parkman avait-il, admirable pionnier, réuni une documentation moins unilatérale que les autres; mais il s'en était servi, avec un talent inégalé, pour mettre de la couleur locale et brosser des tableaux tout en contrastes. Les historiens écrivaient donc du point de vue français ou du point de vue anglais. Pour nous, nous faisions comme s'il était possible de pénétrer le sens de la conquête sans nous enquérir des objectifs de ceux qui l'effectuèrent. Nous ne nous demandions pas s'ils avaient su ce qu'ils faisaient. Comme s'ils s'étaient battus pour rien, pour le plaisir. Ils avaient cependant vu plus clair dans notre avenir que nous dans leur pensée. Franklin a saisi mieux qu'aucun de nos docteurs les conséquences de l'effritement du Canada. Que dire aussi de cet Américain britannique qui donne les vaincus de 1760 pour un groupe humain « brisé en tant que peuple » ? Ce n'est pas un prophète; ce n'est qu'un homme assez intelligent pour noter correctement un fait d'observation.

Que l'on ne parle pas de pessimisme. Ce serait un signe trop manifeste d'inattention. Le sismographe qui enregistre un tremblement de terre est précis ou inexact; il ne viendrait à l'idée de personne de le dire optimiste ou pessimiste selon la violence de la secousse qu'il mesure. L'utilité d'une entreprise historique ne se juge ni aux émotions qu'elle donne ni aux soulagements qu'elle procure, mais à la valeur des éclaircissements qu'elle fournit. Puisque les enjolivements affadissent jusqu'aux fables, on devrait convenir qu'ils sont hors de saison dans les travaux scientifiques. Ceux qui abordent une oeuvre d'histoire en vue d'y trouver des frissons de fierté montreraient autant de bon sens que de bon goût en allant chercher ailleurs les sensations qu'ils préfèrent. Au terme de cette étude, notre conclusion ne peut, en toute honnêteté, qu'être la suivante. Si, comme le dit un excellent méthodologiste anglais, l'histoire est une hypothèse permettant d'expliquer les situations actuelles par celles qui les ont précédées, un examen attentif de la façon systématique et décisive dont le peuple canadien fut « brisé » doit nous mettre à même de voir sous son vrai jour la crise, d'ailleurs évidente, de la société canadienne-française et de constater qu'il ne s'agit pas d'une crise de conjoncture, mais bien de structure, — de structure démolie et jamais convenablement relevée.

Il ne m'échappe pas que cette conclusion est troublante. J'avoue même que, si elle n'inquiétait pas, cela signifierait qu'elle n'est pas comprise. Ne serait-ce point, cependant, raisonner de façon fort singulière que de la juger mauvaise parce que dure et dangereuse parce que démontrée ? Ah ! si l'histoire n'était que jeu, que déploiement d'érudition sans rapport avec le présent ! Mais alors, il faudrait, sous un autre nom, trouver une discipline qui remplit le même office; il faudrait créer une science qui pût mesurer les pressions du passé sur le présent et en déterminer la nature; il faudrait inventer l'histoire. Et la pratiquer froidement. Marc Bloch rapporte le mot qui échappa, en juin 1940, à un officier français désemparé par la défaite : « Faut-il croire que l'histoire nous ait trompés ? » L'homme pouvait parler ainsi parce que la tradition historique du groupe dans lequel il se trouvait pris ne l'avait pas préparé à l'éventualité de la catastrophe et que — considération plus pénible encore — elle ne l'avait pas mis à même, lui et la société à laquelle il appartenait, de travailler avec efficacité à conjurer le désastre. Ce qui l'avait trompé, ce n'était pas l'histoire, c'était la tradition qui passait pour de l'histoire.

C'est justement une des fonctions de l'histoire — la principale, à mon sens, — que de corriger systématiquement la tradition selon laquelle un groupe humain ordonne sa vie. A elle d'expliquer le présent en montrant comment il s'est fait. Si elle refuse cette tâche, la société laissera dériver son attention sur les faux problèmes parce que ce sont les plus faciles ou, ce qui revient au même, elle cédera à la tentation absurde de regarder les problèmes les plus graves comme de vieilles questions depuis longtemps réglées. L'histoire, dit Lucien Febvre, « est un moyen d'organiser le passé pour l'empêcher de trop peser sur les épaules des hommes ». Les hommes ont besoin d'histoire parce que, sans elle, le passé risquerait de les écraser. Mais il va de soi que, s'ils ont un rigoureux besoin d'histoire, ils ont besoin d'une histoire rigoureusement vraie. Il faut d'abord ouvrir les yeux sur le réel, si inquiétant soit-il, pour se mettre en état d'en écarter les périls.

(*La Guerre de la conquête,* 1955)

Marcel Trudel (Né en 1917)

Professeur d'histoire aux universités Laval, Carleton et d'Ottawa successivement, il est membre de l'Académie canadienne-française et président du Conseil des Arts de la province de Québec.

MURRAY FAIT MARCHER L'ÉGLISE DU QUÉBEC

Ce sont là à Montréal et aux Trois-Rivières de rares cas d'ingérence dans l'Eglise. Il en va bien autrement dans le gouvernement de Québec où Murray entend bien obtenir et garder le contrôle de l'administration religieuse. Murray avait constaté la puissance que l'évêque exerçait sur son clergé; il veut donc que cette puissance devienne le privilège du gouverneur afin, comme il l'écrit, de tenir les prêtres *dans un état de sujétion nécessaire.* La capitulation de Québec n'avait pas fait mention des cures; aussi, dès la disparition de l'évêque, Murray convoque-t-il chez lui le grand-vicaire Briand et nous constatons que, par la suite, le gouverneur Murray agit tout comme s'il avait pris en main la direction administrative de l'Eglise québécoise : à l'automne de 1761, il fait passer Petit de la cure de Deschaillons à celle de Saint-Michel-de-Bellechasse; à la demande de Murray, en janvier 1762, le curé de Berthier-en-bas devient curé de Saint-Vallier; Gatien ne prend possession de la cure de Berthier-en-bas qu'après avoir obtenu l'adhésion de Murray; ce même gouverneur, en août 1762, menace le curé de Saint-Thomas-de-Montmagny de l'envoyer à la cure des Grondines; enfin, c'est sur une plainte de Murray que le curé de Saint-Pierre-de-Montmagny est transféré en 1764 à la cure de Lachenaie. Cette prépondérance de Murray est si bien connue que des prêtres y ont recours pour obtenir un ministère de leur choix : le récollet Veyssière réussit de cette façon à demeurer à Saint-Michel-de-Bellechasse malgré les projets du grand-vicaire Briand; Pressart, ex-supérieur du Séminaire de Québec, désire faire du ministère à la paroisse Notre-Dame (alors chez les Ursulines) : Briand s'y oppose, mais Pressart va voir Murray et gagne son point.

Nous retrouvons dans d'autres domaines cette prépondérance de Murray. En 1762, le Séminaire de Paris nomme pour Québec un nouveau supérieur : c'était son droit traditionnel et ce droit demeurait toujours valide puisque le Canada n'appartenait pas encore officiellement à l'Angleterre; mis au courant de cette nomination, Murray convoque les directeurs du Séminaire de Québec et les oblige de procéder à une élection, en excluant d'avance tout prêtre choisi par le Séminaire de Paris. Lorsque Murray a besoin d'une salle chez les Ursulines pour y rendre la justice criminelle, il retient d'abord la salle et ce n'est qu'ensuite qu'il avertit le supérieur ecclésiastique des religieuses. En 1762, Murray veut que l'on prie pour le Roi d'Angleterre; en cela, rien d'anormal : on priait pour George III aux Trois-Rivières et à Montréal, mais seulement dans les prières du prône. Or Murray veut davantage : avant que le Canada soit cédé à l'Angleterre, Murray veut que le roi soit nommé dans le canon de la messe, tout comme l'était le roi de France qui, pourtant, détenait ce privilège parce que l'un de ses devoirs officiels était de maintenir le catholicisme. Sans récriminer et bien qu'aux Trois-Rivières et à

Montréal on continuât de ne nommer George III qu'au prône, le grand-vicaire Briand exécute la volonté de Murray en donnant comme excuse que les ordres sont formels. Chaque fois, Murray trouve devant lui un grand-vicaire disposé à obéir.

Et ce grand-vicaire ne met jamais en doute les dispositions de Murray. Il ne se scandalise nullement quand Murray somme un curé de comparaître à Québec devant l'autorité militaire, avec défense de conférer avec qui que ce soit auparavant. Briand fait même plus pour encourager l'ingérence de Murray : comme le vicaire Parent refuse de sortir de Saint-Vallier, Briand invite l'autorité militaire et protestante à servir de bras séculier. Il a en Murray une telle confiance qu'il propose même que l'élection de l'évêque se fasse en présence du gouverneur et que, si ce dernier n'est pas satisfait, on recommence l'élection.

Le gouverneur Murray (et c'est peut-être ce qui explique le comportement de Briand) ne souhaitait pas la disparition de l'Eglise canadienne, il voyait tout simplement en elle un puissant organisme qu'il serait fort utile de contrôler sévèrement : en lui donnant un caractère plus national et en faisant nommer les curés par le roi ou par le gouverneur, Murray comptait la rendre tout à fait docile. Il avait été assez heureux, depuis les débuts du régime militaire, pour tenir bien en main l'Eglise de Québec. C'est pourquoi, quand vint le temps de régler le problème religieux de la nouvelle colonie, Murray proposa une solution conforme à sa propre politique : l'Eglise canadienne serait toujours administrée par des vicaires généraux, les deux séminaires seraient fusionnés en un seul et le supérieur serait nommé par le roi, on renverrait immédiatement les jésuites avec une pension, la nomination des curés appartiendrait au gouvernement; bref, cette Eglise sans évêque, parfaitement soumise aux obédiences politiques, demeurerait un instrument fort commode de domination.

Ce programme accablant est proposé par le gouverneur Murray à une époque où l'Eglise canadienne subit une diminution désastreuse dans ses effectifs. En janvier 1759, elle comptait 196 prêtres : à la fin de décembre 1764, elle n'en compte plus que 137, ayant donc perdu dans le bref espace de cinq ans, le tiers de ses effectifs. Pour combler ce vide, on ne peut plus compter sur le recrutement de France et l'on ne trouve au pays qu'une dizaine de grands séminaristes qui doivent attendre la venue encore toute problématique d'un évêque. Chez les communautés d'hommes, la situation devient désastreuse : le chapitre a terminé son histoire; les Jésuites, déjà réduits au petit nombre de 16, ont reçu l'ordre de s'éteindre; les Récollets, dont la moitié ne mènent plus la vie conventuelle, devront eux aussi s'éteindre; le séminaire de Québec, qui a subi pour plus de 85,000 livres de dommages, ne doit plus compter que sur lui-même, puisque le séminaire de Paris n'a plus le droit de lui envoyer du renfort, et il doit, de plus, modifier profondément sa formule en créant chez lui de toutes pièces un collège classique qui remplacera celui que les autorités anglaises ont transformé en entrepôt. Des cinq communautés d'hommes, il n'y a vraiment que celle des Sulpiciens qui s'en tire avec le moins possible d'inconvénients. Partout, la pénurie du clergé est très grave : il n'y a plus que 3 prêtres dans l'immense région des Illinois, 3 prêtres dans tout le pays des Grands Lacs; dans l'ancien gouvernement des Trois-Rivières, la moitié des centres de population sont sans prêtre résidant; un seul prêtre doit desservir toute la rive nord depuis les Eboulements jusqu'aux Sept-Iles; sur la rive sud, depuis les Trois-Pistoles jusqu'à la Baie-des-Chaleurs, un seul prêtre, et encore est-ce un septuagénaire ! dans toute l'Acadie (continentale, péninsulaire et insulaire), il n'y a plus là aussi qu'un seul prêtre.

(*L'Eglise canadienne sous le régime militaire, 1759-1764, II, Les institutions,* 1956)

Michel Brunet (Né en 1917)

Professeur d'histoire à l'Université de Montréal, membre de l'Académie canadienne-française, il s'est surtout intéressé aux problèmes que pose la coexistence des deux nationalités au Canada.

FIDÉLITÉ BRITANNIQUE

Quelle a été, en général, l'attitude de l'ancienne métropole du Canada anglais ? A-t-elle cru que celui-ci mettrait brutalement fin à son alliance avec la mère patrie ?

Les plus grands hommes d'Etat du Royaume-Uni — les Dorchester, les Dalhousie, les Durham, les Grey, les Elgin, les Carnarvon, les Chamberlain, les Balfour, les Churchill — n'ont jamais mis sérieusement en doute la fidélité britannique des *Canadians,* qui s'étaient d'abord appelés les *British Americans.* A certains moments, quelques observateurs myopes — dont les déclarations ont eu beaucoup d'écho au Canada français — ont prétendu que l'émancipation politique du Canada anglais et l'acquisition de sa pleine souveraineté le conduiraient infailliblement à la rupture de ses liens séculaires avec la Grande-Bretagne et l'Empire. Ceux qui connaissaient l'histoire du pays et sa volonté de demeurer fidèle à l'idéal qui lui avait donné naissance n'ajoutèrent jamais foi à ces pronostics. Aux heures d'épreuve — 1899, 1914, 1939 et 1945-1946, on se rendit compte que ceux-ci étaient faux.

L'Empire a bien évolué depuis le Statut de Westminster. Le Commonwealth ne compte pas uniquement, depuis la fin de la dernière guerre, des nations d'origine britannique. L'Inde, le Pakistan, le Ceylan et les Boers d'Afrique du Sud constituent les points faibles de cette alliance. Mais le véritable Commonwealth, celui qui n'a pas changé et ne changera pas, c'est le Royaume-Uni, le Canada, l'Australie et la Nouvelle-Zélande. Ces nations-soeurs en sont « l'épine dorsale », selon l'expression de lord Vansittart qui n'entretient aucune illusion sur la fidélité des autres membres.[63] Il en est ainsi parce que la population de ces pays est totalement ou en majorité britannique. Les liens du sang, de la race et de la langue garantissent leur fidélité britannique.

Un récent discours de sir Winston Churchill mérite de retenir l'attention. Lors de sa dernière visite à Ottawa, le premier ministre du Royaume-Uni a adressé un message d'adieu au peuple canadien. Le vieil homme d'Etat, dont la conduite durant la dernière guerre demeurera l'un des grands moments de l'histoire humaine, y affirme sa foi inébranlable en l'avenir du pays qui fut autrefois une modeste colonie anglaise. Il rappelle l'étroite camaraderie « des grands Dominions — si cette expression n'est pas périmée — qui se sont réunis autour de nous dans leur force et leur vitalité ». Il remercie la Providence d'avoir donné à tous les peuples britanniques « cette rayonnante figure qu'est la reine du Canada. C'est à cause d'elle que tous les habitants des terres du Commonwealth sont frères. » Churchill doit être le premier à savoir qu'il faudrait nuancer cette dernière affirmation. L'unité et la fraternité des membres du Commonwealth n'ont jamais reposé et ne reposent pas uniquement sur leur allégeance commune à la Couronne. Cette allégeance elle-même s'appuie sur des bases très concrètes : la race, la langue, les traditions politiques et les intérêts économiques. Mais l'homme d'Etat n'est pas tenu au langage brutalement réaliste de l'historien et du spécialiste en science politique. Certaines fictions sont absolument nécessaires au gouvernement des hommes. En terminant, sir Winston demande aux *Canadians* : « N'ou-

---

63. Voir son article « Commonwealth Gains : Royal Tour Tightens Bonds », *Montreal Star,* 28 mai 1954.

bliez pas le vieux pays, n'oubliez pas cette petite île, perdue dans les vents du Nord, qui a joué un si grand rôle lors de vos débuts. Elle vous regarde maintenant avec admiration et fierté. »[64]

L'historien ne peut pas citer ce discours de sir Winston Churchill sans rappeler les paroles prophétiques d'un autre homme d'Etat du Royaume-Uni qui croyait, lui aussi, en l'avenir du Canada anglais et en la grandeur de l'Empire britannique. Lord Carnarvon, qui collabora à la rédaction et à l'adoption de l'Acte de l'Amérique du Nord britannique, eut le mérite de comprendre qu'il assistait à la naissance d'un puissant Etat. Il appuya et conseilla Macdonald et les autres délégués coloniaux. A la Chambre des Lords, il défendit le projet avec éloquence et déclara : « Nous posons les bases d'un grand Etat — d'un Etat qui peut-être dans l'avenir jettera dans l'ombre notre propre pays. Mais, quoi qu'il arrive, nous nous réjouirons un jour de n'être pas demeurés indifférents à leurs demandes et de n'avoir manifesté aucune jalousie devant leurs ambitions. Au contraire, nous aurons lieu de nous féliciter d'avoir honnêtement et sincèrement, en mettant à contribution toute notre puissance et toutes nos connaissances, favorisé leur développement et leurs progrès, reconnaissant que ceux-ci contribuent directement à notre propre grandeur. »[65]

Heureuse et privilégiée la nation qui a eu de tels hommes d'Etat pour diriger ses destinées ! Qui soutiendrait que lord Carnarvon et tous les dirigeants britanniques et anglo-canadiens qui ont pensé comme lui n'avaient pas vu juste ? L'histoire de la fidélité britannique des *Canadians* confirme toutes leurs prophéties.

(*Canadians et Canadiens,* 1954)

---

64. *La Presse,* 30 juin 1954.
65. Discours de lord Carnarvon à la Chambre des Lords, le 19 février 1867; citation donnée dans Hamilton, éd., *Canadian Quotations,* 20.

Germaine Guèvremont (Née en 1900)

Journaliste, secrétaire de la Société des Ecrivains canadiens, elle publia des contes du terroir, puis les deux premiers romans d'une trilogie : *Le Survenant* (1945) et *Marie-Didace* (1947), évocation poétique d'une famille terrienne qui se meurt et que vient troubler un moment un inoubliable garçon de ferme. Germaine Guèvremont est membre de l'Académie canadienne-française et de la Société royale du Canada.

LE SURVENANT

Le Survenant resta au Chenal du Moine. Amable et Alphonsine eurent beau être vilains avec lui, il ne s'offensa ni de leurs regards de méfiance, ni de leurs remarques mesquines. Mais la première fois que le père Didace fit allusion à la rareté de l'ouvrage, Venant lâcha net la faux qu'il était en train d'affûter pour nettoyer de ses joncs une nouvelle mare de chasse. Ses grands bras battant l'air comme pour s'ouvrir un ravage parmi des branchages touffus, il bondit en face du chef de la famille.

Ainsi que l'habile artisan, au bon moment, sait choisir la planche de pin et, d'une main sans défaillance, y tailler un gabarit parfait, il sut que son heure était venue de parler franchement ou bien de repartir :

— Ecoutez, le père Beauchemin, vous et vos semblables. Prenez-moi pas pour un larron ou pour un scélérat des grands bois. Je suis ni un tueur, ni un voleur. Et encore moins un tricheur. Partout où c'est que je passe, j'ai coutume de gagner mon sel, puis le beurre pour mettre dedans. Je vous ai offert de me garder moyennant asile et nourriture. Si vous avez pas satisfaction, dites-le : la route est proche. De mon bord, si j'aime pas l'ordinaire, pas même le temps de changer de hardes et je pars.

Cette façon droite de parler, ce langage de batailleur plurent à Didace. Cependant, il ne voulut rien en laisser voir. Il se contenta de répondre carrément :

— Reste le temps qu'il faudra !

Venant vint sur le point d'ajouter :

— En fait de marché, vous avez déjà connu pire, hé, le père ?

Mais il se retint à temps : le déploiement d'une trop grande vaillance, une fois la bataille gagnée, est peine perdue.

Ainsi il serait un de la maison. Longuement il examina la demeure des Beauchemin. Trapue, massive, et blanchie au lait de chaux, sous son toit noir en déclive douce, elle reposait, avec le fournil collé à elle, sur un monticule, à peine une butte, au coeur d'une touffe de liards. Un peu à l'écart en contre-bas se dressaient les bâtiments : au premier rang deux granges neuves qu'on avait érigées l'année précédente, énormes et imposantes, disposées en équerre, la plus avancée portant au faîte, en chiffres d'étain, la date de leur élévation : 1908. Puis, refoulé à l'arrière, l'entassement des anciennes dépendances recouvertes de chaumes : remise, tasserie, appentis encore utilisables, mais au bois pourri faiblissant de partout.

Elle ressemblait à une maison par lui aperçue en rêve autrefois : une maison assise au bord d'une route allant mourir au bois, avec une belle rivière à ses pieds. Il y resterait le temps qu'il faudrait : un mois ? Deux mois ? Six mois ? Insoucieux de l'avenir, il haussa les épaules et ramassa la pierre et l'outil. Puis, d'un pouce lent, sensible, humide de salive, ayant pris connaissance du taillant, il continua tranquillement à affûter la faux.

— Arrivez vite, Survenant, le manger est dressé.

Comme il s'avançait vers la maison, Alphonsine lui reprocha :

— Traînez donc pas toujours de l'aile de même après les autres.

Alphonsine se mettait en peine d'un rien. Le plus léger dérangement dans la besogne routinière la bouleversait pour le reste de la journée. De plus, de faible appétit, d'avoir à préparer l'ordinaire, depuis la mort de sa belle-mère, surtout la viande que Didace voulait fortement relevée d'épices, d'ail et de gros sel, lui était tous les jours une nouvelle pénitence. Nul supplice cependant n'égalait pour elle celui de voir à chaque repas la nourriture soumise au jugement du Survenant. Ah ! jamais un mot de reproche et jamais un mot de louange, mais une manière haïssable de repousser l'assiette, comme un fils de seigneur, lui qui n'était pas même de la paroisse. Et cette fantaisie qu'il avait de l'appeler la petite mère ...

Le Survenant prit place sur un banc de côté, goûta au bouilli, fit une légère moue et dit :

— Je cherche à me rappeler où j'ai mangé du si bon bouilli, à m'en rendre malade ...

D'ordinaire silencieux à table, il ne finissait plus de parler, comme par simple besoin d'entendre le son de sa voix :

— Si je pouvais me rappeler ...

Il cherchait. Il repassait place après place. Il cherchait encore, dans le vaste monde, nommant aux Beauchemin des villes, des pays aux noms étrangers qui leur étaient entièrement indifférents : le Chenal du Moine leur suffisait. Il chercha en vain. Au bout d'un instant, de sa voix basse et égale, il reprit :

— Je vous ai-ti parlé d'un couque que j'ai connu dans un chantier du Maine ? Il avait le secret des crêpes et des galettes de sarrasin comme pas une créature est capable d'en délayer. Elles fondaient dans la bouche. Seulement on n'avait pas l'agrément d'en parler à table parce qu'il fallait garder le silence.

Alphonsine, vexée, pensa à lui demander :

— C'est-il là, fend-le-vent, que t'as fait ton apprentissage pour si bien savoir retenir ta langue ?

Mais la présence de son beau-père la gêna.

Incapable de se taire, le Survenant demanda encore :

— Avez-vous déjà mangé des fèves au lard avec une perdrix ou deux au milieu du pot ? Ç'a goût d'amande. Y a rien de meilleur. Ça ramènerait un mort.

Didace l'arrêta :

— Aïe ! La perdrix vaut rien en tout. Parle-moi du canard noir : au moins la chair est franche et la volaille d'eau repose l'estomac. Mais de la perdrix ? Pouah !

— En avez-vous déjà mangé d'abord ?

— C't'histoire ! Un chasseur nous en a laissé une couple, il y a quelque temps. Phonsine les a envoyées dans le chaudron à soupe pour leur faire jeter un bouillon. C'était méchant, le yâble !

Le Survenant arrêta de manger pour regarder Alphonsine.

— De la soupe à la perdrix ! Là vous avez commis un vrai péché, la petite mère, de gaspiller du bon manger de même ! La perdrix, on la mange aux choux avec des épices et des graines de Manille, mais jamais en soupe. Ou encore, comme je l'ai mangée en Abitibi. Le couque prenait une perdrix tout ronde, moins les plumats. Il la couvrait de glaise et la mettait à cuire de même dans les cendres vives, sous terre. Quand elle est à point, il se forme tout autour une croûte qu'on casse pour prendre juste la belle chair ferme.

Phonsine se retint de frissonner. Indifférente en apparence, la figure fermée, elle écoutait le récit de ce qu'elle prenait pour de pures vantardises. Croyant la faire sourire, le Survenant, après avoir mangé trois fois de viande, repoussa son assiette et demanda à la ronde :

— Vous trouvez pas que le bouilli a goût de suif ?

Le visage de la jeune femme flamba. La plaisanterie n'était pas de saison : Venant le vit bien.

Didace se leva de table et sortit. Z'Yeux-ronds, toujours en jeu, sauta au milieu de la place pour le suivre. D'un coup de pied, Amable envoya le chien s'arrondir dans le coin.

— Où c'est que vous avez eu ce chien-là ? demanda le Survenant.

— As-tu envie de dire qu'on te l'a volé ? répliqua Amable, malendurant.

Deux ans auparavant, Z'Yeux-ronds, un chien errant, ras poil, l'oeil toujours étonné, avait suivi la voiture des Beauchemin, jusqu'au Chenal. Une oreille arrachée et le corps zébré de coups, il portait les marques d'un bon chien batailleur.

— Il est maigre raide, avait dit Didace, en dépit des protestations d'Amable, on va y donner une petite chance de se remplumer.

Amable conclut méchamment :

— Si tu veux le savoir, c'est un autre survenant.

— Survenant, survenant, remarqua Venant, vous avez toujours ce mot-là à la bouche. Dites-moi une fois pour toutes ce que vous entendez par là.

Amable hésita :

— Un survenant, si tu veux le savoir, c'est quelqu'un qui s'arrête à une maison où il est pas invité ... et qui se décide pas à en repartir.

— Je vois pas de déshonneur là-dedans.

— Dans ce pays icitte, on est pas prêt à dire qu'il y a de l'honneur à ça non plus.

Le Survenant éclata de rire et sortit avec Z'Yeux-ronds à ses trousses. Amable, les regardant aller, dit à sa femme : Ils font la belle paire, tu trouves pas ?

Mais à l'heure du souper, le Survenant, sans même lever la vue, vit Alphonsine ajouter à la dérobée deux ou trois oeufs à la pâte à crêpe afin de la rendre plus légère. Et le lendemain matin, encore endormie et un peu rageuse de ne plus pouvoir traîner au lit, comme avant l'arrivée du Survenant, et d'avoir à préparer le déjeuner de trois hommes, elle promena sur les ronds de poêle fumants une couenne de lard avant d'y étendre à dos de cuiller la galette de sarrasin, grise et pivelée, aux cent yeux vite ouverts par la chaleur.

Au milieu de l'après-midi, Phonsine, croyant les hommes aux champs, sortit une pointe de velours à sachets et s'amusa à la faire chatoyer, tout en rêvassant.

De son bref séjour au couvent où en échange de légers services on l'accepta parmi les élèves qu'elle servait à table, elle gardait la nostalgie des fins ouvrages. Passer de longues soirées dans un boudoir, sous la lampe, à l'exemple de jeunes Soreloises, à travailler la mignardise, la frivolité ou à tirer l'aiguille à petits points, lui avait paru longtemps la plus enviable destinée. Parfois elle sortait de leur cachette de délicates retailles de satin pâle et de velours flamme, pour le seul plaisir de les revoir de près et de les sentir douces au toucher.

Autrefois, à imaginer les porte-balai, les pelotes à épingles et tous les beaux objets qu'elle pourrait façonner de ses mains et enfouir au fond d'un tiroir dans du papier de soie, une nostalgie gagnait Alphonsine à la pensée qu'elle était plutôt faite pour porter de la dentelle et de la soie que pour servir les autres. Mais son entrée dans la famille Beauchemin lui conféra un tel sentiment de sécurité que, s'il lui arrivait encore de frissonner en revaudant les rudes hardes des hommes, elle s'interdisait des pensées frivoles de la sorte. Du reste elle n'aurait plus le temps de coudre ainsi. Ni l'habileté. Et la raideur de ses doigts l'en eût empêchée.

Perdue dans sa rêverie, Phonsine n'avait pas entendu des pas sur les marches du perron. Venant apportait le bois dans le bûcher. Depuis son arrivée, du bois fin et des éclats pour les feux vifs, du bois de marée pour les feux de durée, il y en avait toujours. Il veillait à emplir franchement la boîte à bois, sans les détours d'Amable qui réussissait, en y jetant une couple de brassées pêle-mêle, à la faire paraître comble.

Alphonsine n'eut pas le temps de soustraire à sa vue la pointe de velours rouge. Il ne dit pas un mot mais quelques jours plus tard, comme elle allait le gronder d'entrer, les pieds gros de terre, dans la cuisine, il lui tendit une brassée de foin d'odeur, en disant :

— Tenez, la petite mère. Ça fera de la superbe de bonne bourrure pour vos petits ouvrages.

Peu habituée à la prévenance, Alphonsine s'en étonna d'autant plus. Inconsciemment elle s'en trouva flattée. Parlait-il donc au diable, l'étranger, pour deviner ainsi ce qui se passait jusque dans l'esprit des gens ? Elle l'aurait cru aisément si, un jour, elle n'avait vu tomber du mackinaw du Survenant une petite croix noire à laquelle un christ d'étain, usé aux entournures, ne pendait plus que par une main.

(*Le Survenant*, 1945)

Gabrielle Roy (Née en 1909)

Née au Manitoba, institutrice, comédienne, elle s'est consacrée à son oeuvre littéraire depuis que son premier roman, *Bonheur d'occasion* (1945) lui valut la célébrité et le prix Femina. Ce grand reportage romanesque sur la misère d'une banlieue de Montréal fut suivi par des récits partiellement autobiographiques qui évoquent son Manitoba natal et par le portrait d'une sorte de Salavin canadien : *Alexandre Chenevert.* Elle est membre de la Société royale du Canada. Le premier texte qui suit est tiré de son premier roman; le second est communément considéré comme un auto-portrait très réussi.

UNE PROMENADE DANS SAINT-HENRI

Il s'arrêta au centre de la place Saint-Henri, une vaste zone sillonnée du chemin de fer et de deux voies de tramway, carrefour planté de poteaux noirs et blancs et de barrières de sûreté, clairière de bitume et de neige salie, ouverte entre les clochers, les dômes, à l'assaut des locomotives hurlantes, aux volées de bourdons, aux timbres éraillés des trams et à la circulation incessante de la rue Notre-Dame et de la rue Saint-Jacques.

La sonnerie du chemin de fer éclata. Grêle, énervante et soutenue, elle cribla l'air à la paroi de la cabine à signaux. Jean crut entendre au loin, dans la neige sifflante, un roulement de tambour. Il y avait maintenant, ajoutée à toute l'angoisse et les ténèbres du faubourg, presque tous les soirs, la rumeur de pas cloutés et du tambour que l'on entendait parfois rue Notre-Dame et parfois même des hauteurs de Westmount, du côté des casernes, quand le vent soufflait de la montagne.

Puis tous ces bruits furent noyés.

Un long tremblement gagna le faubourg.

A la rue Atwater, à la rue Rose-de-Lima, à la rue du Couvent et, maintenant, place Saint-Henri, les barrières de sûreté tombaient. Ici, au carrefour des deux artères principales, leur huit bras de noir et de blanc, leur huit bras de bois où luisaient des fanaux rouges se rejoignaient et arrêtaient la circulation.

A ces quatre intersections rapprochées la foule, matin et soir, piétinait et des rangs pressés d'automobiles y ronronnaient à l'étouffée. Souvent alors des coups de klaxons furieux animaient l'air comme si Saint-Henri eut brusquement exprimé son exaspération contre ces trains hurleurs qui, d'heure en heure, le découpent violemment en deux parties.

Le train passa. Une âcre odeur de charbon emplit la rue. Un tourbillon de suie oscilla entre le ciel et le faîte des maisons. La suie commençant à descendre, le clocher de Saint-Henri se dessina d'abord, sans base, comme une flèche fantôme dans les nuages. L'horloge apparut; son cadran illuminé fit une trouée dans les voiles de vapeur; puis, peu à peu, l'église entière se dégagea, haute architecture de style jésuite. Au centre du parterre, un Sacré-Coeur, les bras ouverts, recevait les dernières parcelles de charbon. La paroisse surgissait. Elle se recomposait dans sa tranquillité et sa puissance de durée. Ecole, église, couvent : bloc séculaire fortement noué au coeur de la jungle citadine comme au creux des vallons laurentiens. Au delà s'ouvraient des rues à maisons basses, s'enfonçant de chaque côté vers les quartiers de grande misère, en haut vers la rue Workman et la rue Saint-Antoine, et, en bas, contre la canal Lachine où Saint-Henri tape les matelas, tisse le fil, la soie, le coton, pousse le métier, dévide les bobines, cependant que la terre tremble, que les trains dévalent, que la sirène éclate, que bateaux, hélices, rails et sifflets épellent autour de lui l'aventure.

Jean songea non sans joie qu'il était lui-même comme le bateau, comme le train, comme tout ce qui ramasse de la vitesse en traversant le faubourg et va plus loin prendre son plein essor. Pour lui, un séjour à Saint-Henri ne le faisait pas trop souffrir; ce n'était qu'une période de préparation, d'attente.

Il arriva au viaduc de la rue Notre-Dame, presque immédiatement au-dessus de la petite gare de brique rouge. Avec sa tourelle et ses quais de bois pris étroitement entre les fonds de cours, elle évoquerait les voyages tranquilles de bourgeois retirés ou plus encore de campagnards endimanchés, si l'oeil s'arrêtait à sa contenance rustique. Mais au delà, dans une large échancrure du faubourg, apparaît la ville de Westmount échelonnée jusqu'au faîte de la montagne dans son rigide confort anglais. Il se trouve ainsi que c'est aux voyages infinis de l'âme qu'elle invite. Ici, le luxe et la pauvreté se regardent inlassablement, depuis qu'il y a Westmount, depuis qu'en bas, à ses pieds, il y a Saint-Henri. Entre eux s'élèvent des clochers.

(*Bonheur d'occasion*, 1945)

PETITE MISÈRE

Mon père, parce que j'étais frêle de santé, ou que lui-même alors âgé et malade avait trop de pitié pour la vie, mon père peu après que je vins au monde me baptisa : Petite Misère. Même quand il me donnait le nom avec douceur, en caressant mes cheveux, j'en étais irritée et malheureuse, comme d'une prédisposition à cause de lui à souffrir. Je me redressais et intérieurement me disais : « Ah non ! je ne suis pas misère. Jamais je ne serai comme toi ! »

Mais, un jour, il me jeta le mot détestable avec colère. Je ne sais même plus ce qui avait pu mériter pareil éclat : bien peu de chose sans doute; mon père traversait de longues périodes d'humeur sombre où il était sans patience et comme accablé de regrets; peut-être aussi de responsabilités trop lourdes. Alors, parfois, un éclat de rire le rejoignant, l'atteignant en plein dans ses pensées moroses, provoquait chez lui un accès de détresse. J'ai compris plus tard que craignant sans cesse pour nous le moindre et le pire des malheurs, il aurait voulu tôt nous mettre en garde contre une trop grande aspiration au bonheur.

Son visage agité, ce jour-là, m'avait paru terrifiant. Il me menaçait de sa main levée; mais, incapable de se décider à me frapper, il me jeta comme un reproche éternel :

— Ah ! pourquoi ai-je eu des enfants, moi !

Les parents peuvent croire que de telles paroles, bien au delà de l'entendement des enfants, ne leur font pas de mal; mais parce qu'elles ne sont qu'à moitié intelligibles pour eux, les enfants les creusent et s'en font un tourment.

Je m'enfuis, je courus à mon grenier où, face par terre, je grattai le plancher rugueux de mes ongles, je cherchai à y entrer pour mourir. Le visage collé au plancher, j'ai essayé de m'empêcher de respirer. Je croyais que l'on peut à son gré s'arrêter de respirer et, ainsi, quitter le mal, quand on le veut, parce que c'est le mal...

Les heures passèrent, et je me retournai sur le dos, ma position étant vraiment trop incommode.

Alors, par la lucarne qui se trouvait à la hauteur de mon visage, j'ai aperçu le ciel. C'était une journée venteuse de juin... et des nuages très beaux, très blancs, se mirent à passer devant mes yeux. Il me sembla qu'à moi seule se montraient les nuages. Au-dessus du toit si proche sifflait le vent. Déjà, j'aimais le vent dans les hauteurs, ne s'attaquant ni aux hommes, ni aux arbres, sans malfaisance, simple voyageur qui siffle en se promenant. Deux grands ormes plantés par mon père poussaient leurs plus hautes branches jusqu'au bord de ma lucarne, et, en tendant un peu le cou, je les voyais se balancer; et cela aussi devait être pour moi seule, puisqu'il n'y avait que moi d'assez haut perchée pour surprendre les branches supérieures de nos ormes.

Et alors, plus que jamais je désirai mourir, à cause de cette émotion qu'un arbre suffisait à me donner... traître, douce émotion !

me révélant que le chagrin a des yeux pour mieux voir à quel point ce monde est beau !

Un instant mon attention fut toute captivée par la vue d'une araignée qui descendait vers moi d'une poutre du plafond, au bout de son chemin de soie . . . et j'en oubliai de pleurer. Mais, plus fort de m'avoir été dérobé quelques minutes, mon chagrin revint et remplit toute mon âme, cependant que j'examinais à travers mes larmes cette pauvre petite vie d'insecte que d'un doigt j'aurais pu faire cesser.

Et je me dis : « Mon père n'a pas voulu de moi. Personne n'a voulu de moi. Je n'aurais pas dû venir au monde. » (Quelquefois, j'avais entendu ma mère, parlant de quelque pauvre femme déjà chargée d'enfants, malade, et qui venait d'en mettre un autre au monde, observer en soupirant : « C'est dur, mais c'est le devoir. Que voulez-vous ? il faut bien qu'elle fasse son devoir ! ») Et, ce jour-là, retrouvant le mot dans mes souvenirs, je m'en emparai et ne sachant encore quel sens terrible il contenait, je me répétai : « L'enfant du devoir ! Je suis l'enfant du devoir ! » Et le seul son de ce mot suffit à me faire pleurer de nouveau, sur des chagrins que je ne connaissais pas encore.

Puis je retrouvai le ciel bleu qui filait au delà de la lucarne. Pourquoi, ce soir, le ciel m'a-t-il paru si beau que, depuis, nulle part au monde je n'en ai vu de pareil ! Etait-ce parce qu'il était si indifférent vis-à-vis de moi qui le regardais ?

Comme j'allais me remettre à pleurer, j'entendis des pas résonner le long du corridor, à l'étage, sous mon grenier. Puis la porte au bas de l'escalier s'ouvrit : une voix, celle de ma mère, annonça :

— La table est mise, le souper prêt. Assez bouder. Viens manger.

J'avais faim malgré tout, et cela même, la honte en plein chagrin d'être tentée par la nourriture, me fit nier la chose et affirmer que je ne pouvais manger, que jamais plus je ne pourrais manger.

Au bas de l'escalier, ma mère dit :

— Eh bien, boude, si tu veux bouder . . . mais après, tu ne trouveras plus rien à manger.

Et elle s'en alla d'un pas leste, encore jeune.

Mon frère ensuite vint au bas de l'escalier me crier qu'il s'en allait pêcher dans la petite rivière . . . et est-ce que oui ou non je voulais l'accompagner ? . . . Il ne s'agissait pas de la Rouge, l'importante rivière de la vallée, mais de notre petite Seine . . . maigre cours d'eau qui se tortillait, s'avançait à la manière d'une couleuvre entre des bosquets pleins de cenelles . . . petite rivière enfouie dans l'herbe, vaseuse, secrète, sans grand danger pour nous, y fussions-nous tombés la tête la première ... ma jolie rivière verte comme les yeux des chats ! ...

J'eus bien de la peine à résister, mais encore une fois l'idée de la joie possible dans une vie corrompue par le chagrin me fit repousser mon frère, crier que je voulais être seule.

Lui aussi s'en alla d'un pas rapide; je l'entendis trotter au long du passage, puis prendre le galop dans le grand escalier menant au bas de la maison.

Alors il y eut un silence.

Ensuite, les petits Gauthier, mes chers compagnons de jeux, tous trois perchés sur leur palissade de planches qui séparait nos deux propriétés — mais je me rappelle : entre elles il y avait encore un champ vague — m'appelèrent longuement. Ils modulaient leur appel, selon notre coutume, sur le chant du Fré-dé-ri-m'as-tu-vu. Mais justement, à cette heure, l'oiseau aussi chantait. Il me fallait beaucoup d'application pour distinguer de la petite phrase chantée celle de mes amis qui scandaient : « Chris-ti-ne-viens-tu-jouer ? Au-mar-chand-viens-tu-jouer ? Au-domp-teur-viens-tu-jouer ? » Enfin, ils varièrent un peu leur ritournelle; parce que c'était là le jeu que j'aimais le mieux et qu'ainsi ils espéraient me voir sortir de la maison, ils lancèrent : « Viens jouer aux enterrements. »

Je ne pus résister alors au désir de les voir; je m'approchai au bord de la lucarne, et je les aperçus en bas, tous les trois hissés sur la haute palissade; mais, pensant tout à coup qu'ils étaient des enfants mieux aimés de leurs parents que je ne l'étais des miens, je plongeai vite la tête avant qu'ils ne m'aient découverte, car leurs petits visages cherchaient pour m'y trouver toutes les fenêtres de notre maison. Je retournai me coucher sur le dos et regarder le plafond sombre.

Longtemps encore, sans me découvrir nulle part, les chers enfants m'appelèrent, avec tout ce désespoir enfantin de voir perdue pour les jeux une si belle soirée d'été. Il faisait presque noir qu'ils m'appelaient encore. Leur mère leur commanda d'entrer se coucher. Je les entendis protester, puis la voix de leur mère insista. Mais avant de m'abandonner, les trois petits sur la clôture me crièrent très fort, avec tant de regret :

— Bon-soir-Chris-ti-ne ! Es-tu-morte-Chris-ti-ne ? A-demain-Cris-ti-nette !

Maintenant, dans la lucarne, le ciel était sombre. Et mon chagrin reprit, mais beaucoup plus mystérieux et inconnu. Il semblait que c'était l'avenir, tout le long, terrible avenir d'un enfant qui sur moi pesait ... et je pleurai à petits coups, sans savoir au juste pourquoi ... peut-être parce que je sentais en moi comme chez les grandes personnes assez de lâcheté pour me résigner à la vie telle qu'elle est ... Et peut-être la vie me tenait-elle mieux encore par la curiosité ...

J'entendais encore aux étages certains bruits qui me renseignaient sur les allées et venues dans la maison. Des portes claquèrent. Sur la galerie puis sur notre petit trottoir de ciment j'entendis le bruit des pas de ma mère dans ses souliers neufs. C'est vrai, elle devait ce soir aller jouer aux cartes chez des amis. Elle se hâtait, ses pas semblaient courir ... et je fus malheureuse que d'un coeur si libre elle partît pour aller se livrer à quelque chose d'aussi futile, ce soir, que de jouer aux cartes.

La nuit me parut monter vers moi des étages obscurs. La grande maison était à présent tout à fait silencieuse ... peut-être vide ... Et mon chagrin fut intolérable, de tous abandonné sauf de moi, sauf de ma seule attention bien trop jeune, bien trop faible pour le comprendre; et sans plus en connaître la cause, je pleurai davantage le chagrin lui-même qui n'est peut-être qu'un enfant seul.

Alors, mon oreille proche du plancher entendit le pas traînant, le pas accablé de mon père.

Il entrouvrit doucement la porte au bas de l'escalier. Il resta là, sans parler, longtemps. Peut-être pensait-il que je ne le savais pas debout, un pied levé vers la première marche. Mais j'entendais sa respiration ... et lui peut-être la mienne, tant le silence entre nous était poignant.

Enfin, il appela :

— Petite Misère !

Oh ! que j'avais la gorge serrée ! Jamais après, je n'y ai eu un tel noeud la serrant à m'étouffer. Et il est bon peut-être qu'on ait eu très jeune un atroce chagrin, car après il ne peut guère plus nous étonner.

Le vieux père reprit :

— T'enfant !

Puis, comme je ne répondais encore pas, mon père me dit :

— Tu dois avoir faim.

Et plus tard, après un autre silence, il me dit si tristement qu'aujourd'hui encore, trouvant son chemin entre des souvenirs touffus comme une forêt, l'inflexion exacte de la voix de mon père me revient :

— J'ai fait une tarte à la rhubarbe ... Elle est encore chaude ... Veux-tu en manger ? ...

Moi, je ne sais plus ! Depuis ce temps, la tarte à la rhubarbe ne m'a jamais tentée; mais avant ce jour, il paraît que j'en raffolais, bien que je fusse malade chaque fois que j'en mangeais. Aussi ma mère n'en faisait plus que très rarement et si, par exception, elle en servait une, alors elle me défendait d'en prendre plus qu'une toute petite pointe. Ainsi donc, mon père avait profité de l'absence de ma mère ce soir... et je l'imaginai roulant ses manches, cherchant la farine, le saindoux — jamais pourtant il ne trouvait les choses dans la maison — allumant le four, surveillant la tarte qui cuisait !... Comment aurais-je pu répondre ! Le chagrin qui m'avait tenue éloignée toute la soirée des jeux de mon âge, qu'était-il auprès de celui qui à présent m'empoignait ! En était-il donc du chagrin comme des mystérieuses routes dans mon livre des *Mille et une Nuits* où chacune menait à une avenue plus large et découvrait de plus en plus de pays ?

J'entendis mon père pousser un soupir. Il referma la porte si lentement que c'est à peine si j'entendis le très léger déclic de la serrure. Il s'en alla.

Ce long pas découragé !

J'attendis quelques minutes pourtant, longtemps à ce qu'il me sembla. Puis j'ai étiré ma robe chiffonnée. Je me suis donné des tapes aux joues pour effacer la trace des larmes; et, avec le bas de ma robe, j'ai tâché de réparer les barbouillages ainsi faits sur mon visage.

Je suis descendue, m'arrêtant à chaque marche.

La table de notre grande cuisine était mise comme pour une fête... une bien triste fête, car, sur la nappe blanche, il n'y avait, au centre, que la tarte et, loin l'une de l'autre, à chaque bout, nos deux assiettes.

Nous avons pris place, sans nous regarder encore, mon père et moi, à cette longue table.

Mon père poussa alors vers moi la tarte qu'il avait taillée d'avance en si gros morceaux que brusquement je fondis en larmes. Mais en même temps j'avais commencé de goûter à la tarte.

Souvent, aux étapes de ses rudes voyages en pays de colonisation, lorsqu'il allait établir des immigrants, mon père avait fricoté lui-même ses repas sur de petits feux de braises en plein air, dans les Prairies, et il avait gardé de ce temps-là, sans doute accompagnée du regret des espaces et de la pureté, l'illusion d'être habile à la cuisine. Mais ma mère disait que les tartes de mon père étaient de plomb.

Et c'était bien en effet une nourriture de plomb que je cherchais à avaler.

Nos yeux se rencontrèrent. Je vis que la bouchée que mon père avait prise ne passait pas non plus.

Et comment alors, à travers mon pauvre chagrin d'enfant ai-je si bien pressenti celui combien plus lourd de mon père, le poids de la vie : cette indigeste nourriture que ce soir, comme si c'était pour toujours, mon père m'offrait !

Cette nuit, je fus bien malade d'une sérieuse indigestion. Ma mère, ne comprenant pas du tout ce qui s'était passé entre le vieil homme et sa Petite Misère, accabla mon père de reproches :

— Lui faire manger de la tarte à dix heures du soir ! Es-tu fou ?

Lui, avec un sourire triste, sans se disculper, pencha la tête; et, plus tard, quand il vint m'apporter un remède, il y avait sur son visage une telle douleur que, parfois, je l'imagine immortelle.

(*Rue Deschambault*, 1955)

Robert Charbonneau (1911-1967)

Journaliste, puis éditeur, il devint directeur du service des textes à Radio-Canada. Membre de l'Académie canadienne-française, il fut président de la Société des Ecrivains canadiens.

Critique pénétrant, romancier d'analyse, il est surtout connu comme l'auteur d'*Ils posséderont la terre* (1941), roman de la liquidation de l'adolescence, analyse des états d'âme de jeunes au moment où ils s'engagent dans la vie.

ADIEU À L'ADOLESCENCE

A quelque temps de là, j'ai rencontré Dorothée dans la rue, et elle m'a dit : « Voilà deux fois qu'on vous invite... Est-ce moi qui vous fais peur ? » Elle tentait de réparer l'injustice dont j'étais l'objet de la part des siens, et même d'Edward.

Comme je m'apprêtais à me rendre à son invitation, grand'mère est venue me rejoindre à la porte et m'a dit sans me regarder : « Ne rentre pas trop tard. J'ai préparé pour le dîner un plat que tu aimes. » Elle souffrait presque autant que moi de me voir souffrir. Mon châtiment avait assez duré, croyait-elle. Une grand'mère ça ne veut plus rien avoir à se reprocher. Grand-père, contre son habitude, se préparait à partir et il profita de ce moment d'émotion de son épouse pour sortir avec moi. Dans la rue, il ne savait quoi dire et il me quitta au premier coin.

Edward pouvait, lui, se payer le luxe d'appréhender toute sa vie son moi. Et cela, je le lui enviais. Se perfectionner en dehors des contraintes inhumaines. Dorothée s'offrait à m'aider. Je la payais en l'accablant. Je lui décrivais mes désespoirs minutieusement jusqu'à ce qu'elle aperçut tout en noir, puis je riais qu'elle prît mes phrases au sérieux. Elle avait sur la vie des naïvetés. Comme ceux qui n'ont pas souffert, elle pouvait se permettre de me prendre au tragique. La fatigue aidant, car nous nous rencontrions dans la rue, elle se déprimait.

Le parc d'équitation était notre promenade préférée. Elle détestait les Juifs et je les aimais pour leur nonchalance, leurs extraordinaires trognes sales et l'étalage qu'ils font de leurs sentiments en public. Chaque sentier me rappelait les discussions avec Jérôme, et pour exorciser de ma vie ce fantôme, j'exagérais mes griefs à son égard. « On dirait que vous vous faites une gloire d'être méchant », disait-elle. Et comme je commençais une explication : « Ce n'est pas la peine, dit-elle, nous, les femmes, nous comprenons bien des choses qui ne sont pas dites. »

Je savais qu'elle trompait sa tante pour me rejoindre et qu'elle se reprochait ce mensonge comme une ignominie. Je la croyais cependant incapable de souffrir longtemps pour une cause morale. Mais un jour que je tentais de l'embrasser, elle s'est brûlé cruellement la main, sans un mot, avec la braise de sa cigarette.

Je l'admirai pour ce geste qui humiliait mon amour-propre. Ses yeux gris luisaient de pureté incandescente. Elle avait le même teint et les mêmes yeux que son cousin, un étrange teint comme un émail, casqué de cheveux noirs à reflets comme un cuir graissé.

Je m'appliquai, pour m'en détacher, à croire qu'une jeune fille qui pouvait tromper sa tante pour me faire plaisir me réservait d'amères trahisons. Je savais par ses confidences que, plus jeune, elle et sa tante faisaient des secrets au père d'Edward de leurs sorties. Quand Dorothée avait deux jours de congé, elle allait en passer un chez ses tantes (alors que son père la croyait au couvent jusqu'au soir). S'il avait fallu que je prenne par écrit tout ce que je ridiculisais dans ma pensée !

Elle m'attirait par ce besoin qu'elle avait d'être aimée. En échange, elle ne me ménageait pas sa pitié. Malheureusement je me fatigue facilement des êtres qui me portent trop d'attention. « Parce que je suis incapable de répondre », me disais-je. « Parce que vous n'allez pas aux êtres », reprenait Dorothée.

Je m'habituais à la voir et la trouvais moins belle.

Après une longue promenade où elle s'était montrée plus coquette qu'à l'habitude, je la suivis dans la maison. Elle portait, ce soir-là, une robe noire laissant à découvert ses bras et la pointe éclatante des épaules. Son chapeau qu'elle avait en entrant rejeté en arrière d'un geste de lassitude, encadrait de lumière son beau visage recru.

— Nous sommes seuls, fit-elle.

Rougissante, elle porta à ses lèvres un peu pâles une cigarette qu'elle tenait à l'extrême pointe de ses longs doigts vernis et se laissa choir dans un fauteuil. Je me levai pour replacer sur la table un livre qu'elle en avait fait glisser. Elle était déjà debout, agressive et poignante de pureté. Elle me fixa un moment de ses pupilles ardentes puis, lentement, elle retraita vers la cheminée.

— C'est triste, dit-elle comme si elle avait aperçu tout à coup que nous nous cherchions tous les deux sur des plans différents. Ses belles dents de carnivore avaient disparu et sur le masque de céruse aux lignes insensibles ne subsistait plus que le désespoir sans fond des yeux gris immobiles.

— Vous n'êtes plus le même, continua-t-elle.

Et malgré mon sourire, elle ne voulut pas croire que rien n'était changé. Mes griefs n'auraient pas résisté à l'expression. Mais j'étais devenu spectateur de ce débat entre elle et moi. « Exercez-vous à la peur du mariage », me dirait Edward.

J'appris par celui-ci que ma tentative d'embrasser sa cousine dans le parc avait provoqué une réaction nerveuse. Elle a fait une crise le soir. On lui a mis des serviettes froides sur la tête.

Edward aussi avait changé. Il parlait d'entrer au séminaire. « La vie ne vaut pas la peine, dit-il. A moins qu'on ne la perde tout d'un coup. »

Mais je ne pouvais le suivre au séminaire. Ce n'eût pas été par pur amour de Dieu. Maintenant inaccessible, Dorothée m'attirait.

« Tu as l'illusion de l'aimer et elle ne t'aime pas, continua mon ami. J'ai cru l'aimer aussi. C'est elle dont je te parlais dans le train. Crois-moi, elle n'éprouvera jamais pour toi que de la pitié. Essaie de l'embrasser pour te convaincre. »

La saison avançait. Je me présentai chez les Pollender. « Viens lundi matin, à neuf heures, on te trouvera quelque chose », m'a dit Hector Pollender. C'était facile, en somme; j'étais embrigadé pour la vie. Trop longtemps, j'avais conjecturé la réaction des êtres, subi leur respect. La leçon que m'avait donnée indirectement Dorothée ne serait pas inutile. Mon scepticisme intellectuel demeurait le même, mais l'effet de plusieurs années d'éducation était aboli, cédait à une éthique nouvelle. Il s'agissait de viser moins haut.

Dorothée voulut une dernière fois retourner à la campagne. Nous avions choisi un sentier escarpé, dangereux. Nous allions allégrement, le sang fouetté par l'air vif et le danger. J'éprouvais une sensation de virilité renforcée par le spectacle de l'effarement de ma compagne. Arrivés sur le plateau, les mains crottées, contractées par le froid, nous avons regardé à nos pieds la pente tachetée de neige et de feuilles jaunes dont il nous restait le souvenir d'un contact tiède et visqueux.

Au chalet, une surprise nous attendait. Ly était assise à une petite table avec un garçon d'une douzaine d'années. Je la saluai discrètement. Elle ne quittait pas Dorothée des yeux. Elle semblait scruter la main fine que ma compagne, se sentant épiée, avait portée à sa lourde chevelure noire. Elle se mirait dans ce teint stellaire, empreint de cette jeunesse qui la fuyait. Dans la pénombre, son visage paraissait saupoudré de vert. Songeait-elle à sa jeunesse perdue ? Ses lèvres prirent une expression de cruauté indéfinissable. Et elle s'élança plutôt qu'elle ne marcha vers la jeune fille. Mais à mesure qu'elle approchait, son visage se transformait. Et ce fut sans affectation qu'elle salua Dorothée et se pencha au-dessus de la jeune fille, qui n'avait pas bougé, pour admirer la triple gorgerette qui irisait de feu cendré son cou de statue.

Dorothée, habillée pour la marche, sans maquillage, était presque terne dans sa robe brune. Ly, en robe montante, portait des bijoux et des brillants. Elle se rendait à un thé et s'était arrêtée là en attendant. Elle se sentait aussi jeune que Dorothée, mais elle avait toujours été épaisse des hanches. Son front haut, un peu bombé, trop pâle, la trahissait. Son aisance aussi. Une jeune fille ne sait jamais quoi faire de ses bras, dont elle s'embarrasse dès qu'elle ne s'occupe pas. Ly ne pouvait retrouver une certaine conception de la vie qu'elle avait vidée à son mariage.

Elle prétextait l'émotion qu'elle ressentait à me parler de Fernand pour ignorer Dorothée. « J'ai gardé, dit-elle, le petit missel où l'enfant (elle insistait sur ce mot comme pour indiquer qu'elle ne l'employait que pour Fernand) a malhabilement tracé : J'offre ma vie pour André ».

Il était passé l'heure de se rendre à son thé. « Viens donc dîner avec nous un soir, comme autrefois. Maman sera tellement contente de te voir », dit-elle.

Je m'aperçus bientôt que j'étais sorti de l'adolescence à un rajustement de mon idéal à mes moyens immédiats. Je n'aspirais plus à dominer, mais seulement à me faire une situation enviable dans un monde que j'acceptais tel qu'il était. Ma grande ambition se portait vers une augmentation de salaire, un congé.

Je voyais souvent Ly qui aimait comme moi les cinémas et me pilotait dans les endroits où l'on s'amuse. Je fuyais autant les livres et la solitude que je les avais recherchés jusque-là.

Edward, l'esprit tourné vers la liturgie qu'il aimait et vers laquelle il allait d'instinct, m'entretenait à chaque rencontre de sa vocation en termes ésotériques. Il ne manquait pas de se moquer copieusement des prédicateurs. L'un d'eux notamment, dont la spécialité, en fait de gestes, était les vagues. « Des vagues, beaucoup de vagues, m'expliquait-il, un teint d'écolière partie sur la mer par une embellie. Des phrases à la main, faites pour la main. Une belle main soignée, glissante, intelligente, oratoire; une main de tête. Entre les gestes, la main s'étendait sur le surplis et s'interrompait un moment pour qu'on ait le temps de l'admirer. Puis elle descendait comme à regret le long de la rampe. Quel dommage de disparaître, une si belle main, une main pour un auditoire de Notre-Dame de Paris, une doublure pour les mains de Stokowski au cinéma. »

Des anecdotes comme celle-là me faisaient pressentir le débat qui se faisait en lui. Il me parlait aussi souvent de Dorothée pour qui son amour semblait grandir à mesure que le temps d'entrer au séminaire approchait. Il s'est débattu ainsi jusqu'à la dernière minute contre son esprit de critique et son amour.

Quant à moi, ma jeunesse était finie et tous ceux qui en avaient été les témoins, sauf Ly, me paraissent appartenir à un monde définitivement dépassé.

(*Ils posséderont la terre,* 1941)

Jean-Jules Richard (Né en 1911)

Pigiste, auteur de poèmes, contes et reportages, son meilleur livre est *Neuf jours de haine* (1948), évocation brutale de la souffrance physique et morale des soldats aux pires jours de la guerre. L'extrait qui suit en convaincra facilement les lecteurs.

LA MORT DE MARTEDALE

Est-ce bien Martedale, cette forme ?

Un casque à la jugulaire défaite a roulé à la tête. C'est un casque comme les leurs.

Sur la poitrine, des papiers enveloppés de lambeaux d'étoffe kaki. McDeen saisit ces papiers du torse. Il les écrase sur le sol pour les éteindre. De sa main libre, il les entrouve. Ce sont les livrets de service et de solde. Les livrets sont en partie calcinés, mais la lettre entre les deux presque intacte.

C'est une lettre adressée au sergent Martedale.

Une lettre de sa femme.

La lettre.

Tous deux en connaissent le contenu. On hait cette lettre. Elle suggère l'idée du suicide. Cette idée est une injure à Martedale.

Mais c'est bien lui.

On l'identifie.

Il a dû se rouler pour essayer de se dépêtrer du liquide gluant. Il est maintenant sur le dos. Des lambeaux d'étoffe bordés de noir (en deuil) sont éparpillés autour de son corps.

Il est nu. Sauf pour ses bottes. Et des filaments de sa ceinture et des courroies de son équipement retenus par les ferrures. Les ferrures se sont creusé des rectangles dans la chair.

Il est chauve.

La figure est un bloc de charbon presque sans forme humaine. Excepté pour le creux des yeux d'où coule un liquide gluant, plus épais que des larmes. Les dents ressortent avec une grimace plus triste que terrifiante.

Le cou ressemble à un bout de boyau. Le corps est pourpre, brun et noir. Quelques pièces d'étoffe calcinée le picotent de taches brunâtres. La brise joue là-dedans. C'est comme si le corps grouillait de vermine.

Sur la poitrine s'écroûtent des plaques de carmin. La boucle de la ceinture chauffe le nombril à blanc. Dans le creux se forme un petit lac de graisse. Sur le ventre, la chair continue de cuire en grésillant. La graisse coule sur un mélange de couleur : rouge, brun, gris, rose, orange, bleuâtre, noirâtre, noir. Le sexe atrophié luit comme une sculpture d'acajou.

La peau des cuisses est comme du cuir trempé. Les jambes, des jambières. Les pieds perdus dans les bottes fumantes. Et il est encore vivant,
    vivant,
    vivant.

La vie se meut en lui. Avec insistance, la vie l'accuse de tous les crimes de la guerre. Payer. Il faut payer. Quelqu'un doit payer. Tant que la mort ne sera pas satisfaite d'atrocités, elle va présenter des additions à la vie. La vie débourse. Martedale, les bras repliés, tient ses mains au niveau de sa tête. Les doigts courbés, réduits, cherchent à écaler la suie croûtée de sa figure. Ou ces mains bizarres présentent-elles une offrande ?

Il continue toujours quelques mouvements.

Des mains. Des mâchoires et des recoins de lèvres qui lui restent. La senteur est abominable. A elle seule ne suffirait-elle pas à l'asphyxier ? A le faire mourir ? Car il va mourir. Mais quand ?

Mais quand ?

Combien de temps va-t-il ainsi souffrir ? Des secondes, des minutes ou des heures ?

McDeen, de sa main libre, sort son revolver de sa ceinture. Sans un mot, il le tend à Noiraud. Noiraud le regarde. Il regarde le révolver avec des yeux surpris. Il regarde McDeen avec des yeux violents. Pas ça. Pas lui. McDeen fait un autre geste. Ça veut dire :

« Prends. Vas-y. C'est beaucoup mieux. Avec ma main gauche, moi, je peux viser mal. »

Noiraud enfin accepte l'arme. Trébuchant comme un infirme, il avance vers la tête de Martedale. Il se penche. Ça sent trop fort. Une nausée lui monte au nez. Un vertige à la tête.

C'est bien Martedale, cette forme. Le jeu raidi des épaules, mais c'est bien son jeu à lui. Il paraît plus grand, ainsi couché. Il paraît aussi plus petit, amoindri. Ça dépend de l'angle d'où on le regarde. Qu'est-ce qu'il a l'air au juste ? Il a l'air de lui malgré ses lèvres charnues rongées. Ces lèvres qui formaient contraste avec sa tendance puritaine. Elles sont maintenant puritaines, ces lèvres.

Le revolver s'approche. Noiraud le pointe derrière l'oreille. Sa main est comme un gros tas de mastic. Son index relâché ne veut pas presser la gâchette.

Accroupi, il se regarde les pieds à travers ses bras. Décidément, il ne peut pas tuer Martedale. Il ne veut pas l'arrêter de penser.

Est-ce que le sergent pense ? Sa cervelle n'est pas brûlée. A quoi pense-t-il, s'il pense ? Plusieurs copains ramassés mourants ont témoigné. Dans ces moments-là, on ne pense pas à ceux qu'on aime. L'approche de la mort ne veut rien dire. On ne pense pas à ceux qu'on laisse. Ni à l'amour. Ni à sa femme. Ni à son pays. A rien de doux ou de consolant.

Un blessé ou un mourant sur le champ de bataille ne pense à rien de tout cela. Il ne pense pas non plus à la divinité en laquelle il peut croire. Il ne regrette pas ses injustices envers l'humanité. Son instinct le domine. Ses réflexes le guident vers la peur et vers la haine. Vers la peur causée par son impuissance à s'évader. Vers la haine dictée par l'irrémédiable.

McDeen attend. Il attend depuis quarante-cinq secondes. Noiraud attend aussi. S'il tire, c'est pour obéir au sergent-major. Ça lui répugne d'obéir, non de tuer. Si une section était là au lieu de McDeen, Noiraud aurait tué tout de suite. Tout simplement comme si c'était son tour. Pour rendre service à Martedale. Pour l'obliger en toute amitié. McDeen est le représentant de l'autorité. C'est insupportable.

Mais McDeen ne représente peut-être pas l'autorité. Il est blessé. Il ne compte plus. Il est là lui aussi par amitié. Cinquante secondes. McDeen dit :

— Tu l'as fait souffrir cinquante secondes de plus qu'il ne le mérite. Vas-y.

Le son de la voix pique les nerfs de Noiraud. Son index se casse à la jointure. Ça presse la détente. Le coup part. Le sergent du 14e perd une expression de surprise dans tout son corps immolé.

Maintenant c'est fini. Ou l'est-ce ? On dit plutôt que tout continue. Noiraud se ferme les yeux aussi hermétiques que possible. Il reste là debout dix secondes pour finir cette minute inouïe.

Pour la finir.

Ses muscles vibrent et se crispent mutuellement. Le goût amer de son esprit s'imprègne sur ses lèvres. Ça goûte le sable. Pour un jeune homme, un jeune homme de vingt ans, cette scène et ce dernier geste sont quelque chose de trop. De réellement trop.

Pourquoi Martedale s'est-il ainsi laissé mourir ? Pour Noiraud, la mort est volontaire. On ne la subit pas sans préméditation. La préméditation peut être inconsciente. Le sergent, troublé par la rupture annoncée par sa femme, a vu son sens de discernement atrophié. Il est allé rencontrer la mort où elle l'attendait sans pouvoir résister à ce rendez-vous à cause de son complexe.

McDeen reprend son revolver. Il ramasse aussi les papiers. Des bottes de Martedale s'élève une petite flamme bleue. Il en approche la lettre. Le papier s'enflamme. La lettre brûle. Le papier s'enroule et part chassé par la brise. La lettre se sauve cacher sa honte.

McDeen entoure les épaules de Noiraud. Il le conduit à travers les buissons fumants. Noiraud s'écroule sur l'herbe. Il aimerait pleurer. Mais ça lui fait trop mal. Sa douleur est trop chaude. Ça lui assèche les larmes. Manier d'abord, puis ça, ça.

(*Neuf jours de haine*, 1948)

André Giroux (Né en 1916)

Publiciste au gouvernement du Québec, attaché de presse à la Maison du Québec à Paris, il occupe maintenant un des hauts postes au ministère des Affaires culturelles de Québec. Fondateur de la revue *Regards* (1940-42), membre de la Société royale du Canada, il est l'auteur de romans et de nouvelles plutôt sombres, où les personnages sont hantés par leur propre misère, par la mesquinerie des autres, par la maladie et par la mort imminente. Le texte qui suit termine son premier roman.

REGARDS

Depuis une demi-heure déjà, le train roulait. Une jeune fille au visage inquiet traversait les wagons. Elle dévisageait les voyageurs, les uns après les autres, sans trouver celui qu'elle cherchait.

Soudain, elle eut un léger mouvement de recul. Là-bas, au fond du dernier wagon, un homme à ses côtés, deux devant, c'est lui ! Ses genoux s'entre-choquèrent et elle dut, l'espace de quelques secondes, se cramponner au dossier d'un banc. Puis, oppressée, elle s'approcha à petits pas, hésitante, les mains glacées, les lèvres agitées d'un tic nerveux. Oui ! C'est bien lui ! C'est Jacques ! Les yeux sont affreusement creux. Les paupières sont closes, la tête appuyée est immobile. Elle se glisse à cette place d'où elle pourra le contempler tout son saoul. Trois bancs la séparent de lui. Elle le regarde de toute son âme.

Enfin, Jacques ouvrit les yeux. La verra-t-il ? La verra-t-il ? Elle est immobile, le corps projeté en avant. Ses yeux exorbités l'aspirent. La verra-t-il ? La regardera-t-il ?

Après avoir erré quelques secondes, les yeux de Jacques se posèrent sur elle. Elle y lut de la surprise, de l'égarement, de la curiosité et une immense détresse. Alors, elle lui sourit, d'un sourire tout intérieur qui montait du coeur et se composait presque sans l'aide d'aucun muscle. Lui ne bronchait pas. Pendant trois heures le lien ne fut interrompu que par les battements de leurs quatre paupières et par des hanches qui passaient rapides. Pendant trois heures, leurs regards se fondirent dans la plus étroite des communions. Au moment de descendre, il lui sourit enfin. Ce fut tout.

Saura-t-elle un jour, Marie-Eve, que pendant ces trois heures, Jacques avait gravé au plus profond de son coeur l'expression de son regard et qu'en entrant dans sa cellule, il allait en fixer au mur l'émouvante tendresse, comme un crucifix ?

Saura-t-elle jamais, cette femme, que Jacques n'allait plus vivre que de la lumière de ses yeux ? Car le jour où il n'en pourrait plus retrouver dans sa mémoire toute la chaleur, toute la vibration, tout l'amour, ce jour-là commencerait réellement sa vie de bagnard.

(*Au delà des visages,* 1948)

Adrienne Choquette (Née en 1915)

Publiciste au ministère de l'Agriculture de Québec, elle a publié des nouvelles et des romans, dont *Laure Clouet* (1961), roman bref et pudique qui analyse le bouleversement d'une vieille fille qui découvre l'amour physique d'un jeune couple qu'elle héberge.

QUÉBEC L'AUTOMNE

Le mois de septembre s'acheva presque sans pluie. Un matin, vues de la côte Sainte-Geneviève, les Laurentides firent l'effet de flamber. De jour en jour, les arbres de la Grande-Allée se transformèrent sous les yeux des promeneurs, filtrant au soleil couchant des rayons de lumière rousse que de jeunes peintres tentaient de fixer sur leurs toiles. Mais l'instant d'après, les feuilles roses n'étaient plus roses, ni l'érable or, ni le hêtre couleur de sang; il fallait attendre au matin suivant. Alors tout recommençait avec violence, et les yeux, pour avoir trop longtemps regardé, se teintaient d'ocre et d'émeraude.

La ville se mit à sa vie d'automne, raffinée à la porte Saint-Louis, faite de bals, de dîners d'Etat; âpre chez les ouvriers. Dans l'entre-deux se situait le peuple du commerce québecois, à partir du petit boutiquier de la côte du Palais et de la rue Saint-Paul, bon enfant sous des dehors abrupts, jusqu'aux grands propriétaires invisibles des magasins à rayons, des compagnies d'assurances, des courtiers en valeurs immobilières. Souvent, dans la masse des travailleurs divisés par grappes humaines aux arrêts d'autobus, on reconnaissait la tête de malchance des chômeurs. Ils formaient une seconde masse d'attente. Les plus âgés étaient vêtus comme s'ils sortaient de l'usine, mais les jeunes usaient leurs costumes de dimanche et taquinaient de propos bruyants les serveuses de restaurants.

Entre les autos couraient les gamins de Québec, toujours au courant de tout, candides et débrouillards, parfois d'une telle joliesse de traits sous leurs grimaces moqueuses qu'on en éprouvait un choc heureux. Ils vantaient celui de la famille qui portait toujours une chemise blanche : « Mon frère du Parlement... » disaient-ils avec respect, en désignant à leurs camarades celui qui, hors de son quartier, tombait dans l'anonymat du service public. Un rouage. Mais qui refusait d'être confondu et rapidement se prenait de mépris pour la classe de petites gens d'où il était sorti. Alors on le voyait miné par une lente fièvre dont il ne mourait jamais. Il prenait rang dans un peuple d'hommes impropres à la gloire du pays, de femmes muettement exaspérées, de jeunes filles qui se regardaient, avec haine et épouvante, ressembler bientôt aux laissées pour compte de leurs bureaux. Tous ils avaient cru se délivrer de quelque chose et voici que chaque jour les ligotait à une nouvelle servitude. Sortes de poids-du-jour aux revanches furtives dans le vin bon marché qui leur donnait vite, comme pour se débarrasser, une ivresse grinçante et rendait les femmes semblables à des chattes folles. Tel un corps de métier, ils faisaient bloc aux grandes funérailles et à l'ouverture de la session provinciale en s'arrangeant pour être dans le champ de vision des caméras, car ils ne manquaient aucune manifestation, affairés, importants, le verbe ironique pour bien montrer qu'ils n'étaient pas dupes. Cependant ils se retrouvaient toujours dans le chemin suivi la veille et bordé de scrupules dévotieux aisément traversés d'agacements érotiques qui leur inspiraient des énormités verbales. Sans doute beaucoup d'entre eux avaient-ils rêvé jadis d'un destin sans mesures et sans conditions; l'aigle qu'ils eussent voulu symboliser, ils vivaient maintenant dans l'attente qu'il surgît de leur corporation. Mais peut-être alors l'attacheraient-ils au sol.

Le jour tombait rapidement sans qu'on y prît garde sous le fluorescent multicolore des panneaux-réclame. Dans l'autobus qui grimpait la côte d'Abraham, parfois des lueurs mauves à courtes veines d'or traversaient les vitres pour se poser sur une épaule, sur un front. L'individu ainsi touché faisait le geste de se débarrasser d'un insecte et ses voisins d'en face le regardaient avec indifférence resplendir quelques secondes d'un éclat fantastique. Soucieux, inquiet même, mais pudique de ses sentiments jusqu'à la gouaille, le peuple de Québec s'agitait nerveusement aux approches de l'hiver. Dès les premières soirées fraîches recommençait, pour les uns, l'éternel calcul du combustible à faire durer et des vêtements à renforcer aux coutures. Pourvu que le syndicat ne votât point de grève ... Pourvu que la femme tînt jusqu'au printemps malgré sa vessie crevée ... Pourvu que le gars ... Pourvu que la fille ... Longtemps, n'importe quel travailleur réfléchissait, pipe au bec, devant son appareil de radio où des drames semblables aux siens toujours se dénouaient.

Le dimanche, parfois, des jeunes gens montaient encore se promener rue Saint-Jean. De là, ils s'aventuraient jusqu'à la terrasse Dufferin, mais ils n'allaient plus aux Plaines et tôt rentraient dans leurs quartiers, déconcertés par l'indifférence de leurs flirts d'été. Peu à peu, les classes sociales reprenaient position. Cela se faisait sans heurts, comme d'un accord tacite : Saint-Roch en bas, Grande-Allée en haut, et jamais si nettement qu'à l'automne les portes de la ville n'assignaient aux habitants leurs limites respectives.

(*Laure Clouet,* 1961)

Yves Thériault (Né en 1916)

Ecrivain d'une rare abondance chez nous, il a publié plusieurs romans et nouvelles et est l'auteur de pièces et de textes écrits pour la radio et la télévision. Il est actuellement rédacteur-en-chef de la revue "Sept-Jours". Il est membre de la Société royale du Canada.

Son oeuvre a peu d'unité de style, l'auteur renouvelant sans cesse sa manière en abordant des sujets nouveaux. On tient habituellement *Agaguk* pour son meilleur roman. C'est, on le sait, l'histoire d'une famille esquimaude. En voici un passage d'une émouvante simplicité.

PREMIERS PAS DE TAYAOUT

Plus vite encore que l'enfant blanc dorloté, l'enfant des villes à qui l'on enlève la moindre initiative animale, Tayaout croissait. Il rampait presque facilement. Ses mains étaient agiles et pouvaient saisir les objets. Son visage était éveillé, ses yeux brillaient.

Aux sons qu'il faisait, grognements et gloussements, il ajoutait parfois des exclamations quasi articulées. Il parlerait tôt, mais il n'était pas en cela différent des autres petits Esquimaux. Laissé à lui-même, habitué dès les premiers temps à pourvoir à ses envies et à ses besoins, il avait tôt appris à se rouler, à s'aider de ses jambes pour ramper de-ci de-là. Il y avait un monde neuf sur la mousse, un pays qui lui appartenait et avec lequel il communiait intimement. Les insectes, les rares plantes crevant le tapis frais, l'eau bruissante du ruisseau, les miroitements et les reflets, tout ceci était à son niveau.

Déjà il savait se garer d'un coup, ou rouler à quatre pattes en criant de frayeur quand un vison bondissait hors des buissons sur la toundra.

Un enfant blanc eût mis bien des mois à atteindre à cette habileté. Deux fois plus de temps que Tayaout qui, à six mois, alors que le soleil d'été était chaud et que le vent tiède enfonçait plus creux encore le permafrost sous la mousse; alors que, bien nourries, les plantes surgissaient plus haut et que les fleurs égayaient la toundra, se tint debout pour une première fois.

Agaguk avait été béat de vénération devant l'enfant nouveau-né, petite masse animale à peu près informe, sans voix définie, sans sourire, à la merci de tout et de tous. Il en avait suivi l'évolution, il s'était pâmé devant le bambin qui avait appris à ramper, à courir à quatre pattes comme un renardeau.

Mais quand Tayaout se tint debout, quand Agaguk l'aperçut ainsi, agrippé à l'un des montants de la hutte et criant de joie, il devint comme fou.

Il bondit vers l'enfant, l'empoigna, l'éleva jusqu'à sa poitrine et se mit à courir en hurlant, cette façon bien esquimaude d'extérioriser les sentiments qui se pressent dans la gorge. Il courait en rond, par seule joie animale, il criait sans mots, un son de bête joyeuse et reconnaissante. On eût dit un chien que la caresse du maître rend fou.

Iriook, debout devant la hutte, criait à son tour, avec la même impulsion d'instinct. Elle criait de voir la joie d'Agaguk, elle criait de savoir que l'enfant marcherait dans peu de temps. Elle criait sans bien savoir pourquoi; parce qu'elle était vivante, parce que le soleil était chaud et parce que son mâle criait.

Agaguk mit de longs instants à se calmer. Quand il vint finalement se jeter sur la mousse devant la hutte, il haletait comme un chien vanné.

— C'est un homme, gémissait-il. Regarde, Iriook, c'est un homme.

Il remettait l'enfant sur pied, lui tenait les mains et Tayaout, debout, riait de sa nouvelle prouesse. Il le fit avancer. Un pas, puis deux, l'enfant trébucha, se retint, en un tour de rein se remit debout.

— Il marche, s'exclamait Agaguk. Il marche !

Iriook vint s'accroupir près du petit. Elle roucoulait des mots doux au fond de la gorge. Elle touchait à l'épaule nue du bout de ses doigts.

L'enfant, extasié, buvait du soleil à grands rires, la tête renvoyée en arrière, la gorge palpitante. Son torse ferme et déjà trapu se bombait sous l'effort. Ses deux jambes arquées, mais dures et rondes se tendaient, les muscles saillaient sous la peau. Il esquissait des pas maladroits, il ne savait comment poser le pied par terre, mais il avançait peu à la fois, ses doigts comme des étaux autour des doigts d'Agaguk.

Un oiseau plongea du ciel, vint raser la hutte, obliqua vers l'enfant, l'effleura de son aile.

Tayaout eut un cri, sa main s'élança dans le vide, l'autre main aussi lâcha les doigts d'Agaguk, et il se trouva soudain sans soutien, oscillant en un équilibre instable, le visage tourné vers cet oiseau qui s'envolait et vers lequel il avait tendu les bras.

Pendant le temps d'une vie, sembla-t-il, l'enfant resta ainsi, petit d'Inuk tout fier sur la toundra sans fin.

Agaguk et Iriook avaient été pris par surprise et maintenant ils ne soufflaient plus, ils avaient comme cessé de vivre; tout en eux s'était enfui, habitait le corps de l'enfant. Ils devenaient sa volonté, son équilibre, la durée et la complaisance de sa réussite.

Puis l'enfant tomba.

Bien assis — un ploc sourd sur le sol — mais la joie qu'il avait était grande, et Agaguk vit perler deux larmes sur les joues d'Iriook.

— Il s'est tenu debout, dit-elle. Tout seul ! Il était debout... Il aurait pu marcher. Personne ne l'aidait !

Agaguk ne trouva qu'un seul mot, le seul.

— Inuk !

C'était un homme, enfin.

(*Agaguk,* 1958)

Jean Simard (Né en 1916)

Professeur à l'Ecole des Beaux-Arts de Montréal, il a publié des récits et romans où ses dons de caricaturiste se sont aussi manifestés, avant de nous livrer ses réflexions sur l'art et la vie dans *Répertoire* et *Nouveau Répertoire*. Il est membre de la Société royale du Canada.

LES FRÉQUENTATIONS

Les fréquentations de Philippe-Joseph et de Stéphanie furent donc singulièrement dénuées de ces chastes privautés qui, à l'ordinaire, n'en sont pas le moindre agrément. Un jour qu'ils étaient seuls, ayant déjoué un moment la vigilance de madame de Valauris, mon père lança soudain, avec la brusquerie du timide qui prend tout à coup, comme on dit, son courage à deux mains :

— Stéphanie, quand... quand nous marions-nous ?

— Mais quand vous le désirerez, mon ami, répondit la jeune fille d'une toute petite voix, en contemplant la pointe de ses bottines.

Et vlan ! Elle reçut sur le coin de l'oeil son premier baiser prénuptial; après quoi, Philippe-Joseph détala, sous prétexte d'aller faire la « grande demande » aux parents. Démarche de pure formalité, d'ailleurs : confirmant, voilà tout, une entente tacite. Il fut décidé que les jeunes gens s'épouseraient quelques semaines plus tard — le temps de faire publier les bans et d'imprimer les faire-part.

Pour comprendre la terreur panique qui s'empara alors de monsieur Navarin, il faut l'avoir soi-même éprouvée, en des circonstances quasi analogues. Plus que tout autre cataclysme, notre homme craignait le *mariage* : soit qu'il pressentît n'avoir pour cet état que peu de dispositions naturelles; ou qu'il eût savouré trop longtemps les charmes indéniables du célibat pour ne pas les regretter un instant, au moment d'en être dessaisi. Il se jetait donc dans cette aventure comme un baigneur grelottant dans l'eau glacée; un martyr sceptique dans la gueule du lion; un conscrit pusillanime dans la mêlée. On sait que ce fut peut-être, dans la circonstance, la pérennité de cette dernière image — rendue plus terrifiante encore par une imagination surexcitée — qui avait induit mon père à adopter, en premier lieu, ce parti désespéré. Mais la veille du grand jour, il n'était pas loin de se demander si une mort héroïque sur le champ de bataille n'eût pas été, à tout prendre, préférable à ceci !

Stéphanie, de son côté, n'était pas sans ressentir quelque frayeur; mais jamais du caractère lancinant de celle qui torturait son fiancé. Non, il s'agissait plutôt, dans son cas, d'une crainte vague et comme de seconde zone, estompée d'ailleurs par le brouhaha des ultimes préparatifs. Alors que l'angoisse de Philippe-Joseph l'empoignait littéralement aux entrailles, sonnait le tocsin dans sa poitrine, l'inquiétude ne pinçait, au coeur de la jeune fille, que des cordes superficielles.

— Parle-lui, ma bonne, grommela mon grand-père, quelques jours avant la noce.

Madame de Valauris fit venir Stéphanie dans sa chambre, lui improvisa un pathos sur le thème de l'obéissance au mari et de l'abandon à la volonté divine. Elle eut vite fait de bifurquer sur les détails du trousseau : on parla rubans, chiffons ... Stéphanie embrassa tendrement sa mère et elles prirent congé, très satisfaites l'une de l'autre.

— Alors, tu lui as parlé ? demanda ce soir-là monsieur de Valauris, avant de souffler la lampe.

— Mais oui, mon ami, bien sûr ! répondit la vieille dame, en fermant les yeux.

Monsieur de Valauris décida que lui-même, de son côté, « parlerait » à son futur gendre puisque, aussi bien, le pauvre garçon n'avait plus de père. Le dimanche suivant, après dîner, il l'entraîna au fumoir et, comme dit le fabuliste, « lui tint à peu près ce langage » :

— Heu ! Mon cher — voulais vous parler ... Oui, n'est-ce pas ? Vous épousez ma fille ... Petits êtres délicats ... Saisissez ? Heu ! Heu ! Enfin, du tact, sapristi ! du tact ... Vous me comprenez ?

Philippe-Joseph comprit tout ce qu'on voulut; et les deux hommes sortirent aussitôt du fumoir, écarlates, honteux et soufflant comme des phoques. Ainsi, les amoureux furent-ils « initiés » aux problèmes de la vie conjugale, aux mystères troublants de la sexualité !

La veille de l'irrémédiable cérémonie, mon grand-père, inquiet malgré tout, prit sa fille à part et lui fit :

— Tu sais, mignonne, il est encore temps de changer d'idée. Tu n'as pas encore dit *oui* . . . Ta mère tient beaucoup à ce mariage, mais ça ne veut rien dire. Tu es libre, et je suis là ! Ton fiancé est beaucoup plus âgé que toi — as-tu bien réfléchi ?

Stéphanie noua ses jolis bras autour du cou de son père, répandit quelques larmes sur son gilet, tout en songeant à la belle cérémonie du lendemain, dont elle serait l'héroïne. Elle pensa aussi à sa mère, à ses soeurs, ses cousines, ses amies; à tous ces gens qui seraient là, demain, et qui avaient envoyé de si ravissants cadeaux . . . Elle sécha ses yeux, expliquant à son père qu'en vérité, elle n'était capable d'aimer que lui; mais que Philippe-Joseph ferait sans doute un bon mari, tout comme elle une épouse dévouée. Elle se sentait adulte, raisonnable. La pendule sonna. Ils éteignirent les lampes. Il était temps de monter. Comme disait Ravaillac, la veille de son exécution, la journée de demain serait rude . . . Bras dessus, bras dessous, le père et la fille s'engagèrent dans le long escalier de bois vernissé. La onzième marche craquait, et ils échangèrent un sourire complice. Sur le palier, ils s'embrassèrent tendrement, se souhaitant bonne nuit comme d'habitude. Très las tout à coup, le vieil homme alla s'étendre silencieusement le long de sa vieille épouse, qui ronflait à petit bruit, la bouche entrouverte et le chapelet au poing. La jeune fille regagna sa chambre d'enfant où elle goûterait, sans pourtant la savourer comme elle aurait dû, sa dernière nuit solitaire.

A des milles de là, en rase campagne, à bord du wagon-lit qui l'amenait vers son destin, mon père, baigné de sueurs, se tournait et retournait sur sa couchette. Il était la proie d'une cruelle insomnie, hachée de brefs cauchemars où s'entremêlaient les images discordantes de catastrophes ferroviaires et nuptiales. Un bon coup de whisky eût sans doute apprivoisé le sommeil et mis en déroute les fantômes. Seulement, Philippe-Joseph Navarin, qui avait peur de beaucoup de choses, craignait aussi l'alcool . . .

En outre, il communiait demain.

(Mon fils pourtant heureux, 1956)

Pierre Baillargeon (1916-1967)

Journaliste, il est maintenant attaché aux relations extérieures des chemins de fer nationaux après avoir longtemps vécu en France. Fondateur de la revue *Amérique française* (1941), membre de la Société royale du Canada, ses livres reprennent sans cesse le procès de nos moeurs. Ce moraliste est aussi un satiriste acide et un styliste impeccable.

MES MAÎTRES

Je ne voyais pas bien ce que mes maîtres auraient pu faire dans le monde. A quelques exceptions près, ils étaient sots, laids, tristes. Sans doute étaient-ce là des titres à l'enseignement.

On leur demandait de nous apprendre à lire, à écrire, à penser par nous-mêmes, toutes choses dont la plupart d'entre eux, faute de préparation, faute de loisir, étaient incapables.

Mais, s'ils avaient pensé, ils n'auraient pu souffrir d'en être empêchés par les élèves; et, plutôt que de leur apprendre à lire, ils auraient fait des livres.

A défaut de science, ils se fiaient à leur conscience. L'intention droite leur tenait lieu de jugement éclairé. (Pour combien d'autres encore est-ce agir sans réflexion que d'obéir à leur conscience !) Il leur suffisait de se sentir de bonne foi pour se justifier leurs décisions mal fondées. Non seulement ils nous induisaient en erreur, mais encore ils se trompaient eux-mêmes.

Qu'on ne croie pas que j'exagère à plaisir. J'ai médit de mes maîtres, bien moins, cependant, que chacun d'eux ne faisait sur le compte de ses collègues. Entre autres médisances, qui étaient, il va sans dire, autant de plaisanteries, chacun se plaignait d'être entouré d'hypocrites, en quoi tous avaient peut-être raison, car il est difficile de vivre en compagnie sans jouer un rôle; ce qui peut donc ne pas être pris en mauvaise part.

Au demeurant, les meilleurs hommes du monde, et cela, pour dire comme l'autre, ne leur enlevait rien. Ils étaient désintéressés et purs : qualités que je ne sus apprécier à leur juste valeur que bien plus tard dans le monde où elles ne se rencontrent pas.

Si, malgré ces précautions oratoires, l'un d'eux me lit et s'offusque, il me pardonnera beaucoup en se rappelant que *sous peine d'être ennuyeux, l'ignorant est forcé d'être médisant,* que *ceux qui médisent toujours nuisent rarement; ils méditent plus de mal qu'ils n'en peuvent faire,* et enfin qu'*il y a moins d'indifférence à médire qu'à oublier...* Tout a été dit, il ne reste plus qu'à médire.

(*Les médisances de Claude Perrin*, 1945)

Roger Lemelin (Né en 1919)

Ecrivain devenu homme d'affaires, il a créé une vive impression par son premier roman, *Au pied de la pente douce* (1944), où ses dons de conteur et de satiriste étaient manifestes, et il a fait une fortune avec *Les Plouffe* (1948) dont il a tiré des continuités pour la radio et la télévision. Membre de la Société royale du Canada, il n'a rien publié depuis 1952. Ses romans de moeurs hauts en couleurs restent vivants.

NAISSANCE D'UNE VOCATION

Chapitre premier

L'hiver avait semblé long à cause de la neige qui s'était prolongée bien avant dans le printemps. Les fleurs avaient été en retard sur le soleil, puis, quand le printemps fut libre enfin de cette hérédité de grands froids blancs et qu'il commençait de sourire, juin l'engloutit. L'été était apparu, tout neuf.

Denis aurait pu se dire que la fonte des neiges avait emporté le passé. Lise, cette mesquine passion d'un automne triste, quelle nuance était-elle devenue parmi la complexité de ses ambitions d'écrivain? Il ne se le demandait même pas dans la solitude des grandes randonnées, au retour de son travail. Il marchait, léger, dans cette paroisse qu'il défiait toujours de le vaincre, il marchait au milieu des Mulots qui, ayant sur l'épaule les uns leur pelle, les autres leur pic, revenaient de leur tâche à l'égout collecteur. Denis se défendait de se sentir supérieur par sa situation dans un bureau, mais rêvait d'une révolution dont il serait le chef.

Un soir de juillet, on le vit tout effervescence. Il serrait précieusement le magazine qui donnait les conditions d'un concours pour jeunes écrivains. Son roman était déjà tout composé. Il avait d'abord échafaudé une intrigue fantastique qui, ensuite, avec la forte dose de vraisemblance dont il devait la lester, dégénérait en petite autobiographie, plate de ses ambitions crevées. La grande difficulté, c'était son coeur qui entonnait de grandioses tirades hérissées de cruauté, tandis que son style s'empâtait dans une série de comparaisons bourrées de sublime, son coeur qui s'enivrait du « toast » d'une victoire anticipée. Il chercha un lieu commun. Denis Boucher, chantre des méconnus! Quelle explosion, dans le Québec, ce roman! Il ne vit pas approcher le char-observatoire, sur lequel les touristes de Montréal et des Trois-Rivières, rehaussés par la présence de quelques Américains authentiques, étaient soigneusement rangés comme des oeufs de Pâques dans un étalage de Samedi Saint. Le conducteur piétinait éperdument sur le gong pour dégager les rails des petits Mulots qui cernaient ce tramway de gala, distributeur de cents. Les jeunes mariés et les touristes des Trois-Rivières se montraient les plus prodigues. Les pseudo-amateurs de vieilles choses lorgnaient les mansardes aux toits penchés, convaincus de revivre l'atmosphère de Jean Talon, et gloussaient, ravis, devant ces débris du passé. Ces cabanes avaient été récemment bâties de rebuts de démolition. Il y avait aussi des bonshommes accompagnés de leurs pieuses bonnes femmes, prospecteurs insatiables de nouvelles mines à prodiges. On en avait presque assez de sainte Anne et du frère André.

— On dit qu'il demeurait ici, le saint jeune homme ?

Une poignée de sous vola dans la direction de Denis et les gamins se ruèrent dans ses jambes. La première phrase de son livre, qu'il avait sur les dents, se transforma en juron. Il talocha les Mulots et vit rire les touristes. Il leur cria :

— On ne vous les a jamais demandés, vos cents. Filez, puants !

Il saisit une pierre et la lança sur le tramway. Les mamans, dans les portes, le huèrent. Les étrangers ne viendraient plus jeter des cents. Elles faisaient apprendre aux petits, en même temps que : « Je vous aime, mon Jésus », « Give me five cents, please ».

— Ça fait son frais, à cause de sa job de bureau.

Denis vit venir à lui madame Chaton et n'eut pas le temps de l'éviter.

— Le v'là-t-y pas qui veut s'sauver. Arrive que j'te vende une carte pour la soirée de lutte à Pinasse. Envoie, avec ta job de bureau, renie pas ta gang, tu peux payer 50 cents comme rien.

Madame Chaton tendait sa carte, faisait signe à ses amies qu'elle les visiterait dans la minute. Denis hésita. Il ne fallait pas qu'on sût qu'il ne gagnait que sept dollars par semaine. Madame Chaton, devant lui, prenait des poses de combat. Elle était maigre, jaunâtre, petite, mais en ébullition comme un précipité d'acide sulfurique.

— Et puis, tu vas apprendre des prises. L'écartillement général, paraît que c'est fameux. On a Kid l'Assassin, qui lutte au Forum.

Madame Pinasse, la femme du candidat au concours de popularité, « faisait » l'autre côté de la rue, convainquait ses amies de ne pas manquer ce spectacle, qui valait dix bingos comme ceux du candidat des Soyeux, Zéphirin. De plus, la police était à la veille de « rafler » les bingos. Les commères les plus habiles obtenaient un rabais de dix cents sur leur carte et s'informaient si la Chaton n'avait pas un pourcentage sur cette vente. Son mari faisait bien assez d'argent avec ses vers et son nouveau commerce : « Modern Refrigeration Company Incorporated », titre trouvé par Denis pour la modique somme de dix cents. Chaton se rendait au dépotoir qui n'avait pas assez de l'été pour fondre, se taillait des cubes de neige durcie, tachée de crottin, et les vendait deux sous aux Mulots qui n'avaient pas de frigidaire. Ceux-ci les mettaient dans la cuve de leur laveuse, et ça gardait froid le beurre et la petite bière d'épinette. C'était beaucoup moins coûteux que les blocs du marché de la glace.

Soudain, les demoiselles Latruche, organisatrices du candidat des Soyeux, accoururent essoufflées, et rencontrèrent à la porte madame Pritontin.

— Madame Pritontin, votre mari et Pinasse sont saouls et se chicanent avec M. Lévesque dans la salle paroissiale.

— Laissez- vous pas emmancher, madame Pritontin. Ça les agace que vot'mari soit l'ami du mien, cria la femme du commandant des « pratiques ».

Madame Pritontin, désespérée de l'évolution de son mari, fit claquer sa porte. Les succès grandissants des demoiselles Latruche, la popularité du saint répandue dans tout le pays et l'étonnante affection que ses deux fils portaient aux héroïnes des historiettes illustrées des journaux, la faisaient dépérir. Elle raidissait son âme, sa foi, pour retenir au foyer cette atmosphère de canonisation dont ses fils semblaient de moins en moins pénétrés. Les vieilles filles, qui se sentaient érudites et ne discutaient qu'avec le curé depuis qu'elles écoulaient des tracts pieux, laissèrent tomber, méprisantes :

— Mulotes, lutteuses !

Elles entrèrent dans leur bureau d'affaires, récemment ouvert. C'était un ancien restaurant de patates frites qui avait fait beaucoup d'argent par la vente des magazines cinématographiques, surtout le numéro d'avril 1938, qui représentait Dorothy Lamour en sarong. Mais avec les vieilles filles, il n'y avait plus moyen de se damner à St-Joseph; maintenant, la vitrine était garnie d'annales, de chapelets, de bérets pour jocistes. Un petit livre bleu pâle donnait les recettes de l'année, qui permettaient de garder dans le mariage une virginité élastique que les nombreuses naissances n'entachent point.

Il n'était donc plus question pour les paroissiens de s'inquiéter de la longueur de la barbe de Dieu et du chemin tortueux des béatitudes : le salut était là, dans la vitrine des Latruche, étalé sous les yeux bienveillants et optimistes d'un futur saint. Des témoignages de guérison étaient affichés et faisaient couronne à la méthode d'un frère de talent : *clef de la chasteté découverte pour les adolescents.* Les lettres venant des Etats-Unis et de la Colombie Britannique étaient les plus en vue : névralgie, angoisses de jeunes mères, emplois obtenus, malaises d'estomac évaporés, vocation éclairée. Le jeune saint avait des débuts prometteurs. Malgré les protestations des pères de l'Oratoire St-Joseph, madame Pritontin avait fait en leur nom une petite enquête sur ces prétendues guérisons. Les demoiselles Latruche, offusquées, l'avaient accusée de dépit, et répliqué que dans vingt ans, avec l'expérience, leur protégé ferait face aux cancers. Et puis ! on était dans un pays de miracles.

Mais on se chicanait sur les chantiers de l'église neuve. Denis y courut, désireux de s'approvisionner d'observations, car il se sentait vibrant d'une grandiloquence dramatique, il éprouvait le besoin des nuances de l'ironie. Le tapage était infernal, les marteaux des maçons résonnaient à travers les heurts des poutres de fer que les camions déchargeaient près des ouvriers. Et c'était une dispute interminable entre les travailleurs et les badauds. Tous les chômeurs de St-Joseph, installés sur les cubes de pierre, donnaient leur opinion, déploraient que le temple fût tout en longueur, pas assez large. D'autres jouaient aux cartes, obstinés, bouillants de vengeance, et les contremaîtres se tiraient les cheveux d'être incapables de les déloger.

— Où est M. le curé ?

M. le curé se réfugiait dans le sanctuaire pour se soustraire à l'indignation des Mulots, qu'il ne pouvait engager comme maçons parce qu'ils ne savaient que creuser des caves. Les travaux de l'égout collecteur commençaient heureusement de le soulager.

Et monsieur le curé calculait l'angle obtus que son siège ferait entre la nef et le tabernacle. Il serait le pivot de la prière. L'abbé Charton arpentait le jubé, parlait fort aux ouvriers et tendait une oreille attentive pour s'assurer que sa voix portait bien. Enfin, ce jubé serait exclusif à la chorale de la grand-messe et l'orgue neuf n'accompagnerait que les chants à parties. La situation se corsait, cet orgue ayant été donné par le père de l'organiste de la messe de neuf heures. Le bedeau, une jambe dans le plâtre, et qui se traînait sur ses béquilles en soufflant, tentait de sortir les Gonzague, qui s'arrogeaient le privilège de visiter le temple avant l'ouverture officielle. Bidonnet ne les aimait pas, ces futurs bedeaux. C'était bien assez des plus importants actionnaires de la Compagnie des Grâces. (Formée par M. le curé Folbèche. Parts et obligations de $10, $100, et $1,000 remboursables à la caisse de la Grâce Sanctifiante.) Ces messieurs se promenaient comme des maîtres dans l'église, et Bidonnet, perché sur des béquilles qui craquaient, sautillait derrière le curé, lui faisait part de plans grandioses pour décorations futures, car son remplaçant, un hypocrite, s'offrait pour un salaire plus maigre.

Monsieur le curé sourit quand on l'avertit de la dispute entre Pinasse et Zéphirin Lévesque, dans la salle paroissiale, en bas.

— J'y vais.

Il descendit tranquillement l'échelle sommaire qui tenait lieu d'escalier. Les Gonzague avaient les bras tendus, le suppliaient de prendre des précautions.

Quelle idée géniale, ce concours de popularité entre Pinasse et Zéphirin ! Il fallait avouer que la température était un peu chaude pour organiser un tel concours qui, d'ordinaire, avait lieu l'automne. Mais les travaux de l'égout collecteur avaient soulevé chez les ouvriers de St-Joseph une trop belle vague de prospérité pour n'y pas tenter un maître coup de filet. Peuh ! L'automne ! Cette saison sans creusage, ni neige à pelleter, était pauvre comme une journée de la Toussaint ! Non ! Elles étaient même désirables, ces disputes entre Zéphirin et Pinasse. M. Folbèche jeta un oeil désapprobateur à l'abbé Bongrain qui, heureux, aidait à attacher les pierres à la chaîne de la grue mécanique. Un peu plus loin, l'abbé Trinchu, qui commençait de mieux priser son séjour à St-Joseph, vu l'église neuve, se tenait aux côtés de l'architecte, lui imposait ses comparaisons entre l'art romain et l'art gothique.

Denis suivit M. le curé dans la salle paroissiale, d'où les exclamations fusaient. La voix puissante de Pinasse, appuyée par les jurons délicats de Pritontin, abasourdissait l'indignation de Zéphirin. Pinasse voulait obliger Zéphirin à lui laisser la salle nette pour le lendemain, car le bingo de ce soir ferait un fameux gâchis de jetons et de sièges renversés. Le brave commandant tenait à ce que les experts de Montréal qui viendraient installer l'arène pussent travailler dans la propreté et que la salle ne laissât pas de trace de l'orgie du bingo. Et puis, cette soirée de lutte ferait époque, car elle lui permettrait certainement de remporter le concours qui se terminait le même soir. Tout serait fait en grand. La garde, commandée par Pinasse, irait recevoir les lutteurs à la gare. Et Zéphirin pestait. En apercevant M. Folbèche, les commandants se turent, devinrent presque aimables entre eux. Zéphirin s'approcha avec force gestes.

— Monsieur le curé, on dit que la police doit faire une descente à mon bingo. Dois-je craindre ?

Le bon prêtre sourit, majestueux.

— L'Eglise a des lois que la loi n'enfreint pas. Jouez en paix.

Pinasse cligna un oeil canaille à Pritontin. Leurs démarches auprès des autorités policières allaient avoir leur résultat, ce soir. Le commandant des pratiques fit éclater son gros rire :

— Je serai en loi, moi, avec ma séance de lutte. Ça attire les hommes, au moins.

M. le curé se tira l'oreille, perplexe. Ces combats en maillot l'inquiétaient un peu. Pourquoi les autres curés n'en organisaient-ils pas ?

— C'est dangereux, cette lutte ? On dit qu'ils se font souffrir, qu'ils se tirent les orteils ? Enfin, vous êtes bien sûr que c'est un spectacle de salle paroissiale ?

— Vous pensez ! Des lutteurs de Montréal, qui luttent au Forum. C'est distingué. Et puis, c'est du « fake ».

M. le curé ouvrit de grands yeux et imagina de formidables corps souples qui flottaient dans l'arène comme des muses, se blottissaient sous les bras ouatés de l'adversaire, donnaient des coups de poings qui fondaient en caresses. Il entendait distinctement le doux murmure de la foule à la vue de cette délicieuse acrobatie de gentilshommes musclés, qui geindraient en souriant dans des étreintes de camarades. On pourrait presque inviter les religieuses.

— Qu'est-ce que tu viens faire ici ?

Monsieur le curé fixait Denis d'un oeil sévère. Qu'avait-il à prendre des notes, ce garnement étrange, si intelligent, et qui avait frustré ses espoirs ? Boucher l'inquiétait plus que les intrigues de tous les Soyeux réunis. C'en était un qu'il faudrait surveiller. Denis enfouit son calepin dans sa chemise. Il se faufila vers la porte, sans bravade. Seule, une tristesse le désespérait, la tristesse de n'avoir rien pu saisir de précis, de simple et de vrai. La vie bouillonnait devant lui et il ne pouvait la saisir, emporté qu'il était dans une rêverie peuplée d'arbres, de fleurs et de fleuves. C'était donc toujours la même fièvre grandiloquente dans laquelle Lise l'avait plongé, et dont il s'était cru débarrassé par la mort de Gaston ? Ainsi, ce n'étaient que réminiscences, cette inspiration fausse, ce bond de son art vers l'avenir ?

Puis il vit les enfants courir vers chez Lévesque comme s'ils y avaient vu du feu. Les mères apparurent aux fenêtres, et les filles sortirent sur les trottoirs. Chez Bédarovitch, la bande s'approcha au bord de la chaussée.

— Qu'il est beau !

— La chanceuse !

— La fraîche !

— Boucher, regarde Colin qui lui montre !

— Prêtez-le-moi une fois, pour voir.

— Mon Dieu, je vais tomber ! s'effrayait Lise, chancelante sur sa bicyclette neuve.

Jean, confus, la soutenait, lui promettait qu'elle apprendrait. Denis voulut d'abord prendre une autre rue, mais une sorte de rage le clouait de voir Lise sourire ainsi à Jean, se confier à son épaule. Pourquoi ce dépit, puisqu'elle ne l'intéressait pas, cette jeune fille ? Il avait cru consumer tout souvenir de la couventine, l'hiver passé, dans le feu de ses désirs et de ses rêves lubriques. Sa passion inassouvie avait accusé Lise de banalité. Malgré tous ces Mulots, malgré Jean qui la soutenait, il ne pouvait la mettre au rang des autres, avec Germaine et ses amies. Il avança, pour se prouver sa froideur. Mais elle était belle, elle lui souriait. Ses cheveux noirs, qui rendaient sa figure plus pâle, se couchaient sur ses épaules et semblaient tirer sa tête à l'arrière. La langueur qui mettait du rêve dans ses yeux l'an passé avait fait place à une sorte de chaleur douce, celle de l'amour qui mijote. Son cou paraissait plus jeune, moins étiré, et l'harmonie s'en continuait jusqu'à ses épaules arrondies. Ses chevilles semblaient se gonfler d'élans qu'elle comprimait du talon sur les pédales. Il se sentit inférieur de la voir devenir femme avant qu'il devînt homme. Mais ses désirs se levaient de nouveau, comme l'an passé, quand ils étaient beaux et qu'ils s'arrêtaient encore loin de la possession. Cela n'était donc pas éteint ? Ce Jean dont il avait vaincu l'amitié suffisait à tout bouleverser par un seul sourire échangé avec Lise ?

Il entra chez lui, examina sa bicyclette, puis brusquement, il eut envie de la démolir. Non ! il était fort, il était un écrivain. Il prit son trouble pour de l'inspiration, passa en revue les métaphores collectionnées dans l'après-midi, cultiva ses rancunes et sa grandeur, puis écrivit la première page. Son histoire le brûlait, mais ses phrases étaient froides et s'excusaient, au lieu de raconter. L'odeur du rôti parfumait le salon, et il décrivait l'arôme d'un jardin, son début.

Jean, à peine bruni par le soleil, rangea sa bicyclette avec joie près de la victoria. Son bonheur d'aujourd'hui lui faisait mépriser tous ses déboires, la maladie étrange qui grossissait son genou, sa misère, l'acceptation morne de l'indifférence de Lise à son amour. Et tout à coup, au moment où il se sentait sombrer de voir Denis monter et s'enfuir dans la supériorité de son emploi de sténographe, au moment où l'amour lui paraissait impossible, Lise lui demandait de l'accompagner demain, à bicyclette. Il se mit à frotter le nickelé de sa bécane. On sentait, dans son sourire ravi, dans les phrases hachées qu'il murmurait, sa reconnaissance à Dieu de ne pas l'avoir oublié. Il était formidable, Dieu ! Lui permettre d'accompagner Lise sans que sa claudication parût ! Ils s'arrêteraient, au bord de la route, dans une clairière de silence, un silence irisé par la lune. Il aurait des pressions de doigts si douces, si émues, qu'elle comprendrait enfin jusqu'à quel point il l'aimait. Il se rappela la colère de Denis, près de cette victoria, quand il lui avait avoué sa première rencontre avec Lise. Non, son amour ne devait pas avoir été un petit amour de paroisse, puisqu'il avait souffert.

Il souleva donc le banc de la victoria, en sortit la grammaire que Denis lui avait prêtée. Il fallait cacher tous les livres, car Tit-Blanc, quand il était ivre, les brûlait, en invoquant l'ignorance des grands-pères, qui avaient tout de même vécu. Cette grammaire, il l'avait abordée le jour où il avait senti que sa mélancolie de gars de manu-facture ne pouvait s'accorder avec les rêveries de cette fille instruite. Il but de longues pages arides, en souriant, fiévreux, mais il ne com-prenait pas. Des yeux, une main, des dents étincelaient entre les lignes. Tit-Blanc avait fait claquer la porte. Jean eut un geste furtif qu'il n'acheva pas.

— T'es encore dans l'instruction, fainéant ! Je t'ai vu avec la Lévesque. C'est elle qui te rend fier. T'as honte de nous autres, t'as honte des vers.

— Je n'ai pas honte. Je vieillis, et puis, je n'aime pas marcher sur les cailloux. Ma jambe me fait souffrir.

Barloute, dans la cuisine, se lamentait, parlait d'aller trouver le patron de la manufacture afin qu'il donnât plus d'ouvrage à Tit-Blanc. C'était la misère, l'humiliation du chômage, quand ses amies étrennaient des chapeaux, allaient aux vues, mangeaient du dessert grâce à l'argent gagné à l'égout collecteur. Elle tempêtait, pleurait de ne pouvoir aller au bingo, accusant Tit-Blanc de garder ses cents pour la lutte. Le père Pitou, les cheveux plus blancs et la figure plus rouge, appuyé sur sa canne, arrivait, furieux. Il n'avait pas chiqué depuis trois jours :

— Vends donc ce machin-là ! On n'avait pas ça, nous autres, dans not' temps.

Il bouscula la bicyclette. Tit-Blanc eut une exclamation ravie.

— On peut en avoir vingt piastres !

Jean bondit et cria :

— Vendez votre victoria, plutôt. Mon bicycle, je le garde. Je m'en irai plutôt.

— Sacre ton camp. Ça va tet-ben faire notre affaire. Pour ce que tu rapportes.

— J'ai parlé trop vite. Je vendrai encore des vers. Tenez, je vous donne tout.

Il vida ses poches de la monnaie qu'il réservait pour sa promenade avec Lise. Il s'enfuit dans la salle et il lui semblait que tout boitait en lui, jusqu'à son coeur.

Barloute haussa les épaules.

— V'là assez longtemps que tu nous joues la comédie du mal de jambes pour pus travailler. L'école, tu n'iras pas, lâche.

Germaine lui glissa, avant de sortir :

— Fais attention de ne pas l'avoir longtemps, ta Lise. J'ai vu Denis examiner sa bicyclette, tantôt. Il l'a huilée.

(*Au pied de la pente douce*, 1944)

Anne Hébert (Née en 1916)

Le début du *Torrent* reproduit ici fera sentir combien la poétesse est aussi un prosateur de qualité et un écrivain né.

LE TORRENT

J'étais un enfant dépossédé du monde. Par le décret d'une volonté antérieure à la mienne, je devais renoncer à toute possession en cette vie. Je touchais au monde par fragments, ceux-là seuls qui m'étaient immédiatement indispensables, et enlevés aussitôt leur utilité terminée; le cahier que je devais ouvrir, pas même la table sur laquelle il se trouvait; le coin d'étable à nettoyer, non la poule qui se perchait sur la fenêtre; et jamais, jamais la campagne offerte par la fenêtre. Je voyais la grande main de ma mère quand elle se levait sur moi, mais je n'apercevais pas ma mère en entier, de pied en cap. J'avais seulement le sentiment de sa terrible grandeur qui me glaçait.

Je n'ai pas eu d'enfance. Je ne me souviens d'aucun loisir avant cette singulière aventure de ma surdité. Ma mère travaillait sans relâche et je participais de ma mère, tel un outil dans ses mains. Levées avec le soleil, les heures de sa journée s'emboîtaient les unes dans les autres avec une justesse qui ne laissait aucune détente possible.

En dehors des leçons qu'elle me donna jusqu'à mon entrée au collège, ma mère ne parlait pas. La parole n'entrait pas dans son ordre. Pour qu'elle dérogeât à cet ordre, il fallait que le premier j'eusse commis une transgression quelconque. C'est-à-dire que ma mère ne m'adressait la parole que pour me réprimander, avant de me punir.

Au sujet de l'étude, là encore tout était compté, calculé, sans un jour de congé, ni de vacances. L'heure des leçons terminée, un mutisme total envahissait à nouveau le visage de ma mère. Sa bouche se fermait durement, hermétiquement, comme tenue par un verrou tiré de l'intérieur.

Moi, je baissais les yeux, soulagé de n'avoir plus à suivre le fonctionnement des puissantes mâchoires et des lèvres minces qui prononçaient, en détachant chaque syllabe, les mots de « châtiment », « justice de Dieu », « damnation », « enfer », « discipline », « péché originel », et surtout cette phrase précise qui revenait comme un leitmotiv :

— Il faut se dompter jusqu'aux os. On n'a pas idée de la force mauvaise qui est en nous ! Tu m'entends, François ? Je te dompterai bien, moi . . .

Là, je commençais à frissonner et des larmes emplissaient mes yeux, car je savais bien ce que ma mère allait ajouter :

— François, regarde-moi dans les yeux . . .

Ce supplice pouvait durer longtemps. Ma mère me fixait sans merci et moi je ne parvenais pas à me décider à la regarder. Elle ajoutait en se levant :

— C'est bien, François, l'heure est finie . . . Mais je me souviendrai de ta mauvaise volonté, en temps et lieu . . .

En fait, ma mère enregistrait minutieusement chacun de mes manquements pour m'en dresser le compte, un beau jour, quand je ne m'y attendais plus. Juste au moment où je croyais m'échapper, elle fondait sur moi, implacable, n'ayant rien oublié, détaillant, jour après jour, heure après heure, les choses mêmes que je croyais les plus cachées.

Je ne distinguais pas pourquoi ma mère ne me punissait pas sur-le-champ. D'autant plus que je sentais confusément qu'elle se dominait avec peine. Dans la suite j'ai compris qu'elle agissait ainsi par discipline envers elle : « pour se dompter elle-même », et aussi certainement pour m'impressionner davantage en établissant son emprise le plus profondément possible sur moi.

Il y avait bien une autre raison que je n'ai découverte que beaucoup plus tard.

J'ai dit que ma mère s'occupait sans arrêt, soit dans la maison, soit dans l'étable ou les champs. Pour me corriger, elle attendait une trêve.

J'ai trouvé, l'autre jour, dans la remise, sur une poutre, derrière un vieux fanal, un petit calepin ayant appartenu à ma mère. L'horaire de ses journées y était soigneusement inscrit. Un certain lundi, elle devait mettre des draps à blanchir sur l'herbe; et, je me souviens que brusquement il s'était mis à pleuvoir. En date de ce même lundi, j'ai donc vu dans son carnet que cette étrange femme avait rayé : « Blanchir les draps », et ajouté dans la marge : « Battre François ».

Nous étions toujours seuls. J'allais voir douze ans et n'avais pas encore contemplé un visage humain, si ce n'est le reflet mouvant de mes propres traits, lorsque l'été je me penchais pour boire aux ruisseaux. Quant à ma mère, seul le bas de sa figure m'était familier. Mes yeux n'osaient monter plus haut, jusqu'aux prunelles courroucées et au large front que je connus, plus tard, atrocement ravagé.

Son menton impératif, sa bouche tourmentée, malgré l'attitude calme que le silence essayait de lui imposer, son corsage noir, cuirassé, sans nulle place tendre où pût se blottir la tête d'un enfant; et voilà l'univers maternel dans lequel j'appris, si tôt, la dureté et le refus.

Nous demeurions à une trop grande distance du village, même pour aller à la messe. Cela ne m'empêchait pas de passer quelquefois mon dimanche presque entier à genoux sur le plancher, en punition de quelque faute. C'était là, je crois, la façon maternelle de sanctifier le jour du Seigneur, à mes dépens.

Je n'ai jamais vu ma mère prier. Mais, je soupçonnais qu'elle le faisait, parfois, enfermée dans sa chambre. Dans ce temps-là, j'étais si dépendant de ma mère que le moindre mouvement intérieur chez elle se répercutait en moi. Oh ! je ne comprenais rien, bien entendu, au drame de cette femme, mais je ressentais, comme on perçoit l'orage, les sautes de son humeur la plus secrète. Or, les soirs où je croyais ma mère occupée à prier, je n'osais bouger sur ma paillasse. Le silence était lourd à mourir. J'attendais je ne sais quelle tourmente qui balaierait tout, m'entraînant avec ma mère, à jamais lié à son destin funeste.

Ce désir que j'avais augmentait de jour en jour et me pesait comme une nostalgie. Voir de près et en détail une figure humaine. Je cherchais à examiner ma mère à la dérobée; mais, presque toujours, elle se retournait vivement vers moi et je perdais courage.

Je résolus d'aller à la rencontre d'un visage d'homme, n'osant espérer un enfant et me promettant de fuir si c'était une femme. Pour cela je voulais me poster au bord de la grand'route. Il finirait bien par passer quelqu'un.

Notre maison s'élevait à l'écart de toute voie de communication, au centre d'un domaine de bois, de champs et d'eau sous toutes ses formes, depuis les calmes ruisseaux jusqu'à l'agitation du torrent.

Je traversai l'érablière et les grands champs tout en buttons durs que ma mère s'obstinait à labourer en serrant les dents, les mains attachées aux mancherons que le choc lui faisait parfois lâcher. Notre vieux cheval, Eloi, en est mort, lui.

Je ne croyais pas la route si loin. Je craignais de me perdre. Que dirait ma mère, au retour de la traite des vaches, quand elle s'apercevrait de mon absence ? D'avance je me recroquevillais sous les coups, mais je continuais de marcher. Mon désir était trop pressant, trop désespéré.

Après le petit brûlé où chaque été je venais cueillir des bleuets avec ma mère, je me trouvai face à face avec la route. Essoufflé, je m'arrêtai court, comme touché au front par une main. J'avais envie de pleurer. La route s'étendait triste, lamentable, unie au soleil, sans âme, morte. Où se trouvaient les cortèges que je m'imaginais découvrir ? Sur ce sol-là s'étaient posés des pas autres que les miens ou ceux de ma mère. Qu'étaient devenus ces pas ? Où se dirigeaient-ils ? Pas une empreinte. La route devait certainement être morte.

Je n'osais marcher dessus et je suivais le fossé. Tout à coup, je butai sur un corps étendu et fus projeté dans la vase. Je me levai, consterné, à la pensée de mes habits salis; et je vis l'homme horrible à côté de moi. Il devait dormir là, et maintenant il s'asseyait lentement. Cloué sur place, je ne bougeais pas, m'attendant à être tué pour le moins. Je ne trouvais même pas la force de me garantir le visage avec mon bras.

L'homme était sale. Sur sa peau et ses vêtements alternaient la boue sèche et la boue fraîche. Ses cheveux longs se confondaient avec sa barbe, sa moustache et ses énormes sourcils qui lui tombaient sur les yeux. Mon Dieu, quelle face faite de poils hérissés et de taches de boue ! Je vis la bouche se montrer là-dedans, gluante, avec des dents jaunes. Je voulus fuir. L'homme me retint par le bras. Il s'agrippa à moi pour tenter de se mettre debout, ce qui eut pour effet de me faire culbuter.

L'homme rit. Son rire était bien de lui. Aussi ignoble que lui. Encore une fois je tentai de me sauver. Il me fit asseoir sur le bord du fossé, près de lui. Je sentais son odeur fauve se mêler aux relents du marécage. Tout bas, je faisais mon acte de contrition, et je pensais à la justice de Dieu qui, pour moi, ferait suite à la terreur et au dégoût que m'inspirait cet homme. Il avait sa main malpropre et lourde sur mon épaule.

— Quel âge as-tu, petit gars ?

Sans attendre ma réponse, il ajouta :

— Connais-tu des histoires ? Non, hein ... Moi, j'en connais ...

Il passa son bras autour de mes épaules. J'essayai de me déprendre. Il serrait plus fort, en riant. Son rire était tout près de ma joue. A ce moment, j'aperçus ma mère devant nous. Dans sa main elle tenait la maîtresse branche qui servait à faire rentrer les vaches. Ma mère m'apparut pour la première fois dans son ensemble. Grande, forte, nette, plus puissante que je ne l'avais jamais cru.

— Lâchez cet enfant !

L'homme, surpris, se leva péniblement. Il semblait fasciné par ma mère autant que je l'étais. Ma mère se retourna vers moi et, du ton sur lequel on parle à un chien, elle me cria :

— A la maison, François !

Lentement, sentant mes jambes se dérober sous moi, je repris le sentier du brûlé. L'homme parlait à ma mère. Il paraissait la connaître. Il disait de sa voix traînante :

— Si c'est pas la belle Claudine ! ... Te retrouver ici ! ... T'as quitté le village à cause du petit, hein ? ... Un beau petit gars ... oui, ben beau ... Te retrouver ici ! ... Tout le monde te pensait défunte ...

— Allez-vous-en ! tonna ma mère.

— La grande Claudine, si avenante, autrefois ... Fâche-toi pas ...

— Je vous défends de me tutoyer, cochon !

Là, j'entendis le bruit sec d'un coup, suivi par le bruit sourd d'une chute. Je me retournai. Ma mère était debout, immense, à la lisière du bois, la trique toute frémissante à la main, l'homme étendu à ses pieds. Elle avait dû se servir du gros bout du bâton pour frapper l'homme à la tête.

(*Le Torrent,* 1950)

Réal Benoît (Né en 1916)

Réalisateur à Radio-Canada, grand connaisseur du cinéma, il vient de se révéler un bon artisan du "nouveau roman", comme en fait foi l'extrait suivant de ce long monologue de *Quelqu'un pour m'écouter* qui lui valut le Grand Prix littéraire de la ville de Montréal.

AU RESTAURANT

Il faut vivre... phrase-clé des soirs de joie, des soirs de déses-poir, dans la joie de ces soirs où l'amour et l'amitié n'étaient pas bien loin, à portée de bras, à portée de voix, dans le désespoir de ce soir... il faut vivre... pauvre cliché que les docteurs et les psycha-nalystes en mal de morale reprochaient tant à leurs patients qui les prononçaient pour excuser leurs bassesses, leurs désertions, (comme ils disent) à tort ou à raison ou les deux à la fois... il faut vivre, il faut vivre, à boire barman ! le restaurant est à moitié vide, à la table de Rémy, l'amour et l'amitié; Rémy est en forme, toujours aussi bavard, toujours aussi silencieux, attentif à tout, captant les ultra-sons, les images en suspension, non encore visibles, les souvenirs à fleur de peau, ne demandant qu'à sortir au grand jour, et lui... lui reprodui-sant tout en sonore, en couleur, sans rien en perdre, pour le bonheur de ses amis, pour la satisfaction profonde de cette femme-souris, de cette Madame de Chou, de cette femme-femme qui est toujours là, qui sourit, indulgente et compréhensive, mais qui ne s'y trompe pas, qui le chérit : tu vivras, mon trésor, mon petit, mon grand homme, qu'est-ce que tu manges ? Il s'agit bien de manger... et il repartait, et elle le laissait repartir, elle le rejoindrait bien, n'importe où...

Sur la table une chandelle, verte, en bouteille, éclaire tout en vert. Les ris de veau, qu'est-ce qu'on boit avec des ris de veau, du blanc ou du rouge ? sommelier, un Château Carbonnieux ! nous aurons l'air de boire de l'eau de mer, de l'eau de mer des Bahamas, la chandelle est verte, en fondant, la cire construit des châteaux en ruines, des cathé-drales décrépites, des immeubles à bureaux bombardés, les creux et les vides deviennent des têtes de squelette et à travers la flamme le restaurant vacille, les ris de veau tremblotent, les garçons ont le mal de mer, un couple entre puis un autre, bien mis, riches, un bon gros fait mille grâces, le garçon les lui rend, les garçons sont les mêmes partout, serviles, ceux d'ici viennent d'Allemagne et disent s'il vous plaît à chaque phrase, ici au moins ils mangent bien, ils sont gras et bien portants, et vos restes ne leur disent rien, le bon gros est avec une blonde en noir, à Belo Horizonte, au Brésil, les garçons engouffrent

vos restes, souvent une moitié d'entrecôte, en cinq secondes, le temps
d'aller de votre table à la cuisine, ils font cela de dos, discrètement, et
s'essuient les doigts sur leur veste avant d'entrer à la cuisine, le bon
gros aux courbettes fait du charme, sa compagne est dingue, quelle
merveilleuse idée, s'écrie-t-elle, elle a reçu une bouteille de cognac
enchâssée dans un coffret de satin ayant la forme et le luxe d'un cercueil de première classe et elle dit, je coucherais dans un aussi beau
cercueil, et elle croise les jambes, on pourrait jurer qu'elle n'a pas de
slip, lui coucherait sur le ciment, dans le fumier, n'importe où, un
dentiste explique une opération délicate au maître d'hôtel, il ouvre la
bouche, l'autre plonge et regarde, le dentiste laisse sa carte, un grand
maigre fait des promesses, il donnerait tout, cela se voit, tout à son
amie : maison, voiture, fourrures, fortune, mais en attendant lui donne
le caviar, le champagne, son coeur, son âme et bientôt son petit monsieur dans le vinaigre, tous se ressemblent, on est, chacun est tout ce
monde, au moins une fois, en partie, on rit, on ne rit pas, se reconnaissant plus ou moins, et toi, à quelle sauce le serviras-tu ton petit monsieur ? au miel ? rêve de jeunesse, manger les bouts de sein au miel,
au caramel, rêve d'une jeunesse passée en maillot de bain, en canot à
travers des dizaines d'îles, les plus osés emmenaient les jeunes filles
le soir dans les joncs, les autres rêvaient, les autres faisaient de ces
îles des symboles de péché, d'orgie, des retraites mystérieuses où se
réunissaient, où habitaient des gens à qui il était facile de tout permettre, et les îles prenaient des noms connus d'eux seuls, de Rémy, et
de ses semblables, l'île du péché, l'île aux grues, rêves éveillés, rêves
véritables dans lesquels les filles apparaissaient nues et invitantes entre
les arbres entourant le camp de bois rond, ces camps avec cheminées,
sofas, tapis épais sur lesquels s'étendre, dévorer les fleurs des seins,
avec caramel si possible . . . possible ou non, caramel ou non, les
seins auront toujours un attrait particulier, sevré à dix-huit mois, cherchant encore la nuit à saisir les seins de sa mère, en somme jamais
sevré . . . Rémy tu es fou, et Madame de Chou qui dit : je ne trouve
pas moi, et elle se lève et l'embrasse sur les yeux, il faut vivre, et
trempe un doigt dans l'eau de mer, et elle lui caresse les lèvres et elle
ferme les yeux, ne voyant plus personne que Rémy baigné d'une lueur
vert pâle, comme après une étreinte, où elle voit tout en couleur, elle
ne se rappellera jamais le mot qui définit le phénomène par lequel
on voit mille couleurs en se frottant les paupières, le vert était ce
qu'elle portait le mieux . . .

(*Quelqu'un pour m'écouter,* 1964)

Isabel Le Bourdais (Born in 1909)

Mrs. Le Bourdais is the wife of the late D. M. Le Bourdais, and sister of Gwethalyn Graham, both writers. Her most notable work is *The Trial of Stephen Truscott*, one of the most controversial Canadian books of the decade. The story below is the first she published. It appeared in the *Canadian Forum* in 1933.

AND MERCY MILD

She sat very still and stared at the picture on the other side of the room. Her eyes were bright and wide and red.

Her fingers clutched the wooden arms of her chair twitching convulsively, but her body was calm and quiet. She could do nothing now.

In the kitchen she could hear the monotonous tapping of her old mother's crutches moving about the room.

There was a bleak whistling wind outside and the snow blew against the window. She got up stiffly and crossed the room. People would look at her if the blind was not down.

She sat down in her chair and began to rock back and forth. She had rocked in that chair before, years before. Tom and Jenny, Mary and - and Ben.

Her eyes stared fixedly at the picture of Ben.

"Nineteen years old," she muttered.

There was a clatter of dishes in the kitchen.

The woman in the rocking-chair dropped her wide red eyes to the small fire in the grate under the photograph.

She had not cried when she had said good-bye to Ben. She had not cried at all since she had heard the sentence.

She began to rock back and forth with quick movements.

"He was drunk," she said, "He got it from Jim Jones."

The wind outside howled dismally. She wondered if they would keep him warm enough. She wondered if he would feel sorry or if he would learn to hate and hate and hate. In the courtroom he did not remember very much about it. He had just gone with the others. That was all. He was not used to liquor, was Ben.

The man they robbed was drunk too," she murmured.

The clock that Ben won in a raffle struck eleven. It would be so nice if only she were able to sleep.

"He did not know anything about my Ben," she cried in a low tone. "He didn't know that he'd had no father, and that he'd had no proper schooling, with me going out scrubbing."

It was growing chilly in the room. She drew her chair across the floor and put another stick on the fire.

Perhaps Ben would see Tom down there. She remembered Tom in court. He had been so different from Ben. He fought and screamed when he heard it. She had cried then.

But not now. There did not seem any sense in crying.

The house was quiet and the wind outside had dropped a little. A short distance down the street there was a band playing.

Hark, the herald angels sing

Glory to the newborn king —

A piece of streaked grey hair fell across the face of the woman but she felt nothing. Her fingers were opening and closing on the flat arms of her chair.

"Three years," she mumbled. "Three years and — twenty lashes." Her voice was dry and cold.

She slipped from her chair and knelt on the hearth.

"After two months — twenty lashes," she said, very still.

For some time she knelt motionless on the hearth, but suddenly she turned her head and looked around the room. She got up quickly and walked out into the hall. She stood at the foot of the stairs and listened to her mother tapping about the kitchen.

She walked very slowly up the stairs. Her feet pressed gently on the steps. Her face was white and rigid. Her wide eyes stared up to the dark hall above.

She reached the top of the stairs. It was so dark that she could scarcely see the doorway ahead of her. She crossed the hall — she pushed the door open slowly and peered in though the crack. She pushed the door wide open and stepped into the dark room. She wanted to see the bed. There was only one window and the moonlight was dim.

He was very black. He was very tall. The whip in his hand hit the ceiling and lashed down on the bed. Once, twice, three times —

She reached the bed and threw herself across it. There was no one there. She raised her head and switched on the light. The room was empty.

She lay very still upon the bed of her son. She felt tired, so tired, but she could not close her eyes.

Holy night, silent night,

All is dark, save the light —

Perhaps it would be easier if she were mad.

Harry West up at the corner was so bad after his wife died in childbirth that they put him in an asylum.

When you went mad you said everything that you wanted to say. You did not have this hammering in your head. You could scream and scream. She could remember Harry screaming that he lost his wife because he could not afford a specialist. She could remember that he tried to kill the hospital interne.

She sat up on the bed and felt her forehead with her hand to see if she could stop the hammering within.

She would like to kill. She was going to kill.

With great care she rose from the bed and walked across the room. She would show them that he ought not to be lashed.

She stopped at the top of the stairs. She stared at the long dark shaft before her, swayed, and sat down. If only the hammering in her head would stop she would be able to walk downstairs instead of sitting like this. She would have to slip very carefully from step to step.

She reached the fifth step and leaned her head on her arms. One, two, three, four. Fifteen more to go. Twenty altogether.

After two months — twenty lashes. One, two, three, four —

Warily she crept from step to step to the foot of the stairs and stood trembling against the door of the living-room.

The fire in the grate was low. She knelt by the fire to warm herself. Perhaps Harry West felt like this when he was going mad. Perhaps she was mad now. She was going to kill.

She stood and walked to the window. One hand raised the blind and she gazed outside.

She stared at the band in the street. The brass instruments reflected the street-lights.

Noel, Noel, Noel, No-el,

Born is the king of Isra-el.

There was a man standing in the centre of the band. He had a stick in his hand. He raised it high and brought it down. He was very black. One, two, three, four —

She ran from the window and knelt again by the fire. Little flames leapt between the two sticks. She saw a long corridor. She saw a row of small rooms with doors. There was a man in each room looking through the bars in the door —

Her forehead pounded mercilessly. One, two, three, four —

Her mother's crutch tapped across the kitchen. One, two, three, four —

The log at the back of the fire slipped from its position. She jumped as though she had been struck. She dashed madly from the living-room. She threw open the front door and ran out into the night.

"Stop! Stop! she cried. *"He's my boy!"*

Peace on earth and mercy mild,

God and sinners —

The singers ceased. They turned and stared at a little woman with grey hair and a cotton dress running wildly down the street.

She did not feel the snow failling on her bare arms. She did not hear the voice of her mother calling after her.

The black man ! She must find him.

She ran faster and faster.

"He's my boy !" she screamed.

Her legs were trembling under her. She would not be able to run much farther. She reached the corner of the street and clung to a post, searching about with her eyes.

There ! there he was. He was coming towards her !

She made a last effort and sprang forward. The black man grabbed her in his arms. She struggled to find the whip in his hand. It was gone.

She tried to free herself but her arms could not push enough. She was very weak.

"Lashes," she gasped.

The man talked to her and called her by name. She did not know what he was saying. She felt very, very weak —

She watched the two long rows of street lamps. There were far more than twenty. They kept going past her, one by one, but her feet were not walking any more.

She heard the man talking. He was saying that she was quite all right and that no one was hurting her.

Jane Van Every (Born in 1896)

Miss Van Every lives at Doon, Ontario, in the heart of the Mennonite country. From her novel of the same name, this piece relates the experience of a non-Mennonite school teacher who marries into the sect. The author is both painter and writer, a niece of Homer Watson.

"ISSES NET PECULIAR ?"

This year, to Machts Gut and family, three things of importance happen.

The first is a birth, which is our son Aaron, and he is like Groszdoddy, which is a fine thing. I can see it. It is there plain, and for this I am glad, for Groszdoddy has travelled the road from life to death with a good conscience and now, "like an angel, he looks," says Berah, and this is true for all to see.

So we rejoice because of Aaron, new in this world. His face will change, I know. He will go up hill and down dale as we do, all of us. But for the beginning, he has this face of Groszdoddy, pure and innocent, but without the wisdom that is there in the face of Groszdoddy. That he must get, and where I will be when this is done, I do not know. It is a lesson to me.

The time will come when I must let him go and travel his own road but not yet awhile. First, I have the opportunity to show him how to go, which I will take in all seriousness. And when I look down into this face I know it is a holy charge I have, the best in a woman's life that can be.

So it is with our small son, and Berah is loving him nearly as much as I. She holds him in her arms and on her face is that which only a mother can have. Because now she is ready for her second life, which is motherhood.

No longer she wants to be a doctor, or a dancer, or a writer. Sam is all, and that, too, is so a beautiful thing in this life. Her dower chest is full with things, "first a little tuck, then wait a little, then another little tuck" sewn fine ; and after long months it is done. The simple life, I say, is the best. Now I have learned.

This marriage, Berah and Sam, is the second thing of importance, and the third, a death. Groszdoddy. All this happens in three short months to be exact. It is life going at a fast pace.

Aaron is as good a baby as anyone can want, in spite of Berah who coddles him too much and, too, worries a little but there is no cause for worrying. Now is a new life to till the soil, to see how good he can make it, simple and fine. No fuss, no frills, like the Mennonite people I wish him to be.

When I see how these people have put Berah and Sam in their fine new house, and also had for them a barn raising, I know this is the best kind of insurance. No policies, but faith and love, and working together. No great fuss for the wedding, but all in order. Good food and beaming faces. I look and wonder, me, with the new life in my arms, and Groszdoddy, at the end of the road, his face white and serene.

No bride is more beautiful than Berah, and no groom more stalwart than Sam. His shoulders are big, he will carry all ; a tear, I have in my eye which I must brush away when no one can see.

They love each other, they begin their new life. They have their farm, the broad fields, the sun and the sky. For this Machts Gut and the Mennonite people are responsible.

So with motherhood I come, with on my grey bonnet and on my grey dress. In the house, the white bonnet. I would not change these people. Too good they are for change.

And now our Groszdoddy smiles on us like a visitor from another planet.

"There are celestial bodies and bodies terrestrial; and the glory of the celestial is one, and the glory of the terrestrial is another," says the Apostle Paul. "There is one glory of the sun and another glory of the moon and another glory of the stars," and of this I think when I look on the face of Groszdoddy.

It is as if he has gone from us already and only his body remains, worn out and thin. He is using up his last strength, and it is as if he wants to use it fast and shake the dust of this earth off his feet.

Groszmommy protects and also protests but it does her no good.

"Ich bin so scradladich," she is saying and gives up, which means she is sick and tired of it all.

Groszdoddy is up with the break of dawn. No longer he sits on the verandah painted in the back blue, and enjoys the sun. Now he must go in the fields. Martin does not stop him. With love he looks on him, and how much he knows, no one knows. His wisdom is behind his beard. Like a false face is that beard which Martin wears to hide much.

But now, Groszdoddy has gone from among us. It was midnight when he elected to go.

"He worked hard all day, in fact he did three days hard work in one," says Martin. But no one knows that now he is ready and satisfied. He lays himself down.

"Ich bin so scradladich," he saying and gives up, which means tired, I want to sleep.

There is clay on his boots when he goes, leaving his face for us to see, clear and beautiful.

And now, looking back, the thing that stands out clear in memory to stay with me always, is only the funeral where Groszdoddy lies white and still. Inside the church is a great hush and all bonnets and beards are down.

Outside the day is still. A May day, sunny and good, but all is still. The church door is open, I can see the sun on the gravestone on the hill. One grave is there, open and ready, but before your eye lifts to that, there are wheels, small and large, dark in the sun with between grass flashing bright to dazzle the eye. Dachwaeglies and buggies, horses standing this way and that ; a large group of Mennonites collected now, to do honour to this one.

But while I am looking on this scene I am thinking of something else. In my mind comes willy-willy the memory of my life before I am a Mennonite. Of hurrying and dressing up, to make more attractive. Of going for the money and learning the things that don't matter. This life I have lived, and when I come to this place and my life here, I have my snoot in the air. I would teach them ! I would change them ! But now it is me that has been taught a thing of greater importance. For me, inside it is a sad joke.

Sitting there I know it, and bow my head with all. Shut out is the vision of shining gravestones and many wheels, each trying to tell me something of the going in the world and the destination.

I look down in the small new face, and, by and by, it seems to me that I must go back to my girlhood and the town where I am raised.

There, there is always a great talk of being saved. One woman with a long pointed nose, pointed chin, and yes, pointed eyes. Such a thing cannot be, but it is as I see her, raising herself up in my mind.

Pointed eyes. Yes that is possible, and a stomach that sticks out something fierce. Little pointed shoes, stepping along, or waggling first east then west when she sits. A hat that is old-fashioned, and that one has saved souls. How many ? She has all written in a book. (St. Peter, I pity, if his is not the same !)

So, they are saved, but when I look, I do not see one with the face of Groszdoddy. No, nor even yet the faces of any of these, pure and clean around me. I look under my bonnet. Is it true ? Of this I am wondering. Is it in a book, where all is written when you come to St. Peter's gate ? Or the face you have when you raise it to his gaze ? So

I am thinking, sitting at the funeral, not listening to what is being said. There is the bishop up front, speaking words of importance, but these I have heard before.   A new thought has come.

Yes, now is Groszdoddy at St. Peter's gate, and there is clay on his boots ; and he has this face, which has looked on the fields.   He has provided food for the world with the sweat of his brow.   He has raised a good family, and if the going was rough, sometimes with Grosz- mommy, because of her sharp tongue, you did not know. With a sad face and maybe an old saying he would put her in her place, but gently so.   Groszdoddy has raised a good family.   They are all there. Martin, and his sisters, and brothers, their children and our children.   Here it is too, the Freundschaft, all bowing heads in reverence.   Even Uncle Moses I see, bows his head, as reverent as any.   But for Groszdoddy, it is not possible to grieve.   There is no sadness, no tear.   Groszdoddy has gone on, we merely stand with a rustle and a sigh to look upon this miracle.

We go out of the church.   There is the broom by the door to keep the place clean.   We go in groups.   The Bishop first, with his book. Groszdoddy next, carried by his sons.   And next, Groszmommy, and Minerva by her side.

It is in this moment when Minerva first grows up.   For all Grosz- mommy's drowning of cats, stern ways and all, Minerva has forgiven her.   Now suddenly she is a woman, standing with Groszmommy. Big, yes — and strong.   The quiet woman she will be, though the light thick braids tied with a string still hang down her back, against her purple dress.

Yes, so it is, and the gravestones winking in the sun, happy as if it is all a joke. White and pure, knowing all. The Bishop stands with open his book. The words are said, what matter the words when all is clear ?

("Isses Net Peculiar?")

Pierre Berton (Born in 1920)

Author, editor and commentator, he is Canada's best-known journalist and television personality. His book *The Comfortable Pew* was one of the most successful ever done in Canada. His books include *The Mysterious North, Klondike, The Big Sell* and *The New City.*

ADVENTURES OF A COLUMNIST

This is a sort of anniversary piece — not about myself, but about another columnist who wrote for the Toronto papers some eighty years ago. His name was Phillips Thompson and, though he is now forgotten, he was one of the best-known journalists of his era.

He could write about anything. Besides his column he also wrote books, magazine articles, skits, poems and even songs. I'm sure if there'd been TV and radio he'd have appeared in those mediums. As it was, he was famous as a platform lecturer.

He worked for the *Mail and Empire,* the *Globe,* the old *Toronto News,* John Ross Robertson's *Telegraph* and many other papers. He was a leading light in the press galleries at Queen's Park and Ottawa. He was an editor as well as a writer ; he founded a political weekly, the *National,* and was associate editor of the famous magazine *Grip.*

He reached the heights of success as a humorist writing under the pseudonym of Jimuel Briggs, a police court column that caught the public fancy and made his name a by-word. In it he poked fun at both the law and its victims and sometimes barely escaped charges for contempt of court.

In 1881, the *Globe* sent him as its special correspondent to Ireland for two months to cover the land campaign of Charles Stuart Parnell. He left Canada sceptical of the Irish in general and Parnell in particular, but he returned an utterly changed man. The plight of the Irish tenants touched him as nothing else had . He bitterly regretted his humorous columns and his final dispatch to the *Globe* gives some hint of his sympathies:

". . . And so, in spite of blunders, and crimes, and defeats — in spite of the greed of the self-seeking and the ambitions of the demagogues — through bloodshed, and tears, and suffering,

the cause of the people will prevail by slow degrees, and
the accumulated and buttressed wrongs of centuries be
overthrown."

His dispatches caused a sensation. The *Globe* reprinted
them in an extra edition. He was tendered a public banquet
and lionized in the press. Every club in the country seemed to
want him as a speaker. For Thompson's despatches had been
models of good reportiing : cold fact piled upon cold fact
without exaggeration or passion.

"He told a plain story," wrote the Buffalo *Courier*. "He
allowed no word of rage to escape him, though it was clearly to
be seen that underneath the man's calmness his blood was
boiling."

As a result of his Irish experience Thompson became a radical and
a socialist and for the rest of his life fought consistently for
lost causes, for minorities, for voiceless people — fought without
quarter, without funds and without hope of winning.

He was reviled, attacked and hounded; but he kept on. He was
suffered, tolerated, even indulged; and he kept on. In the end,
he came to be respected.

It is hard to understand now why so much calumny was heaped
on the head of this earnest and selfless man. So many of his
causes seem mild enough to us today. Sunday streetcars were one
thing he fought for; the Toronto Transit Commission was
another. He was one of a small group who hired halls in a vain
attempt to prevent a private syndicate from grabbing the
city-owned street railway. Thirty years later, when the private
franchise expired, the city once more took over and
Thompson was vindicated.

He supported the Hutterites and Doukhobors. He attacked
censorship and bigotry. He fought for labour unions and was the
first male Canadian journalist to argue in favor of woman
suffrage.

A review of his book *The Politics of Labour* published at his own
expense in 1887, suggested how he ran against the current
of his times :

"One opinion held by Mr. Thompson is not in accord with the
common view. He holds that want does not arise from
dissipation and intemperance, as many reformers maintain.
On the contrary he argues that intemperance is largely
the result of the want, misery and general wretchedness
of mankind."

He wrote angry letters to the press and the politicians and he got angry letters back, such as this one from the Postmaster General dealing with the banning from the mails of a radical publication, *The Appeal to Reason* :

"I have your letter of the 26th instant couched in much the same language as seems to distinguish the columns of *The Appeal to Reason,* with the aims and views of which you appear to sympathize. Anyone who can feel or express approval of the measures it appears to advocate seems to me a man any good citizen ought to shun. The intemperate language in which you have chosen to express yourself in your letter is, I think, a sufficient reason for my declining to discuss the subject further with you."

Such answers did not ruffle Phillips Thompson, nor did his several defeats at the polls on Socialist, Reform and Labour tickets. In the end, the newspapers began to refer to him as the Grand Old Man of Journalism. Young reporters were sent out to interview him on his birthday. His photo, showing a thin-faced, white-bearded figure, began to appear in the press alongside feature stories about a man who, in his eighties, still wrote every day of his life.

For he could not stop writing. He was almost blind with cataracts on both eyes but still he wrote — articles, essays, poems, speeches, tracts, pamphlets, letters, verse. When he could no longer see to write he dictated to one of his daughters. On that day in May, 1933, when the stroke that killed him came, he was still writing.

In the newspapers he had once served, the obituaries were generous, as they usually are for old newsmen. The best epitaph appeared in the *Star* :

"The late Mr. Phillips Thompson was in his day a clear-sighted and just-minded journalist. He was one of the gentlest of men, but utterly incapable of pretending to agree in a matter of opinion with you or with the King of England if he did not so agree. There was a mild but firm force in him. One wonders how many of the newspapermen of today owe something to the example of this always soft-spoken and sincere man who, at the age of ninety, goes forth to his burial at Oakville. He spoke for the inarticulate, he was on the side of lost causes, he could show you that minorities, although outnumbered, were usually right."

He was the best-known columnist of his day. Now his name has been forgotten.

He was my grandfather.

William Toye (Born in 1926)

Toye, one of the founding editors of *The Tamarack Review*, is Editor of Oxford University Press in Canada. He has written *The Saint Lawrence* and edited an anthology of Canadiana, *A Book of Canada*.

THE SAINT LAWRENCE

The cry for a modern seaway started before the First World War, and linked with it was the dream of manufacturing electricity from the river — building an enormous hydro development focused at the International Rapids between Prescott and Cornwall where the boundary cuts the river in two. In 1932 a treaty was signed between the United States and Canada that would have started the building of a 27-foot channel for navigation with two dams for power — if it had passed through the U.S. Senate. It didn't.

Years went by; the Second World War took place, and interests in the United States still blocked it. For every supporter of the idea, it seemed, there was one detractor.

"More wheat will pass through our city," said Montrealers.

"Our trade will be drastically cut," was how they felt in Boston, New York and Buffalo. And eastern railways were just as gloomy about their prospects.

"Direct shipment to Europe of our grain will increase our profits," said western wheat farmers confidently. And so said manufacturers about their products.

"Our business will be ruined," from the owners of canalers, the small vessels that trans-shipped cargoes through the canals.

"Our market will be diminished by the power developments," coal and oil companies complained.

"Cheaper power will bring more industries," said Ontario and New York. "More industries mean more shipping and more tolls to finance the Seaway."

And so it went. But there was one reason for a seaway no one could deny : Labrador was discovered to be more richly veined with iron ore than the mines around the Great Lakes, and a seaway would carry it cheaply in peace or war to steel refineries in the Middle West.

Canada finally announced that it would build the Seaway alone if Congress would not ratify a treaty. This brought results. In May, 1954, the U.S. House of Representatives passed the St. Lawrence legislation and the next day the Senate approved it.

That summer, between Montreal and the Thousand Islands, work began on two projects : a deeper water highway and a harnessing of the river's fall for hydro-electric power.

To all but the engineers who first envisaged it, the task ahead seemed superhuman. Think of draining parts of a great river dry to build huge concrete dams on bed-rock and to carve deep channels through it for canals; dredging the river elsewhere to deepen it; creating a new lake, the fourth one in the river; moving 95 million cubic yards of earth and rock; raising old bridges for higher ships and building ten new ones ; removing towns completely to make way for a wider river. But with hundreds of trucks, bulldozers, giant shovels, dredges, draglines, with the planning and labour of 22,000 men and over a billion dollars, it was all accomplished smoothly, without delays. And the river co-operated, for in the Seaway-Hydro engineers it met its masters.

(The Saint Lawrence)

Lister Sinclair (Born in 1921)

One of the principal contributors to the CBC, Sinclair is a man of amazing versatility. He is writer, critic, lecturer, mathematician, actor and television personality. His plays are in *A Play on Words*.

THE CANADIAN IDIOM

Two or three years ago the Canadian Authors' Association (the largest organization of published Canadian writers) met in Vancouver, and one of its afternoon sessions was devoted to a discussion of the Drama, under Mr. Herman Voaden who spent the afternoon gliding rapidly over every conceivable aspect of the writing and production of plays. But at one point he paused, in the midst of an enumeration of the essentials of any piece of dramatic writing : Conflict, Character, Suspense and so forth. He briskly reeled off a crushingly exhaustive list and then asked (rhetorically, I am sure), "Now is there anything else that should appear in every play ?" Whereupon a lady said, "Yes, there is one thing. Every play should contain a Mountie. The scarlet uniform is so picturesque and they make everything so Canadian." And we all nodded and murmured approvingly, for of course the lady was quite right.

She was speaking from her first experience of much Canadian writing, and had noticed that for the most part the writing is done first, and the Canadianism added afterwards in clear, unmistakable strokes. If a play contains a Mountie, it is undeniably Canadian; if there is no Mountie, we have no idea what to make of it. It constitutes a simple and infallible test and one which can be complied with by a stroke of the pen from the writer, for it suffices to change "Mike O'Reilly, Policeman" into "Mike O'Reilly, Mountie," and Canadian it is, for anybody who is not colour-blind.

Now not every Canadian author is as straightforward or helpful as this. Some of us merely take care to talk about Saskatchewan and Toronto, moose and trilliums, which we may take to be the penny plain equivalent of the twopence coloured Mountie. Similarly, we adjust our "poetic imagery" so that it keeps nudging the reader in the right direction. Things are no longer "as fast as the wind," they are "as fast as the wind in Winnipeg"; things are no longer "as cold as charity," they are "as cold as charity in Toronto." In this way, we can take a story which might be located in New York, or Berlin, or better still one which is really impossible to think of as taking place anywhere at all, and turn it into a regular piece of Canadian literature. The only trouble is that local colour (as we call it) tends to make a good deal of Canadian writing haunted by geography and wild-life.

But all the same, we are quite right to use it, because what we are really doing is trying to make sure that we are using a Canadian idiom : some of us say *the* Canadian idiom. And we feel we ought to do so because we find ourselves unable to write Canadian literature, that is to say writing that means something to Canadians, unless we do use a Canadian idiom. Only none of us knows what it is, which is why we still very often do the writing first and put in the idiom afterwards, like the New Englander who built his house himself but had a fellow from Boston come down to put on the architecture. A lot of us still feel that a Canadian idiom is exactly the same as architecture : you can put it on afterwards. We know, you see, that nowadays the words *Canadian Idiom* are understood to imply : And How to Get It, just as sixty years ago, they implied : And How to Avoid It. We do write with less and less self-consciousness in the Canadian dialect of English, which seems roughly to be the result of applying British syntax to an American vocabulary. We have begun to see that it is a merit for Canadian writers to try to turn out Canadian writing, and we are even beginning to persuade Canadian readers that it is a merit to read Canadian writing, and sometimes a very hard-won merit indeed, doubtless conferring much grace.

Now this change has not entirely been brought about by the gossamer whips of the critics raining their ethereal lashes on our loud check lumberjack shirts. When all is said and done, the influential critics are those who influence the way writing is really done; and these influences are almost always great writers, and the pressure of the surroundings. Some of the great writers that have influenced recent Canadian work have been dead in the body for a long time, but they are still alive in the spirit: Chaucer, I am sure, is alive for Earle Birney; E.M. Forster, Virginia Woolf, and other symbolists for W. O. Mitchell; and Anatole France for Henry Kreisel. I have yet to see direct influence from James Joyce but I am absolutely certain that he will turn out to be a very influential Canadian critic indeed, if a Canadian critic is a man who influences Canadian writing. Indeed, I suspect Earle Birney of coming under the spell already.

And, of course, there is always Sir Walter Scott, who remains the great model for so many of us, both in verse and in prose.

But in spite of these guides and signposts some of us are beginning to feel that there are things which have to be said about Canada to Canadians which need methods not exactly covered by any of these exemplars; not even Sir Walter Scott. We are beginning to realize our position in the world, and it is precarious. We lie between the greatest and grimmest of the Grim Great Powers. We are unlucky enough to possess uranium; and in the middle of the night we sometimes dream of hot breath quietly playing on the backs of our necks. We are very large in extent but we are very small in population : an average population of four to the square mile, enough for a bridge game if you can get the cards. And what tradition we have is a tradition of the frontier, of pioneering, much enhanced by a calculated diffidence which must come from the soil, for it sweeps over newcomers like a wave. With all these things to consider, we wish to be influential; we have a small voice but we wish to make it heard, certainly for our own sakes and, we believe, for everybody else's sake as well. And it seems to me that it is the ability to take all these things and use them artistically that constitute developing a Canadian idiom which lies, therefore, in a certain point of view : the point of view of the still small voice, the gadfly made innocuous-seeming through protective colouration and the little arts of Socrates that bring down giants by their own great strength.

Some of our writers are developing this point of view, the peculiarly Canadian one it seems to me. The most mature and expert writers have seen that social colour is not enough; the outlook must be changed. Some men, like Frederick Grove, felt they did not have the right view of the battle nor the right weapons to make their onslaught carry home, but grimly began to devote their professional lives to the struggle to acquire them. Grove succeeded, I think, at the end of his life. A friend tells me that he read his last novel thinking it the work of a brilliant young fellow of twenty or thereabouts; shortly after, Grove died of old age and overwork, worn out by the struggle to make his weapons that he has recorded in his autobiography.

Others, like Stephen Leacock, were so honestly and candidly parochial that the idea of there being such a thing as a non-Ontario outlook never even occurred to them. These were very fortunate. They found their innocence praised as the height of wisdom, and their artlessness praised as the height of art. Their writing had the ferocious candour of a child coupled with the minute and particular local knowledge of a man who knows one life so well he cannot imagine there being any others. In Leacock's case, I am afraid the praise he rightly received (and which I am happy to add to, now that he is dead, and it can't do him any harm) went to his head, and led him into certain rash excursions into extra-territorial affairs. But even the most extraordinary of these, such as *While There is Time,* can be used as resounding proofs that Leacock's genuis was the incarnation of insularity and that he was dreadfully unarmed and defenceless, unless protected by the Laurentian Shield.

But there are other Canadian writers who, without having the unconscious touch of Leacock, have been able to avoid the mountainous travail of Grove and have been able, almost without an effort, to allow their work to be a direct expression of their minds, already cast in one of the Canadian moulds; for there are as many ways of being Canadian as there are of being French or British, and many more than there are of being American or Irish. Such people include Len Peterson, Earle Birney, Ned Pratt, W. O. Mitchell, James Nablo, and several others who work hard in their writing at a variety of things, but never at being Canadian. They are so interested, all of them, in the life going on immediately around them, and in telling us about it, that they have no time to remember that this life is, if you want to be particular about it, Canadian life.

When Len Peterson holds up his terrifying clear mirror, and makes us look our cowardice in the eyes, he never resorts to local colour. None of his plays, to my knowledge, have a Mountie in them but when, in *Burlap Bags,* he shows us poor unhappy Tannerhill with his dreadful vision of men and women wearing burlap bags over their heads to shut out reality, it is Canadians that we see and Tannerhill is a Canadian too : for the very simple reason that it is Canadians that Mr. Peterson sees. Similarly, when Earle Birney draws his images from the prairies, or lays the scene of *David* in the mountains, there is no sense of effort. He chooses the Rockies because there they are, right in front of him and he wants to talk about some mountains. And in Earle Birney's poems, the land of Canada stands out in natural colour, not local colour.

The same is true of Ned Pratt. He wants to tell us a tale of the ocean : there it is at his back door. The poem is done, and the book is printed before Dr. Pratt bothers to remember that this is the sea that beats on the Maritimes and that other oceans may not behave like this one. This is the one he wants to talk about and this is the one you will find in his books, just as the epic heroism you will find in his books is the epic heroism lying under his nose in the shape of the North Atlantic patrols, or Brébeuf and his brethren. W. O. Mitchell does exactly the same thing. *Who Has Seen the Wind* is the curious story of a boy growing up surrounded by the symbols of life. The boy naturally grows up where W. O. Mitchell grew up, on the prairies, and Mr. Mitchell slyly calls himself the Gopher Poet on the strength of the images which naturally arise under the circumstances, and which have been naturally and gracefully woven in the book. And with James Nablo and his book *The Long November* we return to Len Peterson's vision of judgment, not so cool, perhaps, in Mr. Nablo, not so steady or so humorous, but still the same old bitter vision of judgment : and it is Canada that comes up to be judged. It is such writers as these, whose minds are cast in Canadian moulds and who are not hampered too much by the Scott brothers, Sir Walter and Duncan Campbell, that seem to me to be developing Canadian idiom.

And not every writer whose mind is cast in a Canadian mould is necessarily born or even bred in Canada. Consider Malcolm Lowry, for instance, who is a very complicated mixture of ex-patriotism; yet his book, *Under the Volcano,* has something to say to Canadians. Or consider the even more striking case of Henry Kreisel whose admirable first novel, *The Rich Man,* is mostly about Vienna, which is Mr. Kreisel's principal brackground; none the less it is a moving, clear account of the position of Jews in pre-war Austria which has been written entirely and thoroughly for a Canadian audience, and shows as much grasp of the Canadian outlook as it does of the Austro-Jewish.

But in spite of this strong surface current towards a Canadian idiom, there has been an undertow setting in the opposite direction. Some of our writers seem to have certain suspicions that they have been born too late to become great national writers; that the world is growing past the stage of acute nationalism; and that if what they have to say is only of value to their countrymen, then it is of no value even to them. Curiously enough, this undertow has been easily and cunningly assimilated by most of the people I have mentioned; for all these people are united by one thing : they are experts.

Kildare Dobbs (Born in 1923)

One of the founders of *Tamarack Review*, Dobbs is Managing Editor of *Saturday Night*. An engaging journalist and broadcaster, he wrote a book of reminiscences, *Running to Paradise*. It won a Governor-General's award. His poetry is in the Oxford book.

RUNNING TO PARADISE

But I was seeing Canada, a limitless territory rising from imagination into fact, and now sunk down to memory. The prairies — before I set eyes on the prairies I imagined them a region of unspeakable desolation, as dreary and oppressive to the spirit as they appear on the back of a dollar bill. Now that I had seen them — I knew them to be a region of unspeakable desolation, as dreary and oppressive etcetera, etcetera. There is a sense in which the paradox is true, that travel narrows the mind. Yet you could see what it was about the region that had prairie people by the heart. It was like the open sea, that wide flat under the vast sky, a brown sea now, though winter would soon cover it in greyish white, its loneliness more than earthly, more than mortal. Like the loneliness of God (I told a prairie poet in a fit of Aida-induced confidence) before he made the universe. The poet nodded enthusiastically. "You're right, you're *right* — that's just it!"

I had to go and spoil it for him. "The only trouble is, he couldn't stand it — he made the universe."

Between hotels — from the windows of trains or airliners — it was possible to catch a notion of the country. The hotels, like the cities, tend to merge into each other in memory, so that the commercial palaces of Winnipeg, Regina, Saskatoon, Edmonton, Calgary now seem all one hotel, and the cities themselves — for all their several peculiarities — one city. Smaller cities are more distinct. Moose Jaw, with its heroic public library; Medicine Hat, crouched in a sort of amphitheatre in a bend of its river; Lethbridge, haunted by the sombre figures of Hutterites, black-suited, black-bearded, accompanied by woman like Victorian dolls in their long skirts and headkerchiefs. But the land — as you went westward it changed. At first flat in the continental doldrums, it began to take on a long undulation, like the heavy groundswell of the Western Ocean. Gradually over hundreds of miles it continued to work itself up by ever shorter and steeper waves into a flurry of foothills till at last it broke over the horizon in a storm of jagged mountains, the icy peaks of the Canadian Rockies.

At the Paralyser Hotel, for me the climax of the foothills, I drank late with my brother-traveller Ken Tupper. My room was by the freight yard of the railroad; we could hardly hear ourselves speak above the metallic clank and clash of shunting trains. At 3 A.M. Ken phoned the desk and made his polite enquiry. "What time does the hotel leave for Vancouver?"

For we were impatient to get to the Coast — that by now almost mythical destination. That first time I went by train, climbing slowly till dark by the boulder-strewn Bow River and through the forested passes, looking up with awe at raw crags of the terrible mountains — those mountains that men from flat country fear and feel oppressed by, though to me, brought up in view of Mount Leinster, nostalgic and exciting — and staring, at night-fall, at the last of the light touching faintly a distant white peak.

And I woke to a new light, the soft, changing light of British Columbia, its green grass and blue distances that drew me like a song. Running still westward to the sea, an Irish melancholy came over me, that pleasant sadness which was one of the seven deadly sins of the Middle Ages. Accidia now took Aida by the hand, enfolded her in a damp and mildewy embrace, stiffling her voice so that in Vancouver's Stanley Park I almost forgot her in contemplation of captive king penguins. My employers, bookmen to the backbone, roused me with a telegram: SIT NOT UPON THE ORDERS OF YOUR TAKING BUT MAIL AT ONCE.

Still I was running westward. I took ship for Victoria, some hours away on Vancouver Island, and there checked in at the hotel which is like no other. I had the feeling that they did not care for salesmen, particularly bookmen and bible men.

The bellhop picked up my suitcase. I began to walk toward the main elevator. "No, sir!" he called to me. "Not that one. This way, sir." I turned. He was heading in the opposite direction. I followed him for some distance to a smaller, meaner elevator. We mounted one floor, emerged and walked about a thousand yards or so along a corridor. Then we came to a staircase and walked *down* two floors. From there we began a second long march — I don't know how far, but I would say at a guess at least a mile — along another corridor or tunnel. We might have been in a mine. I had that feeling of being at a great distance from the world.

The bellhop let me into my sample room. It was a vast chamber, carpeted in decaying green felt, and equipped all round with display counters. In a distant corner was the bed I hoped to sleep in. "Good-bye, sir," said the bellhop, pocketing his tip.

I shivered.

Some time later I decided to pick up my mail. Back I went along the tunnel, up those two flights of stairs, along that thousand yards of corridor and down one flight in the little elevator. Somewhat breathless, I asked the desk clerk for my mail.

"It will be delivered to your room, sir."

"But I want to pick it up now."

"I'm sorry, sir. It will be delivered to your room."

I could see that they didn't want fellows like me hanging round where the guests could see us. I turned away, and reluctant to face that descent into the earth again for a while, looked about me for something to do. A notice caught my eye : TO THE GLASS GARDEN. A hand pointed in the direction of a sort of conservatory. I followed it.

There was a fountain like a sort of giantess's *bidet,* ornamented with encaustic tiles. Near it a door opened on a garden, pleasant with lawns and flowers. Another notice pointed into the garden. Out I went and along a path that led to some trees. To one of them was attached a third sign indicating the way to the Glass Garden (whatever it was). I followed. It led me to a blank wall — or wooden fence. I could see no way through it. And so, of the Glass Garden I may not speak properly, for I was not there.

Did I dream this ? Was it a trap set for me by the hotel — as paranoia whispered at the time ? Or was it a hint, perhaps, that that country I was running to, and still seek, was not to be found ? Aida had led me to this, of that I was convinced, so that I realized at last that I was not her favourite. I gave up (or was given up) as a bible man and book salesman.

Months afterwards, on a journey of another sort, a journey made for pleasure, I drove by night farther to the west — to Point No Point on the Pacific Coast of Vancouver Island. As I got out of the car I could hear it, loud as guns in the darkness, the crash of surf from the main deep. I walked down to the shore, behind me the black forests — and behind *them* the whole of Canada and the world and my life, before me the gleam of the Pacific, the waves running over sand and pebbles to my feet, the heavy drum of the surf beating on my brain. I looked out to the open ocean.

And the sea saith, It is not with me.

(Running to Paradise)

Paul Hiebert (Born in 1892)

Hiebert grew up on the prairies, taught school in Saskatchewan during the drought, and later became a professor. He is most noted for *Sarah Binks,* a parody of literary biography and criticism. This spoof at the expense of the supposed "Sweet Songstress of Saskatchewan" is one of the funniest Canadian books since Leacock.

SARAH BINKS

Sarah was finding herself. That unsureness, "Sometimes they don't rhyme, curses !" was to leave her at this stage. It is no exaggeration to say that technically she reached her full perfection during the poems of the patriotic period. One need only compare *The Parson's Patch,* written in the early fall, with *Ode to Spring,* written the following March, to appreciate the tremendous strides she had made :

THE PARSON'S PATCH

Pathetic patch, a turnip or two,
A onion, a lettuce, a handful of maize,
A sprig of parsley, and that is all
That meets our gaze.

Here we can see with what loving care,
Poked and patted by the parson's hand,
They flourished in their meek mild way,
Just as the parson had.

And now as we turn from the parson's patch
Let us turn our eyes inwards,
And after a few minutes contemplation,
The moral will be visible.

Here we have already the Sarah we have learned to love, sweetly lyrical, deeply moralizing. But her touch is unsure. "A onion, a lettuce" is weak, some of the lines do not quite scan, and her rhyming of "visible" with "contemplation" is not in the best traditions of Saskatchewan literature. But hearken to Sarah six months later :

ODE TO SPRING

'Tis not for long the bird shall creep
Beneath a pile of mouldy straw;
Eftsoons, not long the chill winds sweep,
And powdered snow-bank four feet deep,
Pile up, pile up, in roundish heap :
For spring is coming with its mirth,
And breezy breath of balmy warmth
And burbank, bobolink, and snearth,[1]
Shall banish winter's chill and dearth,
And luscious joy shall fill the earth.

The poem created a furore when it first appeared. The editor of *The Horsebreeder's Gazette* who finally accepted it for publication gave it the prominence it so richly deserved. Moreover it struck a deeply sympathetic chord in the hearts of the Saskatchewan people. It had been a backward spring. The roads were blocked, and the home-made thermometers were still registering nightly low temperatures of sixty-eight to seventy-five below zero. Suddenly the voice of Sarah, Sarah Binks, the Sweet Songstress, burst upon them with its message of hope and cheer. Spring was coming; the burbank would be back and the return of the snearth was imminent. No wonder Saskatchewan took her to its broad, flat bosom. Two weeks later a delayed chinook melted the Saskatchewan snows and Sarah awoke to find herself, if not exactly famous, at least something of a local celebrity.

It is difficult, if not impossible, to estimate the effect which the success of *Ode to Spring* must have had upon the young poetess. The reception accorded *The Parson's Patch* had been, if not exactly cold, at least disappointing from Sarah's point of view. *The Hitching Post,* where *The Parson's Patch* first appeared, accepted poetical contributions only when accompanied by six fully paid-up subscriptions, and the selling of these had tended to lessen Sarah's confidence in herself and in her own poetic ability. Moreover, when finally published it had been wedged in between the obituary notices and the half-page advertisement of a recently discovered cure for harness galls and spavin. But with the appearance of *The Ode* Sarah's confidence returned. Letters of congratulation poured in from Ole and Mathilda, and the editor of *The Fertilizer* personally sent her a form letter calling attention to the fact that his columns were open to all subscribers.
(Sarah Binks)

---

[1]   *It is interesting to note here that this is the first recorded instance of the appearance of the snearth in Saskatchewan. Sarah was always a keen observer of nature.*

Wallace Stegner (Born in 1909)

Though born in Iowa, this writer grew up in the Cypress Hills country of Saskatchewan. His novel *Wolf Willow,* from which the following selection was taken, recalls his boyhood life in the Canadian west. Stegner is now head of the Creative Writing Center at Stanford University.

WOLF WILLOW

The Cypress Hills discovered that they had a history when the Old Timers' Association of Maple Creek planted some historical markers in 1942. In coming first to Fort Walsh they acknowledged that this was the true capital of the first stage of that frontier. In the old post cemetery, where the police graves were identifiable but the civilian ones a scramble of unmarked mounds, they erected crosses and, where they knew, they placed the appropriate names : Clark, Dumont, LaBarge, Quesnelle, McKay, Chief Little Bird — white, *métis,* Scotch halfbreed, Indian. From the graveyard they moved on to plant a cement monument where Abe Farwell's post had stood, and another where the wolfers and the Assiniboin had fought across Battle Creek. The foundations of Farwell's post were still faintly discernible after nearly seventy years, but the battlefield they could locate only through the memory of an old *métis* who as a boy of eighteen, in 1880, had kicked up human bones while herding the police beef herd on that ground.

Once discovered, history is not likely to be lost. But the first generation of children to grow up in a newly settled country do not ordinarily discover their history, and so they are the prime sufferers from discontinuity. If I, for instance, wanted a past to which I could be tribally and emotionally committed, I had to fall back on the American Civil War (my grandfather, whom I had never seen, had fought in it), or upon Norway (my maternal grandfather and grandmother had emigrated from it). Being a mama's boy, I chose Norway, which made a real hash of my affiliations. All through my childhood I signed my most personal and private books and documents with the Norwegian name that my grandfather had given up on coming to America. It seems to me now an absurdity that I should have felt it necessary to go as far as the Hardanger Fjord for a sense of belonging. I might have had — and any child who grows up in the Cypress Hills now can have — Fort Walsh, and all that story of buffalo hunter, Indian and halfbreed, Mounted Policeman and wolfer, which came to its climax just here.

The very richness of that past as I discover it now makes me irritable to have been cheated of it then. I wish I could have known it early, that it could have come to me with the smell of life about it instead of the smell of books, for there was the stuff of an epic there, and still is for anyone who knows it right — perhaps for some *métis* or Cree, a descendant of Gabriel Dumont or Big Bear or Wandering Spirit, who can see the last years of the Plains frontier with the distance of history and with the passion of personal loss and defeat. Often as it has been summarized, no one has properly told the story of the defeat of the Plains people, a people of many tribes but one culture. Fort Walsh saw its last years. This was where some of the last hopes flickered out and the irreconcilables gathered in hope of a last stand : Canadian Indians and American Indians, Cree and Assiniboin and Blackfoot who belonged, and Sioux and Nez Percé and Gros Ventre who fled here because of the Medicine Line and because here were the last of the buffalo. A way of life extremely rich in human satisfactions both physical and spiritual came to an end here. From their headquarters at Fort Walsh, a little over a hundred red-coated men patrolled its final agonies. A few years after it was essentially over for the Indians, the *métis* who lived by the same skills and were shaped to a similar habit of life broke out in their own final desperation, drawing with them some of their Indian relatives, and that could be another epic.

All of it was legitimately mine, I walked that earth, but none of it was known to me.

W. O. Mitchell (Born in 1914)

Novelist, short-story and radio writer, Mitchell is most affectionately known for his CBC series, "Jake and the Kid," which won the Leacock Medal for humour. The selection here is from *Who Has Seen the Wind,* set in Saskatchewan in the thirties.

WHO HAS SEEN THE WIND

. . . Throughout the summer Brian found himself with a heightened eagerness to discover again the strange elation he had experienced early in the spring. He found that many simple and unrelated things could cause the same feeling to lift up and up within him till he was sure that he could not contain it. The wind could do this to him, when it washed through poplar leaves, when it set telephone wires humming and twanging down an empty prairie road, when it ruffled the feathers on one of Sherry's roosters standing forlorn in a bare yard, when it carried to him the Indian smell of a burning straw stack. Once the feeling had been caused by Gaffer Thomas's bucksaw wheehawing impatiently on the other side of the O'Connal back fence; another time, by a crow calling; still another, by the warm smell of bread baking. A tiny garden toad became suddenly magic for him one summer day — the smell of leaf-mould, and clover, and wolf willow. Always, he noted, the feeling was most exquisite upon the prairie or when the wind blew.

There had been the day, well on in the summer, that he and Forbsie Hoffman, now called "Fat" by one of the mutations common to boyhood, and Art Sherry had gone out drowning gophers. Bobbie had tagged along with them.

Out Sixth Street toward the spreading prairie they walked, Brian and Fat carrying between them Art's mother's washtub. Each carried in addition a red lard pail; Bobbie's bumped awkwardly against his fat legs as he alternately trotted and walked to keep up with the older boys. Once upon the prairie they turned east towards Haggerty's Coulee, where they had heard there were many gophers. While Fat's dog and Jappy ran ahead, the boys wandered in leisurely fashion, their conversation rambling as it usually did, until it arrived at the question of what a gopher did when he was being drowned out.

"Sometimes," Fat said, "you get three washtubs down their hole, and the water stays there quite a while, and you think he ain't ever comin' up, and then all of a sudden she goes down."

"She goes down." Bobbie always echoed the conversation of the other boys, who paid little attention to him.

"They back into the hole an' plug her up," Art explained, his face, as always, grimacing behind the thick spectacles that rode his nose. "When he unplugs, then the water comes down."

"The water comes down."

"You take the end of the washtub now," Brian said to Art.

"Not yet. I'll carry after Haggerty's Coulee."

"You never carry," Brian accused him.

"He never carries." Bobbie echoed his brother's speech most often.

"I do so," said Art. His glasses twitched; he put out his foot and tripped Bobbie to his face. Bobbie got up unconcernedly with his pants and shirt covered with spear grass, as were the clothes of all of them. At the edge of the prairie they'd had a spear grass fight, pulling the barbed hairs from their stalks and throwing them at each other; it was a good game.

"That is a ant," Bobbie pointed out.

"Anybody can see that," said Art.

"I can see that," said Bobbie. "I saw a girl one once."

"Look !" Fat cried and pointed to the dogs in scurrying chase over the prairie ahead. "They found one !"

"I don't see any !"

"Where ?" yelled Art.

"A girl gopher," said Bobbie mildly. "I knew —"

"There it is !" Brian caught a glimpse of a brown back rolling in frantic gallop, saw the flirt of a tail as the gopher, inches from Jappy's eager nose, was swallowed down the hole. "He's down the hole !"

Both dogs were at the opening. Jappy ecstatically threw the dirt behind him — stopped to insert his nose right to the eyes — took it out — began to dig again. Fat's dog circled anxiously.

"You an' Fat fill the tub !" directed Art. "I'll watch."

"I'll watch too," said Bobbie as Brian and Fat ran off toward the river, the tub between them, the lard pails swinging in their free hands.

They brought back two tubs of water, tipped them carefully down the hole, after each one, watched eagerly for the gopher to come out. Jappy sat with his ears cocked, his head solicitously on one side; he made anxious sounds in the back of his throat.

"Maybe he's got him a back door," suggested Fat after the second tub. "Maybe he's went out the back door —"

"The dogs would of seen him go," said Art. "He hasn't got any back door — more water is what he — look ! She's going down now !" One great bubble burst itself on the surface of the water filling the hole; it was followed by many little ones wobbling to the top. "He's took his ass outa the hole, an' he's comin' up now !" shouted Ike with excitement. "Git ready !"

The gopher's flat head broke the surface of the water; just out of reach in the throat of his burrow, he crouched with his head barely above water, his almond eyes looking up at the boys and the dogs. Out of the corner of his eye, Brian could see Jappy's tapered body quivering.

"More water !" shrieked Art. "All he wants is more water ! Halfa lard pail an' he'll come all the way out !" Ike rushed to the tub himself, tilted it over the lard pail, ran back, and soused the contents down on the waiting gopher. It came out in a lunging rush, its fawn hair dark with water, plastered wet against its skin. The dogs darted for it. Jappy got it by the scruff of the neck, shook his head, and threw it over his back. The gopher hurtled through the air to land near Art; it lay still upon the prairie. Art ran to it. He picked up the wet, tan body. It began to kick. "He's still alive !"

"He'll bite," said Fat fearfully. "They kin bite !"

"No he won't. I got him round the belly. He isn't biting anybody. All he kin do is squeak."

It was squeaking now; the thin and frantic sound threaded from Art's closed hand. Brian looked away. He saw with a start that the Young Ben was standing there; he had come upon them without a sound, and was staring at them with his pale, grey eyes under hair the colour of the prairie itself. He was barefooted, and as he turned toward Art, Brian saw the beginning of the crease of his bare bottom through the tear hanging open in the seat of his faded overall pants held round his middle by several frayed strands of binder twine.

"I'm gonna take the tail offa him," said Art, with the gopher still struggling and squeaking in his hand.

"I knew a girl gopher once," said Bobbie.

Art saw the Young Ben then. "I'm gonna rip the tail off him," he said again.

"She cut off her sister's finger an' it grew back on."

"Their tails grow back on if you let 'em go." Art was speaking to the Young Ben.

"An' she cut off her hand an't grew back on an' she cut off her legs an' they grew back on," chanted Bobbie.

Brian stared at the high and circling cheekbones under the tanned skin, at the freckles under the grey eyes. He looks like a coyote, thought Brian, like a watching coyote. He realized with a start that an excitement, akin to the feeling that had moved him so often, was beginning to tremble within him. His knees felt weak with it; the Young Ben could cause it too. The Young Ben was part of it. He's something I *know*, thought Brian.

Art had taken the gopher by the tip of its tail and was holding it head down by his thumb and forefinger. He raised his arm above his head and began to swing the gopher in a large circle. "Hold yer dogs back !" he cried. He snapped his arm. The tail remained in his hand.

"They all grow back on," said Bobbie sadly as the gopher thudded to the prairie sod.

Now to one side, now to the other, the gopher ran in squeaking, erratic course, both dogs after it. The Young Ben leaped. He passed the dogs, threw himself full length upon the tailless gopher. He lay there with the squeaking under him. While the boys watched open-mouthed, he reached under himself. With one merciful squeeze he choked the life from the animal. As he stood up he dropped it to the ground. He began to walk toward Art.

Fierce exultation gripped Brian as he realized what was about to happen. Face twitching nervously, Art backed away. He knew that something was wrong. Just as he had thrown himself upon the gopher, the Young Ben leaped at Art, who fell backward under his attacker's weight. The Young Ben fought as the boys had never seen anyone fight before. He was a clawing, wild thing on top of Art. He gouged Art's eyes, from which the glasses had fallen; blood sprang in long tracks as he drew his crooked fingers again and again down Art's face. He pounded him about the head, the throat, the ribs. He stood up and kicked Art rolling helpless on the prairie. When he stopped, one felt that he had done so simply because he was exhausted. He looked at the terror on Fat's face, at Bobbie's sobbing, then for long and level moments at Brian.

Brian returned his gaze and watched him wheel and begin to run in the direction of Haggerty's Coulee. In his heart Brian ran with the Young Ben — running with an easy lope each step of which smoothed into the other like the ripples of a broad stream flowing. When he had ceased watching the Young Ben, he saw that Fat had gone to get a lard pail of water from the river. He made no move to help as Fat soaked his shirt, and washed the blood and dirt from Art's face, his clothes unbelievably ripped. Art had a dazed look upon his sharp face, the look that one expects to see upon the face of a man whose home has just been levelled by a prairie tornado. "I didn't do anything to *him*," he said tearfully over and over again.

And Brian, quite without any desire to alleviate Art's suffering, shaken by his discovery that the Young Ben was linked in some indefinable way with the magic that visited him often now, was filled with a sense of the justness, the rightness, the completeness of what the Young Ben had done — what he himself would like to have done.

Art had to be led home like a blind boy; he was unable to see a foot in front of himself without his thick glasses . . .

(Who Has Seen the Wind)

Eric Nicol (Born in 1919)

Nicol — humorist, columnist, playwright — has won the Leacock Medal three times. His centennial book, with Peter Whalley the cartoonist, is *100 Years of What?*

This team also produced *Say, Uncle : A Completely Uncalled for History of the U.S., Russia, Anyone ?* and *An Uninhibited History of Canada.*

FIRST PROVINCE ON THE LEFT
Vancouver Explained

Although Vancouver, British Columbia, is more than sixty years old and its population is nudging the half-million mark, many strangers, including some Eastern Canadians, still don't know exactly where it is. Responsible for this geographical vagueness are several false impressions: for instance, the common belief that British Columbia is a steaming colony in the heart of the South American jungle. Something about the name, British Columbia, apparently suggests a tattered Union Jack fluttering over a few square miles of monkeys and malaria.

As a result of this loose notion about our latitude, those of us who visit other lands and there mention that we are natives of British Columbia often draw surprised comment on the remarkable whiteness of our skin, on our mastery of the English tongue and on our ability to handle a knife and fork without injury to ourselves or to others, although we never entirely dispel our hosts' suspicion that we may be concealing a blowgun or carrying a shrunken human head in our coat pocket.

Another popular misconception about Vancouver's location is that it is on Vancouver Island. In Toronto, Montreal and throughout the United States there are small but well-organized groups who insist that the logical place for Vancouver is on Vancouver Island and who are liable to turn ugly if you try to prove otherwise. Actually, of course, they are confusing Vancouver with Victoria, the capital of the province, thereby annoying the citizens of Victoria who resent being associated with the continent of North America.

Victoria, it may be noted incidentally, has gained considerable celebrity as "a little bit of Old England." When a British colonel anywhere in the world is wounded or feels death at hand, unerring instinct leads him eventually to the windswept waste of whitening flannel that is Victoria, and there, after snorting defiance through the local press, he passes on.

Thirdly, there are a few persons who fail to distinguish Vancouver, B.C., from Vancouver, Washington, which sits just below the border and refuses to go away. And lastly, some people haven't the faintest idea where Vancouver may be, other than perhaps a forest-bound clearing periodically traversed by Indians and Nelson Eddy singing excerpts from "Rose Marie."

The truth is, of course, that Vancouver lies on the mainland, at the foot of the snow-tipped coastal range, between Burrard Inlet and the mighty Fraser River. You can't miss it, the first province on the left.

In 1946 Vancouver celebrated her Diamond Jubilee, enjoying a bumper crop of American tourists, a hardy staple which comes up every year. Many Vancouver residents insisted that the house they were renting was obviously more than sixty years old, failing to realize that, although the city wasn't incorporated until 1886, there was a shack town here for some time before that, known variously as Hastings, Gas-town and Granville. Vancouver was so tough in those days she *had* to keep changing her name.

Vancouver became so excited about being incorporated that she got overheated and burned down. But the hardy pioneers merely spat on their hands, a questionable habit, and built her up again. This discouraged her so thoroughly that she has never tried to burn down since.

The original settlers around Vancouver were, of course, the coastal Indians, who were great canoe-makers and who thought nothing of paddling hundreds of miles to visit another tribe and spend an enjoyable afternoon slaughtering the men and carrying off the women. The fierce Haidas of the Queen Charlottes, for instance, were accustomed to paddle south to California for their scalps, probably because the heads were larger down there. The Indians were interrupted in these cheerful pursuits by the arrival of the Spanish explorers, who sailed in and planted the flag of Spain, only to have the English come right along behind and dig it up. For, just as the Spanish were leaving, Captain George Vancouver rowed in triumphantly. (There is no historical corroboration of the story that, as he passed the Spaniards' ships, Captain Vancouver yelled over : "How many miles do you get to the galleon ?")

Anyhow, Captain Vancouver, as the sharp students in the front row have already guessed, was the man after whom Vancouver was named. Yet, at the time, Vancouver thought he was barquing up the wrong inlet until he saw the Indians' welcoming committee standing on the shore. Approaching the Indians in his yawl, Vancouver hailed them :

"I am Captain Vancouver. I come in my yawl."

"How yawl," drawled the Indians, who belonged to the southern tribes. "Have you any cheap beads or worthless bits of glass you'd care to trade for these priceless furs ?"

"Now that you mention it," chuckled Vancouver, "I have."

Thus the morning was filled with gay chatter and one-sided trading until the Indians suddenly realized that they were late for a massacre and politely excused themselves. Captain Vancouver, well satisfied with the site of the city that was to be named after him, sailed away in his gallant little *H.M.S. Discovery,* the prow of which was already dinted from repeated attempts to find the North-West Passage.

Some years later the Hudson's Bay Company opened a trading post near Vancouver, and soon the traders were busy breaking glass up into worthless bits and destringing cheap beads. Most of the early trading was done at Victoria, which was a lot quieter than Vancouver, where people like Alex McKenzie and Simon Fraser kept bursting out of the bush every few years expecting to be congratulated and put up for the night.

The next big moment in Vancouver's life was the Gold Rush. We may as well face it — a good many of Vancouver's early lovers were interested in her for her money. This was the period of building and lawlessness, when men worked the mines and women worked the miners. Bands of ruffians roamed the streets, until one day Queen Victoria made the whole place into a crown colony, giving Vancouver a respectability from which the city has never recovered.

Shortly afterward the gleaming rails of the Canadian Pacific Railway came down the Fraser Valley, to stop short at Port Moody, about fifteen miles east of Vancouver. The C.P.R. had it on good authority that Port Moody was where the ocean began, and saw no point in taking its locomotives any farther (they would get soaking wet for one thing). While Port Moody was still thumbing its nose at Vancouver (they never had got along very well), a champion, Van Horne, arose to persuade the company to extend the line to Vancouver, the City with a Future. Impressed with the personality of this virile town, which had just burned itself down (Port Moody had never burned *itself* down — a pretty stuffy place), the C.P.R. extended its line. It was a gay and stirring sight as the first transcontinental train puffed into the station, covered with people and freight rates.

The rest of the story is one of phenomenal growth, of Vancouver's rise to the position of third-largest city in Canada. The largest and second-largest are two places called Montreal and Toronto, situated inland. There is a legend that when the good people of Toronto die they go to Vancouver. "Retiring to the West Coast," they call it, to this spawn of mountain and sea, home of the world's heaviest dew — our Vancouver.

(Sense and Nonsense)

Barry Mather (Born in 1909)

Mather has long been a favourite humorist in his home province, British Columbia. He is a Member of Parliament for New Westminster.

THE BRITISH COLUMBIAN

Once upon a time a little boy asked his Old Man : "Daddy, what is a British Columbian ?" The Old Man paused, thought, and then he spoke as follows :

"A British Columbian," he said, "is a man who has a California-type house, a Montreal mortgage, an English car, and a Scottish dog. His wife, who comes from Regina or maybe it is Calgary, either has a cat whose forebears came from Persia, or she has a small bird from the tropics which she keeps in a cage allegedly imported from Eastern Canada, but more likely made in Japan.

"A British Columbian is one who gets his home entertainment listening to an American imitating a Scandinavian on a machine that was made in Ontario by some outfit whose head office is in Pittsburgh.

"A British Columbian is a man who smokes Virginia cigarettes, drinks South American coffee, eats Ontario cheese, California oranges, Norwegian sardines, and Alberta butter.

"A British Columbian gets up when his Quebec alarm clock tells him. He shines his teeth with American tooth paste and he shaves with U.S. steel. His wife feeds him stuff out of a box put out by an outfit in Eastern Canada and from a tin of juice said to be from Hawaii. While eating, the British Columbian reads a New York news agency's report on what the Australians said to the Indians at the London Conference about the Chinese in Korea.

"The British Columbian eats fast so he can catch a vehicle manufactured in Ontario and deposit a small coin made in Ottawa, with a driver who probably comes from Saskatchewan.

"The British Columbian works hard all morning doing his best to stimulate the sale of a gadget manufactured in Quebec by a big company in New Jersey. At noon the British Columbian will either eat in a café owned by a Greek specializing in confusing the public by using French words to describe American foods — or, he will go to the luncheon of some service club founded in the U.S.A. and listen to a European tell how he escaped the Russians in Bulgaria.

"A British Columbian is one who considers himself fortunate if, after work, he can have one drink of a beverage manufactured in

Scotland. He will then rush home in time to coincide with the operations of an Eastern Canadian stove so that his wife will have time to let him take her to a theatre, partially owned by an outfit in Toronto, and see a Hollywood company portray life in the Canadian North.

"I could say more," the Old Man sighed, "but, my boy, that may give you a rough idea —"

However, the little lad had long ceased to listen to his Old Man and was reading a comic book manufactured by some French Canadians in Montreal, about a Texas cowboy saving a Spanish girl from a Mexican.

Roderick Haig-Brown (Born in 1908)

A writer, farmer and fisherman who also acts as magistrate, Haig-Brown lives on Vancouver Island. He is one of North America's ablest nature writers and his articles are often seen in the *Atlantic Monthly*. Here is the final chapter of his novel *On the Highest Hill*, from 1949.

ON THE HIGHEST HILL

As Colin climbed away from the burning cabin he felt an immense loneliness. There was nothing now, there never could be anything again except himself. He passed the little pool in the rock below the falls and thought of Mildred. She would hear about it, somewhere down in California, and know that she was freed from her promise. His last claim on her was burning in the flames that would soon destroy the cabin, had been killed with the bullet that killed Burdick. Not lonely, Colin thought, but alone. And it was not oppressive, nor terrifying, nor even sad to be alone. There was regret in it, regret for Burdick and all the destroyed things. But there was also pride in it and a clean strength and a purpose. To find death alone, away from confusion and fear and contempt and hatred. Not to seek it, not to aid it in any way. But to find it.

He climbed out on to the last broad ledge before the valley began to narrow to the Gap and knew that he was looking into death. It crept slowly towards him across the face of the mountains, blotting out draws and ridges and pinnacles as it came, gray white and silent. He looked behind him then, back down the still unsheeted valley, and saw at once the dark figures of men climbing far below him against the snow. He turned and went on and the front of the blizzard swept past him, hiding the climbing figures, closing everything into silence that waited for the first fierce sound of the wind.

There was death in the blizzard, Colin knew, but still a chance of life. He believed he could still pass safely through the Gap. After that there would be the full force of the wind on the open slopes at the head of Amabilis Valley. Walking, a man might keep himself alive. In the dark, he would not be able to walk. So there was only the tent. If no one had found it from the other side, and if they did not follow from this side.

The thought stopped him. He remembered what Andrew Grant had said of Tom Hughes' death in Windstorm Gap : "If you're ever in a spot like that, make them go back. Never mind the talk and kidding. Make them go back."

He stood for a moment longer, feeling the storm against him, hearing the high hard sound of the strengthening wind. Then he turned back. He picked his place well, a narrow place where the ledge sharply turned a ridge of the mountain. There was a short steep drop from it down to the wide main ledge they must follow if they were still coming against the storm.

Colin waited. He waited without fear, without hope for himself, yet without reluctance. He knew that the storm had almost certainly turned them back already, knew that time was closing in on him, that in an hour or two at the most it would be too dark to travel through the Gap. But he knew also that he had drawn them there and that if there was to be death again it must be for himself, not them. So he waited.

He saw them easily, more easily than he had expected, when they were still two hundred yards away. Six men, climbing grimly against the storm, following the dim outline of his track under the newly fallen snow. He fired once, over their heads, and watched them scatter into cover. Even then he could have killed some of them, because there was little good cover on the ledge. He wondered if they knew it, if they were afraid, and he did not want to fire again though he knew he would have to if he hoped to hold them there.

He saw a man crawling towards better cover and fired near him. There was an answering shot and the bullet sang away from the ridge above him. There was a long wait. Then Colin saw another man crawling forward. He fired once more, but the man did not stop; instead he stood up and began to walk slowly forward across the open ledge. Colin felt panic touch him. He heard himself shout wildly : "Go back," and he brought the sights of his rifle squarely on the center of the man's chest. Then he knew it was Clyde and saw that there was no rifle in his hands.

For a moment Colin hesitated. Then he stood up, his rifle held down at full arm's length across his thighs. He saw Clyde wave, then felt the shock of the bullet solid and heavy against his left shoulder. It threw him back, half-turning his body, and he fell to his knees. He looked back over the ledge and saw that Clyde had dropped down into cover. He fired near a man who moved, waited a moment and fired a second shot towards the other side of the ledge. Then he slipped away behind the ridge and began to climb the next ledge at a run.

He turned two more ridges, still running, then dropped back to his smooth, effortless mountaineer's walk. He was afraid only of Clyde. Clyde had known he would not shoot to kill. And Clyde would follow. It was Clyde who had brought those others up in the face of the storm and it was Clyde who would stand up and walk forward again, to find blood in the snow where Colin had made his stand and know that he was wounded.

Colin climbed on. He had wedged clothing between his coat and the wound and it seemed to him the bleeding had stopped. There was little pain except when he tried to raise his left arm and he could detect no weakening of his body through shock or blood loss. He was still in shelter from the main drive of the storm, but the way turned out now, along the last jutting ridge that marked the entrance to the Gap. As he started towards the point of the ridge he knew he would be exposed to anyone travelling the ledges behind him, but he did not look round. If they're that close, he thought, let them shoot. But let them do it right this time, let them find the heart. At least I did that for Ches Burdick. It could have been the heart for me. A little lower, a little farther over; likely the guy shot for it, held high and pulled off a little. I always thought it would be the heart, I used to think it when I was a kid, used to think it overseas, a bullet in the heart, quickly.

Suddenly he knew he did not want to die. He was almost at the point of the ridge now and he stopped and looked back. He could see the ledge, white and empty around the long curve behind him, empty again through the next curve to where the falling snow shut it from sight. They were slow or they had turned back. It might be either. He climbed over the point of the ridge and met the full, howling violence of the storm. It tore at his face and hands, found openings in his clothing, held his body and battered it with the strength and weight of moving water. He put his head down and faced into it, not hurrying, not straining, yet using his body's strength to make speed from sure and measured movement. There was light still, a dim gray light that would not lessen much for an hour yet.

There were sloping ledges in the gap and rock that had to be climbed and slides that had to be crossed. He slipped once in climbing, because his left arm was not there to help him, but recovered. Once the snow began to move under him, very slowly, but he crossed to safety and turned back to see the slide check itself and hold for lack of weight. He passed the narrow place where Tom Hughes had slipped, and reached the broad ledge beyond. The snow was thigh-deep now, dragging at his legs while the wind resisted his body. Once he stumbled and fell and lay for a moment feeling the warmth and shelter of the deep snow. He knew it would be easy and peaceful to die that way, but his mind turned from death and he got up and went on.

He came to the tiny draw that sheltered the tent and turned into it without caution. He had plowed a dozen paces through the deeper snow of the sheltered place before he saw that someone had gone in before him. He stopped then, but it was too late. The tent flaps opened and he saw a man there. The numbed fingers of his single good hand fumbled with his rifle, dropped it and he stood there, disarmed and helpless. Then he saw that the man was Johnny Harris.

"Colin," Johnny said. "Jesus, I thought you'd never come." He stumbled forward through the snow and touched Colin. "You're hurt," he said.

"How in hell did you get up here?" Colin asked him.

They went into the tent and Colin slid the light pack away from his right shoulder. "I haven't got much time," he said. "They're liable to be coming still."

Johnny looked out at the storm. "Through that? Nobody would come through against that tonight."

"Only Clyde. Clyde would and he's with them."

"They're down at your cabin too," Johnny said. He was heating a can of soup over a spirit stove. "That's what I came up here to tell you."

"Thanks," Colin said. His mind searched for something more, but he knew only that he was afraid for Johnny. "You got blankets?" he asked.

"Sleeping bag," Johnny said. "I'm O.K. Here, drink this." He handed Colin the soup.

While Colin was drinking Johnny came round to look at his wounded shoulder. "Leave it," Colin said. "You'll only start the bleeding again."

"You've got to take your coat off sometime."

Colin shook his head. "I'm pulling out soon as I've drunk this. Think you can get back down O.K.?"

"You can't go any place tonight," Johnny said. "You've got to stay here."

"And let them walk in on me when I'm asleep?" Colin shook his head again. "I've made it this far and I can make it to where they'll never find me."

"You didn't kill that guy, did you? Not like they say you did?"

"I killed him," Colin said slowly. "Jesus, Johnny, you don't know how easy a man dies until you've done it. You do a little thing, just moving your finger. And after that the biggest thing you can ever do won't change it."

"He must have done something to you first," Johnny said.

Colin shifted his body sharply and sat staring at the little flame of the spirit stove for a long while before he answered. "Yes," he said slowly. "He did something. He tried to burn the cabin. It wasn't my cabin, Johnny. It was hers." He looked at Johnny. "You and Robbie knew about her, didn't you? I know Robbie did."

Johnny moved his feet and looked down at them. "Sort of," he said slowly. "You wrote letters all the time."

"Burdick had no business doing that. She never did anything to him." Colin stared gloomily into the flame again. "Don't ever kill a man, Johnny," he said. "Nothing's big enough for that. They're so empty when they're dead." He reached forward and pushed back the tent flap. "I've got to get moving before I stiffen up." His voice was suddenly urgent. "They'll be coming close now."

"They'll never come tonight," Johnny said. "You could sleep. I'd wake you at first daylight."

Colin took his rifle and his pack and stood up outside the tent. "Help me on with it, Johhny," he said.

"You've got no place to go," Johnny pointed out at the storm. "You can't live a night out in that." But he held the pack while Colin slipped his right arm through and settled the tump line.

Colin held out his hand. "Don't worry, Johnny. I've got a place to go to. Tell Robbie I had a place to go to."

They shook hands and Colin went out of shelter into the storm again. It was almost dark now and his body had stiffened during the short rest; but he had taken the spare snowshoes he kept in the tent and travelling was less difficult. For a little way he followed the trail towards the Gully, squarely into the face of the storm. Then he turned off at right angles and began to climb the sharp ridge that led to the face of Amabilis Mountain. He felt fear then, a clear, penetrating, physical fear of death and loneliness, of the growing darkness and the storm and the dangerous way ahead of him. He wanted to turn back to Johnny in the tent, to go in and lie down and sleep until Clyde came to wake him. But his body loosened as he climbed and he felt its strength again and found strength in the sound of the storm about him. Fear died and he felt freedom.

The ridge grew suddenly steeper and there was little snow on it. He kicked his snowshoes off, slung them on his pack and went on again, climbing faster than before. It was almost dark and he could see only a few feet in front of him, but he knew where he was and he turned from the ridge across the steeply sloping face of the mountain. He stepped carefully now, counting his steps, and so found the tiny sheltered crevice he was looking for.

It was scarcely more than a crack, cut deeply into the face of the mountain, protected at the lower end by a sharp turn that killed the winds drawing up it, shut off abruptly thirty or forty feet from the turn by a straight bold face of rock. He had spent a night there once before, many years ago, an uncomfortable night with a single blanket and no fire. The next morning he had gone out and cut half a dozen little stunted trees and piled them at the lower end of the crevice. He found them now, dry and brittle under the fresh snow, and lit a small fire. Then he took the blankets from his pack, rolled into them and was quickly asleep.

He woke suddenly and thought he had slept until daylight. But he saw the embers of his fire still red and knew it could not be daylight. He looked up and found stars in the clear sky above the crevice. His wounded shoulder sent a wave of pain through his body as he sat up, but his mind felt intensely clear. He took more wood and stirred his fire to fresh life and felt the warmth of it against his face and body. He ate a meal from the food in his pack, then folded his blankets away, picked up his rifle and climbed out of the crevice.

The wind met his body like a singing sheet of ice. It poured in swift and sweeping steadiness across the open face of the mountain and drove against the peaks until they gave back a great body of deep sound in vibrations that quivered against the sky. Colin felt the snow strongly crusted underfoot, saw the full moon high and brilliant in the sky, looked down and saw an infinite swirling whiteness of wind-driven clouds over everything below him. He began to walk, coldly upright, striding like a giant, across the steep face of the mountain.

As he walked, pain left him and fear drew far beyond reach or recall. For a little while Burdick walked with him, a quiet calm Burdick who shrugged his shoulders and found death as small a thing as life. Then Martha was with him and Curly Blake and Terry Murphy and laughter was with them all, loud and free on the clean sweep of the storm under the mighty vibration of the peaks. Colin strode across the face of Amabilis Mountain until dawn showed light beyond the clouds in the east and the moon began to pale in the west.

He had used up the mountain then, had traversed the whole head of the valley. But he crossed to the mountains of the west side and followed them down towards the pass to Hidden Valley. New clouds came high on the wind and snow swept under them, blurring the sun as it rose, then burying it behind fold upon fold of sweeping whiteness. Colin came to the narrow corridor and turned along its level floor. All through the night he had sought for Mildred among the others who had come to be with him on the face of the mountain. She came to him now in the snow, in the quiet of the narrow place between the mountains. Her voice was with him and the feel of her and the strength of her. He came to the end of the corridor, looked down into the snow that whirled and drifted over Hidden Valley, and knew surely that she was there also.

He dropped from the corridor into the deep snow of the little platform above the ledge trail. For a minute or two he stood there, kicking the snow away, clearing space for his jump. Blocks of snow dropped away from the movements of his feet, broke, broke again and disappeared among the flakes of falling snow. He tested himself, feeling his arm for pain, and there was no pain. Cold was no longer cold and the sounds of the storm had become silence. There was brownness where whiteness should have been on the falling snow. Colin knew that he was tired, that he must jump to the ledge trail and follow it' down to her while there was still a little strength left to him. He moved his feet again, to clear away a last lump of snow, then felt the platform heave under him. He jumped wildly and with all the strength of his body. For a moment he was crawling on his hands and knees, reaching blindly for the stretcher that had been torn away from him and the wounded man it had borne. Then he knew that his body was falling, that it would find the death his soul had neither sought nor feared.

Ethel Wilson (Born in 1890)

Novelist and short-story writer, Mrs. Wilson's deft satire and quiet humour have gained an international audience. Among her novels are *The Innocent* Traveller, *The Equations of Love,* and *Love and Salt Water.* The author selected the piece below from her book of the same title.

FROM FLORES

Up at Flores Island, Captain Findlay Crabbe readied his fishboat the *Effie Cee* for the journey home and set out in good spirits while the weather was fair. But even by the time he saw the red shirt flapping like mad from the rocky point just north of the Indian's place the wind had freshened. Nevertheless Fin Crabbe told the big man at the wheel to turn into shore because there must be some trouble there and that Indian family was pretty isolated. As the man at the wheel turned the nose of the boat towards the shore, the skipper listened to the radio. The weather report was good, and so he went out on the small deck well satisfied and stood there with his hands on his hips, looking at the shore where the red flag was.

The third man on the fishboat was just a young fellow. Up at Flores Island he had come down to the float with his gear all stowed in a duffel bag and asked the skipper to take him down to Port Alberni. He was an anxious kid, tall, dark, and thin-faced. He said he'd pay money for the ride and he spoke of bad news which with a young man sounds like parents or a girl and with an older young man sounds like a wife or children or a girl. Fin Crabbe said shortly that the boy could come, although the little *Effie Cee* was not geared for passengers. He didn't need to pay.

Captain Crabbe was small. He had come as an undersized boy to the west coast of Vancouver Island and there he had stayed. He had been fairish and was now bald. His eyes were sad like a little bloodhound's eyes and pink under, but he was not sad. He was a contented man and rejoiced always to be joined again with his wife and his gangling son and daughter. Mrs. Crabbe's name was Effie but she was called Mrs. Crabbe or Mom and her name had come to be used only for the *Effie Cee* which was by this time more Effie than Mrs. Crabbe was. "I'm taking home an Indian basket for Mrs. Crabbe," the skipper might say. "Mrs. Crabbe sure is an authority on Indian baskets." Fin Crabbe was his name up and down the coast but at home he was the Captain or Pop, and so Mrs. Crabbe would say. "The Captain plans to be home for Christmas. The Captain's a great family man. I said to him 'Pop, if you're not home for Christmas, I'll . . . !' " Thus they daily elevated each other in esteem and loved each other with simple mutual gratification. In bed no names were needed by Mrs. Crabbe and the Captain. (When they shall be dead, as they will be, what will avail this happy self-satisfaction. But now they are not dead, and the Captain's wife as often before awaits the Captain who is on his way down the coast from Flores Island, coming home for Christmas.)

Fin Crabbe had planned for some time to reach Port Alberni early in Christmas week and that suited Ed, the big crewman, too. Ed was not a family man although he had a wife somewhere; but what strong upspringing black curly hair he had and what black gambling eyes. He was powerful, not to be governed and a heller when he drank. He was quick to laugh, quick to hit out, quick to take a girl, quick to leave her, a difficult wilful volatile enjoying man of poor judgment, but he got along all right with little Fin Crabbe. He did not want to spend Christmas in Flores Island when there was so much doing in Alberni and Port Alberni.

Captain Crabbe's family lived in Alberni proper, which to the dweller in a city seems like a fairly raw small town at the end of a long arm through the forest to nowhere; and to the dweller up the coast or in the Queen Charlottes seems like a small city with every comfort, every luxury, motor cars speeding in and out by the long road that leads through the forest to the fine Island Highway, lighted streets, plumbing, beer parlours, a hospital, churches, schools, lumber mills, wharves. It lives for and on trees and salt water. Behind it is a huge hinterland of giant forests. Before it lies the long tortuous salt-water arm of the open sea.

Captain Crabbe, as the bow of the *Effie Cee* turned towards the pine clad but desolate and rocky shore, cutting across the tricky undulations of the ocean, again gave his habitual look at the sky, north and west. The sky was overclouded but so it usually is in these parts at this time of year. Since these rocky shores are not protected, as are the rocky shores of the British Columbia mainland, by the long stretches of sweet liveable gulf islands and by the high barrier of mountainous Vancouver Island itself, the west coast of the island lies naked to the Pacific Ocean which rolls in all the way from Asia and breaks upon the reefs and rocks and hard sands; and the continuous brewing of weather, up in an air cauldron in the north, seethes and spills over and rushes out of the Gulf of Alaska, often moderating before it reaches lower latitudes; but sometimes it roars down and attacks like all hell. The fishboat and tugboat men know this weather well and govern themselves accordingly. Next morning perhaps the ocean smiles like a dissolute angel. The fishboat and tugboat men know that, too, and are not deceived. So that, although Fin Crabbe knew all this as well as he knew his own thumb, he did not hesitate to turn the *Effie Cee* towards the shore when he saw the red shirt flapping at the end of the rock point but he had no intention of stopping there nor of spending any time at all unless his judgment warranted it, for on this trip his mind was closely set to home.

The turning aside of the fishboat in her journey irked the young passenger very much. Since the weather report on the radio was fairly good and anyway he was used to poor weather, he felt no concern about that. But here was delay and how much of it. He did not know how often he had read the letter which he again took out of his pocket, not looking at big Ed nor at little Captain Crabbe but frowning at the letter and at some memory. He was possessed entirely, usurped, by impatience for contact, by letter, by wire or — best of all — by speech and sight and touch with the writer of this letter. Now that he had started on the journey towards her, now that he had started, now that he was on his way, his confusion seemed to clear. He read again in the letter : "Dear Jason I am very unhappy I dont know I should tell you I've thought and thought before I wrote you and then what kind of a letter because I could say awful things and say you must come to Vancouver right away and marry me or believe me I could just cry and cry or I could write and say plain to you O Jason do I beseech you think if we couldn't get married right away. I could say I love you and I do."

The young man folded the letter again. He looked with distaste at the red flag that signified an Indian's trouble and his own delay and his mind ran backwards again. The letter had found him at last and only two days ago. He had left the camp and had crossed to Flores and there an old man with a beard had told him that Fin Crabbe was all set to go to Alberni the next morning, and he had enquired for Captain Crabbe. As he had walked up and down the float pushing time forward, sometimes a violence of joy rose in him and surprised him. This was succeeded by a real fear that something would happen to prevent the fishboat from leaving, would prevent them reaching Alberni very soon, while all the time Josie did not even know whether he had received the letter. Many feelings were induced in him by what Josie had written, and now he thought ceaselessly about her to whom, only three days before, he had barely given a thought. He unfolded the letter again.

"I gess I dont know too much about love like in the pictures but I do love you Jason and I wouldn't ever be a person who would throw this up at you. I dont sleep very good and some nights I threton to myself to kill myself and tho I am awful scared of that maybe that would be better and easiest for us all and next night I say no. Lots of girls go through with this but what do they do with the Baby and no real home for it and then I am bafled again and the time going."

Jason, looking out to the ocean but not seeing it, was aware of a different Josie. If a person had told me, he thought, that I'd want to get married and that I'd be crazy for this baby I'd say they were crazy, I'd say they were nuts, and impatience against delay surged over him again. The boat neared the mouth of the bay.

"One thing I do know I couldn't go back to the prairies with the Baby," (no, that's right, you couldn't go back) "so where would the Baby and me go. Mother would let me feel it every day even if she didn't mean to tho she would take us but Father no never. Then I think its the best thing for the Baby I should drown myself its quite easy in Vancouver its not like the prairies I do mean that."

The skipper was talking back and forth to the crewman at the wheel and the *Effie Cee* slowed down. There were beams of sunshine that came and went.

"I cant believe its me and I do pitty any poor girl but not begging you Jason because you must decide for yourself. Some people would pay no attention to this letter but I kind of feel you're not like some people but O please Jason get me a word soon and then I can know what. Josie."

From the pages arose the helpless and lonely anguish of little Josie and this anguish entered and consumed him too and it was all part of one storm of anxiety and anger that she was alone and she so quiet, and not her fault (he said), and impatience rose within him to reach a place where he could say to her Don't you worry kid, I'm coming ! He thought with surprise Maybe I'm a real guy and I never knew it, maybe we're all bad and we don't know it. He read once more : "I am bafled again and the time is going . . . I do love you Jason." He put his head in his hands with dumb anger that she should be driven to this, but as soon as he reached a telephone in Alberni everything would be all right. As he suddenly looked up he thought he would go mad at this turning off course for any sick guy, or any kid who'd been crazy enough to break an arm. In his frustration and impatience there was an infusion of being a hero and rushing to save someone. Some hero, he said very sourly to himself, some hero.

The *Effie Cee* slowed to a stop and a black volley of cormorants, disturbed, flew away in a dark line. There was an Indian and an Indian woman and a little boy in a rowboat almost alongside the fishboat. The little boy was half lying down in an uncomfortable way and two rough sticks were tied to his leg. Three smaller children stood solemnly on the rocky shore looking at the two boats. Then they turned to play in a clumsy ceremonial fashion among the barnacled rocks. They did not laugh as they played.

Jason put the letter in his pocket and stood up. The rowboat juggled on the water and Captain Crabbe was bending down and talking to the Indian. He listened and talked and explained. The Indian's voice was slow and muffled, but not much talk was needed. Anyone could see. "Okay," said the skipper and then he straightened himself and turned to look at Ed and Jason as much as to say . . . and Jason said, "Better I got into the rowboat and helped him lift the kid up," and the skipper said "Okay."

All this time the woman did not say anything. She kept her hands wrapped in her stuff dress and looked away or at the child. Jason slipped over the side and the rowboat at once became overcrowded which made it difficult for him and the Indian to lift the child up carefully without hurting him and without separating the boats. The Indian child made no sound and no expression appeared on his face so no one knew how much pain he suffered or whether he suffered at all. His eyes were brown and without meaning like the dusky opaque eyes of a fawn. The Indian spoke to his wife and she reached out her hands and held on to the fishboat so that the two craft would not be parted. Jason and the father succeeded in slipping their arms — "This way," said Jason, "see? do it this way" — under the child and raised him gradually up to where Ed and the skipper were kneeling. Everyone leaned too much to one side of the rowboat and Jason tried to steady it so that they would not fall with the child into the sea. All this time the woman had not spoken but had accepted whatever other people did as if she had no rights in the matter. When the child was safely on board, Jason sprang onto the deck and at once, at once, the *Effie Cee* turned and tore away with a white bone of spume in her mouth and a white wake of foam behind, leaving the Indians in the rowboat and the children on the shore looking after her.

"Best lay him on the floor, he'd maybe roll off the bunk," said Fin Crabbe when they had lifted the child inside. "Mustn't let you get cold, Sonny," he said, and took down a coat that swung from a hook. The child regarded him in silence and with fear in his heart. Another white man taking him to some place he did not know.

"Make supper Ed, and I'll take the wheel," said the skipper. The boat went faster ahead, rising and plunging as there was now a small sea running.

What'd I better do, thought Fin Crabbe and did not consult the crewman who hadn't much judgment. There were good reasons for going on through and trying to make Alberni late in the night or in early morning. That would surprise Mrs. Crabbe and she would be pleased, and the young fella seemed desperate to get to Alberni on account of this bad news; but here was this boy he'd taken aboard and the sooner they got him into hospital the better. I think it's his hip (he thought), I could turn back to Tofino but it'd be dark then and would he be any better off landing him in the dark and likely no doctor. Anyway I can make Ucluelet easy and spend the night. I don't like to take no chances but all in all I think we'll go on. And they went on.

Evening came and black night. It was winter cold outside and Jason crowded into the wheelhouse and looked out at the dark. The coming of night brought him nearer the telephone, so near he could all but touch it, but he could not touch it.

The *Effie Cee* could not make much speed now and plowed slowly for hours never ending, it seemed to Jason, through water that had become stormy and in the dark she followed a sideways course so that she could cut a little across the waves that were now high and deep. Ed had the wheel and Captain Crabbe stood beside him. The storm increased. The boat's nose plunged into the waves and rose with the waves and the water streamed over. There was a wallowing, a sideways wallowing. The little fishboat became a world of noise and motion, a plunging, a rising, a plunging again. Jason wedged the child against the base of the bunk. The child cried out, and vomited with seasickness and fear. "Now now," said Jason, patting him. "Try the radio again," said Captain Crabbe.

Jason fiddled with the radio. "Can't seem to get anything," he said.

"Let me," said the skipper.

"Bust," he said.

But now the storm rapidly accelerated and the waves, innocent and savage as tigers, leaped at the *Effie Cee* and the oncoming rollers struck broadside and continuously. The little boy made sounds like an animal and Jason, in whom for the first time fear of what might come had struck down all elation and expectation, took the child's hand and held it. The little plunging boat was now the whole world and fate to Jason and to Fin Crabbe and to the Indian boy but not to Ed who had no fear. Perhaps because he had no love he had no fear. Standing over the wheel and peering into the dark, he seemed like a great black bull and it was to Jason as though he filled the cabin.

Ed turned the boat's nose towards shore to get away from the broadside of the waves. Fin Crabbe shouted at him to be heard above the storm. The boat had been shipping water and Jason, crouching beside the shaking child in a wash of water, heard the words "Ucluelet" and "lighthouse" and "rocks" but Ed would not listen. The skipper went on shouting at him and then he seized the wheel. He pushed the big man with all his strength, turning the wheel to starboard. Jason and the Indian child saw the big man and the little man fighting in the small space, in the din of the ocean, the howl of the wind, for possession of the wheel. As quick as a cat Ed drew off and hit the older man, a great blow. Fin Crabbe crumpled and fell. He lay in the wash of the water at Ed's feet and Ed had his way, so the fishboat drove inshore, hurled by the waves onto the reefs, or onto the hard sand, or onto the place that Ed knew that he knew, whichever the dark should disclose, but not to the open sea. Captain Crabbe tried to raise himself and Jason crawled over towards him.

The skipper could not stand in the pitching boat. He looked up at Ed who was his executioner, the avenger of all that he had ever done, driving on against death for sure.

The thought of the abandonment of Josie (for now a belief was formed terribly in him that she was to be abandoned) pierced Jason through and through and then in the immediate danger the thought of Josie was no longer real but fled away on the wind and water, and there was nothing but fear. Without knowing what he did, he seized and held the child. Never could a man feel greater despair than Jason in the walnut shell of a reeling boat soon to be cracked between land and water. Ed, bent over the wheel, knowing everything, knowing just where they were, but not knowing, looked only forward into the blackness and drove on. The sea poured into the boat and at the same minute the lights went out and they were no longer together. Then the *Effie Cee* rose on a great wave, was hurled upwards and downwards, struck the barnacled reef, and split, and the following seas washed over.

A few days later the newspapers stated that in the recent storm on the west coast of Vancouver Island the fishboat *Effie Cee* was missing with two men aboard. These men were Findlay Crabbe aged fifty-six and Edward Morgan aged thirty-five, both of Alberni. Planes were continuing the search.

A day or two afterwards the newspapers stated that it was thought that there might have been a third man aboard the *Effie Cee*. He was identified as Jason Black aged twenty-two, employed as a logger up the coast near Flores Island.

On the second morning after the wreck of the *Effie Cee* the skies were a cold blue and the ocean lay sparkling and lazy beneath the sun. Up the Alberni Canal the sea and air were chilly and brilliant but still. Mrs. Crabbe spent the day waiting on the wharf in the cold sunshine. She stood or walked or sat, accompanied by two friends or by the gangling son and daughter, and next day it was the same, and the next. People said to her, "But he didn't set a day? When did he *say* he'd be back?"

"He never said what day," she said. "The Captain couldn't ever say what day. He just said the beginning of the week, maybe Monday was what he said." She said "he said, he said, he said" because it seemed to establish him as living. People had to stop asking because they could not bear to speak to Mrs. Crabbe standing and waiting on the busy wharf, paying the exorbitant price of love. They wished she would not wait there because it made them uncomfortable and unhappy to see her.

Because Josie did not read the papers, she did not know that Jason was dead. Days had passed and continued to pass. Distraught, alone, deprived of hope and faith (two sovereign remedies) and without the consolation of love, she took secretly and with terror what she deemed to be the appropriate path.

The Indian, who had fully trusted the man who took his son away, heard nothing more. He waited until steady fine weather came and then took his family in his small boat to Tofino. From there he made his way to Alberni. Here he walked slowly up and down the docks and at last asked someone where the hospital was; but at the hospital no one seemed to know anything about his only son.

(Mrs. Golightly & Other Stories)

Claire Martin (Née en 1914)

Speakerine à la radio, plus tard présidente de la Société des Ecrivains canadiens, elle a débuté par des nouvelles abondant en observations cruelles, avant d'écrire des romans où elle analyse les ressorts de l'amour humain et deux livres de souvenirs d'enfance, *Dans un gant de fer*, et *La Joue gauche* qui lui a mérité le Prix du Gouverneur général 1966. Suit le dernier chapitre de *Doux-Amer*.

DOUX - AMER

Je repartis. Il n'y avait pas encore de lumière à ses fenêtres. Je sillonnai son quartier. Je revins vers ce boulevard où je l'avais perdue. Comme je revenais chez elle, je la vis qui entrait. Je la rejoignis dans l'escalier.

— J'ai attendu ton appel toute la journée, me dit-elle.

Ce disant, elle montrait son manuscrit. Je n'avais pas remarqué en la suivant, tout à l'heure, qu'elle le portait sous le bras.

— Je suis allée chez toi, ce soir encore. Mais tu n'es jamais là. Mon travail ne t'intéresse plus ?

Je l'écoutais comme, dans un cauchemar, on écoute, venant on ne sait d'où, des voix qui tiennent des propos insensés. Je la voyais toute occupée de ce manuscrit qu'elle serrait sur elle et je ne savais comment l'amener à l'objet de ma démarche. Nous étions, maintenant, dans l'antichambre. Le téléphone pouvait sonner d'une seconde à l'autre et ce qu'on aurait à lui apprendre ne serait peut-être plus la même chose. Je tendis la main.

— Donne-le-moi. Je vais t'expliquer. J'ai été très occupé.

— Moi aussi, je suis très occupée. Je pars.

— Mais tu ne peux pas faire ça.

— Oh ! si, je peux. Je pars demain. Je m'en vais à la campagne.

Elle se mit à me parler du repos qu'elle cherchait, d'une petite auberge. Ce téléphone allait sûrement sonner.

— Le rêve, ce serait une auberge déserte, tenue par des gens parlant une langue qui m'est inconnue, le hongrois ou le turc. Tu as ça dans ton carnet d'adresses ?

Elle riait. Depuis que je tenais dans mes mains son gros cahier cartonné qu'elle avait emporté deux soirs de suite sans pouvoir s'en défaire, elle avait perdu son air morne.

— Tu sais, j'ai renvoyé Barbara.

— Ah ? Viens donc avec moi dans ma chambre : je n'ai pas terminé mes préparatifs.

Je la suivis. Elle se mit à plier des tricots.

— Tu comprends, je ne vais pas là pour exhiber des robes du soir. Qu'est-ce que tu as ? C'est d'avoir renvoyé Barbara qui te met dans cet état ?

— Ecoute. Bullard a eu un petit accident de voiture.

— Ça devait arriver. Il boit trop. Rien de grave ? Tu sais que je l'ai mis à la porte.

Et le téléphone sonna.

Tout le temps que dura la communication, elle garda un visage impassible. Elle disait « oui, oui », sans plus. Elle regardait dans ma direction. Je fis, sans qu'elle me réponde, un geste interrogatif, et je me rendis compte que ce qu'elle regardait c'était, derrière moi, son image dans la glace. Ce n'était pas, comme Barbara, sa beauté intacte qu'elle y cherchait. Je pense que c'était le reflet rassurant de ce visage sans pâleur. Bullard pouvait râler, sangloter, mourir, ce fait sans importance venait se brouiller et se dissoudre sur le tain des miroirs. Elle ne me regarda qu'en répétant le nom de la rue où l'accident avait eu lieu. Puis, ses yeux m'outrepassèrent de nouveau, à la rencontre de leurs calmes jumeaux.

— Bon. J'y vais tout de suite.

La main sur l'appareil, elle restait immobile. Derrière notre zone de silence, on entendait une voix irritée qui répandait une cascade de mots.

— Ils sont ennuyeux tes voisins. Ils se disputent tout le temps.

— Tu sais, j'aurais mauvaise grâce à leur faire des reproches.

— Veux-tu que je te conduise à la clinique ?

— Tu es gentil. Dis donc, c'est arrivé bien près de ton bureau, cet accident. On m'a dit vers cinq heures et demie. Il avait été chercher Barbara, je suppose ?

— Oui, et il est parti en colère parce que je l'avais renvoyée. Il avait un peu bu, tu sais.

Elle me mit les mains aux épaules.

— Tu ne vas pas te croire responsable, dis ? Et elle ? Est-elle blessée ?

— Très peu. Mais Bullard l'est beaucoup plus gravement. T'a-t-on dit quelque chose à ce sujet ?

— Non. Nous verrons cela là-bas.

Je l'aidai à passer un manteau. Au moment de sortir, elle avisa le manuscrit que j'avais posé sur une table avant de la suivre dans sa chambre. Sans un mot, elle le prit et me le remit dans les mains.

Dans la voiture, pendant que nous roulions par les rues désertes, elle me demanda de lui raconter ce qui s'était passé à mon bureau. A chaque réverbère, son visage surgissait de l'ombre, attentif, pour s'y renfermer de nouveau. C'était, à chacun, comme un bref aveu. Un aveu complexe que je n'avais jamais le temps de démêler tout à fait. Sur un fond de sérénité qui me semblait voulue, des ondes de cruauté ou de désespoir naissaient, s'amplifiaient au moment le plus vif de l'éclairage, puis se résorbaient.

Je racontai, d'abord, comment j'avais décidé le renvoi de Barbara, la journée qui avait suivi, l'arrivée de Bullard, les invectives échangées.

— Ont-ils parlé de Blondeau ?

Cette préoccupation, que j'avais eue pourtant, me déplut. Il y a quelque chose d'inhumain dans l'inutile rappel d'une folie.

— Non. Et je préférerais que tu n'en parles pas non plus.

— Pourquoi ?

— Parce que cela m'humilie.

Elle eut un rire sec.

— Tu aurais été attendrissant dans une carrière politique.

— Aussi m'en suis-je tenu éloigné. Mais je n'ai pas terminé mon récit.

Je lui racontai ce que j'avais vu de l'accident. Elle écoutait sans m'interrompre. Entre les réverbères, j'aurais pu croire que je parlais pour moi seul. Puis, je lui dis que je l'avais longtemps suivie dans la rue.

— Comprends-moi. Je ne savais pas comment t'annoncer ça.

— C'est ce que tu crois. Mais j'ai une meilleure explication.

Nous arrivions devant la clinique. Je stoppai brutalement. Un peu de sueur me vint au creux des mains.

— Laquelle ?

— Celle-ci : à chaque minute qui passait, la probabilité que je le revoie vivant diminuait. Veux-tu m'attendre ? Je ne serai pas longue à revenir.

Elle sauta hors de la voiture et l'ombre la happa aussitôt. Qu'y avait-il de vrai dans cette assertion ? J'avais beau m'assécher les mains, elles redevenaient tout de suite moites.

— Romancière ! Si elle arrive trop tard, ne va-t-elle pas m'en accuser à présent ? Disons tout de suite que c'est moi qui ai tué Bullard. Bon Dieu ! je ne suis tout de même pas un assassin.

J'avais parlé haut, mais l'endroit était désert et je pouvais m'offrir cette thérapeutique. Informulées, mes pensées s'évadaient, tournaient en rond et se désagrégeaient. Cet accident, Bullard seul en était responsable. Je n'étais coupable en rien. Mais j'y étais bien pour quelque chose. Je n'étais coupable en rien mais, sans moi, Bullard ne serait pas mourant derrière ces murs. Je sentis poindre, au plus profond de moi, un sentiment extraordinaire, tel que je n'en avais jamais ressenti. Quelque chose d'aigu et de fuyant comme la volupté, mais lucide. Et pourtant, songeais-je, je n'aime plus Gabrielle. Cela devrait m'être indifférent. Puis, je pensai qu'au contraire c'était une raison de plus de n'être pas indifférent. Pourquoi aurais-je cessé d'en vouloir à Bullard ? Parce que, après m'avoir enlevé la femme que j'aimais, il était aussi la cause, immédiate ou éloignée, de tout ce qui avait contribué à détruire mon amour ? Il y avait plutôt aggravation.

La portière s'ouvrit brusquement et Gabrielle monta près de moi.

— Fracture du crâne. Il est dans le coma.

— Tu ne restes pas ?

— Que veux-tu que je fasse là ? Il paraît que cela peut durer plusieurs jours. Il faut que j'aille terminer mes malles.

— Tu pars quand même ?

— Oui, je pars quand même, dit-elle d'une voix coléreuse. Crois-tu que je vais rester dans le corridor de cet hôpital à attendre que ce monsieur se décide à rester ou à partir ? Mon séjour là-bas est tout arrangé, depuis des jours. Je ne renoncerai à rien. Je ne renoncerai plus jamais à rien.

— Et s'il meurt ? Il faudra t'avertir.

— J'ai donné ton numéro de téléphone en disant que c'était la façon la plus facile de me rejoindre.

Je mis en marche. Dieu sait que le sort de Bullard ne m'inspirait aucune pitié. Mais la décision de Gabrielle me laissait pantois. Je ne suis qu'un bourgeois hypocrite, pensais-je, mais je ne pouvais m'empêcher d'être scandalisé. Elle n'en avait cure. La bouche grossie par une moue courroucée, elle restait silencieuse.

— Monte avec moi. Je vais te donner le numéro de téléphone de l'auberge.

Elle poussa un sac de voyage pour que je puisse m'asseoir sur le lit, écrivit sur une carte le nom et le numéro de l'hôtel. Sa main, en me la donnant, tremblait très fort.

— Pourquoi m'as-tu dit que je voulais que tu arrives trop tard ? Il est encore vivant et tu n'es pas restée une demi-heure.

— Tu prends tout pour des reproches. Je crois que c'est la vérité. Mais je ne t'ai rien reproché.

Elle retourna à ses préparatifs tout en parlant de son séjour à la campagne. Quand les vêtements épars furent rangés, elle tourna les yeux vers la penderie ouverte, franchit, très vite, la distance qui l'en séparait et y saisit une robe noire qu'elle plia et déposa avec le reste. De ma vie, je n'avais assisté à rien de semblable. Je me sentais flotter sur une sorte de brume, comme dans une hallucination. Je me levai pour aller regarder la nuit par la fenêtre.

Le bruit d'un corps qui s'écroule, suivi de violents sanglots, me fit sursauter. Gabrielle était assise sur le parquet. La tête enfouie dans ses bras, elle pleurait, appuyée sur le lit.

C'était la première fois que je la voyais pleurer de vraies larmes qu'elle n'essayait pas de retenir. Je tentai de la relever, de la prendre dans mes bras, mais elle balbutiait « laisse-moi, laisse-moi » et se faisait lourde et inerte, de sorte que je n'y parvenais pas. Elle pleura longtemps. Du moins, cela me sembla interminable. Je ne disais rien : j'étais stupéfié. Enfin, elle se calma peu à peu et vint s'asseoir près de moi sur le lit.

— Ma pauvre Gabrielle, tu n'en peux plus. Et puis, tu t'es fait mal à feindre l'indifférence. Reste donc, va.

Elle leva un visage que les larmes avaient rendu indéchiffrable et me regarda longtemps.

— Je cherche mes mots, dit-elle enfin. Ce n'est pas ce que tu crois. Je n'ai pas feint l'indifférence. Je n'ai pas envie de rester. C'est la première fois que je pleure depuis ... (et elle indiqua, de la main, la hauteur d'une fillette), et c'est sur moi que je pleure. L'affaire Bullard, l'affaire Blondeau, et tous les autres, rien n'est propre, rien n'est viable, rien ne dure. Je me sens poussée, bousculée. Ce n'est pas juste. Plus je vais, et plus les pages tournent vite. Quand j'ai commencé à écrire, je croyais qu'avec cela, je me moquerais bien de vieillir. Ce n'est pas vrai. Tout m'échappe. Regarde-moi.

Elle avançait, avec une sorte de défi, un visage rouge et vernissé où les larmes avaient recommencé à couler. Plein d'étonnement, je contemplais cette femme qui s'était refusé vaillamment les pleurs arrachés par l'amour, au temps où Bullard la torturait et qui, cette nuit, sanglotait sur son propre destin.

— Tu sais, j'ai pensé à me tuer. J'y ai beaucoup pensé. Je me disais que, sitôt ce roman terminé, je me tuerais.

Je ne pus m'empêcher de sourire. C'était toujours « travail d'abord ».

— Ça me fait peur. Moi qui ai poussé tant de gens au suicide, dans mes livres, le coeur me tourne rien qu'à imaginer le revolver sur ma tempe.

Elle essayait de rire et ne parvenait qu'à grimacer. Elle était un peu pénible à regarder.

— Ce serait pourtant une solution. Tu sais pourquoi cela a tourné ainsi ? C'est que j'ai confondu l'amour et la peur de vieillir. J'ai pris peur, comme n'importe quelle sotte.

Elle se leva et s'approcha de la glace.

— Si tu n'avais pas tant pleuré, tu verrais que tu es encore très jeune.

— Je le sais. Mais je suis fatiguée de lutter. Retarder une ride de six mois, ça ne vaut plus le coup. Je ne veux plus d'hommes dans ma vie pour qui je me battrai contre l'âge. Dans un an, je serai peut-être comme ces femmes qui ont remplacé l'amour par la nourriture. Sur quoi écrit-on quand on en est là ?

Ayant mis le doigt, après ces propos qui n'étaient incohérents qu'en apparence, sur son souci capital, elle se tut. Puis, elle me prit par la main.

— Allons, viens prendre un verre avec moi.

Je la suivis à la cuisine. Entre ses mains agitées, les verres et les bouteilles tintaient. Elle avala d'un trait un grand verre d'eau.

— J'ai trop soif, je boirais trop vite. Pourquoi ne viendrais-tu pas me voir, un dimanche, à la campagne ? Tu pourrais amener Corinne, si tu veux.

Elle continua à parler sur ce ton tout le temps que dura l'alcool dans nos verres. La nuit s'achevait. Il me fallait partir.

— Qu'as-tu fait de mon manuscrit ?

— Il est dans la voiture. Je commencerai à le lire dès demain. A moins... écoute, Bullard va peut-être mourir. Il n'y a rien que tu veuilles retrancher ?

— Non.

Je la pris dans mes bras. Ce faisant, je songeais que j'aurais pu forcer à l'abandon ce corps dont je connaissais toutes les ressources. Mais, cet abandon, je n'aurais su qu'en faire. Si je l'avais enlacée, c'est qu'elle me faisait pitié, que j'étais triste, que la nuit avait été dramatique. Je laissai retomber mes bras.

— Au revoir, Gabrielle.

— Au revoir, répondit-elle, avec ce visage en désordre, vaillant et désespéré, tiraillé par la montée des larmes et la volonté de les refouler, ce visage qu'une fois déjà je lui avais vu sur un chemin de son village.

Elle ouvrit la porte et, comme je passais le seuil, je sentis sa main sur mon dos qui me poussait un peu.

(Doux-Amer, 1960)

Gérard Bessette (Né en 1920)

Docteur ès lettres, il a enseigné aux universités de Saskatchewan, Duquesne, R.M.C., Queen's et Laval. Poète et critique, il est surtout connu comme romancier grâce au *Libraire,* dont est extrait le texte ici reproduit, et à *L'incubation.*

L'OFFRE D'EMPLOI

Au début de février, comme je me trouvais sans emploi depuis près de deux mois et qu'il ne me restait que cinquante dollars en poche, j'ai décidé de chercher du travail. Je me suis rendu au bureau de placement gouvernemental et j'ai jeté un coup d'oeil au tableau d'embauchage. On demandait plusieurs bûcherons, des commis-voyageurs, deux mécaniciens, trois tourneurs, une demi-douzaine de comptables, des laveurs de vaisselle et des manoeuvres. Bref, rien de bien tentant. J'ai demandé à un chômeur qui se trouvait là si c'était tout. Il m'a dit que non : on avait d'autres listes dans les bureaux. L'espace manquait pour les afficher toutes. Il m'a demandé ensuite si j'avais ma carte. C'était la première fois que j'en entendais parler. Il s'agit d'un petit certificat émis par le bureau de placement et attestant que le postulant n'a pas de dossier criminel et cherche « de bonne foi » du travail. La tournure me parut ridicule. Je ne concevais pas qu'on pût chercher du travail « de mauvaise foi ». C'était de ma part un manque d'expérience. Le type m'a expliqué que bien des sans-travail se présentent au bureau dans l'unique but de toucher leur assurance-chômage et s'arrangent pour refuser les emplois qu'on leur offre. Je trouvai le procédé ingénieux et regrettai de ne pouvoir l'utiliser. Malheureusement, en ma qualité de répétiteur au collège Saint-Etienne, « institution de charité », je n'étais pas protégé par l'assurance-chômage.

De toute façon, pour obtenir ma carte, il me fallait subir une interview. Cette perspective ne m'enthousiasmait pas. Mais, comme j'étais plutôt fatigué, je me suis assis sur la banquette près du type; et j'ai attendu. Au moins une quinzaine de sans-travail nous précédaient. On les appelait à tour de rôle, et alors nous glissions nos fonds de culotte le long du siège de bois poli par l'usure. Le type ne parlait plus. Il semblait nerveux. Il craignait de ne pouvoir faire estampiller sa carte. Je me souviens que j'ai allumé un cigare et tiré quelques bouffées; puis je me suis endormi.

Au bout de quelques minutes, un coup de coude de mon voisin m'a fait sursauter. J'ai ouvert les yeux. Je pensais que l'on m'appelait déjà pour l'interview et je trouvais que je n'avais pas attendu longtemps. Mais je me trompais. En levant la tête, j'ai vu un gros type en complet bleu marine qui se tenait devant moi la main tendue.

— Comment ça va, Hervé ? me demanda-t-il. On ne te voit plus. Qu'est-ce que tu deviens ? Toujours dans l'enseignement ?

Je reconnus Martin Nault, un ancien condisciple. C'était jouer de malchance. Avec son menton en galoche et sa trogne de boxeur, Nault m'avait toujours paru repoussant. Je fis mine de ne pas voir sa main tendue et lui répondis avec indifférence que je n'étais plus dans l'enseignement.

— En effet ! fit Nault en se grattant le menton. Je me souviens maintenant. Qui est-ce qui m'a dit ça ?... Ah ! oui, c'est Massé. Il s'est rendu au collège pour te voir et tu n'étais plus là ...

Que Nault fût au courant ne me surprenait pas. C'est le genre de crétin qui s'attache aux potins de classe et aux souvenirs d'*alma mater* comme certains « campagnards » aux nouvelles de cousins du huitième degré qu'ils ne connaissent même pas. Un autre chômeur venait d'être appelé et je me glissai d'une place sur le banc sans m'occuper de Nault. Mais il ne se décontenança pas pour si peu. Il faut dire aussi que, chez mes confrères, on m'a toujours pris pour un excentrique, un cynique. Si bien que je peux leur faire les pires impolitesses sans qu'ils s'en formalisent. Il fut un temps où je prenais plaisir à forcer mon personnage, car il est agréable de pouvoir injurier impunément les gens. Mais ça offre aussi des inconvénients, par exemple quand on veut se débarrasser d'un emmerdeur. Jamais je ne m'en rendis mieux compte qu'à cette minute où, bedonnant et fessu, la figure épanouie, Nault m'examinait avec condescendance, avec gourmandise, dans l'espoir que je lui raconterais mes déboires.

— Qu'est-ce que tu fais ici ? me redemanda-t-il en voyant que je n'ouvrais pas la bouche.

Je rallumai posément mon cigare; puis je lui déclarai que le décor me plaisait, que c'était sympathique et luxueux.

En fait ce bureau de placement occupe des locaux sordides. Murs gris, crasseux, carreaux salis d'une couche de suie, parquets recouverts d'un linoléum échancré, ça fait penser à la salle d'attente d'une gare de province.

Nault éclata d'un rire gras, sonore. Ma réponse ne l'avait même pas piqué. Il me mit la main sur l'épaule, une grosse main boisée d'une toison noire.

— Viens donc à mon bureau, dit-il. Nous serons plus tranquilles pour causer.

Je le suivis, je ne sais trop pourquoi, ou plutôt je m'en doute : depuis l'apparition de Nault, mon voisin me poussait du coude et s'éclaircissait la voix pour attirer mon attention; il voulait que je le présente. Nault, je l'ai appris quelques minutes plus tard, est surintendant-adjoint de ce bureau. Mais le chômeur pouvait toujours se démerder tout seul. Je préférais encore une entrevue avec Nault.

A peine installé dans son bureau, dont je constatai avec satisfaction qu'il était à peine moins terne que la salle d'attente, Nault reprit son interrogatoire :

— Comme ça, tu as laissé tomber les bons pères de Saint-Etienne ? Qu'est-ce que tu fais maintenant ?

Il frottait l'une contre l'autre ses grosses mains velues, un sourire vorace aux lèvres. Il savourait d'avance le plaisir qu'il aurait à raconter mes ennuis à nos anciens condisciples. Je lui déclarai donc que j'étais présentement recteur de l'université, mais que je songeais sérieusement à changer de poste, vu que mes secrétaires, vieilles filles constipées, ne me laissaient pas tripoter les étudiantes aussi méticuleusement que je l'eusse souhaité. Nault se tordit de rire à cette réponse stupide. Voilà le genre « d'esprit » qui m'a valu ma réputation auprès de mes condisciples.

— Et qu'est-ce que tu envisages comme situation ? me demanda Nault, sa crise d'hilarité passée.

Je lui répondis que ça m'était égal pourvu qu'il n'y eût rien à faire.

Après un nouvel esclaffement, Nault se mit à se frotter le menton, l'air perplexe. Il voulait m'aider, c'était évident, mais sans nuire à son prestige. Je ne le blâme pas d'avoir nourri des doutes sur mes aptitudes à obtenir un job. Mes vêtements ni mes manières ne sont de nature à inspirer confiance à un employeur. Je n'ai pas eu, comme on dit, l'occasion de renouveler ma garde-robe depuis longtemps. Comme « pédagogue », on s'était habitué à me voir toujours les mêmes hardes sur le dos et on ne faisait plus d'observations. On se contentait de me payer un salaire de famine et de me laisser croupir dans les basses classes.

Tout à coup, la binette de Nault s'illumina. Il fit claquer ses doigts boudinés en un geste triomphal.

— Tu aimes toujours les livres ? me demanda-t-il.

Esquissant une moue d'indifférence, je lui déclarai que les livres brûlaient moins longtemps que le charbon, mais que, faute d'autre combustible, il m'arrivait de m'en servir.

Le rire de Nault se déclencha de nouveau; puis, soudain, il prit son masque sérieux de surintendant-adjoint.

— Ecoute, fit-il, je connais un type, un libraire, qui cherche quelqu'un... Je ne sais pas si ça t'intéresserait ?... (Il consulta un petit fichier.) Le seul inconvénient, c'est que c'est un peu loin de Montréal, à Saint-Joachim...

Inutile de décrire plus longtemps cette interview d'opéra-comique. J'ai accepté l'offre de Nault. Saint-Joachim ou ailleurs, je m'en balançais.

(Le libraire, 1960*)*

Eugène Cloutier (Né en 1921)

Romancier, chroniqueur et grand voyageur, il a été directeur de la Maison canadienne à Paris et écrit aujourd'hui pour la radio. Ses romans curieux dénotent le goût de l'insolite et du mystère.

LE GRAND COUP

— Ce qu'ils ne savent pas, dit Jean, c'est que leurs lits ramollissent la colonne vertébrale.

Il fut tenté de se relever, en quête d'une planche qu'il eût glissée sous son matelas. Mais une douce chaleur l'engourdissait. Et puis, il y avait de la tristesse dans le noir. La misère des chambres d'hôtel quand vient la nuit ! Le souper avait été joyeux, enlevé, et pourtant, voici qu'une mystérieuse langueur avait commencé de s'insinuer partout.

Antoine ne parvenait pas davantage à s'endormir. Il transpirait de toute la surface de son corps. Les monstres de la nuit dernière sortaient lentement de l'ombre et s'avançaient par glissements saccadés, les yeux brillants, la dent éclatante. De longs fils de soie, nerveux et mobiles, descendaient en même temps du plafond et se tordaient vers lui comme des tentacules. Antoine avait rejeté ses couvertures et se roulait sur son lit. Dans quelques instants, la nuit bondirait sur lui, de toute part, à la hauteur de la gorge, et serrerait ... Mais soudain, la voix chaude de Jean prit toute la place dans cette chambre :

— Le moment est arrivé de t'expliquer le « grand coup ».

Il y eut un silence pendant lequel Antoine se sentit revivre. Il se rappela avec reconnaissance qu'au cours de leurs dernières nuits de là-bas, Jean avait pris l'habitude de lui faire la conversation, pour l'aider à combattre ses monstres. Et c'est ainsi que, petit à petit, il avait entendu chuchoter que sa « guérison approchait ». Encouragés par leur victoire de la nuit dernière, les monstres n'avaient pas tardé à vouloir le reprendre ... mais Jean était là pour le défendre, et aussi longtemps qu'il serait là ... Il sentit un frisson bienfaisant se répandre en lui. La voix de Jean le cherchait comme une caresse :

— Sans argent, la partie est perdue d'avance. Sans argent, tout est toujours perdu. Et nous ne sommes pas ici pour le déplorer. Les faits sont les faits et, quels qu'ils soient, nous devons prendre l'habitude de les accepter. C'est la seule façon d'aller au-delà.

Il n'était pas question pour eux de travailler à gagner cet argent. Le travail n'était admissible que pour les oisifs. Et ils avaient tant à faire au cours des prochains jours. D'ailleurs, pouvaient-ils se sentir liés par l'une ou l'autre des lois ou des habitudes d'une société qui les avait délibérément écartés ? Non. Ils devaient agir en toute liberté de conscience et prendre sans hésiter les chemins de raccourci qui s'offraient. Ils voulaient de l'argent, beaucoup d'argent, assez d'argent pour accomplir leur mission sans perdre un temps précieux à faire des calculs ... Eh bien, ils iraient en chercher là où il s'en trouvait de trop. En fin d'après-midi, il avait soigneusement repéré la banque qui répondait le mieux à ses goûts pour la simplicité et la discrétion. Rue déserte, ou à peu près. Caissière jeune et d'une nervosité prometteuse. Elle n'hésiterait pas longtemps avant de pousser l'argent à son agresseur et l'aiderait, au besoin, à tout engloutir, sans exiger de détails sur le calibre et la portée de l'arme qu'on voudrait bien lui mettre sous le nez. Au comptoir, un vieux commis à grosses lunettes, aux réflexes lents et d'une démarche alourdie par sa crise annuelle de rhumatisme.

Les complications ne pourraient venir que des clients ou du gérant ... Or, à compter de deux heures trente de l'après-midi, les clients se faisaient de plus en plus rares et le gérant avait depuis toujours l'habitude de quitter les lieux un quart d'heure avant la fermeture.

— L'agression ne peut donc avoir lieu qu'entre deux heures cinquante et trois heures, déclara Jean.

Mais attention ! Ils ne devraient s'intéresser qu'aux billets. Jean se grisait de tous les détails qu'il avait soigneusement arrêtés. Les titres, les obligations, les bons d'épargne... tout cela n'était pour lui que raffinements d'une société qui s'ennuie. Il remplirait sa serviette de billets en accordant sa préférence aux coupures de dix et de vingt dollars.

Puis, un gros agent apparaîtrait dans la porte, s'avancerait vers lui, le prendrait au collet, lui passerait les menottes et l'entraînerait en gesticulant dans la rue : ce serait Antoine.

Grâce à cette intervention, la caissière retrouverait sa respiration normale, le vieux commis son lumbago et la petite succursale son ambiance pacifique. On n'aurait plus qu'à téléphoner au gérant pour lui signaler le vol en même temps que l'extraordinaire efficacité des policiers municipaux. Tout à fait rassuré, le sympathique gérant ne songerait qu'à savourer par anticipation le plaisir de lire son nom quelque part en première page des quotidiens... tandis que chacun de son côté, ils auraient largement le temps de regagner l'hôtel par le double itinéraire qu'il avait mis au point et qu'il lui expliquerait le lendemain matin à la première heure.

— La grande erreur des professionnels, conclut Jean, c'est de ne pas fournir eux-mêmes la silhouette pacifiante de l'agent. Ils font attendre une voiture noire, se garnissent de mitraillettes, font un gaspillage de personnel... Ils pensent à tout, sauf à l'essentiel. Grâce à ton intervention, au bon moment, je n'aurai même pas d'arme à produire. Il me suffira d'enfoncer profondément la main dans la poche de ma veste et de la pointer sur la caissière. Elle me croira sur parole, ou les jeunes filles ont bien changé.

Il se lança dans une grande période oratoire qu'une réflexion d'Antoine fit pourtant tourner court : « Et la morale ? » avait-il lancé sur un ton angoissé. En voilà un qui avait de curieuses questions. Le parfum de la fille flottait encore dans la chambre. Antoine répétait, angoissé :

— Et la morale ?... Tu y as pensé à la morale ?

Non. A la vérité, il n'y avait pas pensé. Pour Jean, la morale n'était pas quelque chose de surajouté comme un vêtement. S'il avait voulu le « grand coup », c'est qu'il était nécessairement moral. Mais

Antoine avait peu de chances de se rallier à un modus vivendi aussi personnel. Il fallait trouver autre chose, et vite ! Jean se décida pour une référence biblique.

— Tu te souviens, dit-il, de ce passage où le Christ prétend qu'il sera plus facile à un chameau de passer par le trou d'une aiguille qu'à un riche d'entrer dans le Royaume des Cieux ?

Antoine se le rappelait si bien qu'il commença par rectifier la lettre de la citation pour ensuite la placer dans son contexte, avec une aisance qui eût impressionné un spécialiste. Jean le lui fit remarquer, ne ménageant pas ses compliments, en vue de l'amener à maturité pour son argumentation maîtresse :

— Le « grand coup » aura le mérite de rendre à la pauvreté des dizaines, peut-être même des centaines de personnes. Plus d'argent nous prendrons et plus de pauvres nous aurons livrés repentants à la Bible ! Ne crois-tu pas que la morale y gagne, et que si nous la trahissons, c'est pour mieux la servir ? Il est clair que notre sacrifice nous attirera les bénédictions du Ciel ! . . .

Un ronflement l'interrompit. Antoine s'était endormi en souriant aux anges.

(*Les Inutiles*, 1956)

André Langevin (Né en 1927)

Journaliste, puis réalisateur à Radio-Canada, il a débuté par un roman où il forçait son talent et a atteint à la maturité dès *Poussière sur la ville* (1953) qui a la rigueur d'une tragédie racinienne (et dont on trouvera ici les premières pages). Il n'a rien publié depuis *Le Temps des hommes* (1956), où se manifeste encore sa compassion pour les déshérités qui luttent pour sortir de leur désespoir.

POUSSIÈRE SUR LA VILLE

Une grosse femme, l'oeil mi-clos dans la neige me dévisage froidement. Je la regarde moi aussi, sans la voir vraiment, comme si mon regard la transperçait et portait plus loin, très loin derrière elle. Je la reconnais vaguement. Une mère de plusieurs enfants qui habite dans le voisinage. Cela dure une demi-minute au moins, j'en jurerais. Puis elle s'en va d'un pas lent et lourd qui troue silencieusement la neige. J'écrase ma cigarette sur le mur contre lequel je suis adossé et je comprends tout à coup. La bonne femme a dû me croire fou ou ivre. Il est presque minuit. Un vent violent fait tournoyer une neige fine dans la rue déserte. Et, tête nue, sans pardessus, je contemple ma maison.

Dans la cabane de Jim, le chauffeur de taxi, le téléphone sonne sans répit, comme toutes les nuits. Un son grêle, haché par le vent. On a l'impression que le gros Jim est mort et que la sonnerie ne s'interrompra que lorsqu'on aura découvert le corps.

Je refais les cent pas en regardant la chambre de Madeleine, encore illuminée, où la neige tend un illusoire écran.

— Moi, je ne sais pas ce qu'elle vient chercher ici... Mais les gens parlent. J'en connais qui ne viennent au restaurant que pour la voir. Moi, ça ne me regarde pas... Enfin, je tenais à vous avertir.

Kouri furetait sous le comptoir et je ne voyais que ses cheveux couleur de poussière. Mais à sa voix chevrotante je pouvais reconstituer le visage : les yeux noirs, sans eau, abrités derrière la paupière épaisse; la bouche indécise comme la voix, un peu tordue par la gêne ou la pudeur. Ses paroles étaient demeurées en suspens sur le comptoir; elles ne m'avaient pas atteint. Je devais avoir l'air hébété.

Puis Kouri redressa son grand tronc oscillant dans une ample blouse grise et me tendit les cigarettes sans me regarder, les yeux fixés sur la caisse. C'est à ce moment-là que quelque chose me remua dans les entrailles, comme une angoisse. Je quittai le restaurant sans mot dire et traversai la rue pour arpenter le trottoir devant la maison du docteur Lafleur, face à la mienne.

Je ressentais un peu l'impression de l'automobiliste qui se jette sur la victime qu'il veut éviter. La grosse femme vient de me remettre en mouvement et j'essaie de trouver un sens aux paroles de Kouri.

« Je tenais à vous avertir... ». Il y a peut-être dix jours qu'il cherche les mots, les mots qui m'inquiéteraient sans rien m'apprendre. Il a sans doute voulu me parler avant ce soir, mais sa pudeur le bâillonnait. « Moi, ça ne me regarde pas... » Je vois très bien Kouri consoler ainsi un homme qui jouerait devant lui avec un revolver. Sa discrétion d'oriental l'a bien servi. En dix ans il a transformé une petite gargotte en établissement luxueux. Le plus important restaurant de la ville, aux murs peints de rose et de bleu poudre, aux banquettes moelleuses, non encore trouées par les cigarettes. Et une glace immense qui couvre tout un mur.

Le Syrien a dû m'épier, me voir traverser la rue. Il me regarde peut-être, abrité derrière le givre de la vitre.

Je n'arrive pas à m'expliquer mon émoi, la chaleur intérieure qui m'a bouleversé. Parce que Kouri me révélait une part de la vie de Madeleine que je ne connaissais pas ? Peut-être. Comme s'il avait levé le rideau et m'avait montré derrière une vitre un être dont j'aurais ignoré complètement l'identité et qui eût été ma femme. Madeleine m'échappait par plusieurs points. C'était cela mon émotion. Je ne la soupçonnais quand même pas. Et la soupçonner de quoi ? Il ne faut surtout pas que je me laisse séduire par le jeu des images. Imaginer Madeleine dans le restaurant du Syrien souriant à quelqu'un qui lui parle. Quand même cela serait, il y aurait mille interprétations possibles en plus de celle que ma chair appelle. Non. Je n'ai ni le goût, ni le temps de ces sortes de jeux.

Qu'a-t-il voulu dire le Syrien ? Je ne sais pas. Question de bienséance sans doute. Macklin ne doit pas priser que Madeleine soit vue seule chez Kouri tous les jours. Hé bien ! Macklin n'a qu'à se faire une raison. Cela ne concerne que Madeleine et moi.

Le téléphone continue de sonner sans arrêt chez Jim, aussi vain, aussi stupide que les pensées qui tournent à vide dans mon cerveau. La fenêtre de Madeleine est toujours illuminée. A part cela, un calme irritant que troublent à peine les volutes effrénées de la neige. Pas un passant. Pas une voiture. Quelques clients doivent encore flâner chez Kouri. Des mineurs qui tuent le temps avant de descendre dans les puits pour la nuit.

Kouri a certainement voulu dire davantage. Autrement, il n'eût pas parlé. Il sait, lui, ce que Madeleine fait dans son restaurant, à qui elle sourit, à qui elle adresse quelques mots. Il sait aussi ce qu'on en peut dire dans la ville. De tout cela il a tiré une conclusion, qui était de m'avertir. Bah ! le Syrien est assez simple d'esprit et s'est alarmé pour quelques mots mal entendus. Trois mois de mariage seulement. Ce simple chiffre brille comme l'innocence. Ces sortes de choses n'arrivent qu'après dix ans, et encore faut-il avoir un peu le goût des attitudes théâtrales. En trois mois nous n'avons pu connaître le mot *irrémédiable*. Les longs soirs insupportables où on peut s'accuser l'un l'autre de la fatigue de vivre ensemble. Cela ne se goûte pas sans masochisme.

Je contemple toujours la fenêtre de notre chambre. Aucune ombre ne s'y profile. Est-ce que j'attends une révélation de ce rectangle de lumière ? J'aurais déjà des instincts de victime !

— Ça ne va pas, docteur !

Le gros Jim. La chassie de ses yeux se discerne encore dans la poudrerie et son visage lui faiblement. Enorme, mou, pataud, Jim me renifle doucement. La neige lui a permis de s'approcher de moi sans que je l'entende. De ses yeux malsains il trace à deux reprises sa petite trajectoire, depuis mon visage jusqu'à la fenêtre de Madeleine. Puis il se fouille une narine d'un gros doigt velu.

— Vous prenez l'air ?

Sa voix est comme un gros graillon. Vous avez l'impression de la voir : visqueuse et molle. Je ne puis que lui murmurer :

— Ça sonne chez vous.

Il continue à se fouiller la narine en regardant la neige sur le trottoir.

— Vous pensez pas que je vais travailler par une nuit pareille !

D'un lent hochement de tête il montre la neige qui patine sur l'asphalte. Puis il s'en va, languide et écrasé, en me lançant du milieu de la rue, le dos tourné :

— C'est pas un temps pour prendre l'air sans pardessus.

Je le vois entrer dans sa petite cabane de bois. Quelques secondes plus tard le téléphone se tait. Il a dû décrocher pour la nuit.

Jim passe plusieurs heures par jour chez Kouri. Il y était sans doute quand... Je le vois m'épiant sans en avoir l'air pendant que Kouri me parlait. Lui aussi connaît cette part de la vie de Madeleine qui m'échappe. Il n'aime pas ma femme, qui le lui rend bien. Cela doit lui donner une certaine perspicacité. Ce gros homme malsain a lu mes pensées. J'ai l'impression d'avoir déshabillé Madeleine devant lui, de la lui avoir révélée.

Je suis gelé. Je traverse la rue et prends mon chapeau et mon pardessus dans la voiture que je laisse dans la rue. Si j'ai un appel d'urgence durant la nuit, la vieille Chevrolet ne démarrera sans doute pas. Tant pis. Je suis trop las.

Je m'assieds sur une des chaises de la petite salle en bas et j'écoute la vie dans la maison. Le ron-ron monotone du moteur dans la cave, le bois qui craque ici et là sous la chaleur des tuyaux. C'est tout. Du côté de chez Kouri, dont le restaurant occupe tout le rez-de-chaussée de la maison à part les deux petites pièces où j'ai mon bureau et ma salle d'attente, une maigre rumeur que ne perce aucun son particulier.

Je suis un intrus. Il faudrait que je me passe la main sur les yeux, que je secoue la tête pour découvrir que je n'ai rien à faire ici. Ce bureau n'est pas le mien et la femme qui dort ou lit en haut ne m'appartient pas. J'ai rêvé et, somnambule, je m'éveille dans la maison d'un autre. Je réussis presque à considérer ma nouvelle vie — mon mariage et mon cabinet de médecin — en étranger, comme au retour d'une absence de vingt ans qui me ferait ne reconnaître ni ma femme, ni la maison. Par la porte entrouverte de mon bureau je vois briller sur ma table le stéthoscope que j'avais oublié. Et ce simple objet, qui m'identifie aussi sûrement que le marteau le charpentier, ne m'est plus familier. Que tout cela est laid : les chaises recouvertes de moleskine noire qui ont peut-être passé par dix salles de médecin avant d'échouer dans la mienne, le pupitre que l'usure a rendu poreux, les crachoirs de cuivre, les hautes armoires vitrées dont on chercherait en vain la réplique dans les plus anciennes pharmacies. Il n'y a de neuf que ma table d'examen au chrome étincelant, au jeu de positions complexe, qui fait l'admiration de Madeleine. Cette table, ainsi que les fers sous la vitrine, elle s'y intéressa avec l'avidité qu'elle apporte devant tout ce qui est neuf, différent. Tout le reste, l'appartement et mon bureau, elle le découvrit avec indifférence, sinon avec ennui. Le parfum sec et rance de la maison, comme si tous les humains qui y ont vécu avant nous avaient laissé un peu de leur sel dans le bois, m'aide à comprendre le désaccord profond qu'il y a entre Madeleine, jeune et libre, d'une liberté quasi animale, et les souvenirs morts, ces meubles revêches d'avoir trop longtemps survécu. Je songe au jeune médecin qui occupait l'appartement avant nous. A-t-il quitté la ville parce que sa femme ne pouvait supporter l'hostilité de la maison ?

Au fond, le désaccord survient toujours entre Madeleine et les choses l'instant qu'elle les a connues. Elle ne s'attache qu'au mouvement et préfère le train lui-même à l'endroit où il permet de se rendre. Elle ne goûte jamais avec économie. Elle exprime le suc de tout dès l'abord et connaît ensuite une dépression où elle s'abandonne avec nonchalance. Forcément sa vie est faite de moments d'ardeur et de grands espaces vides où elle est d'une passivité déconcertante. Aussi l'appartement serait-il plus attrayant que son ennui, en fin de compte, ne s'abolirait pas. Agit-elle de même avec les êtres ? Je ne pourrais l'affirmer. Leur mobilité, leur instabilité devraient la retenir davantage. Il faut plus de temps pour épuiser les possibilités de transformation d'un être. Mais un jour la chaîne doit se boucler et les rapports doivent n'être plus qu'une perpétuelle répétition.

(*Poussière sur la ville,* 1953)

Claude Jasmin (Né en 1930)

Peintre, romancier et critique d'art, il cherche à peindre en traits rapides et violents les sentiments durs des jeunes en révolte contre la société qui les étouffe. De son oeuvre déjà abondante on a retenu ici le début de *Délivrez-nous du mal.*

MONOLOGUE

Je me parle.

La nuit enfin va s'achever. J'ai honte d'avoir tant pleuré. Montréal a chaud, c'est juillet. Juillet 1960. Je suis là, debout, dans le silence affreux, derrière une des fenêtres du douzième étage du Victoria Queen Building. Montréal a très chaud. Un trafic continuel sillonne constamment la rue Ste-Catherine. Pendant que mes yeux, enfin, — enfant — se sèchent, je relis pour la centième fois les flamboyantes enseignes dont l'aube, bientôt, rendra leurs cris clignotants inutiles : leurs petits cris de PARKING — PARKING — PARKING — PARKING — PARKING... en jaune; de GRILL, COMING UP, DANSE — GRILL, COMING UP, DANSE — GRILL, COMING UP, DANSE en jaune et rose; de DUNLOP, TIRES, PNEUS, DUNLOP, TIRES, PNEUS en vert; et puis, comme un exercice d'optique, loin à l'ouest, ICI RADIO-CANADA, ICI RADIO-CANADA, ICI RADIO-CANADA... en bleu et blanc... Assez ! Ma mère avait bien raison : « tu n'es qu'un braillard comme ton père ! »

Mon Dieu, faites que je ne lui ressemble pas... pas tant que ça !

Je suis là, rôdant, seul et enfermé sous clé depuis six heures hier soir. Un coup de trompe, freins, démarrage nerveux, un coup de trompe, deux coups de trompe. Ils se répondent, suivant un code indéchiffrable, mystérieux, fantaisiste ! Devant moi, au nord, la montagne, monstre calme qui ne bouge pas, étrangère, vieille bête dormant derrière les blocs à appartements de la rue Sherbrooke, de la rue McGregor, de l'avenue des Pins; derrière des cheminées, des antennes de télévision, elle dort avec sa grosse croix de fer allumée, plantée dans le dos comme un poignard. Les blocs de ciment, de briques, percés de multiples carreaux bleus, noirs, mauves, quelques-uns, rares, jaunes de veille, veillent.

Je me parle.

D'heure en heure, j'écoute, retenant mon souffle, le pas traînant du gardien de nuit. Il vient tout près de ces bureaux où je me suis fait bêtement enfermer. Dans le mur, de l'autre côté, invisiblement, il fait entrer sa petite machine à marquer les heures. Cling ! Et voilà la preuve, en cas d'incendie, que monsieur le surveillant a fait sa ronde régulièrement. Il s'éloigne, même pas traînant. Il reviendra dans une heure. Dans l'état où j'étais — braillard que je suis — je n'osais pas l'appeler. Maintenant que ça sèche — enfin, enfin — à la prochaine tournée, je vais lui manifester mon insolite présence. Je suis plus calme. Extérieurement du moins. Je pourrai inventer quelque chose : que je me suis endormi, tout bonnement ! C'est peut-être un fieffé bavard et demain, cinq minutes après la rentrée du personnel, tout le monde, avec excitation, se répétera qu'un dénommé André Dastous a passé la nuit enfermé dans l'édifice ! André Dastous ? André Dastous ? Vous les entendez chuchoter ? « Dastous ? L'ami de Georges ? Oui, oui, oui, oui, oui ... l'« ami » de Georges. Georges Langis, l'ami de Dastous. Le couple, le charmant petit couple ». Oh, je les entends très bien : ronronnements, sifflements, commérages, radotages, vous entendez ? C'est affreux ! médisances, calomnies, persiflages, moqueries, railleries, affreux !

Je me fiche pas mal de cette petite société des petits employés de la McCormick Publishing Corporation Limited. Je ne me fiche pas — vous pouvez rigoler — de lui. Que dira-t-il ? Que dira Georges ? Qu'en pensera-t-il ? Il me croyait parti. Il était bien certain que j'étais sorti de l'édifice quand, hier à cinq heures, dans ce vestiaire tout à côté de la salle de toilette ... pendant que je me peignais dans la glace et que lui, à trois pas de moi, caché par la cloison, endossait son veston, reprenait son sac, son journal et que sais-je ... Oh ! ce rire ... et ces mots, lui, Georges, mon ami, le seul ami, l'unique Georges, il osait dire cela, parler ainsi de moi. Oh ! hasard maudit qui fit que, me trompant, je voulais prendre l'ascenseur, je poussai cette porte, la mauvaise porte, ah oui, la mauvaise porte, celle du vestiaire et de la toilette ... J'en profitai pour pisser, me laver les mains puis pour me peigner et je ne savais pas, je ne pouvais pas savoir que Georges viendrait, là, tout à côté ! Il était donc déjà cinq heures !

Pourquoi avoir dit cela, Georges ! Pourquoi ? Oh, qu'il m'a fait mal, jamais je n'ai eu si mal ! Ils riaient tous, les chers camarades de Georges, ils riaient, grossièrement ! Georges, tu ne cessais pas, je tremblais, accroché aux petits éviers, comme je tremble encore en y repensant. Tout se mit à tourner, les carreaux de céramique du parquet, les robinets se multipliaient, la glace fondait devant mon regard mouillé, les ampoules me cuisaient, me brûlaient, tout chavira sur ces mots horribles de sa voix : « pire qu'une teigne, les gars, pire qu'une punaise, pire qu'un pou, c'est une sangsue, ce Dastous ! »

Je me réveillai : silence, le robinet que j'avais ouvert coulait toujours. Par la fenêtre, les reflets clignotants d'une enseigne. J'étais demeuré ainsi, étendu par terre, plus de deux heures ! Les portes étaient fermées à clé par l'extérieur. Je ne voulais pas sortir, pas tout de suite . . .

Je me parle encore.

J'allai m'asseoir à son pupitre. J'essayais d'imiter son rire, son rire net, franc et cascadeur. J'essayai tout haut. Je n'y parvenais pas, impossible. Je pris du papier, son stylo, et je voulus, pour lui, écrire ses propres mots, ses affreuses paroles à faire rire la « galerie ». Je n'y parvins pas non plus ! Et c'est là, à ce moment, que, couché sur son cartable, je me mis à pleurer. Puis, j'entendis le pas traînant pour la première fois. Je retins mon souffle, me mordis la lèvre, réprimai de force des sanglots, m'essuyai les yeux de ma manche — un enfant — et je n'entendis que le « cling » et les pas du gardien qui s'éloignait. Ainsi, je pouvais me relever, aller aux fenêtres ouvertes et regarder le monde en bas, les passants, le monde que je commençais à haïr, à haïr vraiment, là, je pouvais pleurer tout doucement, je pouvais pleurer en paix, comme un fou. J'avais toute la nuit pour pleurer.

Et c'est ce que je fis . . . pendant que Montréal, qui avait si chaud, se promenait sur tous ses trottoirs !

(*Délivrez-nous du mal*, 1961)

Jacques Godbout (Né en 1933)

Poète, romancier et cinéaste, il a enseigné à Addis-Abéba et est maintenant cinéaste à l'Office national du Film. Il a beaucoup voyagé. Le passage qui suit, tiré de *l'Aquarium*, fera sentir l'originalité de cet écrivain qui allie à une tendresse souriante une ironie dévastatrice.

DERNIERS INSTANTS

Dehors la pluie tombe comme d'un robinet rouillé. Et de temps à autre le toit séché par le vent se surprend à chanter. J'ai fumé, compté l'argent, je l'ai distribué dans toutes mes poches et puis sous ma chemise. Andrée a terminé les malles que j'ai bouclées et descendues à la porte arrière de l'immeuble.

En bas, il y a de la mousse jusque sur l'escalier de service. Mais dans la mousse, ici et là, une tige blanche. Et puis la lumière était

telle que je me suis attardé à l'écouter s'avancer vers les murs du
palais. La lumière. Comme un faisceau coloré sous une tente de
cirque.

Bras dessus, bras dessous, nous regardons vers le jardin. Le monticule qui couvrait Israël s'est affaissé. Mais il reste la pierre. Et puis
par centaines, comme des cigarettes mouillées, des vers de terre, mie
de pain des corbeaux.

Il nous reste trente minutes.

. . . qui serons-nous dans trente ans ?

Il nous faudrait une chanson pour ne pas oublier. Pour que nous
puissions dire : tu te souviens ? Pour qu'un jour, nous promenant à
New York nous l'entendions, dans le haut-parleur d'une école de
danse et que nous puissions avoir l'air attendri. Mais nous n'aurons
ni chanson, ni danse. Tout simplement des rafales de pluie, de vent.

Vingt-huit minutes. Et si ma montre s'arrêtait ? Comment pourrais-je mesurer le temps du départ ? Il me faut rester calme, et ne
plus penser qu'à eux maintenant. Ne plus penser qu'à eux.

— Si nous vidions la cafetière ?

— C'est une manie.

— Non, un prétexte.

Pendant que l'eau s'agite, je vais chercher le Mauser. Andrée
s'affaire et je frotte la crosse avec l'huile de lin qui me reste, j'insère
à tout hasard quelques balles dans le chargeur. J'essaie de me persuader que nous allons à la chasse dans les herbes sèches.

Puis à nouveau le silence. Depuis une demi-heure nous ne nous
sommes pas dit vingt mots. Nous nous regardons, inquiets sûrement
de tout ce qui nous arrive sans que nous le voulions vraiment. Et puis
à quoi bon se cabrer ? Il ne m'est jamais arrivé de faire exactement
les gestes que j'aurais voulus, le mouvement s'impose toujours sans
demander la permission. Aujourd'hui de même, c'est tout !

— Chéri, ça te paraît grandiose ce que nous vivons ?

— Non, tout simplement con.

— Tu as déjà fait quelque chose d'extraordinaire ?

— Je n'ai jamais fait que des conneries.

Andrée sourit. Nous nous embrassons. Nous avons gagné cinq
minutes : il en reste vingt-trois.

— Comment te dire ? J'ai très mauvaise mémoire; alors hier, ce
que j'ai pu faire . . . ou ce que je ferai demain . . . je ne sais prévoir.
Je suis le quotidien fait homme. Tantôt soucieux, tantôt heureux. Je
n'ai qu'un but : m'en sortir.

Elle me regarde et pointe le fusil du doigt.

— Et ça, c'est pour t'en sortir ?

— Peut-être.

— Tu vas tirer s'ils refusent de monter ?

— Oh ! entre ça et la chasse aux grands singes . . .

Andrée me regarde, langue entre les lèvres. Et puis, que devrais-je dire ? Que j'ai le coeur battant, que j'ai peur ? Que je crains qu'ils ne veuillent monter. Que je ne me sens pas assez riche pour trouver une solution à tout ?

— Pas la peine de laver les tasses.

Elle se lève et les laisse se briser sur la céramique du plancher.

— Pourquoi as-tu fait cela ?

— Sais pas.

— Pourquoi ?

— Pour bien marquer notre première querelle de ménage.

Puis elle s'en va au salon regarder par la porte-fenêtre que jadis empruntaient mes sorcières.

Vingt minutes. Ce sera bientôt le voyage. Mais il me faut, avant, faire monter mes hôtes. Andrée se retourne :

— Quel droit avons-nous de . . .

Elle a vu que je haussais les épaules. Nous sommes à cran. Epuisés avant même de fuir.

Assis en silence.

Pourquoi cet air de jazz me hante-t-il, suivi d'applaudissements ? Puis encore les cuivres, la tête qui éclate, les cuivres et le tambour au loin.

Ou est-ce Gayéta qui appelle au secours ? Et si le décor se mettait à fondre comme crème glacée au soleil, et si les briques se désagrégeaient sous la pluie ? Et si la couleur disparaissait dans une improvisation infinie ?

Il me faut y aller, il me faut me décider; dix-huit minutes en équilibre instable, sur le bout des pieds. Le temps de respirer. Cependant, Andrée et moi sommes aussi distants que si nous ne nous connaissions pas. Nous ne savons plus nous rejoindre. Elle erre dans l'appartement et remet les objets en place, et je ne trouve pas les mots.

. . . Indifférents à tout ce qui nous entoure, au paysage surtout. C'est cela (j'entends la contrebasse qui insiste et encore les applaudissements); il est temps que nous changions de décor. Celui-ci ne nous sied plus. Comme un soulier trop petit, trop usé. Nous ne pouvons plus demander à ces murs, à cette table placée à angle droit, nous ne pouvons plus demander aux objets familiers le droit de vivre. Ou même le plaisir. Et pourtant tout cela nous appartient, tout est propre, net. Peut-être était-il trop tard pour remettre les choses à leur place.

Qu'adviendra-t-il de Vladimir, Stan, Monsignore, Jerry, Paul, Lauzon (Lauzon surtout qui m'a toujours attendri) et des Australiens ?

Nous avons vécu ensemble, nous avons bu ensemble et puis fumé les mêmes cigarettes. Je les mène à la mort ? Je leur offre le suicide exemplaire que l'on consignera dans le livre d'or de la Casa Occidentale ? Cela est ridicule : s'ils n'opposent aucune résistance ils en seront quittes pour la peur.

Et s'ils résistaient ? Je ne sais plus . . .

. . . Je me souviendrai, c'est cela, je me souviendrai. Et ce sera le remboursement de ma dette. Trois mois contre des souvenirs, trois ans contre deux jours de peine. Madame, je vous donne mon coeur contre votre beauté. Echangeons la neige contre les vents, et les vents contre la pluie et la pluie contre le mur; essoufflée, la pluie; je sais : il faut troquer ceci contre cela pour être heureux. Et n'avoir point de remords.

La porte du grand salon, brune avec des marques de doigt. Je me souviendrai. Et j'ai le Mauser au bout des bras, pour les mieux persuader.

Je me souviendrai qu'Andrée m'attendait au bas de l'escalier, près de la cave où j'avais déposé les malles, cachée par un pilier de ciment. Je me souviendrai des yeux de mes victimes, mi saoules, mi hébétées — qui regardent par-dessus mon épaule parce qu'elles craignent l'armée. Quatorze minutes, mes petits. A l'heure où les corbeaux croassent . . . où en sommes-nous ? Je lève le Mauser.

— Monsignore, rassemblez la milice !

Trop ivres ou effrayés, ils ne m'ont pas posé de questions. Pendant qu'ils se pressent, je ne bouge pas de l'entrée : Monsignore est parti raccoler ceux qui étaient allés se coucher. Je leur accorde cinq minutes avant le rassemblement. Ceux qui sont au salon me regardent, peut-être étonnés de l'air décidé que j'aimerais qu'ils lisent sur mon visage.

. . . Il fait chaud, très chaud tout à coup. Et puis il y a Stan le Danseur qui m'a regardé. Vladimir aussi. Stan. Où donc ai-je vu une tête de cette allure ? La princesse ! la salle du Rotterdam-Café . . . il y avait Mary l'acrobate jaune au fil de fer immense. Il y avait Joey, le professeur d'histoires-à-la-sauvette. Deux ou trois autres que je ne connaissais pas. A ma droite la princesse Weunssaskij, à ma gauche Paulo dit le duc de Kent depuis le vol des bijoux un hiver.

. . . Il y avait surtout cette salle vaste comme le bureau de poste de Tripoli, avec des ventouses à la place des électroliers, une salle jaune avec d'affreux dessins roses issus de cerveaux paranoïaques en bordée.

. . . Les Syriens souriaient de tout l'or de leurs dents du dimanche, Paulo alias le duc pelotait l'acrobate-sans-filet-protecteur. Un Lithuanien se promenait de long en large, massacrant sur son violon des airs allemands, parfois des valses, parfois de fausses complaintes. Puis la Princesse cria. Le Lithuanien bon enfant se mit à jouer *Cosaque und fraulein* ou quelque chose d'approchant. Quelle joie !

... Pour l'accompagner, il fallait monter sur les tables avec nos souliers pointus et des verres tout autour et puis claquer du pied, des doigts et de la bouche à chaque demi-mesure. L'excitation était à son comble et je crois bien nulle part au monde n'aurait pu se trouver gaieté à ce paroxysme.

... Et puis un Syrien a voulu pincer les jambes de la princesse et de colère je lui ai botté la gueule. Et puis le Syrien sur le dos grimaça, comme une grenouille, en hurlant. Alors nous on a bien ri et on se tapait dans le dos et on s'est juré qu'on s'aimait bien et que l'on ne se quitterait jamais. Le duc de Kent a juré de même à l'acrobate de jamais non plus la quitter.

... Ces promesses ne nous coûtaient pas cher car le duc et moi avions déjà en poche nos billets d'avion. Nous nous souviendrons, nous disions-nous.

... Stan est toujours là à me regarder.

Je m'accroche à des souvenirs comme s'ils étaient raison de vivre. Et puis peut-être le sont-ils, au fond, tout au fond. Ce qui reste après le geste.

Mais si j'étais seul à me souvenir ?

(*L'Aquarium,* 1962)

Hubert Aquin (Né en 1932)

Cet écrivain est un des penseurs du mouvement indépendantiste au Québec, et il a tiré de son expérience un roman, le seul à date, où la conscience du héros est hantée par les souvenirs et les rêves d'un révolutionnaire qui ressemble étrangement à l'auteur.

UNE RENCONTRE DANS LA NUIT

Entre le 26 juillet cubain et la nuit lyrique du 4 août, entre la place de la Riponne et la pizzeria de la place de l'Hôtel-de-Ville, à Lausanne, j'ai rencontré une femme blonde dont j'ai reconnu instantanément la démarche majestueuse. Le bonheur que j'ai éprouvé à cet instant retentit encore en moi tandis qu'attablé dans cette pizzeria lausannoise, rendez-vous des maçons du Tessin, je me laisse aller à la tristesse qui m'engourdit progressivement depuis que je suis ressorti de mon hôtel où je n'ai fait que passer quelques minutes stériles après être allé au cinéma Benjamin Constant. C'est dans cette pizzeria que j'ai échoué.

Et quand le juke box émit pour la troisième fois les premiers accords de Desafinado, je n'en pouvais plus de nostalgie. Je me suis dégagé du comptoir au rythme des guitares afro-brésiliennes et j'ai réglé mon addition à la caisse. Et me voici à nouveau dans cette nuit antérieure, étranglé une fois de plus dans l'étau de la rue des Escaliers-du-Marché que je remonte comme si cette dénivellation avait la vertu de compenser ma chute intérieure. C'est à quelques pas de la place de la Riponne et me dirigeant vers elle, que j'ai aperçu la chevelure léonine de K. En pressant le pas, je me suis vite trouvé à côté d'elle, tout près de son visage détourné. Comme je craignais de la faire fuir par la soudaineté de mon approche, je me suis empressé de conjurer un malentendu et j'ai prononcé son prénom, avec une inflexion qu'elle se devait de reconnaître. C'est alors que l'événement merveilleux, notre rencontre, s'est produit, alors même que nous approchions tous deux de la grande esplanade de la Place de la Riponne. Nous avons tourné sur notre gauche, après avoir découvert la colonnade sombre de l'université et le bonheur aveuglant de nous retrouver. Je ne me souviens plus de l'itinéraire que nous avons suivi après, ni quelles rues sombres nous avons parcourues lentement, K et moi, avant de nous arrêter un moment sur le grand pont, juste au-dessus de la Gazette de Lausanne et face à la masse sombre du Gouvernement cantonal qui nous cachait le lac Léman et le spectre des Alpes. Douze mois de séparation, de malentendus et de censure s'achevaient magiquement par ce hasard : quelques mots réappris, le frôlement de nos deux corps et leur nouvelle attente. Douze mois d'amour perdu et de langueurs se sont abolis dans le délire fondamental de cette rencontre inespérée et de notre amour fou, emporté à nouveau vers la haute vallée du Nil, dans une dérive voluptueuse entre Montréal et Toronto, le chemin de la Reine Marie et le cimetière des Juifs portugais, de nos chambres lyriques de Polytechnique à nos rencontres fugaces à Pointe-Claire, quelque part entre un 26 juillet violent et un 4 août funèbre, anniversaire double d'une double révolution : celle qui a commencé dangereusement et l'autre secrète, qui est née dans nos baisers et par nos sacrilèges.

Notre vie a déjà tenu dans quelques serments voluptueux et tristes échangés dans une auto stationnée à l'île Sainte-Hélène, près des casernes, par un soir de pluie. Avant de te rencontrer, je n'en finissais plus d'écrire un long poème. Puis un jour, j'ai frémi de te savoir nue sous tes vêtements; tu parlais, mais je me souviens de ta bouche seulement. Toi tu parlais en attendant et moi j'attendais. Nous étions debout, tes cheveux s'emmêlaient dans l'eau-forte de Venise par Clarence Gagnon. C'est ainsi que j'ai vu Venise, au-dessus de ton épaule, noyée dans tes yeux bruns, et en te serrant contre moi. Je n'ai pas besoin d'aller à Venise pour savoir que cette ville ressemble à ta tête renversée sur le mur du salon, pendant que je t'embrassais. Ta langueur me conduit à notre étreinte interdite, tes grands yeux sombres à tes mains humides qui cherchent ma vérité. Qui es-tu, sinon la femme finie qui se déhanche selon les strophes du désir et mes caresses voilées ? Dans notre plaisir apostasié, germaient tous nos projets révolutionnaires. Et voilà que par une nuit de plein été, quelque part entre le vieux Lausanne et son port médiéval, sur la ligne médiane qui sépare deux jours et deux corps, nous retrouvons notre ancienne raison de vivre et d'avoir mille fois souhaité mourir plutôt que d'affronter la séparation cruelle dont la terminaison subite nous a inondés de joie.

Nous avons marché longtemps cette nuit-là, jusqu'à ce que la vallée tout entière du Rhône s'emplisse de soleil et que, petit à petit, l'ancien port d'Ouchy résonne du bruit des moteurs et du travail, et que les garçons disposent les chaises sur la terrasse de l'hôtel d'Angleterre où Byron, en une seule nuit dans le bel été de 1816, a écrit le Prisonnier de Chillon. Nous nous sommes attablés à la terrasse de l'hôtel d'Angleterre pour prendre un petit déjeuner et garder le silence à la hauteur du miroir liquide qu'une haleine brumeuse voilait encore. Après douze mois de séparation et douze mesures d'impossibilité de vivre un mois de plus, après une nuit de marche depuis la Place de la Riponne jusqu'au niveau du lac antique et à la première heure de l'aube, nous sommes montés dans une chambre de l'hôtel d'Angleterre, peut-être celle où Byron a chanté Bonnivard qui s'était jadis abîmé dans une cellule du château de Chillon. K et moi, inondés de la même tristesse inondante, nous nous sommes étendus sous les draps frais, nus, anéantis voluptueusement l'un par l'autre, dans la splendeur ponctuelle de notre poème et de l'aube. Notre étreinte aveuglante et le choc incantatoire de nos deux corps, me terrassent encore ce soir, tandis qu'au terme de cette aube incendiée je me retrouve couché seul sur une page blanche où je ne respire plus le souffle chaud de ma blonde inconnue, où je ne sens plus son poids qui m'attire selon un système copernicien et où je ne vois plus sa peau ambrée, ni ses lèvres inlassables, ni ses yeux sylvestres, ni le chant pur de son plaisir. Désormais seul dans mon lit paginé, j'ai mal et je me souviens de ce temps perdu retrouvé, passé nu dans la plénitude occulte de la volupté.

Les rythmes déhanchés de Desafinado qui éclatent par surprise dans le Multivox me hissent au niveau du lac amer où j'ai retrouvé l'aube de ton corps, dans une seule étreinte bouleversante, et me ramènent à ton rivage membrané où j'aurais mieux fait de mourir alors, car je meurs maintenant. Ce matin-là c'était le beau temps, celui de la jointure exaltée de deux jours et de nos deux corps. Oui, c'était l'aube absolue, entre un 26 juillet qui s'évaporait au-dessus du lac et la nuit immanente de la révolution. Les mots qui s'encombrent en moi n'arrêtent pas le ruisseau clair du temps fui de fuir en cascades jusqu'au lac. Le temps passé repasse encore plus vite qu'il n'avait passé ce matin-là, dans notre chambre de l'hôtel d'Angleterre avec vue sur le glacier disparu du Galenstock qui descendait un jour sur la terrasse de l'hôtel à l'endroit même où K et moi nous nous étions assis à l'aube. Glacier fui, amour fui, aube fugace et interglaciaire, baiser enfui très loin sur l'autre rive et loin aussi de la vitre embuée de mon bathyscaphe qui plonge à pic sous la fenêtre de la chambre où Byron a pleuré dans les stances à Bonnivard et moi dans la chevelure dorée de la femme que j'aime.

Ce soir, si je dérive dans le lit du grand fleuve soluble, si l'hôtel d'Angleterre se désagrège dans le tombeau liquide de ma mémoire, si je n'espère plus d'aube au terme de la nuit occlusive et si tout s'effondre aux accords de Desafinado, c'est que j'aperçois, au fond du lac, la vérité inévitable, partenaire terrifiant que mes fugues et mes parades ne déconcertent plus. Au fond de cette liquidité inflationnelle, l'ennemi innommé qui me hante me trouve nu et désarmé comme je l'ai été dans l'étreinte vénérienne qui nous a confirmés à jamais, K et moi, propriétaires insaisissables de l'hôtel d'Angleterre, qui se trouve à mi-chemin entre le Château de Chillon et la villa Diodati, Manfred et la future libération de la Grèce. Que vienne l'ennemi global que j'attends en dépérissant ! Que l'affrontement se produise et qu'advienne enfin l'accomplissement de la vérité qui me menace. Ou alors qu'on me libère au plus vite et sans autre forme, moi, prisonnier sans poète qui me chante. Et je me noierai une fois de plus, au fond d'un lit chaud et défait, dans le corps brûlant de celle qui m'a gorgé d'amour entre la nuit d'un hasard et la nuit seconde, entre le fond noir du lac de Genève et sa surface héliaque. Les mots de trop affluent devant ma vitre, engluent ce périmètre de mémoire dans l'obscuration, et je chavire dans mon récit. L'hôtel d'Angleterre, était-ce un 24 juin ou un 26 juillet; et cette masse chancelante qui obstrue mon champ de vision, est-ce la Prison de Montréal ou le Château de Chillon, cachot romantique où le patriote Bonnivard attend toujours la guerre révolutionnaire que j'ai fomentée sans poésie ? Entre cette prison lacustre et la villa Diodati, près de Genève, dans une chambre divine d'un hôtel de passage où Byron s'est arrêté, j'ai réinventé l'amour. J'ai découvert un soleil éclipsé par douze mois de séparation et qui, ce matin-là, s'est levé entre nos deux corps assemblés, réchauffant le milieu suprême de notre lit pour jaillir enfin, éclatant et intolérable, dans le lac antique qui dévalait glorieusement de nos deux ventres. Ah, qu'on me rende la chambre soleil et notre amour, car tout me manque et j'ai peur. Que se passe-t-il donc en moi qui fasse trembler le granit alpestre ? Le papier se dérobe sous mon poids comme le lac fluviatile. La dépression me déminéralise insidieusement. Mer de glace je deviens lave engloutissante, miroir à suicide. Trente deniers, et je me suicide ! En fait, je réduirais encore le prix pour me couper avec un morceau de vitre : et j'en aurais fini avec la dépression révolutionnaire ! Oui, finies la maladie honteuse du conspirateur, la fracture mentale, la chute perpétrée dans les cellules de la Sûreté. Finis le projet toujours recommencé d'un attentat et le plaisir indécent de marcher dans la foule des électeurs en serrant la crosse fraîche de l'arme automatique qu'on porte en écharpe ! Et que je vole enfin ! Que je me promène encore incognito et impuni au hasard des rues qui s'échappent de la place de la Riponne et ruissellent en serpentant jusqu'aux rives de Pully et d'Ouchy pour se mêler au grand courant de l'histoire et disparaître, anonymes et universelles, dans le fleuve puissant de la révolution !

Seul m'importe ce laps de temps entre la nuit de la haute ville et l'aube révolutionnaire qui a foudroyé nos corps dans une chambre où Byron, pour une nuit écrite, s'est arrêté entre Clarens et la villa Diodati, en route déjà pour une guerre révolutionnaire qui s'est terminée dans l'épilepsie finale de Missolonghi. Seul m'importe ce chemin de lumière et d'euphorie. Et notre étreinte du lever du jour, lutte serrée, longue mais combien précise qui nous a tués tous les deux, d'une même syncope, en nous inondant d'un pur sang de violence !

Je ne veux plus vivre ici, les deux pieds sur la terre maudite, ni m'accommoder de notre cachot national comme si de rien n'était. Je rêve de mettre un point final à ma noyade qui date déjà de plusieurs générations. Au fond de mon fleuve pollué, je me nourris encore de corps étrangers, j'avale indifféremment les molécules de nos dépressions séculaires, et cela m'écoeure. Je m'emplis de père en fils d'anti-corps; je me saoûle, fidèle à notre amère devise, d'une boisson nitrique qui fait de moi un drogué.

(*Prochain épisode,* 1965)

Marie-Claire Blais (Née en 1939)

Cette enfant précoce étonna par l'évocation des rêves étranges d'une adolescente trop sensible (*La Belle Bête,* 1959) et elle a depuis approfondi son art et élargi son expérience comme le prouve *Une saison dans la vie d'Emmanuel* dont voici le début. Elle vit maintenant sur la péninsule de Cape Cod.

GRAND-MÈRE ANTOINETTE

Les pieds de Grand-Mère Antoinette dominaient la chambre. Ils étaient là, tranquilles et sournois comme deux bêtes couchées, frémissant à peine dans leurs bottines noires, toujours prêts à se lever : c'étaient des pieds meurtris par de longues années de travail aux champs (lui qui ouvrait les yeux pour la première fois dans la poussière du matin ne les voyait pas encore, il ne connaissait pas encore la blessure secrète à la jambe, sous le bas de laine, la cheville gonflée sous la prison de lacets et de cuir...) des pieds nobles et pieux, (n'allaient-ils pas à l'église chaque matin en hiver?) des pieds vivants qui gravaient pour toujours dans la mémoire de ceux qui les voyaient une seule fois — l'image sombre de l'autorité et de la patience.

Né sans bruit par un matin d'hiver, Emmanuel écoutait la voix de sa grand-mère. Immense, souveraine, elle semblait diriger le monde de son fauteuil. (Ne crie pas, de quoi te plains-tu donc? Ta mère est retournée à la ferme. Tais-toi jusqu'à ce qu'elle revienne. Ah! déjà tu es égoïste et méchant, déjà tu me mets en colère!) Il appela sa mère. (C'est un bien mauvais temps pour naître, nous n'avons jamais été aussi pauvres, une saison dure pour tout le monde, la guerre, la faim, et puis tu es le seizième...) Elle se plaignait à voix basse, elle égrenait un chapelet gris accroché à sa taille. Moi aussi j'ai mes rhumatismes, mais personne n'en parle. Moi aussi, je souffre. Et puis, je déteste les nouveaux-nés; des insectes dans la poussière! Tu feras comme les autres, tu seras ignorant, cruel et amer... (Tu n'as pas pensé à tous ces ennuis que tu m'apportes, il faut que je pense à tout, ton nom, le baptême...)

Il faisait froid dans la maison. Des visages l'entouraient, des silhouettes apparaissaient. Il les regardait mais ne les reconnaissait pas encore. Grand-Mère Antoinette était si immense qu'il ne la voyait pas en entier. Il avait peur. Il diminuait, il se refermait comme un coquillage. (Assez, dit la vieille femme, regarde autour de toi, ouvre les yeux, je suis là, c'est moi qui commande ici! Regarde-moi bien, je suis la seule personne digne de la maison. C'est moi qui habite la chambre parfumée, j'ai rangé les savons sous le lit . . .) Nous aurons beaucoup de temps, dit Grand-Mère, rien ne presse pour aujourd'hui . . .

(Sa grand-mère avait une vaste poitrine, il ne voyait pas ses jambes sous les jupes lourdes mais il les imaginait, bâtons secs, genoux cruels, de quels vêtements étranges avait-elle enveloppé son corps frissonnant de froid ?)

Il voulait suspendre ses poings fragiles à ses genoux, se blottir dans l'antre de sa taille, car il découvrait qu'elle était si maigre sous ces montagnes de linge, ces jupons rugueux, que pour la première fois il ne la craignait pas. Ces vêtements de laine le séparaient encore de ce sein glacé qu'elle écrasait de la main d'un geste d'inquiétude ou de défense, car lorsqu'on approchait son corps étouffé sous la robe sévère, on croyait approcher en elle quelque fraîcheur endormie, ce désir ancien et fier que nul n'avait assouvi — on voulait dormir en elle, comme dans un fleuve chaud, reposer sur son coeur. Mais elle écartait Emmanuel de ce geste de la main qui jadis, avait refusé l'amour, puni le désir de l'homme.

— Mon Dieu, un autre garçon, qu'est-ce que nous allons devenir ? Mais elle se rassurait aussitôt : « Je suis forte, mon enfant. Tu peux m'abandonner ta vie. Aie confiance en moi ».

Il l'écoutait. Sa voix le berçait d'un chant monotone, accablé. Elle l'enveloppait de son châle, elle ne le caressait pas, elle le plongeait plutôt, dans ce bain de linges et d'odeurs. Il retenait sa respiration. Parfois, sans le vouloir, elle le griffait légèrement de ses doigts repliés, elle le secouait dans le vide, et à nouveau il appelait sa mère. (Mauvais caractère, disait-elle avec impatience.) Il rêvait du sein de sa mère qui apaiserait sa soif et sa révolte.

— Ta mère travaille comme d'habitude, disait Grand-Mère Antoinette. C'est une journée comme les autres. Tu ne penses qu'à toi. Moi aussi j'ai du travail. Les nouveaux-nés sont sales. Ils me dégoûtent. Mais tu vois, je suis bonne pour toi, je te lave, je te soigne, et tu seras le premier à te réjouir de ma mort . . . .

Mais Grand-Mère Antoinette se croyait immortelle. Toute sa personne triomphante était immortelle aussi pour Emmanuel qui la regardait avec étonnement. « Oh ! Mon enfant, personne ne t'écoute, tu pleures vainement, tu apprendras vite que tu es seul au monde ! »

— Toi aussi, tu auras peur . . .

Les rayons de soleil entraient par la fenêtre. Au loin, le paysage était confus, inabordable. Emmanuel entendait des voix, des pas, autour de lui. (Il tremblait de froid tandis que sa grand-mère le lavait, le noyait plutôt à plusieurs reprises dans l'eau glacée . . .) Voilà, disait-elle, c'est fini. Il n'y a rien à craindre. Je suis là, on s'habitue à tout, tu verras.

Elle souriait. Il désirait respecter son silence; il n'osait plus se plaindre car il lui semblait soudain avoir une longue habitude du froid, de la faim, et peut-être même du désespoir. Dans les draps froids, dans la chambre froide, il a été rempli d'une étrange patience, soudain. Il a su que cette misère n'aurait pas de fin, mais il a consenti à vivre. Debout à la fenêtre, Grand-Mère s'est écriée presque joyeusement :

— Les voilà. Je sens qu'ils montent l'escalier, écoute leurs voix. Les voilà tous, les petits-enfants, les enfants, les cousins, les nièces, et les neveux, on les croit ensevelis sous la neige en allant à l'école, ou bien morts depuis des années, mais ils sont toujours là, sous les tables, sous les lits, ils me guettent de leurs yeux brillants dans l'ombre. Ils attendent que je leur distribue des morceaux de sucre. Il y en a toujours un ou deux autour de mon fauteuil, de ma chaise, lorsque je me berce le soir . . .

Ils ricanent, ils jouent avec les lacets de mes souliers. Ils me poursuivent toujours de ce ricanement stupide, de ce regard suppliant et hypocrite, je les chasse comme des mouches, mais ils reviennent, ils collent à moi comme une nuée de vermines, ils me dévorent . . .

Mais Grand-Mère Antoinette domptait admirablement toute cette marée d'enfants qui grondaient à ses pieds. (D'où venaient-ils ? Surgissaient-ils de l'ombre, de la nuit ? Ils avaient son odeur, le son de sa voix, ils rampaient autour du lit, ils avaient l'odeur familière de la pauvreté . . .)

Ah ! Assez, dit Grand-Mère Antoinette, je ne veux plus vous entendre, sortez tous, retournez sous les lits . . . Disparaissez, je ne veux plus vous voir, ah ! quelle odeur, Mon Dieu !

Mais elle leur distribuait avec quelques coups de canne les morceaux de sucre qu'ils attendaient la bouche ouverte, haletants d'impatience et de faim, les miettes de chocolat, tous ces trésors poisseux qu'elle avait accumulés et qui jaillissaient de ses jupes, de son corsage hautain. « Eloignez-vous, éloignez-vous », disait-elle.

Elle les chassait d'une main souveraine (plus tard, il la verrait marchant ainsi au milieu des poules, des lapins et des vaches, semant des malédictions sur son passage ou recueillant quelque bébé plaintif tombé dans la boue) elle répudiait vers l'escalier — leur jetant toujours ces morceaux de sucre qu'ils attrapaient au hasard, tout ce déluge d'enfants, d'animaux, qui, plus tard, à nouveau, sortiraient de leur mystérieuse retraite et viendraient encore gratter à la porte pour mendier à leur grand-mère . . .

(*Une saison dans la vie d'Emmanuel,* 1965)

Robert Elie (Né en 1915)

Journaliste, critique d'art, directeur de l'Ecole des Beaux-Arts de Montréal, attaché culturel à la Maison du Québec à Paris, il est maintenant directeur associé du bureau du bilinguisme au Conseil privé à Ottawa. Membre de la Société royale du Canada, il a publié des romans et des pièces de théâtre, dont *L'Etrangère* dont on reproduit ici la quatrième scène.

L'ÉTRANGÈRE

SCÈNE QUATRIÈME

Lou - Nik

Lou se dirige vers la fenêtre où elle regarde attentivement. Puis, elle revient au centre de la scène, où elle reste debout, face à la salle. Elle porte ses mains à son visage. On entend la porte d'entrée s'ouvrir lentement, puis Nik apparaît. Il l'aperçoit avec surprise. Long silence.

LOU, *sans se retourner.* — Entre, Nik.

NIK — Tu savais que je viendrais ?

LOU — Tu rôdes autour de cette maison depuis trois jours, attendant le moment où je serais seule.

NIK — Tu m'attendais ?

LOU — Je t'attendais, mais il est maintenant trop tard.

NIK — Que veux-tu dire ?

LOU — Il y a une heure à peine j'hésitais encore, mais je sais maintenant que plus personne n'entrera dans ma vie.

NIK — Tu as donc oublié ?

LOU — Je n'oublie rien, Nik, mais tu es mort en moi avec les autres, parti pour un monde meilleur, sans doute.

NIK, *s'approchant de Lou et la saisissant par les épaules pour l'obliger à le regarder, mais elle ferme les paupières.* — Mais regarde-moi donc ! Ne suis-je pas venu d'assez loin pour que tu me regardes ?

LOU, *elle ouvre les yeux et crie.* — Ah ! (*Elle se dégage.*)

NIK — Je te fais peur !

LOU — Comme tu es las et vieux ! . . . C'était vraiment trop lourd ce mal que tu m'as fait, et pourtant tu étais beau quand tu portais ce défi au monde, à la vie . . . Mais, maintenant, ce n'est plus un défi, on dirait que tu as consenti au mal, que tu as pardonné au monde.

NIK — Je n'ai jamais eu de remords.

LOU — Oui, là-bas, tu es venu à moi comme une brute. Tu n'étais plus qu'une bête, et je t'aurais abattu comme un chien si je n'avais su que tu n'étais pas responsable.

NIK — J'ai traversé le monde comme une bête.

LOU — Le silence, la fatigue t'ont dégrisé. La bête s'est endormie et tu penses maintenant pouvoir l'éveiller.

NIK — Tu lis mal sur mon visage. La bête vient de mourir; elle est morte cette nuit.

LOU — Elle doit être toute chaude encore.

NIK, *la prenant par les épaules.* — Ne te moque pas ou je te tuerai !

LOU — Tu as souvent tué pour venir jusqu'à moi ?

NIK — Tais-toi.

LOU — Raconte-moi donc ce grand voyage.

NIK — Tu les connais bien ces voyages des sans-patrie.

LOU — Je m'en souviens à peine.

NIK, *radouci.* — Du fond de l'Europe jusqu'ici sans vrai passeport, sans vrai métier, c'est toute une aventure ! Et je pensais retrouver un femme que j'avais aimée !

LOU — Une femme que tu avais haïe comme ta chair.

NIK — Oh ! je t'ai prise sans en attendre la permission, mais tu ne m'as jamais repoussé.

LOU — J'aimais encore mieux la bête que tu étais que ces hommes sans âmes, ces mendiants qui avaient peur de toi.

NIK — J'étais venu pour obtenir ton consentement.

LOU — Il est trop tard.

NIK — Il est trop tard.

LOU, *le regardant, étonnée.* — C'est donc vrai que la bête est morte ?

NIK — Cette nuit, j'ai tué une vieille femme, une horrible créature, mais c'est le visage d'une enfant que j'ai vu avant de fuir.

LOU — Tu n'as donc rien refusé à la bête !

NIK — Rien, Lou, je ne lui ai rien refusé. J'avais faim, j'avais froid; je n'ai plus de passeport, je n'ai plus de terre, étranger au monde, inclassable.

LOU — Pourquoi n'es-tu pas venu plus tôt ?

NIK — Il n'y avait plus que la mort dans mon destin, je savais que la bête ne désirait rien d'autre, et je n'ai pas voulu te tuer.

LOU — C'était moi, et non pas cette vieille femme, qui devais mourir. Que feras-tu ?

NIK — J'irai droit devant moi sur la première route que je rencontrerai, jusqu'à ce qu'ils me trouvent.

LOU — Personne ne t'a accueilli ?

NIK — Je n'ai demandé à personne de m'accueillir. Je ne suis pas de cette race.

LOU — C'est vrai, Nik. Tu es de la race de ceux qui prennent, qui exigent tout . . . Et tu n'as rien trouvé ici ?

NIK — Je hais cette terre.

LOU — On y rencontre, comme partout ailleurs, des hommes et des femmes ordinaires, de bonnes bêtes apprivoisées.

NIK — J'avais dix-sept ans quand l'ennemi m'a amené comme une bête de somme, dans cette ville où je t'ai prise. J'ai vécu dans un monde sauvage où l'on abattait les bêtes apprivoisées.

LOU — C'est la paix ici.

NIK — La paix ! Ah ! oui, comme on y dort bien, comme on y est sage et propre. La propreté, surtout, c'est extraordinaire ! Comme on doit faire l'amour gentiment dans ce pays ! Avec quel sourire ne doit-on pas s'y haïr !

LOU — Console-toi : les bonnes bêtes savent parfois se souvenir de la forêt.

NIK — Eh ! oui, on ferait un très bon administrateur de chambre à gaz avec ce gendarme qui sourit à chacune des voitures qui l'éclaboussent. Et ces collégiens, qui chantent dans la rue, feraient des tortionnaires pleins d'imagination.

LOU — Pourquoi te révolter ? C'est la paix des hommes : elle est veule et lâche. Mais la guerre des hommes ne vaut pas mieux.

NIK — Au moins, personne ne cherche plus à se justifier.

LOU — Mais les hommes font de si sales bêtes. Tu étais vraiment une exception.

NIK — Que c'est gentil ! Et le compliment vient trop tard : je ne suis même plus une bête sauvage.

LOU — Je n'ai rien à te dire, Nik. Je suis brisée comme toi.

NIK — Tu n'attends rien ?

LOU — Je n'ai rien à offrir.

NIK — Mais cette maison est gentille. Quelle paix savoureuse !

LOU — Pauvres mensonges !

NIK — Vraiment, Lou, tu as mauvais goût. Je n'aurais jamais pu te prendre ici.

LOU — Tu préférais les maisons en ruine.

NIK — Tu te souviens ? Une mine pouvait éclater sous nous, à chaque pas.

LOU — Un soldat ivre pouvait s'amuser à nous abattre comme des chats de gouttière.

NIK — Oh ! ce cri rauque des ruines dans la nuit, cette odeur d'incendie !

LOU — L'amour aime la mort. Les chats se déchirent.

NIK — Mais, dans cette paix, les désirs meurent en naissant. Et le nouvel amant, il est gentil ?

LOU — Il est gentil.

NIK — Et tu lui dis : je t'aime ?

LOU — Je lui ai dit : je t'aime.

NIK — Il vient aussi de mourir, comme moi ?

LOU — Je le crois.

NIK — Et c'est tout ce que nous avons à nous dire ?

LOU — C'est tout ce que nous avons à nous dire.

NIK — Pourtant, je t'ai aimée.

LOU — Pourtant, je ne t'ai jamais repoussé.

NIK — Ah ! Lou, cessons. On doit pouvoir échapper à cette paix. La vieille était riche et nous ferons danser les bêtes apprivoisées. Allons au moins dans un cabaret leur crier notre dégoût.

LOU — Tu aurais la force de crier ?

NIK — Et d'éteindre d'une balle le rire gras du premier fêtard, et de mettre un peu d'angoisse dans les yeux mouillés d'une belle jeune fille.

LOU — Va-t-en, Nik, nous n'avons plus rien à nous dire.

NIK, *Nik la saisit brutalement et il vient pour la renverser sur le divan, mais elle glisse de ses bras, épuisée. Il la regarde. Elle ouvre les yeux.*

LOU — Va-t'en, Nik. (*Il sort lentement.*)

Rideau

(*Ecrits du Canada français, I*, 1954)

Marcel Dubé (Né en 1930)

Auteur de plus de dix pièces déjà, ce jeune dramaturge a surtout mis en scène des jeunes au moment où ils découvrent que la vie est laide et que cette expérience trouble profondément. Ces tranches de vie réalistes révèlent un sens inné du théâtre, et les dialogues sont vivants et vrais. On trouvera un bon exemple de ce style populaire dans la dernière scène de *Zone* (1953) reproduite ici.

LA MORT DE TARZAN

CIBOULETTE — C'est la première fois et la dernière peut-être qu'on est seuls ensemble, faut pas perdre de temps : prends-moi dans tes deux mains.

TARZAN — Mes mains sont pas belles, mes mains ont tué un homme.

CIBOULETTE — C'est des mains de chef, c'est des mains sans péchés.

TARZAN — Laisse-moi finir mon dessin, je veux t'avoir en image avant de te toucher. Quand je mourrai, c'est ton portrait que je veux voir.

CIBOULETTE — Touche-moi et t'auras plus jamais besoin d'image.

TARZAN — Je ferme les yeux, je regarde dans ma caboche pour être certain qu'y a rien qui manque, que toutes les couleurs y sont, que tous les traits sont gravés : rien manque à ton visage Ciboulette. J'ouvre les yeux et l'image change pas; y a qu'une Ciboulette qui est à deux endroits en même temps : devant moi et dans ma tête. Devant moi pour une minute et dans ma tête pour toujours. (*Il va vers elle et prend sa tête entre ses mains.*)

CIBOULETTE — Embrasse-moi, doucement, comme un enfant qui joue. (*Il l'embrasse en l'effleurant.*)

CIBOULETTE — Embrasse-moi fort comme un vrai amoureux. (*Il l'embrasse sur les lèvres mais elle se dégage.*) Est-ce que j'ai la manière, Tarzan ? Est-ce que j'ai l'air d'une amoureuse ?

TARZAN — Oui, Ciboulette.

CIBOULETTE — Est-ce que je suis raisonnable aussi ?

TARZAN — Plus que toutes les autres filles.

CIBOULETTE — Qu'est-ce que ça veut dire « raisonnable » ?

TARZAN — Ça veut dire « qui comprend ».

CIBOULETTE — Embrasse-moi encore Tarzan. (*Il la serre très affectueusement dans ses bras et l'embrasse. Mais ils se séparent quand ils entendent des bruits et des voix.*)

TIT-NOIR — On l'a eu, on l'a eu, Tarzan.

Entrent Moineau et Tit-Noir tenant Passe-Partout par les bras.

MOINEAU — Y était caché dans la cour de Johny. Il comptait l'argent.

PASSE-PARTOUT — Lâche-moi, vous me faites mal. Lâchez-moi.

MOINEAU — Oui, on va te lâcher, attends. (*Moineau jette un coup d'oeil à Ti-Noir qui comprend tout de suite. Ensemble ils poussent Passe-Partout qui tombe à plat ventre aux pieds de Tarzan.*)

MOINEAU — Le v'là, chef.

TIT-NOIR — Livraison rapide et courtoise.

CIBOULETTE — C'est Judas !

Il y a un long silence. Tarzan ne se décide pas à parler et Passe-Partout n'ose se relever.

MOINEAU — Qu'est-ce qu'on lui fait, chef ?

TARZAN, *étrange*. — Appelle-moi pas chef, appelle-moi Tarzan.

TIT-NOIR — Veux-tu qu'on le brasse un peu, Tarzan ?

TARZAN — Non. On n'a pas le temps et on se salirait les mains. (*Doucement, à Passe-Partout*) Lève-toi, Passe-Partout. (*Passe-Partout se relève lentement, très apeuré.*) Donne l'argent, Passe-Partout.

PASSE-PARTOUT — Quel argent, Tarzan ? J'ai pas d'argent.

TARZAN — Tu sais ce que je veux dire. Donne. Fais vite, on est pressé. (*Tarzan jette un regard à Ciboulette comme si elle seule pouvait comprendre. Passe-Partout sort lentement l'argent de sa poche et le tend à Tarzan. Tarzan le prend.*) Maintenant, tu peux t'en aller, Passe-Partout.

Mouvement de surprise générale.

TIT-NOIR — Quoi ?

TARZAN — Va-t'en tout de suite, Passe-Partout, parce que si t'es pas parti dans dix secondes, je t'assomme.

Passe-Partout regarde tout le monde et sort en reculant. Tit-Noir lui donne un croc-en-jambe et le fait trébucher.

PASSE-PARTOUT — Non, pas ça, je veux pas, je veux pas.

TARZAN — Tit-Noir ! Laisse-le sortir . . . c'est moi qui mène ici.

PASSE-PARTOUT, *qui s'est relevé*. — Merci, Tarzan, merci . . . je t'ai pas trahi, je t'ai pas trahi . . . c'est pas moi qui l'a dit.

TARZAN, *crie soudain*. — Va-t'en !

Passe-Partout sort en courant.

CIBOULETTE — C'est mieux comme ça, Tarzan. T'as bien fait. Maintenant, faut que tu partes toi aussi. T'es en danger si tu restes plus longtemps.

TARZAN — Pas tout de suite. Je vas séparer l'argent avant.

TIT-NOIR — Mais, t'es fou !

MOINEAU — On n'en veut pas nous autres. C'est toi qui en as besoin, pas nous autres.

TARZAN — Vous en avez besoin autant que moi et vous avez pas à répliquer . . . Tiens, Tit-Noir, prends ça. (*Il lui tend une liasse de billets.*)

TIT-NOIR — Non, Tarzan, je peux pas.

TARZAN — C'est la dernière fois que je te demande de m'obéir, Tit-Noir . . . la dernière fois . . . prends : t'en auras besoin si tu veux te marier un jour. (*Il lui met l'argent dans la poche.*) V'là ta part, maintenant, Moineau. Avec, t'apprendras la musique, tu deviendras un bon musicien et personne te dira après que tu sais pas jouer.

MOINEAU — Quand tu seras parti, la musique m'intéressera plus.

TARZAN — Demain, t'auras oublié ce que tu viens de dire. Prends ton argent, tu l'as gagné. (*Il le lui met de force dans la main puis il leur tourne le dos et remonte la scène un peu.*) Une dernière chose maintenant ... Je veux que vous me laissiez avec Ciboulette. Partez sans parler, c'est le seul service que vous pouvez me rendre.

TIT-NOIR — Tarzan, je ...

TARZAN — Fais ce que je t'ai demandé, Tit-Noir.

MOINEAU, *à Tit-Noir.* — Viens ... Bonsoir, chef ... Bonne chance, chef. (*Il se met à jouer de l'harmonica et se retire lentement.*)

TIT-NOIR, *ému.* — Salut, mon Tarzan ... Bon voyage ...

Ils sortent. Ils s'éloignent et la musique avec eux. Ciboulette se dirige lentement vers Tarzan.

CIBOULETTE — Pourquoi que t'as fait ça ?

TARZAN — Le restant, c'est pour toi ... je t'ai jamais rien donné ... Ce sera mon premier cadeau. Avec, t'achèteras tout ce que tu veux ... donne rien à tes parents ... tu t'achèteras une robe, un collier, un bracelet ... tu t'achèteras des souliers neufs et un petit chapeau pour le dimanche. (*Il lui prend la main et dépose l'argent dedans; il lui ferme les doigts autour.*)

CIBOULETTE — T'as beaucoup changé depuis une minute.

TARZAN — Je suis pas venu ici pour avoir de l'argent, je suis venu pour t'embrasser et te dire que je t'aimais.

CIBOULETTE — Faut que tu partes alors et que tu m'amènes avec toi si c'est vrai que tu m'aimes. L'argent ça sera pour nous deux.

TARZAN — Je peux pas faire ça, Ciboulette.

CIBOULETTE — Pourquoi ?

TARZAN — Parce que je suis fini. Tu t'imagines pas que je vas leur échapper ?

CIBOULETTE — Tu peux tout faire quand tu veux.

TARZAN — Réveille-toi, Ciboulette, c'est passé tout ça ... je m'appelle François Boudreau, j'ai tué un homme, je me suis sauvé de la prison et je suis certain qu'on va me descendre.

CIBOULETTE — Pour moi, t'es toujours Tarzan.

TARZAN — Non. Tarzan est un homme de la jungle, grand et fort, qui triomphe de tout : des animaux, des cannibales et des bandits. Moi je suis seulement qu'un orphelin du quartier qui voudrait bien qu'on le laisse tranquille un jour dans sa vie, qui en a par-dessus la tête de lutter et de courir et qui aimerait se reposer un peu et être heureux. (*Il la prend dans ses bras.*) Regarde-moi ... vois-tu que je suis un peu lâche ?

CIBOULETTE — Mais non, t'es pas lâche. T'as peur, c'est tout. Moi aussi j'ai eu peur quand ils m'ont interrogée; j'ai eu peur de parler et de trahir, j'avais comme de la neige dans mon sang.

TARZAN — Je vous avais promis un paradis, j'ai pas pu vous le donner et si j'ai manqué mon coup c'est seulement de ma faute.

CIBOULETTE — C'est de la faute de Passe-Partout qui t'a trahi.

TARZAN — Si Passe-Partout m'avait pas trahi, ils m'auraient eu autrement, je le sais. C'est pour ça que j'ai pas puni Passe-Partout. C'est pour ça que je veux pas de votre argent. Ça serait pas juste et je serais pas capable d'y toucher. C'est de l'argent qui veut plus rien dire pour moi puisque tout est fini maintenant. J'ai tué. Si je t'avais aimée, j'aurais pas tué. Ça, je l'ai compris en prison. Mais y est trop tard pour revenir en arrière.

CIBOULETTE — Veux-tu dire qu'on aurait pu se marier et avoir des enfants ?

TARZAN — Peut-être.

CIBOULETTE — Et maintenant, on pourra jamais ?

TARZAN — Non.

CIBOULETTE — Tarzan ! Si on se mariait tout de suite ! Viens, on va s'enfermer dans l'hangar et on va se marier. Viens dans notre château; il nous reste quelques minutes pour vivre tout notre amour. Viens !

TARZAN — Tu serais deux fois plus malheureuse après.

CIBOULETTE — Ça m'est égal. Je suis rien qu'une petite fille, Tarzan, pas raisonnable et pas belle, mais je peux te donner ma vie.

TARZAN — Faut que tu vives toi. T'as des yeux pour vivre. Faut que tu continues d'être forte comme tu l'as toujours été même si je dois te quitter . . . pour toujours.

CIBOULETTE — Quand un garçon et une fille s'aiment pour vrai, faut qu'ils vivent et qu'ils meurent ensemble, sans ça, ils s'aiment pas.

TARZAN — Pauvre Ciboulette. On sera même pas allés au cinéma ensemble, on n'aura jamais marché sur la rue ensemble, on n'aura jamais connu le soleil d'été ensemble, on n'aura jamais été heureux ensemble. C'est bien ce que je te disais un jour : être amoureuse de moi, c'est être malheureuse.

CIBOULETTE — Mais non. On fait un mauvais rêve et il faut se réveiller avant qu'il soit trop tard.

On commence à entendre les sirènes de police en arrière-plan.

TARZAN — Y est trop tard, Ciboulette. Ecoute, on entend les sirènes. Moineau, Tit-Noir et Passe-Partout sont partis, je les reverrai jamais. On est tout seul et perdu dans la même cour qu'on a rêvé au bonheur, un jour. T'es là dans mes bras et tu trembles de froid comme un oiseau. Mes yeux sont grands ouverts sur les maisons, sur la noirceur et sur toi; je sais que je vais mourir mais j'ai seulement qu'un désir : que tu restes dans mes bras.

CIBOULETTE — Embrasse-moi . . . une dernière fois . . . pour que j'entende plus les voix de la mort . . . (*Il l'embrasse avec l'amour du désespoir. Les sirènes se rapprochent sensiblement.*) Maintenant, tu vas partir, Tarzan. Tu vas te surmonter. Tu penseras plus à moi. T'es assez habile pour te sauver.

TARZAN — Et t'auras cru en moi jusqu'à la fin. J'aurais pas dû revenir, Ciboulette; comme ça t'aurais eu moins de chagrin.

CIBOULETTE — Mais non, Tarzan, t'as bien fait, t'as bien fait. L'important maintenant c'est que tu penses à partir.

TARZAN — T'as raison, Ciboulette. (*Il la laisse et se dirige vers l'ouverture de la palissade. Il regarde un peu au loin et il revient.*) Ça va pas tarder. Dans cinq minutes, ça va être pourri de policiers ici. Je les sens venir.

CIBOULETTE — Faut que tu te dépêches, Tarzan.

TARZAN — Oui, Ciboulette. (*Il s'écarte d'elle et se dirige vers la gauche, il regarde l'ouverture entre les deux maisons puis de nouveau il revient vers Ciboulette.*) Par là, je me découvre tout de suite.

CIBOULETTE — Passe par les toits comme t'es venu.

TARZAN — C'est le seul chemin possible, je pense. (*Il se dirige du côté des toits, il regarde, il inspecte puis il s'approche de son trône, se penche, soulève la caisse et prend son pistolet. Puis il revient vers Ciboulette.*) Ecoute. Je sais qu'ils vont m'avoir au tournant d'une rue ... Si je pouvais me sauver, je le ferais, mais c'est impossible.

CIBOULETTE — Il te reste une chance sur cent, faut que tu la prennes.

TARZAN — Non. Y est trop tard. J'aime mieux mourir ici que mourir dans la rue. (*Il vérifie le fonctionnement du pistolet et le met dans sa poche.*) J'aime mieux les attendre. Quand ils seront là, tu t'enfermeras dans l'hangar pour pas être blessée. S'ils tirent sur moi, je me défends jusqu'à la fin, s'ils tirent pas, je me rends et ils m'emmènent.

Les sirènes arrivent en premier plan et se taisent.

CIBOULETTE — T'es lâche, Tarzan.

TARZAN — Ciboulette !

CIBOULETTE — Tu veux plus courir ta chance, tu veux plus te battre et t'es devenu petit. C'est pour ça que tu m'as donné l'argent. Reprends-le ton argent et sauve-toi avec.

TARZAN — Ça me servira à rien.

CIBOULETTE — Si t'es encore un homme, ça te servira à changer de pays, ça te servira à vivre.

TARZAN — C'est inutile d'essayer de vivre quand on a tué un homme.

CIBOULETTE — Tu trouves des défaites pour faire pardonner ta lâcheté. Prends ton argent et essaie de te sauver.

TARZAN — Non.

CIBOULETTE — Oui. (*Elle lui lance l'argent.*) C'est à toi. C'est pas à moi. Je travaillais pas pour de l'argent, moi. Je travaillais pour toi. Je travaillais pour un chef. T'es plus un chef.

TARZAN — Il nous restait rien qu'une minute et tu viens de la gaspiller.

CIBOULETTE — Comme tu gaspilleras toute ma vie si tu restes et si tu te rends.

TARZAN — Toi aussi tu me trahis, Ciboulette. Maintenant je te mets dans le même sac que Passe-Partout, dans le même sac que tout le monde. Comme au poste de police, je suis tout seul. Ils peuvent venir, ils vont m'avoir encore. (*Il fait le tour de la scène et crie :*) Qu'est-ce que vous attendez pour tirer ? Je sais que vous êtes là, que vous êtes partout, tirez . . . tirez donc.

CIBOULETTE, *elle se jette sur lui.* — Tarzan, pars, pars, c'était pas vrai ce que je t'ai dit, c'était pas vrai, pars, t'as une chance, rien qu'une sur cent c'est vrai, mais prends-la, Tarzan, prends-la si tu m'aimes . . . Moi je t'aime de toutes mes forces et c'est où il reste un peu de vie possible que je veux t'envoyer . . . Je pourrais mourir tout de suite rien que pour savoir une seconde que tu vis.

TARZAN, *il la regarde longuement, prend sa tête dans ses mains et l'effleure comme au premier baiser.* — Bonne nuit, Ciboulette.

CIBOULETTE — Bonne nuit, François . . . Si tu réussis, écris-moi une lettre.

TARZAN — Pauvre Ciboulette . . . Même si je voulais, je sais pas écrire. (*Il la laisse, escalade le petit toit et disparaît. Un grand sourire illumine le visage de Ciboulette.*)

CIBOULETTE — C'est lui qui va gagner, c'est lui qui va gagner . . . Tarzan est un homme. Rien peut l'arrêter : pas même les arbres de la jungle, pas même les lions, pas même les tigres. Tarzan est le plus fort. Il mourra jamais.

Coup de feu venant de la droite.

CIBOULETTE — Tarzan !

Deux autres coups de feu.

CIBOULETTE — Tarzan, reviens !

Tarzan tombe inerte sur le petit toit. Il glisse et choit par terre. Il réussit tant bien que mal à se relever tenant une main crispée sur son ventre et tendant l'autre à Ciboulette. Il fait un pas et il s'affaisse. Il veut ramper jusqu'à son trône mais il meurt avant.

CIBOULETTE — Tarzan !

Elle se jette sur lui. Entre Roger, pistolet au poing. Il s'immobilise derrière les deux jeunes corps étendus par terre. Ciboulette pleure. Musique en arrière-plan.

CIBOULETTE — Tarzan ! Réponds-moi, réponds-moi ... C'est pas de ma faute, Tarzan ... c'est parce que j'avais tellement confiance ... Tarzan, Tarzan, parle-moi ... Tarzan, tu m'entends pas ? ... Il m'entend pas ... La mort l'a pris dans ses deux bras et lui a volé son coeur ... Dors mon beau chef, dors mon beau garçon, coureur de rues et sauteur de toits, dors, je veille sur toi, je suis restée pour te bercer ... Je suis pas une amoureuse, je suis pas raisonnable, je suis pas belle, j'ai des dents pointues, une poitrine creuse ... Et je savais rien faire; j'ai voulu te sauver et je t'ai perdu ... Dors avec mon image dans ta tête. Dors, c'est moi Ciboulette, c'est un peu moi ta mort ... Je pouvais seulement te tuer et ce que je pouvais, je l'ai fait ... Dors ... (*Elle se couche complètement sur lui.*)

RIDEAU

(*Zone,* dans *Ecrits du Canada français 1955*)

Jacques Languirand (Né en 1930)

C'est le goût de l'insolite, et parfois du sordide, qui caractérise l'oeuvre de ce jeune dramaturge influencé par Beckett et Ionesco et à qui on doit aussi un bon roman, *Tout compte fait*. On trouvera ici une version corrigée et inédite d'une scène caractéristique du *Gibet*.

UN RECORD

LE POLICIER — Alors, c'est le neuvième jour, monsieur Perplex ?

PERPLEX — Oui.

LE POLICIER — Ah ! Il y a de quoi être fier. Les nôtres ont du courage... Franchise et ténacité ! Les discours politiques auront servi à quelque chose...

PERPLEX — C'est souvent la peur qui nous empêche d'aller jusqu'au bout...

LE POLICIER — Lorsque vous aurez battu le record mondial, Monsieur Perplex, vous devriez vous présenter aux élections. Le pays a besoin de gars comme vous. Et avec Gus comme organisateur, vous seriez élu dans le temps de dire « ouf » !

PERPLEX — Vous croyez ?

LE POLICIER — Il est très fort, Gus ! Ça me fait mal quand je suis obligé de le mettre en prison... D'ailleurs, j'ai toujours prétendu qu'il n'y avait pas de travail sérieux dans le quartier : je préfère revenir bredouille le plus souvent possible, afin de le prouver — vous comprenez ?

PERPLEX — Il y va souvent, Gus, en prison ?

LE POLICIER — De moins en moins. Il a plus d'expérience. Il va finir par connaître la loi par coeur. C'est toujours plus facile de s'en tirer quand on peut jouer avec la loi. Un jour, Gus aura son mot à dire au gouvernement... Dites-moi, il est venu beaucoup de monde vous voir ?

PERPLEX — Aux heures de pointe, c'est impressionnant. Je ne pourrais jamais regarder cette foule en face, mais d'en haut, c'est plus facile... Savez-vous ce qui m'a frappé le premier jour ? La diversité des crânes. Parfois, ça me donne le vertige. Alors, je regarde le ciel...

Luna paraît à la fenêtre, et se retire aussitôt.

LE POLICIER — ... Hier soir, je crois avoir aperçu votre femme.

PERPLEX — Elle est allée rendre visite à la tante.

LE POLICIER — Elle était avec Gus . . .

PERPLEX — Il n'aura pas voulu qu'elle aille seule . . .

LE POLICIER — . . . Ils étaient au « Bar de Minuit » !

PERPLEX — . . . Ils avaient peut-être donné rendez-vous à la tante au « Bar de Minuit » . . .

LE POLICIER — C'est une tante à elle ou à vous ?

PERPLEX — A moi . . . La pauvre, elle est impotente . . .

LE POLICIER — Ah . . . Votre famille doit être fière de son Perplex : on parle de vous dans les journaux ! Avez-vous lu tous les articles ?

PERPLEX — On me les a montrés d'en bas.

LE POLICIER — Il y en a qui sont défavorables.

PERPLEX — Ah ! . . .

LE POLICIER — On dit que ce serait un moyen de gagner de l'argent sans travailler.

PERPLEX — Pensez-vous ! C'est de l'art pour l'art !

LE POLICIER — Oui, bien sûr . . . Sacré Gus ! Moi, je ne demande qu'à fermer les yeux. Pourvu que l'affaire ne fasse pas trop de bruit . . . Au revoir.

PERPLEX — Au revoir.

On entend quelques bruits de chemin de fer.

LUNA — *Elle passe la tête par la porte entrouverte.* — Il est parti . . . *Puis, elle s'avance, vêtue d'une robe aguichante.* Vous pouvez sortir . . .

GUS — Ce n'est pas que les policiers m'intimident, mais je suis superstitieux . . . Chaque fois que j'en rencontre un, ça me porte malchance : ou bien il se met à pleuvoir et j'ai oublié mon parapluie . . . ou bien je perds mon mouchoir ! C'est bête, mais je suis superstitieux . . . Et maintenant, si on s'occupait de l'artiste. Ça va ?

PERPLEX — Bonjour, Luna, je t'embrasse.

LUNA — Ton imprésario te demande si ça va . . .

PERPLEX — . . . Ça va.

GUS — Tu vas tenir bon ?

PERPLEX — Oui . . .

GUS — Bravo ! On pense à sa femme, on devient ambitieux, on va tenir bon ! Mais si tu étais sur le point de tourner de l'oeil, n'hésite pas à le dire : je te ferais monter une bouteille de vinaigre. Je ne connais rien de meilleur comme stimulant !

LUNA — D'ailleurs, tu n'es pas mal là-haut.

PERPLEX — Ça va beaucoup mieux, depuis que je ne sens plus mes membres . . . Mais je suis loin de toi, Luna, et je ne peux pas être vraiment heureux loin de toi.

LUNA — Je ne te comprends pas, Perplex, tu es installé sur le poteau le plus près de la maison ... Nous ne pouvions tout de même pas planter un poteau dans notre chambre !

PERPLEX — Tous les matins, il me semble que le poteau s'est allongé durant la nuit, et que nous sommes de plus en plus loin l'un de l'autre ...

LUNA — Est-ce que tu deviendrais myope ?

PERPLEX — Il ne faut pas voler le grain d'une poule aveugle !

GUS — Bravo ! Tu diras des phrases un peu nébuleuses aux journalistes, ce sera parfait !

LUNA — Tu comprends, Perplex, le moment est mal choisi pour un tête-à-tête.

PERPLEX — Je comprends ...

GUS — Tout va très bien, il est conscient de ses responsabilités. Précisément, Perplex, j'ai une proposition à te faire. Es-tu disposé à l'entendre ?

LUNA — Il écoute.

GUS — Demain, à midi, tu auras battu le record d'endurance sur un poteau ! Bravo ! ... Mais le moment est venu de voir grand ! Puisque la température a été clémente, puisque tu es en pleine forme, une décision grave paraît s'imposer ...

LUNA — Très grave décision, Perplex. Ecoute attentivement.

PERPLEX — J'écoute.

GUS — Pourquoi ne pas pousser plus loin l'expérience ? Pourquoi ne pas établir un record d'envergure qui découragerait tous tes adversaires ? — Ils sont nombreux qui se proposent de relever le défi ...

PERPLEX — Qu'est-ce que je devrais faire ?

GUS — Presque rien.

PERPLEX — Mais encore ?

GUS — Tout simplement, Perplex, demeurer là-haut deux ou trois jours de plus ...

PERPLEX — Encore deux ou trois jours ... Je veux connaître l'opinion de Luna.

GUS — Elle n'a pas été facile à convaincre, crois-moi. Luna était partagée entre le désir de te voir de plus près, et la satisfaction de te laisser réaliser ton destin. Elle a choisi.

PERPLEX — Et qu'est-ce qu'elle a choisi ?

GUS — Ta femme clairvoyante a choisi le plus difficile pour elle : le devoir.

PERPLEX — C'est-à-dire ?

LUNA — Perplex, tu dois aller jusqu'au bout. Je ne suis pas de ces femmes qui gardent leur mari au foyer, prisonnier d'une paire de pantoufles ... Tu es très haut, Perplex, dans mon estime. Et tu ne dois pas me décevoir ...

GUS — Imagine la tête des journalistes de la presse, de la radio, de la télévision, venus pour assister à la descente, à qui nous annoncerons que tu vas pousser plus loin, encore plus loin, l'expérience ! Tu deviendras l'homme du jour aux quatre coins du globe, Perplex ! ... Déjà, ta renommée s'étend d'heure en heure. Mais pour vraiment posséder le monde, pour que ton nom soit imprimé dans tous les journaux de la terre, prononcé sur toutes les longueurs d'ondes, et que ta photographie apparaisse sur tous les écrans ... il suffit de si peu : cinq, peut-être six jours de plus !

LUNA — Gus a pensé à tout, Perplex. C'est extraordinaire ! Tu vas devenir l'homme du siècle ... Je ne devrais peut-être pas te le dire maintenant, mais il est question que tu fasses le tour du monde !

PERPLEX — Moi ?

GUS — Oui, toi ! ! !

PERPLEX — A quel titre ?

GUS — « Monsieur Perplex, recordman mondial d'endurance sur un poteau » ! ... Et nous allons parcourir la terre ! ...

PERPLEX — Je ne comprends pas.

LUNA — Monsieur Gus, je vous en prie, exposez-lui le grand projet.

GUS — Perplex, l'avenir t'appartient ! Nous allons, ta femme, toi et moi, parcourir le monde, et dans chaque capitale, tu vas battre ton propre record ! ... Washington, dix-huit jours ! Mexico, vingt jours ! Santiago du Chili, vingt-deux jours ! Londres, un mois ! Paris, six semaines ! Berlin, sept semaines ! Tokio, deux mois ! Et caetera, trois mois ! ...

LUNA — N'est-ce pas merveilleux ?

PERPLEX — Tu trouves ?

LUNA — Le monde à tes pieds !

GUS — « Perplex, recordman des recordmen. » « Il bat son propre record, de capitale en capitale ! »

LUNA — Tu hésites ?

PERPLEX — Je n'avais pas envisagé que je devrais un jour vivre des années sur un poteau.

GUS — Dans la vie, il faut être disponible ! Si le cheval de la chance vient manger dans ta cour, il faut l'attraper par la bride et monter dessus ! ... Moi-même, j'étais loin de penser que j'allais un jour devenir l'imprésario du recordman des recordmen. Mais j'ai toujours été disponible ... Perplex, me voici ! « On a souvent besoin d'un plus petit que soi. »

LUNA — « La chance sourit aux audacieux. »

PERPLEX — ... « La nuit porte conseil. »

On entend siffler un train.

LUNA — Je vais aller te chercher à manger.

PERPLEX — Je n'ai plus faim.

GUS — Tu ne manges presque pas ...

PERPLEX — L'air est bon, ici ...

(*Le Gibet,* 1960)

E. Austin Weir (Born in 1886)

Weir was responsible for the first series of Sunday Symphonies in America (1929), featuring the Toronto Symphony Orchestra. He made a major contribution to the development of Canadian radio drama by commissioning Merrill Denison to write the Romance of Canada series for the CBC, which was produced by the noted director, Tyrone Guthrie.

THE STRUGGLE FOR NATIONAL BROADCASTING
IN CANADA

On January 1, 1941, the CBC's first National News Service commenced under D.C. McArthur with five newsrooms across the nation. The great drama that made everyone both participant and spectator compelled this addition. At the end of 1939, news bulletins occupied 9.4 per cent of total programme time, but by the autumn of 1941, this had risen to over 20 per cent. The day Pearl Harbour was attacked, thirteen special bulletins were given, in addition to those carried on American exchange programs. During the following week, network bulletins were provided every hour on the hour.

The simple presentation of news without embellishment and free of sponsorship was regarded as paramount. A clearly defined policy was laid down, and sensationalism was as sedulously avoided as dullness. Special precautions against rumours, inaccuracies, and misinterpretation had to be taken without resorting to censorship. Truth, with no attempt to modify the news, however disagreeable, so long as it was from a reliable source, was deemed imperative. In this respect, it was modelled very much upon the BBC. The extensive knowledge and experience of Gladstone Murray, the General Manager, were of untold value in the first five years of the CBC. Murray was highly imaginative and demanded a high standard of artistic achievement. He loathed overstatement, and insisted on fostering Canadian talent.

With the help of the Canadian Legion, the voices of friends at home were brought to the troops overseas. Recordings of community events and personal messages from family groups were retransmitted to Europe by the BBC. In this popular feature, private stations were very helpful. The BBC News Service also prepared a weekly news-letter featuring such sports as National Hockey League games. And there were transatlantic conversations between war guests and their parents at home. "Neighbourly News," begun in 1940, soon spread nationally. In 1941, thirteen plays by famous authors under the title "Theatre of Freedom" were produced.

Vicki Branden

A teacher and a former editor of the now defunct *Farmer's Advocate,* Mrs. Branden has contributed to CBC's "Stories with John Drainie." This was selected by Drainie as one of the most successful pieces.

THE RELUCTANT GENIUS

My Aunt Agnes is one of those comfortable dumplings of women who never seem to have an idea from one year's end to the other. Aunt Agnes's dumbness, in fact, has grown into a family legend and a favourite joke.

We often used to wonder how Uncle Owen could stand it. Uncle Owen is artistic and sensitive and bad-tempered; how he has escaped being bored to death by Aunt Agnes is a marvel.

I suppose that the explanation is that Uncle Owen thinks Aunt Agnes is funny. Her artless remarks send him into convulsions. He saves up collections of "Aunt Agnesisms" and gloats over them.

Example of an Aunt Agnesism : A gossipy neighbour had just delivered a long scandalous story about one of the local belles, ending with the information that some of her gentlemen friends didn't leave until four A.M.

"Hedges' sakes," said Aunt Agnes, "what do they find to talk about until that hour ?"

"Hedges' sakes" is my aunt's vilest oath, although she has spent most of her life with one of the most resourceful cussers in the province. Uncle Owen is invariably floored by "hedges."

Once I went into their house and found Uncle Owen writhing on the floor, groaning and choking with mixed pain and joy. It seems that he had been tacking down the carpet, had hit himself on the thumb and had let loose with the most awful stream of blasphemy and invective; and Aunt Agnes had said, after about fifteen minutes of unbroken profanity,

"Hedges, Owen, stop fussing."

It was the total inadequacy of it, Uncle Owen said, wiping away his tears, that struck him as having a classic quality.

In spite of seeming almost spectacularly ill-matched Uncle Owen and Aunt Agnes lived together in perfect happiness and affection for about twenty years, until Aunt Agnes began to paint.

Please note that Aunt Agnes *began to paint*. She didn't take up art. The word art, which was of vital significance to her husband, meant absolutely nothing to her. Uncle Owen talked at length and with fervency of the Artistic Experience; Aunt Agnes said, Hedges.

She began to paint because the Women's Institute sponsored an oil painting contest. The leading spirits in the Institutes may have talked a good deal about spreading culture and the joys of the creative, but Aunt Agnes entered the contest out of loyalty to the Institute. She thought that everyone should take an interest in Institute work, and of course she hoped that she would win the prize.

Aunt Agnes was a great prize-winner. She had won hundreds of prizes for her marvellous home-made bread, her pickles and jam and so on. Then (also an Institute project) she entered rug-making and quilt-making contests. She won prizes for them, too.

I suppose we should have found a clue to Aunt Agnes's painting career in her rugs, because they were very nice ones. She made the designs herself, and worked them in pure cold shades of blue and green, with white. Sometimes they were not very practical, because they showed soil. (She had been given a second instead of a first in one contest because of this.) It was the one indication of impracticality in Aunt Agnes's nature that, although she knew her rugs would soil, she kept right on working them (as if under some compulsion) in her clear frosty colours.

Don't misunderstand me — we all admired Aunt Agnes's rugs. The workmanship in them was impeccable; anyone could see that they were, altogether, very unusual rugs. But somehow we never connected them with Art, capital A. Aunt Agnes sitting by the fire hooking away at her rugs was such a remarkably homely sight, so ordinary, so non-artistic.

After all, there was nothing surprising about Aunt Agnes's creating homemade bread so superb that a mere whiff of it wrung cries of anguished desire out of everyone who passed; so why should her rugs and mats be surprising? No reason she shouldn't make good rugs and mats.

We were inclined to class all of Aunt Agnes's production in the same category with her bread, her pineapple upside-down cake, her gooseberry jam. They were all works of art. The memory of the fragrance of one of Aunt Agnes's blueberry pies is more haunting than the strains of a Mozart concerto, more delicately evocative than a line from Keats. There was no doubt that the woman was an artist.

Nevertheless when she began to paint we, for some reason or other, were sure that she would produce amateurish and unsightly daubs. We expected her to make copies of calendars. We looked for lumpish sheep grazing under comic trees on poison-green meadows.

We called her Mrs. Dali, Mrs. Gauguin, Mrs. Van Gogh and so on (Hedges, said Aunt Agnes, who had never heard of any of them). Uncle Owen had never found his wife more insanely diverting. He tried to persuade her to wear a beret and smock, and advised her that she would be expected to smoke marijuana.

Aunt Agnes, naturally, paid no attention. She did her painting in a house dress and a large gingham apron, with newspapers spread to protect the floor. We hung about and chortled, making witty suggestions about pop art and the resurgence of Cubism and the vogue for Piet Mondrian. Then, to our embarrassment, even to our dismay, we realized that Aunt Agnes's painting was good.

Consider our position. We are, as a family, all sensitive, intelligent, rather unusual people. We really are, seriously. We've always been profoundly affected by the arts. I suppose all of us have tried to write. We love music and theatre. We've never actually *done* anything successfully in any of these fields, you understand, none of us; but they are important to us and we had persuaded ourselves that somehow we were important to them. Here we were, and here we had been for years and years, enjoying Aunt Agnes as a sort of dull background for us to scintillate against. And we had never distinguished ourselves in the least; but here was Aunt Agnes, painting her disquieting pictures.

She had never painted anything before, except kitchen chairs. She had never even thought about painting. We felt faintly outraged, as if Aunt Agnes had done something dishonest. We stopped making jokes about Picasso.

The picture Aunt Agnes entered in the contest was a snow scene. It had a sort of realism — that is, she had caught the effect of snow slanting down in a way that almost made you feel it melting on your eyelashes. But the picture was by no means a piece of naive realism. It had an odd, austere formality of design that gave it a kind of Oriental look, although it was all done in Aunt Agnes's favourite icy colours.

All this was very hard on Uncle Owen. He stopped discussing the picture, and used to watch Aunt Agnes (stolidly painting in her gingham apron) with a confused air, half admiring and half resentful. It was rather like entertaining angels unawares, or having a pet hen turn into a cockatrice.

Only Aunt Agnes remained unaffected by her art. Aproned and impassive, she painted amiably and placidly while Uncle Owen and the rest of us talked. If a neighbour dropped in, Aunt Agnes continued to paint, just as she would have continued to knit. She listened with mild pleasure to radio soap operas.

If the picture had been more commonplace, or Aunt Agnes less commonplace, it wouldn't have been so bothersome. But the incongruity of the combination became an obsession with us.

We would find ourselves prodding and digging at Aunt Agnes's mind, prospecting for the strange vein of lightness and grace and austere beauty that flowed somewhere in her dumpling anatomy. But no spark ever shone in Aunt Agnes's eye, no word betrayed any consciousness that she was creating beauty. We could only conclude that Aunt Agnes had no idea of what she was doing, or that it was in any way different from baking a pie. She was doing her best, of course; she always did her best. But she wasn't feeling any spark of divine inspiration.

My aunt in her painting days sometimes rather frightened me. You know the theory of the apes at the typewriters — if you sat a group of apes down at a typewriter each, and let them bang away, if they banged long enough they would eventually, quite by accident, write all of the world's masterpieces of literature. But suppose one ape sat down and at first go wrote *Paradise Lost* ? I wondered if Aunt Agnes mightn't be possessed by a spirit. Her painting was rather like spirit-writing — as if something supernatural had appropriated her body without the body's awareness of what it was doing. The hair on the back of my neck used to prickle as I watched Aunt Agnes placidly splashing away, humming "What A Friend We Have in Jesus," while she produced a masterpiece.

It wasn't much of a surprise that Aunt Agnes won the contest; although it was interesting to see that all sorts of slender, willowy women with delicate hands and ethereal expressions, who talked passionately about art, had submitted copies of calendars and lumpish sheep grazing under comic trees on poison-green meadows.

The contest was judged by three distinguished Canadian artists. Until they came to Aunt Agnes, they had been confronted with the usual run-of-the-mill amateur efforts — some promising, some indifferent, some perfectly awful. Aunt Agnes staggered them.

But they were generous, when they had recovered from their shock. They ungrudgingly acclaimed the genius of this unknown amateur. In the blink of an eye, Aunt Agnes was famous.

It didn't particularly affect Aunt Agnes. She was an old prize-winner. She had won prizes for her quilts, her rugs, her jam, her catsup, her oatmeal cookies — She had often had her picture in the paper. (She always said she looked a sight, however.) She had given demonstrations of hooking rugs, at a handicraft show at the Exhibition. Fame was nothing new to Aunt Agnes.

But if his wife saw no difference in the quality of this present fame, and that of her other triumphs, Uncle Owen did. He had wondered, up until then, whether he had been imagining the quality of the painting. Now the tribute of the judges confirmed his suspicions — his worst fears, in fact. Aunt Agnes was a genius. You can't go around guffawing about a genius. It took all the fun out of his marriage.

In the new world that swept down on their household, Uncle Owen hardly counted at all. Before that, he had always been the centre of the stage, with his gift for witty conversation and his skill as a raconteur. People had barely noticed Aunt Agnes, except to eat her baking and laugh at the Aunt Agnesisms.

But now no one noticed Uncle Owen.

An Aunt-Agnes-cult sprang up in the art world. Our relative was continually being asked to go to odd affairs — a cocktail party at the Art Gallery (Hedges !), a meeting of the Artists and Writers Club. She was asked to speak at dinners and banquets.

"What do they think I'd talk about ?" complained Aunt Agnes, and refused to go.

She refused all invitations, explaining that she didn't have a thing fit to wear. Her real reason was that she coudn't be bothered. The whole business struck her as silly : Aunt Agnes had never been one for gadding about.

The newspapers, therefore, built her up as a mystery woman. They frequently compared her to Grandma Moses, although Aunt Agnes's painting was in no sense similar, and the comparison irked her greatly. She had seen a Grandma Moses Christmas card and thought it was pitiful.

"I've seen kiddies in kindergarten do every bit as good," sniffed Aunt Agnes.

Since she would not go to the art world, it came to her in the form of disciples. Young men in beards and eccentric haberdashery appeared on her doorstep; tousled girls in paint-smeared leotards asked her for guidance. Aunt Agnes fed them raspberry tarts, and urged them to comb their hair. She tried to be civil to them, but she disapproved because they were not neat.

"There's no excuse for untidiness," she said broodingly. "Anyone can afford soap and water."

A wealthy Toronto collector bought Aunt Agnes's prize picture. When asked for her price, she said daringly that it would be twenty-five dollars. She was not greedy but she wanted to donate the money to the church for some repairs to the roof, which was leaking like a sieve. But the millionaire's secretary had never heard of pictures which cost twenty-five dollars, and the cheque that arrived was for twenty-five hundred.

It frightened Aunt Agnes. Twenty-five hundred dollars was approximately half of what Uncle Owen earned in a year, after thirty years of school teaching.

Art lovers came and bought every picture she painted. They commissioned her to paint more. There was turmoil in the souls and lives of my aunt and uncle; their whole world seemed to be topsy-turvy.

I felt rather shy of Aunt Agnes in her new character of Genius, when I wasn't actually with her; but when I found myself in The Presence, she was so exactly just Aunt Agnes that I always forgot she was a genius. The only difference was that she was inclined to be grouchy.

One day I found her painting away in the kitchen, with rather a surly expression on her usually pleasant, bun-like face.

"Hedges' sakes," she grumbled, "they never give you a minute to yourself, they're in such a rush for their old pictures."

"Is it true," I asked diffidently, "that they want you to give a one-woman show?"

Aunt Agnes snorted.

"Oh, that old show. I'm tired of hearing about them and their old show. All the time I ever get to myself any more — there's Owens' shirts with buttons off, and no baking done for the bazaar — might as well be going out doing cleaning, like poor Mrs. Wilkins."

"Going out doing cleaning" — was the big shame, the last ditch, of Aunt Agnes's generation. It meant that your husband wasn't a good provider, if you had to go out cleaning.

She mumbled away, dourly. Her painting didn't suffer for her bitter mood; it wasn't in Aunt Agnes's nature to skimp a job.

"When I finish this one," she said defiantly, "it's the last one I'm doing. I told them that, and I'm sticking to it. So there."

"But Aunt Agnes!" I cried. "You can't do that! You have a great gift — it's wicked not to use it!"

"Wicked," scoffed my aunt. "You show me any place in the Bible that says a body has to paint pictures they don't want to."

"The parable of the talents !"

"That says anything about wasting time painting pictures ? I'll just thank you to show me a word about it ! Just the same," said Aunt Agnes, "I'm just relieved you mentioned that. 'Cause that's what I'm doing, wasting my time and talents painting these fiddling pictures when I should be thinking about seeing your uncle's got his buttons sewn on his shirts right — him the principal of the school, going around looking as if he hadn't a wife to look out for him."

The outburst restored my aunt's equable temper and she sent me to the kitchen to sample a piece of devil's food cake; she had been trying out a new recipe, between pictures, for the church bazaar. I forked down a melting mouthful and cried that it was a work of art.

"Oh for hedges' sakes not that !" cried Aunt Agnes. It was the closest she ever came in her life to making a joke.

When she finished the current picture, Aunt Agnes, true to her word, abandoned painting. She refused all commissions. She rebuffed her admirers.

"Haven't the time," Aunt Agnes told her scandalized followers, with irritated finality.

"My sakes," said Aunt Agnes, when her painting career was over. She was knitting diamond socks for Uncle Owen. "All that fuss about a picture. All that taking on. Why, they don't know much. It isn't half the job hooking a rug is."

Uncle Owen, sitting back in his arm chair, went into a paroxysm of helpless laughter.

"And then, what's the use of them when you've got them ? Well, some are pretty, I grant, and I like a nice picture on the wall. But it isn't like a quilt or a rug that you can get some use of. I call it a lot of silly nonsense. Hedges, Owen, what's funny about that ?"

Aunt Agnes's knitting needles clicked severely; speechless with mirth, Uncle Owen writhed in his chair. He was reading *The Moon and*

(Sixpence.)

Vinia Hoogstraten

Mrs. Hoogstraten has written for Canadian and American magazines and radio networks. | This selection is from the CBC radio feature, Matinée.

THE PASSING OF THE BIG M

Nobody raised in a family of girls, as I was, has any inkling of the earth-shaking importance of a boy's first car. When our son drove up in his, my reaction was more pity then anything else, coupled with thanksgiving that we were safely through the motorcycle period. The car, immediately christened The Big M, was a 1948 model with the beaten, overwrought look of one who has laboured in the vineyards too long and too hard. It made me think of a weary old horse who should long since have been put to pasture. I didn't realize that in Bill's eyes it was a shining, flawless chariot.

Mealtimes became periods of scintillating conversation about things like differentials and exhaust manifolds. Our daughter and I became thoroughly bored with The Big M and paid as little attention to it as we could manage. Then one day as I watched it tootling down the street with Bill at the wheel it dawned on me that something almost uncanny had happened to it. It no longer looked tired. It looked cocky, almost rakish. The countless hours Bill and half a dozen of his friends had spent on it had done more than give it a dazzling polish. They had restored its self-confidence. It carried its cracked windows with a devil-may-care attitude, and its new white fender skirts contrasted gaily with its worn maroon paint. Its crowning touch was a fuzzy pink rug on its front seat called, I regret to say, a passion mat.

In the next two years The Big M became part of our lives. It stood out unprotesting through all kinds of weather, since ours is a one-car garage, and responded to Bill's demands on it with the unquestioning faithfulness of a good old dog. At first we kept expecting something to go wrong with it. Nothing ever did and we soon took it for granted that nothing would.

Bill's father bought a new car and offered him a very generous deal on the old one. Bill's reaction couldn't have been more appalled and would, I'm afraid, have been less so had my husband suggested we turn me in on a newer model. The subject never was mentioned again.

Then one tragic bitterly cold evening Bill came home from a hockey game and plugged in the car for the night. (In our prairie area cars are equipped with engine heaters. If they weren't, winter traffic would cease. You plug in your car like you would a toaster and the heater usually keeps the engine warm enough so that the car will start in the morning). We were sitting in the living-room catching up on the day's activities when the two lamps at the end of the room went out. We found the kitchen and bathroom lights out too. Bill started down to the basement and gave a cry of anguish. Through the back-door window the cause of our difficulties was cruelly apparent. The Big M was burning.

I always had assumed naively that when faced with an emergency ours would be one of those coolly behaved families we all admire so much. Looking back, I can scarcely believe the chicken-headed way we all ran around in the dark yelling instructions at each other. We all soaked towels and filled pails oblivious to the fact that there were several tons of snow within ten feet of our stricken servant.

Bill ran out with me on his heels shrieking that he wasn't to go near it because it might explode. He ignored me and I went back in to tell my husband he wasn't to let Bill stay there and he wasn't to go near it himself. I must have been pretty noisy about the whole thing because for the first time in our long and happy marriage he told me to shut up. I was so astounded I did shut up. He also told me to phone the fire department and then went to join Bill so that if there *was* an explosion it would get both of them.

I went to the telephone and there learned that it is almost com-pletely impossible to remember an exchange and five digits long enough to dial them when you are expecting your mate and your firstborn to be blown to fragments at any minute. Emergency numbers are things with which I'm in the heartiest possible accord. I finally got the fire department and they came and helped put the fire out.

I did The Big M an injustice. I should have known it wouldn't harm Bill, even in its death throes. It didn't explode, but it was a total loss, going out literally in a blaze of glory. We never did learn what caused the fire.

"Anyway," Bill said, from the depths of his sorrow, "it'll never have to rot away in a wrecking yard. That's something."

He has a new car now. It's a much newer model and infinitely smarter looking. Its windows are intact and it has no spots where its paint has been polished out of existence. Fender skirts are not for it and the pink passion mat perished with The Big M. He's pleased with it, even proud of it, but it's a respectable car, a man's car. It pulls up to the house regularly, filled with carefree youngsters, but things are not the same. There's something lacking, an intangible, mysterious something that has to do with boyhood and the irreplaceable thrill of a first car. I like to think that some day when it's old and weary, and reaching the end of the highway, this car will fall into the loving hands of another boy and be to another family the gay, rejuvenated, beloved old ruin The Big M was to us.

(Trans-Canada Matinée)

David MacDonald (Born in 1928)

An engaging writer on sports, MacDonald is an associate editor of the Canadian edition of the *Reader's Digest*.

CANADA'S GAME SCORES ABROAD

During a National Hockey League game in Montreal this winter, Gordie Howe of the Detroit Red Wings went gliding down the ice with long, flowing strides and took a quick pass in front of the Canadiens' nets. As goalie "Gump" Worsley came sprawling out to block him, the 200-pound six-footer spun delicately on his skates, drew back his stick and drove the puck home with a whoop of joy. It was Howe's six-hundredth goal in NHL competition — a previously "impossible" record — and such a thrilling moment that even Montreal's fifteen thousand wildly partisan fans were moved to cheer the Detroit superstar.

Two minutes later, however, they were screaming for his scalp. For when a Canadien slammed him into the rinkside boards, Howe lashed back with an elbow and broke the rude chap's cheekbone. "It may seem crazy," as Howe had reflected once before, after belting another player into hospital with an awful but lawful body check, "yet that's what I'm paid to do."

Crazy or not, the lusty yet lovely game he plays so well is now the world's fastest-growing team sport, a rousing spectacle of speed and colour that is exciting crowds from Los Angeles to Leningrad.

Indeed, as NHL pros wage it, no contest outside the bullring provided such a stirring, improbable blend of beauty and brutality. Montreal's Jean Béliveau is all grace and Gallic élan, a swooping skater whose crisscross passing plays dazzle the eye. Chicago's explosive

Bobby Hull rockets around so fast (forty-four feet per second) and shoots so furiously (one hundred and twenty mph) that the Chicago *Tribune* calls him "the most exciting athlete in sports today." When Toronto goalie Johnny Bower does the splits, into a swirl of oncoming blades, he's a nerveless Nureyev. And then there are the slam-bang bruisers like Boston's Ted Green and New York's Arnie Brown, who bring fans to their feet by bouncing opponents on their rears.

Refined from the ancient European game of bandy, a formless free-for-all that nineteenth-century Canadians took up to ward off the winter cold, ice hockey has become one of the hottest commodities in North American professional sport. According to New York *Times* columnist Arthur Daley, the National Hockey League is "the most productive money-maker in the entire history of athletics." Last year, NHL teams in Toronto, Montreal, Chicago, Detroit, New York and Boston drew three million patrons into their rinks — ninety-seven per cent of capacity — and grossed almost twelve millions from rapid, rugged jousts that have been likened to "a combination of soccer, golf, prizefighting and tong war."

Yet hockey is uniquely itself. "There is no game that moves so swiftly, so continuously and so poetically," author Paul Gallico once noted. "It is played by a group of the most violent and reckless men on the face of the globe."

"Hockey's great appeal to spectators," says Dr. John Lohrenz, a Montreal psychoanalyst who used to coach the game, "is the thrill of speed and danger, without the risk."

Thus, while NHL team-owners often deplore rough play and fisti-cuffs, by *other* teams, they know better. "If we don't stamp out that sort of thing," a Toronto official mused after one rousing brawl, "we'll have to print more tickets."

Indeed, such is the clamour for hockey's thrills and spills that the NHL is about to extend franchises to six more major U.S. and Canadian cities — at two million dollars a throw.

From Canada, where hockey is a national mania, the game has spread to thirty-odd lands — even to Mexico and Japan — and won millions of avid new fans.

In 1946, Russia had no hockey players; today she boasts five hundred thousand, and crowds of fifteen thousand often pack Moscow's huge open-air rink at minus thirty degrees. Second only to soccer in popularity in Sweden, hockey has become *the* game in Czechoslovakia and Finland. For the World Amateur Hockey Tournament this March in Yugoslavia, most of the important matches were sold out last year. "It's a sign of our times," says Helge Berglund, head of the Swedish Hockey Federation. "People want things to happen fast."

Hockey's playing surface, two hundred by eighty-five feet of glare ice, is the fastest in sport. The players are chosen for their ability to skate swiftly and shoot hard; to improvise instant plays and, in so far as a lenient rule-book allows, to clobber the other guys. When two such teams square off, each intent on firing the puck into the other's goal, the action is bound to be exciting for all concerned. "During a hockey game," runs one maxim, "the only sane person in the rink is the referee."

Perhaps so. For when otherwise normal people play the sport, or merely watch it, strange things happen. In New York's Metropolitan League, whose four amateur teams compete for the sheer love of it, a truck driver recently had a stick broken over his head — by a Columbia University math professor.

It was ever so. During "King" Clancy's first term with the Toronto Maple Leafs, in 1930, a priest talked him into donning a cassock and helping out as a ringer in a game between two Catholic seminaries. "By Heaven," recalls Clancy, one of the hardiest pros of his day, "that was the roughest game I've *ever* been in."

Rough as it may be, hockey has edicts against slashing, boarding, tripping and such, plus graver felonies like fighting and deliberate bloodletting. If a man's offence is noticed by the referee, he's banished to a penalty box that is unique in sport — and in penology. For there the players who flay together stay together, still packing their shillelaghs. Predictably, some of the game's biggest brawls have begun in the "cooler."

"Even when we only go to *watch* hockey," says psychoanalyst Lohrenz, "we unconsciously prepare to *play* it. Blood pressure rises, adrenaline flows faster. In short, we build up steam. When that lets go, even timid people can become tigers."

Another reason why hockey fans get carried away is that they're close to the action, in relatively small arenas, where they can hear and almost feel a thumping body check. "They're not just spectators," says NHL President Clarence Campbell, — "they're *participants!*"

As such, all scream, cheer or gnaw their nails. Some have pelted the enemy forces with eggs or ink — a Detroit man once threw an octopus! — while a few fight in the stands. But most patrons vent their fury in purely vocal ways.

In the heat of battle, hockey teams rarely hear — or need — incitements to mayhem. Once, however, before a minor-pro game in Quebec City, a visiting player hurled hunks of raw meat into the hostile mob. "You wolves have been howling for blood all year," he shouted. "Maybe this will keep you quiet."

Still, according to Dr. Lohrenz, hockey provides a healthy outlet for repressed tensions. "More than in most sports," he says, "the fans identify with the players. To a woman, say, a burly defenceman may represent her domineering husband; when he's knocked down, she feels better. And when Jean Béliveau scores for Montreal against an English-speaking goalie, it's a triumph for *all* French Canadians."

While hockey is easy to understand, it is possibly the hardest of all sports to master. Like most top athletes, an NHL player needs speed, stamina, split-second reflexes, agility, balance and strength — plus an instinct called "hockey sense."

Above all, because hockey is a punishing business, it requires rugged individuals who shrink not from pain nor the sight of blood. A true pro is recognizable by the stitch-marks on his face — Detroit defenceman Bill Gadsby has 500 ! — and by his pearly dentures. "You're not really a hockey player," says one veteran, "until you've lost a few teeth."

During the NHL playoffs in 1963, Bobby Hull played one game for Chicago with a broken nose so badly swollen that he could hardly see past it, yet he scored three of his team's four goals and set up the other. Another time, in 1964, Boston's Dean Prentice was tripped from behind and crashed into the boards. Not until he'd scored on a penalty shot would he leave the ice — with a fractured back. "You know," former New York goalie Chuck Rayner once remarked to the rink physician who was sewing up a four-inch gash in his face, "a fellow could get hurt in this job."

Goaltenders are a breed apart. Their task, the most hazardous in sport, is to brave slashing sticks and blades — merely incidental risks of the trade — in order to throw themselves at flying pucks that can break bones and scramble their features. This calls for quick hands, the audacity of a Kamikaze pilot, and some forty pounds of protective gear. Even so, blistering shots have torn the huge gauntlets from goalies' hands and bruised them through four-inch leg pads.

Apart from physical harm, goaltenders are prone to edgy nerves. Detroit's brilliant Roger Crozier earned an ulcer as a seventeen-year-old junior player, while veteran Chicago goalie Glenn Hall still gets nauseated before most games. Small wonder. For a single mistake, or a fluke of fate, can be disastrous. In a sudden-death overtime period to end the 1954 Stanley Cup finals, Montreal goalie Gerry McNeil was about to catch a long, easy shot when one of his own defencemen swung in front, screened his view and accidentally knocked the puck past him — at a cost of fifteen hundred dollars in bonuses for each member of the team. After stewing all summer over that one shot, McNeil gave up his fifteen thousand-dollar job. "No money," he said, "is worth that misery."

The strain of their last-ditch responsibilities tends to make goalies age fast. Once, watching Terry Sawchuk in the Detroit nets, an old NHL hand asked, "How old is that boy?"

"Twenty-four."

"Next year," he said sadly, "he'll be *thirty*-four."

If working conditions are less than ideal for the one hundred and nineteen Canadians and one American in big-league hockey, the hours and wages are excellent. In fact, the average income of NHL players tops that of any other profession in Canada — $21,600, including bonuses and awards, for seven months' toil — and some earn twice that much. Mere rookies become household names, glamour boys.

The most glamorous of all, golden-haired Bobby Hull, was a muscular young farm boy of thirteen when a Chicago scout first spotted him on an outdoor rink. Today, at twenty-seven, he earns about one hundred thousand dollars a year in salary and fringe benefits, and gets more fan mail than most movie stars.

Yet even Hull hasn't approached the adulation heaped on Maurice "The Rocket" Richard, perhaps the most famous Canadian of all time. In eighteen years with Montreal, the fiery superstar became a French-Canadian idol, unable to walk down the street without stopping traffic. In 1960, slowing to the speed of ordinary stars, The Rocket was paid twenty-five thousand dollars *not* to play, lest his lustre dim with age.

The plain fact of the matter is that Canadians, divided by language, are united by a deep love for their nation's best-known art form. "Hockey isn't just a game," one Canadian columnist recently wrote, "but an essential element of our culture."

In Toronto, English Canada's greatest city, the NHL Maple Leafs have filled their fourteen thousand-seat rink for every game since 1946. There's a waiting list of ten thousand for season tickets — so prized that they've been left in wills. And in Montreal, heart of the French minority, *Le Club de Hockey Canadien* is revered to the edge of fanaticism. In 1955, after the beloved Rocket Richard was suspended for attacking a referee, a riot resulted which caused one hundred thousand dollars worth of damage.

All across the country, each Saturday night from October to April, six and half million Canadians — a third of the population — watch NHL games on TV. It's a sacred rite, not to be denied. When Ottawa police were summoned to a rowdy domestic fight last winter, the husband pleaded extreme provocation: "She turned off the hockey game!"

In their passionate dedication to the sport, Canadians sometimes reach weird and wonderful heights. As far back as 1906, in a memorable grudge match between Cobalt and Haileybury, Ontario, a Cobalt lawyer bet forty-five thousand dollars — a fortune then — and went broke. The happy Haileybury sponsor, who won fifty thousand dollars, rewarded his team handsomely — with a silver mine. More recently, in Glace Bay, N.S., five thousand coal miners chipped in to build a rink for their own semipro team, then threatened to strike when their star goalie was disqualified on a technicality.

Hockey fans are notoriously fickle. For years, for example, Toronto partisans cheered Gordon Drillon, a high-scoring forward with a deceptively lazy style. Then, abruptly, they razzed him for loafing on the job. When a newspaper photo showed six Maple Leafs serving as pallbearers at the team doctor's funeral, one wag sent it to the coach with the query: "Is Drillon carrying his share of the load?"

The current Toronto favourite is helter-skelter Eddie Shack. When Shack joined the Leafs, he was rumoured to be illiterate. But no. Once, as he was barging up the ice, a Detroit coach shouted, "G'wan, stupid, you can't even spell." Seconds later Shack scored, then skated back to the Detroit bench. Leaning over the rail to face the coach, he declaimed, "G-o-a-l."

Big-league hockey is essentially as serious as any other multi-million-dollar industry. Its raw material grows wild on thousands of playground rinks where most Canadian boys start skating as soon as they can walk. Like other industrial recruiters, NHL scouts beat the bush leagues for talent, ranging all across Canada, into United States hockey hotbeds like Massachusetts, Michigan and Minnesota — even as far afield as Sweden.

They especially watch for speed, size and spirit. Toronto's Conn Smythe once hired a hard-driving athlete named Syl Apps after watching him play only one game — of *football.* "Anyone with that kind of spirit," he said, "*has* to become a great hockey player." Sure enough, Apps is now in the Hockey Hall of Fame.

By the age of fifteen, a promising prospect may have several NHL scouts bidding for his services. Once signed by New York, say, the prodigy starts climbing up through various farm teams from junior to minor-pro, hoping to reach Madison Square Garden.

For developing pro hockey to its present high degree, however, Canada has paid a stiff price in prestige at the World Amateur Hockey Tournament, which, begun in 1920, has lately become a not-so-cold war.

For years, Canadians so dominated the game that they could win the international title with almost any third-rate amateur team. But in 1954, at Stockholm, Russia competed for the first time — and won. Canadians were stunned, their pride sorely hurt.

One year later, in Germany, a stronger Canuck team regained the championship by blanking the Soviet upstarts 5-0. Since then, however, Russia has taken over again, winning the last three tourneys. In 1965, when Canada finished a dismal fourth, newspapers cried : "Shame !" and pointed questions were even raised in Parliament.

One answer is that Canada's best players — six hundred admitted pros and hundreds of excellent amateurs — are too busy making money at home to defend the national honour abroad. (The team competing in Yugoslavia in March is composed of college students and a few superpatriots.)

In Russia, thirty-two farm teams cultivate talent for the Soviet national squad. Standout players are sworn in as Red Army officers, then posted to Moscow and paid to practice together all year. The result is better teamwork than many Canadian pros display.

Oddly enough, there's bitter rivalry between Russia and satellite Czechoslovakia, which has eighty thousand hockey players. When the favored Czechs lost to the U.S.S.R. in 1964, angry citizens of Prague demonstrated outside the coach's home.

The third big power in European hockey is Sweden, whose players have multiplied from three thousand to one hundred and thirty thousand since 1948. One of them is young Crown Prince Carl Gustaf. Sweden's Number One sports hero is "Tumba" Johansson, whose fame as a hockey star brings him roughly fourteen thousand dollars a year, without somehow impairing his amateur status.

In the United States, too, hockey is booming as never before. The number of all-weather artificial ice rinks has grown from ninety-six to two hundred in fifteen years, and has meant a proportionate increase in school-boy teams. In Detroit alone, four hundred youngsters play in organized leagues. So popular is one hockey clinic, in Princeton, New Jersey, that many fathers enroll their sons at birth to make sure they get in. Moreover, minor-pro hockey is now thriving in such unfrozen places as Memphis, Tennessee, and Houston, Texas. When the NHL expands in 1967 or 1968, St. Louis, Los Angeles and San Francisco-Oakland are almost sure to get franchises, along with two other major United States cities and Vancouver, British Columbia.

The game's excitement is winning thousands of fans in — lo ! — Mexico City. Hockey was introduced there in 1948, by graduates of Canadian colleges. Now the city has a five-team senior league and twelve junior clubs. "The fire and action of hockey appeals to Latins," says junior-league president Jaime Roberts, whose grandfather came from Canada. "For big games, we need lots of police."

As hockey continues to spread, the day may come when we'll see a truly *world* playoff for the Stanley Cup, the seventy-year-old NHL championship bowl. If a Cup playoff should ever pit Russian against Canadian pros, it probably wouldn't supplant Brotherhood Week. For the Soviets play, as *Sports Illustrated* has noted, "as though the future of the communist world depends on their sticks and blades." As for Canadians, their commitment to success in hockey knows no bounds, not even family ties.

Not long ago, a Montreal player who flubbed an easy shot was pained to hear his own son razzing him from the stands. Later, at home, he demanded an explanation.

"When you score, you're my father," the lad replied. "But when you miss an open goal, Daddy, you're a bum."

(Hockey Pictorial)

George Johnston (Born in 1913)

Johnston has written two books of poems, *The Cruising Auk* and *Home Free*. His work has been printed in various magazines, from the *London Mercury* to the *Atlantic Monthly*.

MR. GOOM

Earth fills her lap for Mr. Goom
With gifts, of which in studied measure
And with the savoir-faire of doom
He makes selection for his pleasure.

Yet life is often very sad
For Mr. Goom, he doesn't know
Whether it's really good or bad
Its sweetest moments sour so.

And though he cherishes his gifts
— His lovely clothes, his lovely friends —
His dilettante attention shifts
From time to time to mortal ends

And then he finds he needs a drink
Or else a Turkish bath to chase
His apperception from the brink
Of darkness to a brighter place.

Always around the door he knows
The brink of darkness drops away
And sure enough the door will close
After him over it one day.

The tears I shed for Mr. Goom
Are soft in character and fine
As his own amiable perfume :
They fall between his fate and mine.

(The Cruising Auk)

Anne Marriott McLellan (Born in 1913)

Miss Marriott's best-known work is *The Wind Our Enemy* (1939), which, in the words of C. F. Klinck and B. Conron, expressed "with vivid and moving imagistic pictures the disheartening effect of continuous drought..."

BEAVER POND

Not furred nor wet, the pointing words yet make
a feel of plush slip moistly through the mind.
Tires grate to gravelled stops; tourists, lumpy in jeans,
question and clatter round the still, small pool.
Twigs, peanuts flip
on the wrought island on the farther side —
its basket crown, cunningly cut,
entangles all eyes, but none in return

looks through the sealed lattice. Water absorbs
nut, cry and pebble, offers in reply
no waking head, and no binocular
searching route to the shelter but reveals
on the shut surface only its blind, mirrored eye.

And yet I feel the water in my ears,
nose sucks the strong root-smell
and light refracts among the embroidered weeds
in rich deep greens and browns that grow
more coloured with acquaintance.
The velvet bodies of our infrequent kind
press here beside me. Deep beaver I
greet you under the masked water from my secret house,
neither will break the public surface against my wish
for sticks or stones or softest coaxing words.

(Fiddlehead and *Canadian Anthology)*

Fred Cogswell (Born in 1917)

Cogswell is editor of *The Fiddlehead,* | His own best poems have been
which prints poetry and some stories. | collected in *Descent from Eden* (1959).

THE WATER AND THE ROCK

Hard rock was I, and she was water flowing,
Over sharp stones of opposition going;
Shaping herself to me as to a cup,
She filled the valleys of my ego up
With a cool, smooth compliance, everywhere
As yielding and unhurtable as air.

Soft was my love as water, and I forgot
In the calm wash of compliant rhythm caught
How water shapes and softens, sculpts and smooths
The channel of the rock through which it moves.

(Descent from Eden)

P. K. Page (Born in 1916)

Miss Page now devotes much time to the visual arts of drawing, painting, print-making. But a new collection of her poems is imminent. She is highly regarded for *As Ten As Twenty* and *The Metal and the Flower.*

PHOTOS OF A SALT MINE

How innocent their lives look,
how like a child's
dream of caves and winter, both combined :
the steep descent to whiteness
and the stope
with its striated walls
their folds all leaning as if pointing to
the greater whiteness still,
that great white bank
with its decisive front,
that seam upon a slope,
salt's lovely ice.

And wonderful underfoot the snow of salt,
the fine particles a broom could sweep,
one thinks
muckers might make angels in its drifts,
as children do in snow,
lovers in sheets,
lie down and leave imprinted where they lay
a feathered creature holier than they.

And in the outworked stopes
with lamps and ropes
up miniature matterhorns
the miners climb,
probe with their lights
the ancient folds of rock —
syncline and anticline —
and scoop from darkness an aladdin's cave :
rubies and opals glitter from its walls.

But hoses douse the brilliance of these jewels,
melt fire to brine.
Salt's bitter water trickles thin and forms
slow fathoms down
a lake within a cave
lacquered with jet —
white's opposite.
There grey on black the boating miners float
to mend the stays and struts of that old stope
and deeply underground
their words resound,
are multiplied by echo, swell and grow
and make a climate of a miner's voice.

So all the photographs like children's wishes
are filled with caves or winter,
innocence
has acted as a filter,
selected only beauty from the mine.
Except in the last picture,
it is shot
from an acute high angle. In a pit
figures the size of pins are strangely lit
and might be dancing but you know they're not.
Like Dante's vision of the nether hell
men struggle with the bright cold fires of salt
locked in the black inferno of the rock :
the filter here, not innocence but guilt.

(The Metal and the Flower)

Louis Dudek (Born in 1918)

Dudek is editor of Delta Press, which publishes a poetry magazine and books of poems. His own books include *The Searching Image, The Transparent Sea, Laughing Stalks,* and *Literature and the Press,* also two anthologies.

SPILLED PLASTER

A young and unfortunate artist I once knew
who modeled in clay and cast statues
in plaster of Paris was always amazed
at the lovely forms which
the white stuff he accidentally spilled
would make, on his hands, on chairs,
on the floor, in an earthenware bowl :
great white mushrooms of it, clouds,
cliffs and trees,
frozen waterfalls of milk and cream,
or just nothing, imaginary
nooks in the Gobi Desert, Antarctic caves;
not his work, not claimable
as artistic property, often destroyed
as soon as made, yet ironically
superior to his
club-faced Peruvian women.
So life, he said, spills outside the artist's pail
past the reach of brush or poem.

(Twenty-Four Poems)

Alfred Purdy (Born in 1918)

Purdy, perhaps more than any other contemporary English-Canadian poet, presents the people of this country and their varied, distant landscapes. His *The Cariboo Horses* has been acclaimed by readers of all ages.

THE COUNTRY NORTH OF BELLEVILLE

Bush land scrub land —
    Cashel Township and Wollaston
Elvezir McClure and Dungannon
green lands of Weslemkoon Lake
where a man might have some
    opinion of what beauty
is and none deny him
    for miles —

Yet this is the country of defeat
where Sisyphus rolls a big stone
year after year up the ancient hills
picnicking glaciers have left strewn
with centuries' rubble
    days in the sun
when realization seeps slow in the mind
without grandeur or self deception in
    noble struggle
of being a fool —

A country of quiescence and still distance
a lean land
    not fat
with inches of black soil on
    earth's round belly —
And where the farms are it's
    as if a man stuck
both thumbs in the stony earth and pulled

    it apart to make room
enough between the trees
for a wife
    and maybe some cows and
    room for some
of the more easily kept illusions —
And where the farms have gone back
to forest

are only soft outlines and
shadowy differences —
Old fences drift vaguely among the trees
        a pile of moss-covered stones
gathered for some ghost purpose
has lost meaning under the meaningless sky
        — they are like cities under water and
the undulating green waves of time are
        laid on them —

This is the country of our defeat and
        yet
during the fall plowing a man
might stop and stand in a brown valley of the furrows
        and shade his eyes to watch for the same
        red patch mixed with gold
        that appears on the same
        spot in the hills
        year after year
        and grow old
plowing and plowing a ten-acre field until
the convolutions run parallel with his own brain —

And this is a country where the young
        leave quickly
unwilling to know what their fathers know
or think the words their mothers do not say —

Herschel Monteagle and Faraday
lakeland rockland and hill country
a little adjacent to where the world is
a little north of where the cities are and
sometime
we may go back there
        to the country of our defeat
Wollaston Elvezir Dungannon
and Weslemkoon lake land
where the high townships of Cashel
        McClure and Marmora once were —
But it's been a long time since
and we must enquire the way
        of strangers —

(The Cariboo Horses)

Margaret Avison (Born in 1918)

A CONVERSATION

"First comes the queer pocket of quiet," he said.
He had no particular listener
For few can listen, on Saturday afternoon,
And the whirr of the ventilators, and the din
Of cellar-lights under cement-walled skylights
And cigar-smoke, made listening too hard.
Yet: "Before the debacle," he said
"Comes the queer peace." And he heard
Not the din, but that.
"Fish have a way of wavering through water.
They don't beat with their fins. What is their death
To me? I can't confront
A tree to really know it, and feel odd
To exchange glances with a squirrel,
And wish to keep my springs of life
Private from the Big Eye.
Well then. The fish has died. I'll not intrude there."
(Night over ocean after, and then day
Magnificently, as immaterial
As it is now, going on now out there,
To us . . .
And then the ivory slivers of the skeleton
Sidling, and sifting, in a slope, through green
and blue-green down . . . .

"Is it a new thing to be still?" A stranger
Entered the friendly circuit of his unfocus
And: "I remember," he went on,
"How it was, many years ago, to wait,
Lonesome and happy, in the organloft
On a May evening, with the applegreen
And the robin song stirring with delicate largeness
The tall cathedral shadows, till your fingers
Rounded the tips of your fingers, and you dared
Not move, as if a fresh sweet-flowing wound

Would open if you did, and let you lie
In lovely death there on the crimson steps
Under the long pale windows."
(And as if it had happened and were over
You felt a distinct, elegant compassion
To hear the children on their rollerskates
Out in the darkening street.)

"Elegant ?" said the first man,
"Those little vertebrae down on the ocean-floor ?"
(And smiled). "But in the shallow water
Sea is a burning-glass to sun,
And to look down, at those unwinking starfish,
Your eyeballs could explode."

The waiter dabbed his mop-cloth at the blur
Of half-moon spill and ash among their elbows.

"I want the loud sun," said the man,
"Through jungle, and a big brass horn
To wet my lips on. See, my lips are swollen.
The sun does that. Thundering down in hundredweights
Swarmed on the sun that thundered down before it
And beats you down and makes you fight.
                              I want
A big brass horn to blow."
    "But the debacle . . ." said the stranger, rising with
An unhappy, nervous smile.

(Winter Sun)

Peter Miller (Born in 1920)

Born in England, Miller came to Canada in 1939, and is now with the Canadian Bankers' Association.

Active in the publishing programme of Contact Press, his own most recent book is *A Shifting Pattern*.

DEMENAGEMENT

Firefly of pleasure
has sparked this place;
echo of whippoorwill
has sounded it for sorrow.

Now I leave this gentle street
as at an era's end.
Gravely turns back
my silvered judas-hand
and waves its betrayal
of lovely time :
years that I kiss
before I foresake them
while the future lies barren
as a potter's field.

With friends, I have here sipped night
(wet our tongues with starlit laughter);
alone, have kindled dawn awake
and, alchemist, transmuted rain to sun,
golden my wishes.

In this once-smiling hall
the mirrors refuse my face.
The walls, all rouge rubbed clean,
wear their plaster as the mask
of a waxen mannequin.

I sit here, of faded ink,
a pronoun in my own diary.
Its pages tell me that my self
has left this dwelling where my body lingers
blind, embalmed, mouthing through linen
a mute riddle to the sky.

(A Shifting Pattern)

James Reaney (Born in 1926)

Three times winner of Governor-General's medals, Reaney is best known for *The Red Heart* and *A Suit of Nettles*. His plays, such as *The Kildeer* and *The Easter Egg*, are gaining considerable attention. A most prolific writer and teacher, Reaney edits the magazine *Alphabet*.

DARK LAGOON

Here lies the newborn child
Who, lately, lay within his mother
And stood beside a dark lagoon
Beneath a sunless, starless sky.
Great trees of thick foliage and stout trunks
Hid someone who, far away,
Seemed to be knocking out this epitaph
With muffled chisel on muffled stone :
"This child will someday die."
But these sounds came really
From his secret Sun,
His mother's heart that hung
Unseen in that dark sky.
The heart, whose tick-tocking
Was life to him, still prophesied
The ticking chisel of the monument-maker
As it should someday carve his name,
His mother's heart, the reason for his being,
Was yet the first clock he ever heard.

Here lies the baby innocent.
He is hardly as large
As the Gettysburg Address
And has never heard
The cry of "Eenie, meenie, minie, moe,"
By which children choose a loser in a game
And by which Fate seems to choose
Which children shall be which :
One-eyed, wilful, hare-lipped, lame,
Poor, orphans, idiots, or rich.
Nor has he read stories where
People cry, "I
Am betrayed"; a notion
That shall haunt him all his life

As also shall that dark lagoon
Where once he stood
And seemed in a grave
Though he had not yet been born;
And seemed to hear his mother's heart
Though also a clock
That with little clicking mouthfuls
Began to eat his time.

(The Red Heart)

Raymond Souster (Born in 1921)

An urban poet, whose particular milieu is Toronto, Souster's books include *City Hall Street, A Local Pride, Place of Meeting, Ten Elephants on Yonge Street,* and *The Colour of the Times,* his Collected Poems, which won the Governor-General's award. The life force of Contact Press, he edited *New Wave Canada,* an anthology of young Canadian poets.

MAY 15TH

May 15th :
                the birds begin to nudge me
awake before the dawn. When I finally look out
into the morning the Manitoba maples
have finally put out their first
clusters of leaves shape of a clenched fist. A squirrel
climbs warily up onto the white-faced oval
of the bird bath and takes a long cool
drink. At least he only comes there
the same as the birds, with nothing on his mind
but thirst. The cats are a different matter.
In no time at all they've sensed
the possibilities — one of them is always lurking
not too far off hoping for a kill . . . .
                                kill or be killed,
that's the law of nature, and the law
of the lawless of the world, with their inter-continental
missiles, their bombers, their bombs, all trigger-happy
to prove it

                    but it's not my law, even though
the only ones listening to the poets these days
are the poets themselves, inbred generation
of lost souls, with their "little" magazines
their private presses their government grants
to get away from a country they secretly hate
but don't know how to come to terms with :
                                        and they've taken poetry
to the universities, buried it under text-books, mythologies,
so what comes out is as dead as the walls
they hide behind, as brittle as the chairs
their fat asses vegetate on, as pointless
as the anthologies they edit, one eye
on the Foundations . . .
                        (but why the hell talk about poetry
on such a day ?)
                    over in Geneva
the statesmen of the power cults are assembling
behind round and square tables to decide
the fate of the world — state regimentation
or capitalistic automation — this will be decided
more by the fitness of livers
after a month of vodka and Canadian Club
than by any honesty, humanity . . . .
                            (but why the hell talk about Geneva
and the statesmen of death on such a day ?)
                                here in Toronto
the long-hanging green tits of the willows
almost arouse the muck and filth of the Don
and for a moment bring life back
into this cancerous stream : the sky above Queen Street
is so maiden blue that one can almost forget
the bug-crawling food in these windows, spit on the sidewalks
and the worn lungs coughing it up : while at noon a naked woman
clad only in three yards of ticker-tape stands up in the
                        Stock Exchange
and cries out : how much am I offered ? (she is sold
for ten thousand shares
of a penny mining stock and trading resumes as usual) :
                                            I myself
take the road along the Humber valley, where workmen
struggle with huge concrete blocks, changing the course of
                this river (pus carrier
garbage dump of excretement) where still a few birds

keep to the trees, where there's no gasoline stench, where
                    ducks can waddle up on the shale
without being fired at, where the sky is still visible, sun warm,
with no soot-ivied buildings cornering the spring air, distilling it
with furnace-ash, street dust, and exhaust fumes :
                                          I look down
in the depths of a green-slimed rock-clustered pool
where nothing moves to the eye but small bubbles rising and rising
to the surface, now here, now there . . . .
                              in these times
keep your mind calm as this pool, go out into life
and let it burst around you, let it blossom through your
                    heart like this spring that today
promises to never end :
                    and be earth's forerunner.

(Place of Meeting)

Joan Finnigan (MacKenzie) (Born in 1925)

Miss Finnigan has been a | Her best-known work is
teacher and journalist. | *A Dream of Lilies.*

IN MEMORY OF ELIZABETH
(DEC. 16, 1962, AGED 37)

By the time I got the news here
she had folded her hands in the ground,
Ophelia of the First Snows,
adrift in a valley of flakes.

I suspect her of a dream larger than ours
suspended on a too-high hook
or of a view from other windows
that gave her no hope.

No hawsers nor lanyards
of love
could anchor her

on the tidal seas
in which she sailed;
the eye of her storm
defied riding out
or refuge

and last Sunday morning
she hung our despair
in her garage
as the murderer
bears to the gallows
our guilt.

the quixotic stars
breaking on the dark
shores of this night
light the way she fled

light where we all stand
between cliff
and web.

(A Dream of Lilies)

Eli Mandel (Born in 1922)

Mandel has a new book of poems, and is well regarded for his work in *Fuseli Poems* and *Black and Secret Man.* In collaboration with Jean-Guy Pilon he edited *Poetry 62,* and is now compiling another anthology. In 1963 he was awarded the President's Medal for poetry.

ENTOMOLOGY

Listen. There are some rooms
        sticky with the gut of lies
where spidery ladies squat
        over the husks of dead blue
        reputations

and I have seen the grasshopper mouths
of men nibbling at the green
branching words of poets

and from minds like shut closets
little white thoughts
sometimes flutter out

I shudder to think of what they have eaten,
especially when they were fat pale larvae,
the massed grave thoughts of mediocrity.

(Fuseli Poems)

Francis Sparshott *(Born in 1926)*

Professor of Ethics at University of Toronto, Sparshott has written *The Structure of Aesthetics* and *An Enquiry into Goodness*. His most recent book of poems is *A Divided Voice*.

A CASE OF PSYCHASTHENIA IN A SCHOOL-TEACHER

During the first year he would stand bewildered,
Speechless. The children roared,
Buffeted him. At evening he went home,
Told no one. At last they found him.

In the second year the wards received him,
Drugs shocked and soothed. He fell sick,
Nearly died, but his strength saved him.
He was helpful around the wards, but nothing could be done
For him, he went home.

By the third year he was given a testimonial and
Left the county, to plant beans and lettuce;
Read novels, greeted his friends
Loudly and cheerfully by the wrong names.

In the fourth year he could not remember
How potatoes are planted; muttered, hummed cheerlessly,

Snapped his fingers; if left alone
Would bicycle through the town, searching, till he fell
Fainting. Strangers brought him home.

In the fifth year he could neither read nor
Chat; lay long abed. His weakness
Grew beyond woman's helping; strength stayed
Past guidance. The wards received him.

In the sixth year the wards held him.
He did not look for his wife if she could not come;
If she came, he knew. He sickened, nearly died.
But his strength saved him.
His last word was "yes."

In the seventh year his son made these verses.
Thinking this useful knowledge : what may come
To a gentle and good man, loved by many,
Who had worked long and painfully for small reward;

Thinking it right, too, to proclaim
A wife's endurance
Who with patient care and without hope tended
Her husband's grave
For those years till the wards received him.

(A Divided Voice)

Phyllis Webb (Born in 1927)

Miss Webb is a programme organizer for the CBC's "Ideas" series, and has written three books of poems: *Even Your Right Eye, The Sea Is Also a Garden* and *Naked Poems*. Earlier work is found in *Trio*.

FLUX

Who would call me to still centres
needs a lesson in desire.
I am fire's ephemeral
boast on Heraclitean air.

Who would label me with names
needs my unbaptizing touch;
requisite of entities
is the constant, moving ash.

Who would kiss me on the mouth
claiming me another self
needs my body on their flesh
tasting little bites of death,

death rerising in desire
naming nothing but its hope,
spiralling in calling flights
flaming into nothing's throat.

Nothing finally is final —
every love is a rain
opening the bud to fire
asking and receiving its own Easter.

(The Sea is Also a Garden)

D. G. Jones (Born in 1929)

Jones' first book of poems, *Frost on the Sun,* appeared in 1957, and the second, *The Sun is Axeman,* in 1961. He teaches English at the University of Sherbrooke.

BEAUTIFUL CREATURES BRIEF AS THESE

Like butterflies but lately come
From long cocoons of summer
These little girls start back to school
To swarm the sidewalks, playing-fields,
And litter air with colour.

So slight they look within their clothes,
Their dresses looser than the Sylphus's wings,
It seems that even if the wind alone
Were not to break them in the lofty trees,
They could not bear the weight of *things.*

And yet they cry into the morning air
And hang from railings upside down
And laugh, as though the world were theirs
And all its buildings, trees, and stones
Were toys, were gifts of a benignant sun.

(The Sun is Axeman)

Jay Macpherson (Born in 1931)

Miss Macpherson wrote *Nineteen Poems* and *O Earth Return,* but her major work is *The Boatman,* which won the Governor-General's award. *Four Ages of Man* is her book on the classical myths, for students.

STORM

That strong creature   from before the Flood,
headless, sightless,   without bone or blood,
a wandering voice,   a travelling spirit,
butting to be born,   fierce to inherit
acreage of pity,   the world of love,
the Christian child's kingdom,   and remove
the tall towered gates   where the proud sea lay
crouched on its paws   in the first day —
came chaos again,   that outsider
would ride in,   blind steed, blind rider;
till then walls at windows,   denies relief,
batters the body   in speechless grief,
thuds in the veins,   crumples in the bone,
wrestles in darkness   and alone
for kingdoms cold,   for salt, sand, stone,
forever dispossessed.

          Who raised this beast,
this faceless angel,   shall give him rest.

(The Boatman)

Mary Allan (Thomson)

Miss Allan is an Albertan. | *Dark Road*, won the Donald
Her most successful work, | French award for poetry.

LANDING IN VICTORIA, B. C.

Against the scrawny comfort of the crane-legged pier
the ship shudders, feeling the shore coils tighten.
Sullen, she subsides and the brackish port-locked water
touching tentatively, laps her sea-knowing hull.

Deep within, the voyagers crowd one another,
poking like trees above the luggage bushes,
tightening their arms around satchels, around babies,
around themselves, awaiting release.

Thrust of forward motioning.
Hands clutch at straps, elbows clamp, heads bend,
shuffling and shouldering down the gangplank.
Damp-nosed, the land wind nuzzles necks.
Into the wooden passageway their heels tap sharply.
The floor clatters a story, over and over.
Flowing and flapping through the sheathing corridor
they burst to the flowering sunlight.

The cluster of waiting people, like a sponge,
soaks them up and away.

(Canadian Poetry Magazine)

Alden Nowlan (Born in 1933)

Nowlan's most recent books of poems are *Under the Ice, Wind in a Rocky Country* and *The Things Which Are.*

His work is also found in *Five New Brunswick Poets;* his short stories in the Pacey and Rimanelli volumes.

THE GENEALOGY OF MORALS

Take any child dreaming of pickled bones
shelved in a coal-dark cellar understairs
(we are all children when we dream) the stones
red-black with blood from severed jugulars.

Child Francis, Child Gilles went down those stairs,
returned sides, hands and ankles dripping blood.
Bluebeard and gentlest saint. The same nightmares
instruct the evil as inform the good.

(Five New Brunswick Poets)

Leonard Cohen (Born in 1934)

Cohen has written four books of poems : *Let Us Compare Mythologies, The Spice Box of Earth, Flowers for*

Hitler and *Parasites of Heaven.* He has also done two novels : *The Favourite Game* and *Beautiful Losers.*

FOR E.J.P.

I once believed a single line
in a Chinese poem could change
forever how blossoms fell
and that the moon itself climbed on
the grief of concise weeping men
to journey over cups of wine
I thought invasions were begun for crows
to pick at a skeleton
dynasties sown and spent
to serve the language of a fine lament

I thought governors ended their lives
    as sweetly drunken monks
telling time by rain and candles
    instructed by an insect's pilgrimage
      across the page — all this
so one might send an exile's perfect letter
to an ancient hometown friend

I chose a lonely country
    broke from love
      scorned the fraternity of war
I polished my tongue against the pumice moon
    floated my soul in cherry wine
      a perfumed barge for Lords of Memory
to languish on to drink to whisper out
    their store of strength
      as if beyond the mist along the shore
their girls their power still obeyed
    like clocks wound for a thousand years
I waited until my tongue was sore

Brown petals wind like fire around my poems
    I aimed them at the stars but
      like rainbows they were bent
before they sawed the world in half
    Who can trace the canyoned paths
      cattle have carved out of time
wandering from meadowlands to feasts
    Layer after layer of autumn leaves
      are swept away
Something forgets us perfectly

(Flowers for Hitler)

John Robert Colombo (Born in 1936)

Colombo is Managing Editor of *The Tamarack Review,* and his most recent books are *The Great Wall of China* and *Abracadabra.*

He calls the following "found poems," poetic rearrangements of letters by William Lyon Mackenzie, written prior to the Rebellion of 1837.

IMMIGRANTS

Quebec,
April 22nd to 25th,
1831.
One forenoon
I went on board the ship
Airthy Castle,
from Bristol,
immediately after her arrival.
The passengers were in number 254,
all in the hold or steerage;
all English, from about Bristol,
Bath, Frome, Warminster, Maiden Bradley, etc.
I went below,
and truly it was a curious sight.
About 200 human beings,
male and female,
young, old, and middle aged;
talking, singing, laughing, crying, eating, drinking,
        shaving, washing;
some naked in bed, and others dressing to go
        ashore;
handsome young women (perhaps some)
and ugly old men,
married and single;
religious and irreligious.
Here a grave matron
chaunting selections
from the latest edition
of the last new hymn book;
there, a brawny plough-boy
"pouring forth the sweet melody
of Robin Adair."
These settlers were poor,
but in general
they were fine-looking people,

and such as I was glad to see come to America.
They had had a fine passage
of about a month,
and they told me
that no more ship loads of settlers
would come from the same quarter
this year.
I found that it was
the intention of many of them
to come to Upper Canada.
Fortune may smile on some,
and frown on others;
but it is my opinion
that few among them will forget
being cooped up below deck
for four weeks
in a moveable bed-room,
with 250 such fellow-lodgers
as I have endeavoured to describe.

NEGROES IN UPPER CANADA

One day last summer a poor black girl,
who had escaped from the whip-lash to this side
        the water,
was seized on a Sunday, near Queenston,
in broad daylight, between eleven and noon,
by two hired scoundrels,
who hauled and pulled her through that village;
she screaming and crying in the most piteous and
        heart-rending manner,
and her ruffian cream-coloured tormentors
laughing at her distress,
and amusing the villagers with the cock-and-bull
        story
that she had stolen five hundred dollars,
and that the money had been found in her bundle.
To the everlasting disgrace of the inhabitants of
        Queenston,
they stood by, many of them,
and allowed the poor African lass
to be placed by main force on board the ferry-boat
which was to carry her back into slavery

of a far worse nature than she had formerly
    experienced.
Her lot would now be, 1st, exemplary punishment,
and 2nd, a slow murder (for so it may be called)
in the unhealthy climate of the rice or sugar
    plantations.
Is it not time that kidnapping of this sort, in Upper
    Canada,
were put an end to
by the strong arm of the law ?

CANADIANS ALL

So let it be with British America —
let every national distinction cease from among us —
let not the native Canadian
look upon his Irish or Scottish neighbour
as an intruder,
nor the native of the British Isles
taunt the other about stupidity and incapacity.
Rather let them become as one race,
and may the only strife among us
be a praiseworthy emulation
as to who shall attain the honour of conferring
the greatest benefits on the country of our birth —
or the land of our choice.

George Bowering (Born in 1936)

Bowering is editor of the Poetry magazine *Imago,* and his own books of poems include *Points on the Grid* and *The Silver Wire.*

Now with the Department of English, University of Western Ontario, he has written a novel, entitled *Mirror on the Floor.*

RED BOOTS (kick Coleridge in Wordsworth's ass)

My brain grew in a greenhouse,
vine as winding as a thought
of white pastures,
real dancing boots,
the globes of water waiting at its roots.

The boots (though) red
as blood in the brain,
let me have off supposition & see

less than divine brown legs
stand in them & are bare
above the knee.

    No green-
house grows a thing that moves
as lovely. Let me feel

those legs among mine, &
the red boots may walk
off the edge of my mind.

Daryl Hine (Born in 1936)

Hine's books of poems include *The Carnal and the Crane, The Devil's Picture Book* and *The Wooden Horse.*

He wrote a novel, *The Prince of Darkness,* and *Polish Subtitles,* based on his Warsaw experiences.

WHEN SUMMER WAS ENDOWED

When summer was endowed with tongues of fire
and the difficult parley of the spirit spoke,
forgetting forms, confusing here and there
the word, the touch, the language and the look,
indifference brought together for an hour
the deaf-mute and his silent paramour.

When autumn saw the ash upon the tree,
the phoenix singing in the burning wood,
the air grown perilous with falconry
the earth made scarlet by the quarry's blood,
religion claimed them, and morality,
as darkness falls upon the golden eye.

As winter heard the key within the lock
turn softly, and the hawk upon the air,
alarm within the crowing of a cock
awoke adultress and adulterer.
The cold that had its way through earth and rock
controlled them in the ardour of their look.

The priest that gave the sermon spoke of spring,
the sun reflected in a thousand groves,
and twigs as if diseased with burgeoning;
he stopped to lay the blame on primal love.
But primal lovers in his chorus sing,
too well acquainted with the season's sting.

(The Fiddlehead)

Lionel Kearns (Born in 1937)

One of the most promising poets in the West, Kearns' work is found in both the Oxford and Penguin Books of Canadian Verse. Publication of *Pointing* is imminent and a second manuscript completed.

REMAINS

Have you ever noticed
how a dead man's
personal articles

Take on a certain
contentious
air

As if they're offended
at being left
and are making things
difficult
out of spite ?

What to do with them ?

Books
aren't a problem
but what about

These other
scraps
of uselessness :

A piece of shabby lace
this old photograph
of god-knows-who
with something
scribbled on the back

Or that unfinished manuscript
an inch in dust
and dedicated
to his son ?

JOHN NEWLOVE

Imagine that
and him
with no family
at all

John Newlove (Born in 1938)

Newlove grew up in Saskatchewan but is now living in Vancouver. He is best known for his verse collections *Elephants Mothers and Others* and *Moving in Alone*. He is an interesting and gifted writer.

BY THE CHURCH WALL

The mocking faces appear in the churchyard,
appear as I curl on the hard ground
trying to sleep — trying to sleep
as the voices call me, asking why
must I always be frightened and dreaming ?

I have travelled this road many times,
though not in this place, tired
in the bones and the long blistered feet,
beneath a black mass of flat clouds,
dry in a damned and useless land.

Frogs croak hollowly, the loons cry
their thin bewildered song on a far-off lake,
the wind rises and the wet grass waves;
by the wall of the white rural church
I count a thousand to go to sleep.

But it will not happen. The faces
float before me, bloated and grinning,
succubus and incubus, a child
screams in a house across the road;
I turn and turn in my fear.

There is nothing to hurt me here,
and I know it, but an ancient dread
clenches my belly and fluttering heart,

and in the cold wet grass I count
what may happen and what has.

All the mistakes and desires are here,
old nameless shame for my lies,
the boy's terrible wish to be good and
not to be alone, not to be alone,
to be loved, and to love.

I remember a letter a friend sent,
trivial and gossiping, quite plain,
of no consequence to him, casually typed
and then signed easily by hand,
All our love, and wish I could say that.

But I lie alone in the shadowed grass,
fond only, incapable of love or truth,
caught in all I have done, afraid
and unable to escape, formulating
one more ruinous way to safety.

(Moving in Alone)

Saint-Denys-Garneau (1912-1943)

Membre de l'équipe de *La Relève,* puis vivant de plus en plus retiré du monde, écrivant des poèmes et son journal, il est décédé à l'âge de trente et un ans. Son destin exemplaire a peut-être exercé une plus grande influence que son oeuvre écrite. On a publié son *Journal* (1954), ses *Poésies complètes* (1949) et ses *Lettres à ses amis* (1967). Ses *Regards et Jeux dans l'espace* (1937) furent avec les poèmes de Grandbois à l'origine du renouveau poétique au Canada français. Ils marquent la fin du régionalisme et du romantisme.

ACCOMPAGNEMENT

Je marche à côté d'une joie
D'une joie qui n'est pas à moi
D'une joie à moi que je ne puis pas prendre

Je marche à côté de moi en joie
J'entends mon pas en joie qui marche à côté de moi
Mais je ne puis changer de place sur le trottoir
Je ne puis pas mettre mes pieds dans ces pas-là
                              et dire voilà c'est moi

Je me contente pour le moment de cette compagnie
Mais je machine en secret des échanges
Par toutes sortes d'opérations, des alchimies,
Par des transfusions de sang
Des déménagements d'atomes
                    par des jeux d'équilibre

Afin qu'un jour, transposé,
Je sois porté par la danse de ces pas de joie
Avec le bruit décroissant de mon pas à côté de moi
Avec la perte de mon pas perdu
                    s'étiolant à ma gauche
Sous les pieds d'un étranger
                    qui prend une rue transversale.

ACCUEIL

Moi ce n'est que pour vous aimer
Pour vous voir
Et pour aimer vous voir

Moi ça n'est pas pour vous parler
Ça n'est pas pour des échanges
                    conversations

Ceci livré, cela retenu
Pour ces compromissions de nos dons

C'est pour savoir que vous êtes,
Pour aimer que vous soyez

Moi ce n'est que pour vous aimer
Que je vous accueille
Dans la vallée spacieuse de mon recueillement
Où vous marchez seule et sans moi
Libre complètement

Dieu sait que vous serez inattentive
Et de tous côtés au soleil
Et tout entière en votre fleur
Sans une hypocrisie
en votre jeu

Vous serez claire et seule
Comme une fleur sous le ciel
Sans un repli
Sans un recul de votre exquise pudeur

Moi je suis seul à mon tour
autour de la vallée
Je suis la colline attentive
Autour de la vallée
Où la gazelle de votre grâce évoluera
Dans la confiance et la clarté de l'air

Seul à mon tour j'aurai la joie
Devant moi
De vos gestes parfaits
Des attitudes parfaites
De votre solitude

Et Dieu sait que vous repartirez
Comme vous êtes venue
Et je ne vous reconnaîtrai plus

Je ne serai peut-être pas plus seul
Mais la vallée sera déserte
Et qui me parlera de vous ?

(Regards et Jeux dans l'Espace, 1937)

Rina Lasnier (Née en 1915)

Journaliste, bibliothécaire, membre du Conseil des Arts du Québec et de l'Académie canadienne-française, son oeuvre abondante est un des sommets de la poésie canadienne-française. D'un lyrisme de plus en plus dépouillé, cette oeuvre diverse est d'inspiration essentiellement religieuse. On trouvera ici le début d'un de ses plus longs poèmes, *La Malemer,* qui est l'expression de la quête de la lumière et de la pureté au milieu de la nuit agitée des tourments humains.

LA MALEMER

> *L'homme cherche sa densité et non pas son bonheur.*
> Saint-Exupéry

Je descendrai jusque sous la malemer où la nuit jouxte la nuit — jusqu'au creuset où la mer forme elle-même son malheur,

sous cette amnésique nuit de la malemer qui ne se souvient plus de l'étreinte de la terre,

ni de celle de la lumière quand les eaux naissaient au chaos flexueux de l'air,

quand Dieu les couvrait du firmament de ses deux mains — avant la contradiction du Souffle sur les eaux,

avant ce baiser sur la mer pour dessouder la mer d'avec la mer — avant le frai poissonneux de la Parole au ventre de l'eau la plus basse,

avant la division des eaux par la lame de la lumière — avant l'antagonisme des eaux par l'avarice de la lumière.

Toute salive refoulée de silence — je regoûterai aux eaux condamnées de ma naissance;

eau fautive de la naissance cernant l'innocence du sang — et tu pends à la vie comme le fruit de l'arbre contredit;

est-il nuit plus nouvelle que la naissance — est-il jour plus ancien que l'âme ?

maternité mystérieuse de la chair — asile ouvert aux portes du premier cri, et la mort plus maternelle encore !

Face fiancée de la haute mer axée sur la spirale du souffle — malemer séquestrée aux fosses marines de la fécondité;

haute mer ! oeil fardé du bleu des légendes — moire des images et des étoiles éteintes;

eau joyeuse au trébuchet des ruisseaux — danseuse au nonchaloir des fontaines;

chair plastique de ta danse — parole aventurière de ta danse et phénix de ton esprit voyager par la flamme verte de la danse;

amoureuse livrée au vertige des cataractes et tes lentes noces au lit des fleuves — fidèle à la seule alliance zodiacale comme à ta hauteur originelle;

eau circulaire et sans autre joug que le jeu de tes voies rondes — c'est toi l'erre de nos fables et la sécheresse de notre bouche;

à l'envers des nuages, nous avons vu tes métamorphoses — et ton sommeil de cristal, ô momie couchée sur les pôles;
eau ascensionnelle — j'ai entendu la rumeur de ton mensonge redescendre dans l'oreille étroite de la conque;

tu joues aux osselets avec les coquillages — tes mains jouent sur toutes les grèves du monde avec le bois mort des cadavres;

sur toutes les tables de sable — tu prends l'aunage de ta puissance et de ton déferlement;

tentative du guet des falaises — j'ai vu l'épaulée féminine de tes marées pour effriter leur refus de pierre;

fiancée fluente des vents durs et précaires — comment te délieras-tu de la fatalité de ton obéissance ?

Purifiée par l'eau la plus lointaine — comment te laveras-tu de la salure des morts ?

Haute mer ! je refuse ta rose d'argent dispersée sur les sables — et ton essor dispersé en écume;

je ne serai plus la mouette de tes miroirs — ni l'hippocampe droit
de tes parnasses houleux;

haute mer! je salue la croix du sud renversée sur ton sein —
et je descends amèrement sous la nuit océanique de la malemer!

Malemer, mer stable et fermée à la foudre comme à l'aile —
mer prégnante et aveugle à ce que tu enfantes,

emporte-moi loin du courant de la mémoire — et de la longue
flottaison des souvenirs;

hale-moi dans ta nuit tactile — plus loin dans ton opacité que
la double cécité de l'oeil et de l'oreille;

malemer, toi qui ne montes plus sur la touffe fleurie des prés —
comme une pensée fatiguée des images,

toi qui ne laboures plus les grèves au cliquetis des cailloux —
remuement de pensées au hasard des vocables,

toi que n'enchaîne plus la chaîne des marées — ni le bref honneur
des révoltes verticales,

que je sois en toi ce nageur rituel et couché — comme un secret
aux plis des étoffes sourdes;

sans foulée calculée — que je circule par tes chemins sans
arrivages,

malemer — rature mon visage et noie cette larme où se refont
des clartés,

que j'oublie en toi les frontières ambiguës de mon propre jour —
et la lucide distance du soleil.

NAISSANCE OBSCURE DU POÈME

dans la pourpre muette de l'amant,
Comme l'amante endormie dans l'ardente captivité — immobile

fluente et nocturne à la base du désir — obscurcie de sommeil et travestie d'innocence,

ses cheveux ouverts à la confidence — telles les algues du songe dans la mer écoutante,

la femme omniprésente dans la fabulation de la chair — la femme fugitive dans la fabulation de la mort,

et l'amant pris au sillage étroit du souffle — loin de l'usage viril des astres courant sur des ruines de feu,

elle dort près de l'arbre polypier des mots médusés — par l'étreinte de l'homme à la cassure du dieu en lui,

par cette lame dure et droite de la conscience — voici l'homme dédoublé de douleur,

voici la seule intimité de la blessure — l'impasse blonde de la chair sans parité;

voici l'évocatrice de ta nuit fondamentale, malemer — la nuit vivante et soustraite aux essaims des signes,

malemer, mer réciproque à ton équivoque profondeur — mer inchangée entre les herbes amères de tes pâques closes,

toute l'argile des mots est vénitienne et mariée au limon vert — tout poème est obscur au limon de la mémoire;

malemer, lent conseil d'ombre — efface les images, ô grande nuit iconoclaste !

Malemer, aveugle-née du mal de la lumière — comment sais-tu ta nuit sinon par l'oeil circulaire et sans repos de paupière ?

pierrerie myriadaire de l'oeil jamais clos — malemer, tu es une tapisserie de regards te crucifiant sur ton mal;

comment saurais-tu ta lumière noire et sans intimité — sinon par le poème hermétique de tes tribus poissonneuses ?

ô rime puérile des étages du son — voici l'assonance sinueuse et la parité vivante,

voici l'opacité ocellée par l'oeil et l'écaille — voici la nuit veillée par l'insomnie et l'étincelle;

entre les deux mers, voici le vivier sans servitude — et le sillage effilé du poème phosphorescent,

mime fantomatique du poème inactuel — encore à distance de rose ou de reine,

toute la race du sang devenue plancton de mots — et la plus haute mémoire devenue cécité vague;

pierre à musique de la face des morts — frayère frémissante du songe et de la souvenance;

malemer, quel schisme du silence a creusé ta babel d'eau — négation à quels éloges prophétiques ?

assises du silence sur le basalte et le granit — et sur les sinaïs noirs de tes montagnes sans révélation,

le vent n'a point de sifflement dans ton herbage — la pluie est sur toi suaire de silence,

veille la parole séquestrée dans l'éclair — faussaire de tes silences catégoriques,

tu l'entendras draguer tes étoiles gisantes, tes soleils tout démaillés — la haute mer lui portera ferveur,

pleureuse de la peine anonyme — la nuit lui est remise à large brassée amère,

chanteuse encore mal assurée — et c'est toi socle et cothurne inspiré,

fermentation de la parole en bulles vives — roses hauturières et blanches pour une reine aveugle.

(*Mémoire sans jours,* 1960)

Anne Hébert (Née en 1916)

Poétesse, romancière, scénariste et dramaturge, membre de la Société royale du Canada, mieux connue en France que la plupart des écrivains canadiens, son oeuvre, d'abord dominée par la hantise de la solitude, de la maladie et de la mort, indique une lente et progressive réconciliation avec la vie. On le constatera en comparant les deux poèmes qui suivent. Son récit *Le Torrent* (1950), dont on a lu le début dans les pages précédentes est un des récits les plus bouleversants de la littérature canadienne.

LE TOMBEAU DES ROIS

J'ai mon coeur au poing.
Comme un faucon aveugle.

Le taciturne oiseau pris à mes doigts
Lampe gonflée de vin et de sang,
Je descends
Vers les tombeaux des rois
Etonnée
A peine née.

Quel fil d'Ariane me mène
Au long des dédales sourds ?
L'écho des pas s'y mange à mesure.

(En quel songe
Cette enfant fut-elle liée par la cheville
Pareille à une esclave fascinée ?)

L'auteur du songe
Presse le fil,
Et viennent les pas nus

Un à un
Comme les premières gouttes de pluie
Au fond du puits.

Déjà l'odeur bouge en des orages gonflés
Suinte sous le pas des portes
Aux chambres secrètes et rondes,
Là où sont dressés les lits clos.

L'immobile désir des gisants me tire.
Je regarde avec étonnement
A même les noirs ossements
Luire les pierres bleues incrustées.

Quelques tragédies patiemment travaillées,
Sur la poitrine des rois, couchées,
En guise de bijoux
Me sont offertes
Sans larmes ni regrets.

Sur une seule ligne rangés :
La fumée d'encens, le gâteau de riz séché
Et ma chair qui tremble :
Offrande rituelle et soumise.

Le masque d'or sur ma face absente
Des fleurs violettes en guise de prunelles,
L'ombre de l'amour me maquille à petits traits précis;

Et cet oiseau que j'ai
Respire
Et se plaint étrangement.

Un frisson long
Semblable au vent qui prend, d'arbre en arbre,
Agite sept grands pharaons d'ébène
En leurs étuis solennels et parés.

Ce n'est que la profondeur de la mort qui persiste,
Simulant le dernier tourment
Cherchant son apaisement
Et son éternité
En un cliquetis léger de bracelets
Cercles vains jeux d'ailleurs
Autour de la chair sacrifiée.

Avides de la source fraternelle du mal en moi
Ils me couchent et me boivent;
Sept fois, je connais l'étau des os
Et la main sèche qui cherche le coeur pour le rompre.

Livide et repue de songe horrible
Les membres dénoués

Et les morts hors de moi, assassinés,
Quel reflet d'aube s'égare ici ?
D'où vient donc que cet oiseau frémit
Et tourne vers le matin
Ses prunelles crevées ?

(*Le Tombeau des Rois,* 1953)

MYSTÈRE DE LA PAROLE

Dans un pays tranquille nous avons reçu la passion du monde, épée nue sur nos deux mains posée

Notre coeur ignorait le jour lorsque le feu nous fut ainsi remis, et sa lumière creusa l'ombre de nos traits

C'était avant tout faiblesse, la charité était seule devançant la crainte et la pudeur

Elle inventait l'univers dans la justice première et nous avions part à cette vocation dans l'extrême vitalité de notre amour

La vie et la mort en nous reçurent droit d'asile, se regardèrent avec des yeux aveugles, se touchèrent avec des mains précises

Des flèches d'odeur nous atteignirent, nous liant à la terre comme des blessures en des noces excessives

O saisons, rivière, aulnes et fougères, feuilles, fleurs, bois mouillé, herbes bleues, tout notre avoir saigne son parfum, bête odorante à notre flanc

Les couleurs et les sons nous visitèrent en masse et par petits groupes foudroyants, tandis que le songe doublait notre enchantement comme l'orage cerne le bleu de l'oeil innocent

La joie se mit à crier, jeune accouchée à l'odeur sauvagine sous les joncs. Le printemps délivré fut si beau qu'il nous prit le coeur avec une seule main

Les trois coups de la création du monde sonnèrent à nos oreilles, rendus pareils aux battements de notre sang

En un seul éblouissement l'instant fut. Son éclair nous passa sur la face et nous reçûmes mission du feu et de la brûlure.

Silence, ni ne bouge, ni ne dit, la parole se fonde, soulève notre coeur, saisit le monde en un seul geste d'orage, nous colle à son aurore comme l'écorce à son fruit

Toute la terre vivace, la forêt à notre droite, la ville profonde à notre gauche, en plein centre du verbe, nous avançons à la pointe du monde

Fronts bouclés où croupit le silence en toisons musquées, toutes grimaces, vieilles têtes, joues d'enfants, amours, rides, joies, deuils, créatures, créatures, langues de feu au solstice de la terre

O mes frères les plus noirs, toutes fêtes gravées en secret; poitrines humaines, calebasses musiciennes où s'exaspèrent des voix captives

Que celui qui a reçu fonction de la parole vous prenne en charge comme un coeur ténébreux de surcroît, et n'ait de cesse que soient justifiés les vivants et les morts en un seul chant parmi l'aube et les herbes

(*Poèmes,* 1960)

Gilles Hénault (Né en 1920)

Journaliste, critique d'art, maintenant conservateur du Musée d'Art contemporain de Montréal, ce poète marqué par le surréalisme a cherché à retrouver et à exprimer les instincts primitifs de l'homme soumis aux forces telluriques.

TU M'EXORCISES

Mets ta main sur mon front
que je sache encore un peu ce que c'est que la vie
qui déplie sa fleur.
Ta main masque la mort
Tes yeux ont la couleur de mon bonheur
Ton sourire

débâcle d'horizon fermé
m'ouvre un chemin d'eau vive
Tes mots lancent des chevaux fous
dont l'écume se mêle au vent rouge de mon sang
Mets ta main sur mon front
que je sache encore ce que le mot présence veut dire.

Iles couleur d'orange et d'été
Iles je traverse vers vous sur l'arche de sa confiance.
Main lance des amarres
Qu'importe si le croc heurte le coeur
Je lirai tes vestiges sur les sables
Main tu peuples le monde
et par toi je sais que le présent n'est pas une
            étoffe illusoire
que je pourrais m'y rouler pour dormir

hamac suspendu hors du temps
avec autour un paysage immobile.
Des pensées nues se baignent dans tes yeux

Je reconnais leurs formes d'algue et de corail
leur transparence de poissons lumineux et aveugles.
Main fraîche palmée de rivières, joie fluide, jour vaste
et sonore, neige lente sur la calcination des heures
Toi seule a ce pouvoir
de dégivrer l'absence
de modeler les contours d'un jour minéral
de courber la lumière vers la planète où je m'exile
pour échapper aux girations des gestes inutiles.

(Sémaphore, 1962)

Paul-Marie Lapointe (Né en 1929)

Journaliste, maintenant directeur du *Magazine Maclean,* il fut aussi scénariste et a publié trois recueils de poésies inspirés par la misère des hommes et la puissance créatrice de la nature. Ses poèmes sont improvisés comme le meilleur jazz dont il est grand amateur.

ÉPITAPHE POUR UN JEUNE RÉVOLTÉ

tu ne mourras pas un oiseau portera tes cendres
dans l'aile d'une fourrure plus étale et plus chaude que
        l'été
aussi blonde aussi folle que l'invention de la lumière

entre les mondes voyagent des tendresses et des coeurs
des hystéries cajolantes comme la fusion des corps
en eux plus lancinantes
comme le lever et le coucher des astres
comme l'apparition d'une vierge dans la cervelle des
        miracles
tu ne mourras pas un oiseau nidifie ton coeur
plus intense que la brûlée d'un été quelque part
plus chaud qu'une savane parcourue par l'oracle
plus grave que le peau-rouge et l'incandescence

(les âmes miroitent
particulièrement le soir
entre chien et loup
                dans la pâleur des lanternes
                dans l'attisement des fanaux
                dans l'éblouissement d'une ombre au midi
                    du sommeil)

tu ne mourras pas

quelque part une ville gelée hélera ses cabs
une infanterie pacifique pour mûrir les récoltes
et le sang circulera
au même titre que les automobiles
dans le béton et la verdure

tu ne mourras pas ton amour est éternel

(*Pour les âmes,* 1965)

Roland Giguère (Né en 1929)

Graveur et poète, éditeur
à ses heures, Giguère a publié
quelques minces plaquettes réunies
dans *L'Age de la parole* (1965).
On y observe d'abord une révolte
contre l'univers ennemi,
puis une lente réconciliation
avec la vie grâce à l'amour
qui s'est exprimé surtout dans
Adorable femme des neiges (1959).

ROSES ET RONCES

à Denise

Rosace rosace les roses
roule mon coeur au flanc de la falaise
la plus dure paroi de la vie s'écroule
et du haut des minarets jaillissent
les cris blancs et aigus des sinistrés

du plus rouge au plus noir feu d'artifice
se ferment les plus beaux yeux du monde

rosace les roses les roses et les ronces
et mille et mille épines
dans la main où la perle se pose

une couronne d'épines où l'oiseau se repose
les ailes repliées sur le souvenir d'un nid bien fait

la douceur envolée n'a laissé derrière elle
qu'un long ruban de velours déchiré

rosace rosace les roses
les jours où le feu rampait sous la cendre
pour venir s'éteindre au pied du lit
offrant sa dernière étoile pour une lueur d'amour
le temps de s'étreindre
et la dernière chaleur déjà s'évanouissait
sous nos yeux inutiles

la nuit se raidissait dure jusqu'à l'aube

rosace les roses les roses et les ronces
le coeur bat comme une porte

que plus rien ne retient dans ses gonds
et passent librement tous les malheurs
connus et inconnus
ceux que l'on n'attendait plus
ceux que l'on avait oubliés reviennent
en paquets de petites aiguilles volantes
un court instant de bonheur égaré
des miettes de pain des oiseaux morts de faim
une fine neige comme un gant pour voiler la main
et le vent le vent fou le vent sans fin balaie
balaie tout sauf une mare de boue
qui toujours est là et nous dévisage

c'est la ruine la ruine à notre image

nous n'avons plus de ressemblance
qu'avec ces galets battus ces racines tordues
fracassés par une armée de vagues qui se ruent
la crête blanche et l'écume aux lèvres

rosace les ronces !

rosace les roses les roses et les ronces
les rouges et les noires les roses les roses
les roseaux les rameaux les ronces
les rameaux les roseaux les roses
sous les manteaux sous les marteaux sous les barreaux
l'eau bleue l'eau morte l'aurore et le sang des garrots
rosace les roses les roses et les ronces

et cent mille épines !

roule mon coeur dans la poussière de minerai
l'étain le cuivre l'acier l'amiante le mica
petits yeux de mica de l'amante d'acier trempée jusqu'à l'os
petits yeux de mica cristallisés dans une eau salée
de lame de fond et de larmes de feu
pour un simple regard humain trop humain

rosace les roses les roses et les ronces
il y avait sur cette terre tant de choses fragiles
tant de choses qu'il ne fallait pas briser
pour y croire et pour y boire

fontaine aussi pure aussi claire que l'eau
fontaine maintenant si noire que l'eau est absente

rosace les ronces
ce printemps de glace dans les artères
ce printemps n'en est pas un
et quelle couleur aura donc le court visage de l'été.

(*Les armes blanches,* 1954)

Sylvain Garneau (1930-1953)

Journaliste, puis comédien et annonceur à la radio, ce poète mort très jeune a laissé deux recueils de poésies où se mêlent un sentimentalisme suranné et une fantaisie souriante.

MON ÉCOLE

J'ai quatre bons amis, quatre rois fainéants.
Leurs fronts sont boucliers abritant mille rôles.
Ils dorment, à midi, du sommeil des géants,
Sur le bord des trottoirs, à l'ombre des écoles.

Comme les chats rétifs qui chassent dans les cours,
Ils voient, dans les buissons, des jungles éternelles;
Leurs ongles aiguisés claquent sur les tambours
Et le message va de poubelle en poubelle.

Leurs châteaux, malheureux derrière la cité,
Ont des carreaux brisés; et dans chaque fontaine
Croissent des nénuphars, au soleil de l'été,
Tandis que les gardiens s'en vont avec les reines.

Pendant ce temps, on voit sauter sur les trottoirs
Les enfants du quartier, légers comme des bulles;
Mais demain il pleuvra et, dans leurs yeux trop noirs,
Sous leurs fronts obstinés et doux comme le tulle,

Les châteaux d'autrefois, les princes, les géants,
Reviendront, pour danser au son des barcarolles.
— Les enfants du quartier sont des rois fainéants
Qui dorment, allongés sur les bancs des écoles.

(*Objets trouvés,* 1951)

Jean-Guy Pilon (Né en 1930)

Avocat, superviseur des émissions littéraires à Radio-Canada; il a fondé les Editions de l'Hexagone, la revue *Liberté* et organisé les Rencontres des poètes canadiens.

Sa poésie virile et laconique chante surtout la réconciliation du poète avec son pays et son peuple, après avoir surmonté les tentations du refus et de l'exil volontaire.

JE MURMURE LE NOM DE MON PAYS

Je murmure le nom de mon pays
Comme un secret obscène
Ou une plaie cachée
Sur mon âme
Et je ne sais plus
La provenance des vents
Le dessin des frontières
Ni l'amorce des villes

Mais je sais le nom des camarades
Je sais la désespérance de leur coeur
Et la lente macération
De leur vengeance accumulée

Nous sommes frères dans l'humiliation
Des années et des sourires
Nous avons été complices
Dans le silence
Dans la peur
Dans la détresse
Mais nous commençons à naître

A nos paroles mutuelles
A nos horizons distincts
A nos greniers
Et nos héritages

Oui
Nous sommes nus
Devant ce pays
Mais il y a en nous
Tant de paroles amères
Qui ont été notre pâture
Qu'au fond de l'humiliation
Nous allons retrouver la joie
Après la haine
Et le goût de laver à notre tour
Notre dure jeunesse
Dans un fleuve ouvert au jour
Dont on ne connaît pas encore
Les rives innombrables

Nous avons eu honte de nous
Nous avons des haut-le-coeur
Nous avons pitié de nous

Mais l'enfer des élégants esclaves
S'achèvera un jour de soleil et de grand vent

Je le dis comme je l'espère
Je le dis parce que j'ai le désir de mon pays
Parce qu'il faut comprendre
La vertu des paroles retenues

Aurions-nous seulement le droit
De serrer dans nos bras
Nos fragiles enfants
Si nous allions les ensevelir
Dans ces dédales sournois
Où la mort est la récompense
Au bout du chemin et de la misère
Aurions-nous seulement le droit
De prétendre aimer ce pays
Si nous n'en assumions pas
Ses aubes et ses crépuscules

Ses lenteurs et ses gaucheries
Ses appels de fleuves et de montagnes

Et la longue patience
Des mots et des morts
Deviendra parole
Deviendra fleur et fleuve
Deviendra salut

Un matin comme un enfant
A la fin d'un trop long voyage
Nous ouvrirons des bras nouveaux
Sur une terre habitable
Sans avoir honte d'en dire le nom
Qui ne sera plus murmuré
Mais proclamé

(*Pour saluer une ville*, 1963)

Fernand Ouellette (Né en 1930)

Licencié en sciences sociales, puis libraire, il est maintenant réalisateur à Radio-Canada. Poète austère et quelque peu cérébral, il est hanté par le soleil, source de lumière et de vie. Il a écrit la première biographie de Varèse.

NAISSANCE DE LA PAIX

à mes parents

Le blanc des ailes
oppresse la nuit.

Le long du temps
où l'Esprit se concentre.

Au corps pur de la Vierge
le sang repose.

La Paix fraîche comme une pousse,

lente comme une vague,
soulève le ventre lisse.

Peu à peu la sommeillante
    se fait geignante
et se resserre dans la froidure.

Trop tiède est l'haleine
    pour l'Amour qui va déchirer
                        la ténèbre.

La terre ne sait qu'une chair,
la fragile, la douloureuse,
la terre contracte le Verbe
    comme un fils de femme.

Au roc les cris se heurtent,
mais s'éteignent les grappes d'étincelles;
les cris longs et lilas
quand l'Infini pousse les fibres.
Ah! si pierre
    pouvait prendre flamme.

Les bêtes sont graves.

L'angoisse s'abat sur l'homme,
                le présent.

Déjà la paille est pourpre.
La Vie va venir près du givre.

Comme une oiselle vive
que la Vierge respire !

La foi
    dans ses prunelles monte forte et flambe.

Une aube de cire germe dans son visage.

        Le temps s'en retourne.
Sur Marie s'appuie le silence,
le grand silence
            avant le gémissement de l'Etre.

Si proche,
          si lointaine paraît la planète
pendant que le Christ s'enracine.

LA PAIX OUVRE SES PAUPIÈRES
                    ET LONGTEMPS FIXE LA MORT.

(*Le Soleil sous la mort*, 1965)

Gatien Lapointe (Né en 1931)

Docteur ès lettres, professeur de littérature, sa poésie simple, directe et dense a la rigueur intellectuelle d'apophtegmes et célèbre surtout la connaissance et la parole par lesquelles le poète impose son ordre aux choses. Incarnée, cette poésie affirme l'identification du poète avec son pays.

PRÉSENCE AU MONDE

C'est le premier matin du monde et j'interroge
Homme demeure errante dans le temps
Un nid fait son feu sous la pluie
Une femme enceinte fleurit son seuil
Un arbre tremble de mille paroles
La chaleur enveloppe l'univers
La lumière creuse des sources
Un secret bouge entre la terre et moi.

Je trouve d'instinct les mains du soleil
J'apprivoise l'odeur sauvage
Je pèse le temps d'un fruit qui rougit
Je dis le temps qui mûrit dans mon coeur
Un frisson élargit ma main
Un sourire aggrave mes yeux
Ma langue remplit d'eau le nuage flétri
Je ne vis que dans la lueur du combat.

Je fais des digues je plante des phares
Je souffle sous l'écorce du plaisir
Toute forme caresse un mot nouveau
Je parle au nom de tous les hommes
Je tends des filets et j'écoute
J'approche la terre de mon oreille
Je tire des images du fond de la terre
De mon toit je salue l'aurore de chaque homme.

Douce déchirante merveille d'être
Je me grise de voir et de toucher
Je m'enflamme de chaque floraison
Et chaque grain dore en moi ses épis
J'oriente le cours d'eau je donne élan au feu
Je révèle et je définis dans l'éphémère
Je touche le ciel du bout de la main
Et c'est le ciel qui me brûle les yeux.

Chaque mort de l'homme agrandit ma tombe
J'entends la plainte des oiseaux qu'on tue
Je vois le bond des bêtes qu'on enchaîne
Je conduis au jour l'arbre aveugle
Et je veille au fond de chaque blessure
Un destin m'identifie à chaque être
Je quitterai la peine du voyage
Je regarde au plus près de ma maison.

J'assemble des mots d'ombre et de lumière
Je traduis en oracles chaque souvenir
Et demain m'ouvre aujourd'hui sa demeure
Le monde est ma présence
Je borde mon chemin j'aiguise mes outils
Je sème et récolte au rythme du soleil
Et la nuit qui tombe ne me surprend pas
J'appelle un grand amour.

Je souffre et le sapin cache sa bouche
Quel secret coupe mon visage en deux
Quel mot à mi-chemin de naître et de mourir
J'ai un grand besoin d'habiter

Je mets des nids dans chaque main
Dans chaque pas je plante un mot d'espoir
Un feuillage établit l'harmonie de ma table
D'ici je dis oui au temps de la terre

J'abolirai la mort je vivrai à tout prix.

(*J'appartiens à la terre,* 1963)

Suzanne Paradis (Née en 1936)

Femme du poète Louis-Paul Hamel, romancière et essayiste, elle est surtout poète. Auteur prolifique, elle écrit dans l'enthousiasme des poèmes souvent diffus dont les meilleurs chantent la joie de vivre et d'aimer.

LA MALEBÊTE

Nous enverrons la mort pâlir dans un grand coffre
derrière un vieux visage osseux et des mains jointes

avec des fleurs à coeur fané et des mains ointes
d'huile et de sang, sous les éclats de cires d'ocre.

Nous chargerons son lit brûlant d'amère flamme
de plâtre et d'os, d'âmes en croix aux bouches d'ordre,

des vins figés, des pains qu'on a cessé de mordre
cessé de rompre en parts de faim, mie, croûte et lame.

Nous coucherons la mort sans front au lit d'épine
que le rosier ouvre à la rose au coeur du songe.

Que la douleur aux dents polies la broie et ronge
mort de poussière au teint de poudre et d'aveline !

Je veux sourire au pire orgueil, au pire outrage
mais l'amour tremble et veut pleurer du poids qu'il porte,

je veux survivre au pire mal de pire sorte,
l'ombre s'allume un feu de joie sur mes courages.

La mort déploie d'étranges ailes sur mes villes
roule, aux linteaux des chambres bleues où j'ai dormi,

des sommeils sourds poreux et doux comme une mie.
J'ai mal de mort au fond des yeux, l'aile immobile.

On m'avait mise à mieux me voir sur la colline,
on m'avait mise à mieux me fuir sur la montagne,

on a souillé de brouillards rouges la campagne
j'ai perdu l'aube et le midi dans les ravines.

Nous enverrons la mort brunir dans les solives
et les bois secs que les mois d'août ne mouillent plus

dans les clartés de lune opaque et continue
quand les vents fuient les cimetières et les grives.

Nous enverrons la mort pourrir dans nos blessures
puisqu'aucun lieu n'a plus de paix pour qu'on y veille,

puisqu'aucun sein n'a plus de lait, ni la groseille
de suc léger qu'on boit au fruit, à la chair sure.

Mains de douleur, gorges du temps, membres malades,
liez la mort en fagots noirs près des murailles,

que nos regards montés du fond de nos entrailles
lèvent enfin sur l'arbre vif, des yeux de jade.

(*La Malebête,* 1962)

Michèle Lalonde (Née en 1937)

Licenciée en philosophie, femme du Dr Yves Duchastel de Montrouge, sa poésie imagée et symboliste évoque surtout le mensonge du monde et la solitude du poète incapable de communier vraiment avec les autres.

IL Y A TROIS SAULES

il y a trois saules
qui s'enracinent au creux de nos mains
deux oiseaux d'ébène
à la hauteur de nos prunelles
une cicatrice d'argent
sur notre tempe

nous sommes au confluent des ciels
immobiles
rivés à l'espace impérissable
soustraits au fastidieux rythme des heures
la présence du sang dans nos veines
est inaltérable

nous voici devenus ce chant astral que nous percevions
et chacun de nos souvenirs
nous réinvente dans l'infini

(*Geôles,* 1959)

Saint-Denys-Garneau (1912-1943)

Ce poète a tenu un journal qui est un témoignage tragique sur la souffrance intérieure d'un artiste qui se sent impuissant à accepter le quotidien et incapable d'exprimer parfaitement cette impuissance. On y trouve des méditations sur les sujets les plus graves et des réflexions sur l'art.

INSOMNIE

Mercredi, 17 avril [1935]
puisque c'est le matin. 2 heures et demie.

Encore une comédie. Sottise ! Une comédie, et cela est bien loin d'être amusant. Quel ennui ! Et tout ce qu'on fait pour tâcher de le secouer. En vain.

Je me suis réveillé. Impossible de me rendormir. Alors, l'idée m'est venue de sortir. C'est la première fois que, dans mes insomnies l'idée me vient de sortir. J'ai lutté, indifféremment, car cela après tout m'était égal. Enfin ma petite curiosité a gagné, ma petite curiosité et mon petit espoir moribond qui me mènent toutes parts, « au cas où », comme je traîne ce livre ou ce papier dont je ne fais jamais rien.

Je suis sorti. J'ai pensé que peut-être le jour se lèverait bientôt. Alors la vie renaît dans le sépulcre des villes. Le bruit recommence dans la lumière blafarde. Les lumières pâlissent. Plus blêmes que la flamme des cierges dans le jour. En arêtes dures les maisons sur-gissent, les bâtisses carrées, les maisons mortes. Tout prend une couleur également terne, comme un long tableau d'ennui. Les rails luisent jusqu'au bout des rues, d'un dur reflet, aigus comme une lame. Le bruit renaît, l'acier contre l'acier crisse; un geignement acide. Où se croisent les rails, ces heurts qui brisent les nerfs. Les tramways : exas-pérations. Les roues des voitures des laitiers. Leur roulement sur le pavé et le trot lourd des chevaux. Les tramways se succèdent de plus en plus nombreux. D'abord vides, ils se peuplent petit à petit des pauvres hommes pour qui la vie recommence chaque jour, éternelle-ment pareille; l'effort, la subsistance, et plus rien. Figures mornes, rési-gnées, vidées par l'habitude. Et puis certaines, quel mystère ! qui sem-blent renaître chaque matin avec une énergie nouvelle, comme si cette journée allait être autrement que la veille avec son ennui.

(Les oiseaux chantent, frères de la lumière, mais comme étrangers, perdus parmi ces cahots sans voix.)

Lamentables matins des sépulcres dans la côte. Rien ne renaît, rien ne chante, rien ne correspond à la lumière qui vient du ciel. La clarté seule renaît; elle frappe les sépulcres, les dépouille de toutes ombres, de tous mystères. Elle s'étale crue sur leur nudité, et dévoile leur mort immobile : les voilà figés dans leur rigidité cadavérique. L'homme y passe, y vit, y souffre en étranger; et tout cela après sa mort n'aura pas changé d'un cheveu. D'autres prendront la place des morts et les mêmes caveaux les abriteront.

Ah ! songe aux matins de la nature où les mille souffles de la vie renaissent et répondent au jour, chantent avec la lumière et jaillissent à l'appel de la joie. Rien ne demeure indifférent. Les coqs sonnent l'éveil. La brise coule des montagnes, ondule selon les méandres de la vallée. Elle glisse sur le lac, en ondes successives de rides qui s'avancent. Elle agite les feuillages d'un frémissement immatériel, clair bruissement. C'est un soupir de toutes choses, comme une caresse très douce qui réveille sans heurt le calme de la nuit. Les oiseaux ont commencé de rouler leur note liquide, fluide, en même temps que le ciel de pâlir. Le voile se lève petit à petit, avec une douceur extrême. Le firmament s'immatérialise. La brume parfois glisse sur les collines et se ramasse aux creux que les souffles n'ont pas encore visités et qui retiennent plus longtemps l'ombre transparente de la nuit, comme jaloux de cette quiétude. Le voile se lève, et la lumière tranparaît. Discret avertissement. Et tout à coup, *l'évolution* s'accélère, quelques nuages attardés sont roses sur le ciel qui verdit. Et dans un éclatement soudain les rayons jaillissent jusqu'au zénith. Comme une cymbale au son d'or clair le soleil paraît à l'horizon, grandit, et la lumière revêt toutes choses, de son éclatante chanson de joie. C'est le jour.

Mais il n'est que 3 heures; tout est calme. La lumière ne se balance pas encore au ciel. Il pleut avec un triste bruit, l'eau se bouscule en gloussant dans les égouts. Dans les ruelles, les chattes se lamentent parmi leur jouissance déchirante. Les rues sont désertes, à peine ce restaurant où je viens échouer pour écrire ces lignes. [...]

(*Journal,* 1962)

Jean Le Moyne (Né en 1913)

Journaliste, traducteur, éditeur de Saint-Denys-Garneau, auteur d'essais personnels, pénétrants et discutés sur des sujets religieux et littéraires qui ont été réunis dans *Convergences* (1961). L'essai qui suit donnera une idée de l'homme et de son style.

DIALOGUE AVEC MON PÈRE

Longuement préparé par la curiosité intense et solitaire devant laquelle j'ai grandi, un dialogue s'amorça un jour entre mon père et moi, dialogue qui demeure l'expérience capitale et inépuisable de ma vie, dialogue ininterrompu par la mort et devenu un événement permanent, forme de tous mes autres événements et en dehors duquel en vérité il ne m'arrive rien.

Un garçon de dix-huit ans, de vingt ans, s'entretient avec son père du concile de Chalcédoine et du Brigandage d'Ephèse; le père met en garde son fils contre un saint Augustin détesté et l'initie aux gnostiques, et le fils reproche à saint Jérôme, que son père aimait comme un ancêtre de Lagrange, d'avoir tenu Jean Cassien pour un ivrogne. Ensemble ils essaient d'imaginer l'enseignement de Gamaliel, de mesurer l'ardeur de Paul, les élans de Pierre, et d'apprécier l'autorité de l'un et de l'autre; ils discutent la sainteté de David, en rêvent et s'en troublent. Ruth, Esther, Judith, Job, Tobie et Jonas, les patriarches, et les grands prophètes et les sages de l'Ecclésiaste et des Proverbes, passent de la familiarité savoureuse du père à l'attention présomptueuse du fils, pour qui tous ces personnages veulent devenir des proches.

Le chêne de Mambré, le Carmel, le Garizim, le puits de Jacob, les plages de Tibériade, les gués du Jourdain, la route de Béthanie, aucune composition de lieu, si minutieusement exercée fût-elle, ne me rendrait ces lieux-là dans la lumière et le relief de désir qui me les montra d'abord.

Le père rencontrait en son fils le premier ami avec qui il pouvait s'entretenir de ces choses, dont il n'avait sans doute pas parlé depuis ces années où, jeune médecin à Paris, avant l'autre guerre, en ce temps-là où on croyait encore au Grand Soir, des confrères anarchistes ou nihilistes avaient poussé à bout l'angoisse de son interrogation et déterminé sa quête.

Moi, au hasard et à la liberté des conversations, je recevais la Parole, non pas par un enseignement sûr, orthodoxe et figé, mais dans une incertitude passionnée, dans un risque de vie qui allait faire des Mots un piège certain, car ces Mots, les seuls auxquels il importe absolument de se laisser prendre sans égard à aucune convenance, avaient écorché quelqu'un avant de me parvenir. Ils ne valent qu'ainsi empâtés de chair.

Nos pilpouls n'étaient pas toujours paisibles, ni subtils, loin de là ! Nous étions deux pôles de même charge et nos divergences disposaient de violences égales, la sienne inusable et la mienne toute neuve. Il nous arrivait de nous quitter en fort mauvais termes, si mauvais que saint Jérôme lui-même y eût trouvé à redire. Bien entendu, j'étais ignorant comme un âne; quant à mon père, malgré ses énormes lectures, il n'était pas un savant. Mais nos échanges étaient de vie; j'étais gonflé d'anticipation jusqu'à l'angoisse et lui, il ne me disait rien qui n'eût en lui sa caution de douleur.

Qu'un exemple suffise à faire voir le prix extraordinaire de ces entretiens presque quotidiens. Un jour il m'appela pour m'apprendre la nouvelle suivante : « Savais-tu, me dit-il atterré, bouleversé, savais-tu que Jésus a très probablement été crucifié nu ? » Il m'avait appelé parce qu'il ne pouvait endurer tout seul sa compassion. Et quel diable aurait empêché que j'en reçoive quelque chose ?

Mon père avait une certaine préférence pour le troisième évangile, entre autres excellentes et péremptoires raisons, parce que Luc, médecin, était un confrère, comme Rabelais et le docteur Anton Tchékhov ! Il éprouvait aussi pour Marc une grande affection à cause de sa manière si concrète et de sa dépendance de Pierre. Sur saint Paul, notre accord était entier et nous rivalisions de ferveur et d'admiration. Seigneur ! qui me relira comme lui les salutations de l'Apôtre ? Qui saurait refaire pour moi le geste ému qu'il avait en me citant la fin de l'Epître aux Galates : « Voyez quels gros caractères ma main trace à votre intention ! » Ou ceux qu'il avait encore en désignant l'un après l'autre les différents personnages, objets de conseils et de souhaits, comme si ces amis de Paul l'eussent entouré, lui docteur Le Moyne, pour l'entendre lire la lettre !

Aux évangiles synoptiques, j'opposais Jean, comme étant plus réfléchi, plus évolué, plus mystique, surtout plus pascal, et par là achevé d'exemplaire façon. La Résurrection me mettait en joie. Pas lui. Le « ne me touche pas » du Christ à Madeleine, le blessait et renouvelait à chaque fois un vieux désarroi, un quasi-scandale. Et il se consolait à l'apparition aux disciples réunis en l'absence de Thomas, où le Seigneur, pour leur montrer la réalité de sa présence, mange avec eux, et à cette autre où Jésus lui-même prépare le déjeuner au bord du lac. Mais chaque apparition retenait pour lui le Sauveur dans sa présence fraternelle, dans cette familiarité quotidienne qu'il enviait aux apôtres d'une envie si terriblement charnelle, et bénie, je le sais maintenant.

Le don d'évocation qui lui faisait animer saint Paul avec tant de vérité, nulle part il ne l'aura exercé de plus saisissante façon que sur l'épisode d'Emmaüs. « Reste avec nous, car le soir vient... » Il se taisait à ces mots, fermait les yeux sur la nuit proche. Puis, se reprenant, il poursuivait et, à l'exclamation des deux disciples, « Notre coeur n'était-il pas brûlant en nous, tandis qu'il nous parlait dans le chemin... » se penchait vers moi, ouvrait les bras pour faire place à ce souvenir ardent, résumé de toutes les choses entendues en route, puis serrait les poings sur son coeur.

Je croyais qu'au départ du Christ sa foi défaillait; en réalité, elle rencontrait à ce moment son objet invisible. La défaillance était de sa chair et alors, son besoin de présence incarnée le faisait accourir à saint Paul, qu'il suivait pas à pas.

Je voyais donc là un détournement qui faussait le sens de Pâques, escamotait l'Ascension et compromettait l'économie de la Pentecôte. Je croyais discerner quelque complicité malsaine en sa sympathie pour Nicodème et Thomas, Madeleine et Pierre, Pierre surtout. Or j'avais lieu de me méfier, car mon père était un vrai Karamazov. Il avait des Karamazov la double nature, leurs dons spirituels, leur charme envoûtant, leurs appétits terrifiants. « Il est venu vers moi comme un saint, » m'écrivit un ami qui l'avait consulté. Il pouvait aussi devenir dangereux — dangereux comme David — et se montrer une masse d'instincts aveugles, sourds, têtus, ravageurs.

Longtemps après sa mort, me souvenant d'un thème fréquent de ses considérations évangéliques, j'avais conclu sans indulgence que mon père avait dressé sa tente sur le Thabor. J'osais me croire tellement mieux logé ! Plus tard, à un simple mot de contradiction, je découvris soudain, ébloui, que la montagne de la Transfiguration est le seul lieu de l'Evangile et de la terre où le Christ ait séjourné en gloire, que cet immense événement s'inscrit une semaine environ après la confession de Pierre, après le scandale de la Passion et de la Résurrection prophétisées pour la première fois, et après le terrible reproche essuyé par ce même Pierre traité de Satan. Du même coup je comprenais l'itinéraire obscur et tortueux, mais sûr comme la grâce et la vie, qui conduisait mon père, homme de violence et de tendresse, à ce sommet de l'Evangile, à cette réunion du Verbe incarné et de ses intimes du ciel et de la terre : les deux morts vivants, Moïse — homme hésitant, homme fulgurant, Elie — homme retiré, solitaire des cavernes de contemplation, appeleur de feu, prophète enlevé dans le feu; les trois vivants assurés de renaître, Pierre, confesseur et renieur, ce Pierre éternel, homme de la promptitude et de la faiblesse, et roc de foi amoureuse, et Jacques et Jean, fils du tonnerre de Dieu, fuyards aux

Oliviers, colonnes de l'Eglise. Je comprenais comment par ses propres errements et attardements, à travers les miséricordes de Luc et parmi les détails de Marc, mon père possédait le Christ des jours et me l'enseignait dans la réalité quotidienne de l'Incarnation, type, garantie et salut de la nôtre, loi déterminante de tout art et de toute pensée. Enfin m'apparaissait qu'il n'existe nulle part, sur aucun plan surnaturel ou naturel accessible à l'homme, d'autre anticipation que celle-là, en cet endroit-là seulement où Pierre trouva qu'il faisait si bon. Dans la nuée, Jésus, Moïse et Elie n'ont pas besoin de tentes pour parler de ce qui doit bientôt s'accomplir à Jérusalem. Nous, nous pouvons bien nous endormir là. Quelqu'un nous touchera en disant : « Levez-vous et n'ayez pas peur. » Et nous ne descendrons pas seuls dans la vallée, nous n'irons pas seuls sur le chemin sans raccourcis de Pâques.

(*Convergences,* 1961)

Paul Toupin (Né en 1918)

Journaliste, puis professeur, dramaturge et essayiste. Membre de l'Académie canadienne-française, il a réuni dans

Souvenirs pour demain (1960) trois récits inspirés par son enfance, dont sont extraits les pages qui suivent.

HÉRITAGES

Ce que six ans de latin, ce que cinq ans de grec ne m'apprirent pas, toute cette antiquité de lumière, toute cette humanité de belles-lettres que j'étais censé connaître et que je ne connaissais pas, il a suffi d'une visite au British Museum pour que je les découvre. Cette fois, sans autre maître que mon goût, sans autre guide que mon caprice, sans autre curiosité que mon émerveillement, les frises du Parthénon me révélèrent ce que le génie humain peut édifier de beau quand il met sa grandeur à être ce qu'il est. La Grèce naissait par un matin de juin, sous le ciel de Londres. Et dans ce défilé des Panathénées, dans cette succession de formes, que ce fussent celles d'hommes ou d'animaux, une sculpture, un style, un art, une civilisation ressuscitaient. Pour moi qui les voyais pour la première fois, ces jeunes cavaliers athéniens qui ajustaient leur ceinture, l'ajustaient aussi simplement que l'avaient fait ces autres cavaliers de la House Guard à la relève desquels je venais d'assister. Et ce qu'ils me disaient était plus émouvant encore que les paroles d'Antigone puisque tous me disaient qu'avant d'être nés pour l'amour ils étaient nés pour la vie. Il n'était plus question de péché, de remords, de rachat, de jugement, d'athlétisme. Personne ici n'énonçait de faux problèmes. Il n'y avait pas de fausse réponse. La pureté après quoi je gémissais et que j'avais confondue avec la chasteté — ainsi l'avais-je appris — la pureté trouvait enfin son expression dans cette liaison du corps et de l'âme, du corps qui ne sacrifiait pas à l'âme, de l'âme qui ne se sacrifiait pas au corps, mais les deux se portant mutuellement.

D'autres vont se convertir à Damas. Ils lancent des cris, tombent foudroyés. Dans la salle Elgin, je pris la résolution silencieuse de réconcilier ma vie avec la vie. La tâche était immense. Il y avait bien des nuages à chasser, bien des noirceurs à nettoyer. Dieu, qui était Dieu, avait mis six jours à créer le monde. Il s'était reposé le septième jour. Je n'étais pas Dieu et je savais que le jour de mon repos serait celui de ma mort. Mais pourquoi voulais-je écrire ? Pourquoi ce désir ? Venait-il de tous les silences que je m'étais imposés ? Il était insensé de me créer une vision du monde. Si j'avais été grec et sculpteur, oui. Mais je n'étais ni l'un ni l'autre. Je vivais en plein vingtième siècle, et de ce côté de l'Atlantique, dans un pays dont la jeune ambition convoite l'argent, l'honneur, la considération. J'assistais déjà à la montée de ceux de mes camarades qui avaient choisi de gagner leur pain par la médecine et le droit. Il leur était facile de me démontrer qu'il était inconséquent de *faire de la littérature* comme si j'eusse ignoré que tout paralyse l'écrivain, depuis la fausse publicité qui lance des fausses valeurs, jusqu'à l'intrigue de salon, la cabale de parti. J'avais une idée fixe, que j'ai encore. Je suis toujours convaincu que ce ne sont pas les raisonnements, ni l'influence, ni les relations, ni l'argent, ni les diplômes, ni les académies, ni les prix qui confèrent du talent à qui n'en a pas, ou qui le dérobent à celui qui en a. Celui qui veut écrire le fera toujours envers et contre tous, souvent malgré lui, parfois contre lui. Je me détachais d'ambitions trop encombrantes. Je me fis insensible à l'opinion publique, indifférent aux gloires régnantes. J'entrai en solitude comme on entre au couvent. Là, j'appris à devenir plus attentif aux autres.

Extérieurement, j'étais très calme. C'est intérieurement que je brûlais. Un naturel peu liant, une certaine méfiance, un dédain réel, aucun mépris toutefois, beaucoup de fierté, pas d'arrogance, trop de timidité, une teinte de snobisme, une émotivité bridée, ceci ou cela me valut la réputation d'être à part. Il est vrai que les amusements ordinaires ne m'ont jamais amusé. Et si à l'université où j'étais, les cartes, la bière et les obscénités étaient de rigueur, j'évitais de donner dans de telles conventions. J'avais jugé intolérable qu'on me commandât d'étudier. Je jugeais plus intolérable encore d'en être empêché. Ma chambre devint ma ruche. J'y faisais miel de tout.

C'était aussi le temps de ces interminables promenades qui ne me menaient nulle part. Je pensais les idées que je croyais avoir. Je rentrais comme le jour pointait, plus fatigué que les noceurs que je rencontrais, plus courbatu. Je serais bien en peine de préciser ce que je cherchais. Dans la verrière du souvenir, je vois toujours un peu de ce Parthénon un instant entrevu et sur les ruines duquel ma vie voulait s'édifier. Mais enseveli sous les livres, avec mes lunettes, mon air scholar trompait. Je n'avais pourtant pas l'esprit scientifique. Le détail ne m'a jamais retenu. Je ne pouvais pas chicaner sur référence. En dépit de cela, mon professeur de philologie fut chagriné d'apprendre que son studieux élève ne se destinait pas à l'enseignement, et que sa science chérie m'était tout juste un point de repère dans mon pèlerinage vers l'antique. Un autre professeur, un autre maître, et quel maître ! m'aida à franchir l'obstacle que tant de siècles et d'idées avaient dressé entre la Grèce et moi. Je ne suis ni le premier, ni le dernier à devoir à Nietzsche les connaissances essentielles, indispensables.

Grâce à lui, je me tiens aujourd'hui à l'écart des grands mensonges. Il m'apprit que le sens de la liberté la plus accomplie est de n'avoir jamais honte de soi-même — surtout pas de rougir de la honte originelle — et que le geste le plus humain est d'épargner la honte à quelqu'un. Je pus devenir mon meilleur ami et mon pire ennemi. J'ai rejeté aussi certains préjugés qui sont encore dans nos lois, nos croyances, nos moeurs, nos arts. Pour m'approprier Nietzsche, il me fallut plus d'une lecture, plus d'une traduction. Il me fallut avant tout le dépouiller de sa vanité mythologique, adoucir son accent quelque peu guttural, rabaisser sa prétention germanique. Sans Nietzsche, me serais-je satisfait de l'apparence des choses ? Aurais-je compris l'attitude de tant de personnages de la tragédie grecque ? Et mon propre appel, l'aurais-je entendu ? Et dans un accent exempt de tout ridicule ? Ma sexualité pouvait porter le masque de son choix. Est-ce que Phèdre n'est pas plus belle sous le joug de son amour ? Mon instinct ne devait pas se renier, mon idéal non plus. Le ciel et la terre, les êtres et les choses étaient faits pour s'accorder et moi, pour les inscrire.

Mais ma plus belle inscription, je la fis sur les registres de Paris car dans mon cas aussi, Paris a eu mon coeur. Il l'a encore. La Seine suit en moi un cours qui m'en a plus appris que toutes les universités réunies en une seule. Il n'y a pas long de Notre-Dame à la Concorde. Que de siècles cependant un tel parcours me faisait franchir.

C'est que j'y promenais toutes ces illusions dont il faut bien que jeunesse se repaisse. Paris m'a éveillé au meilleur comme au pire de moi-même. Si je n'y avais pas vécu, je serais différent de ce que je suis. Car si elle est la capitale de tout ce qu'on lui attribue, elle m'a paru la capitale du spectacle, celui de la rue comme celui des théâtres, donc, celui auquel on participe, celui auquel on applaudit, tout comme celui que l'on observe et qui nous transporte dans son déroulement même. J'ai regardé Paris avec tous mes visages, qui, comme les siens, étaient ou bien légers ou bien graves, ou bien sereins ou bien tourmentés. Je suis si souvent allé de Notre-Dame à la Concorde que je n'ai plus qu'à me regarder pour voir en moi ce paysage que j'aimais tant. Je m'accoude sur les pierres du souvenir comme autrefois sur celles de la Seine pour m'apercevoir, solitaire, inconnu, regagner ma chambre au 7, rue de la Chaise. C'est là que je dévorais livres et papiers.

J'écrivais comme tout jeune homme qui écrit, avec des mots qui n'étaient pas à moi, des sujets qui ne m'appartenaient pas. C'étaient des romans, des essais, des contes, mais jamais mes romans, mes essais, mes contes. Malraux se demande avec raison combien de jours il faut à un écrivain pour écrire avec le son de sa propre voix. Que de mots j'écrivais et que je croyais de moi parce que je les traçais sur le papier. C'étaient les mots les plus récemment lus et qui m'avaient le plus impressionné. Mon apprentissage a été long, difficile. J'en ai mis du temps à croire à ma vie, la vie des autres me paraissait tellement plus intéressante que la mienne. Il ne me semblait pas qu'un amour malheureux pût être de l'amour, ni que des sentiments, tels que ceux que je ressentais, méritassent d'être exprimés. Par pudeur, je me taisais. Aujourd'hui, si ce livre contient des mots qui ne sont pas de moi, c'est qu'ils m'auront échappé. Jamais comme ici mon expression n'a tant dépendu de moi et de moi seul. Je n'imite personne. Je ne cherche même qu'à m'imiter. Je ne suis plus Claudel, Montherlant, Colette, Gide, Proust, même si je suis né de ces auteurs puisqu'il faut bien naître de quelqu'un. Je suis le père légitime de ce que mes souvenirs ont d'authentique. Je me reconnais maintenant à mon accent, à mon ton, à mon allure. Je suis ma veine.

J'accepte d'écrire mais sans m'y résigner car si je m'y résignais je me vouerais à un autre genre de littérature, celui par exemple qui m'assurerait tout le confort matériel et moral voulu. En m'exprimant comme je le fais, je n'exécute aucune corvée. Ce n'est sans doute pas là travailler pour ma gloire et pour mes intérêts. Peu m'importe. Ma moi et c'est là le scandale impardonnable. Qu'on ne me parle surtout bourse est plate et je ne récolte ni succès ni notoriété. J'écris pour pas de littérature engagée, de message à délivrer. Je ne tiens pas au rôle de témoin. J'ai assez d'être le mien sans me charger d'être celui de l'époque. Oh! si j'avais pensé à l'argent comme à mes livres, je serais riche. Si j'avais soigné l'éclairage de ma publicité, je serais installé au sommet de la renommée. J'ai manqué du tact le plus élémentaire en ne me prenant ni pour un génie, ni pour un autre. Je connais mes limites. Car si j'avais donné à l'amour le temps passé à écrire, comme je serais aimé! Mais je manque d'argent — autre aveu qui en fera rougir — d'amis, d'amour. Heureusement que je n'ai pas de fille à marier, car sa dot serait constituée de manuscrits. Tel que prévu, mes enfants sont en papier. Cette absence d'enfant, de femme ne me frustre en rien. Je ne tire vanité ni de mon célibat ni de ma profession d'écrivain. Mon ambition n'est pas de faire la vedette. J'y réussirais gauchement. Je tiens seulement à écrire un bon livre.

Là est ma vie. Quant à l'autre, celle de tous les jours, je la laisse se débrouiller comme elle peut. Elle ne peut pas grand'chose et j'entretiens avec elle des relations tantôt tendues, tantôt cordiales. Il m'arrive de la maltraiter. Elle ne me comprend pas toujours. Pourquoi me critiquer parce que j'écris? Il peut sembler anormal d'écrire pour qui n'écrit pas. Et, par la porte de ma chambre qui ferme difficilement, j'entends des bruits qui me dérangent, le téléphone qui sonne, la voix qui répond, certains propos. Je me demande souvent, comme Flaubert, si je suis dans le vrai, car à quoi tient ma vie? Je suis peut-être dans le faux en ne partageant pas les plaisirs et les peines de ceux qui m'entourent et qui s'affairent. Je renie souvent ce que je fais, je me désapprouve parfois de perdre un temps que je ne retrouverai plus. Je me prends en haine de jouer la partie de cette vie qui ne se joue qu'une fois. La tendresse se flétrit et je m'en veux d'avoir suivi des chimères. Je songe à la douceur qu'il y aurait à ne rien faire. Puis, ce mauvais moment passe, comme passe le bon moment d'après. Le jour se lève sur d'autres illusions : pain quotidien de ceux qui ne sont pas les invités de la première heure. Et comme je ne suis ni assez vieux pour me désabuser, ni assez jeune pour m'abuser, je m'agrippe à ce que mon dégoût de la veille n'a pas désagrégé. Je relis la page froissée. Elle n'était pas si mauvaise que cela. En la corrigeant, elle sera même pas mal. Alors, j'en serre le sens, en varie le rythme, modifie une tournure syntaxique, substitue un verbe au nom. Et les heures passent, comme elles passaient sur les plages de mon enfance, quand j'édifiais des pâtés de sable. Qui peut se vanter de ne pas croire à sa propre fable? de ne pas s'alimenter à ses rêves? Le plus grand comme le plus petit souhaite l'éternité, qui est pour l'écrivain, la page blanche de l'infini...

(*Souvenirs pour demain,* 1960)

Pierre Trottier (Né en 1925)

Avocat, diplomate (Moscou, Djakarta, Londres et Paris), poète et essayiste, il a chanté l'amour et la mort et médité sur le temps et l'espoir.

Ses essais sont très personnels, comme en fait foi le début de *Retour à l'hiver,* extrait de *Mon Babel.*

RETOUR À L'HIVER

Un long séjour ininterrompu à l'étranger me permit d'échapper à six hivers canadiens. Aussi ne fut-ce pas sans inquiétude que, de retour au pays, j'abordai pour la première fois depuis six ans le mois de janvier. L'objet de mes craintes n'était pas le froid physique, car je connaissais l'excellence du chauffage central de nos maisons, mais plutôt l'engourdissement de l'esprit, un certain étouffement ou écrasement de l'âme sous le poids de la neige opaque. Je redoutais en somme une sorte de refroidissement par l'intérieur et je me troublais d'avance à l'idée que le froid pût saper les fondations et disloquer les pierres du musée personnel, du musée de mémoire auquel, depuis plusieurs années déjà, j'avais consacré tant de loisirs, d'efforts, d'étude et d'amour.

La question, pour moi, dépassait de beaucoup celle de la simple reprise des sports d'hiver que l'on me conseillait pour tromper la longue et passive attente de la belle saison. Pour éviter l'engourdissement, me disait-on, soyez actif, faites du ski ! Cela ressemblait trop aux mots d'ordre du collège : pour éviter les mauvaises pensées, faites du sport ! Guerre à la délectation morose ! *Mens sana in corpore sano !*

Je ne prise guère l'aspect tout négatif de semblables préceptes et conseils, fruits de la pensée conceptuelle et antinomique qui, ayant postulé un état, enjoint la pratique du contraire. C'est comme si, au jeu de dames, on décidait de jouer sur les carreaux blancs quand l'adversaire emploie les carreaux noirs. Ainsi, je ne vois pas du tout en quoi l'activité peut vaincre la passivité, le sport, les mauvaises pensées, et les sports d'hiver, l'hiver. Plus exactement, je ne crois pas que le sport, pour lequel j'ai beaucoup de respect, doive naître d'un quelconque activisme physique, pas plus que la poésie, d'un activisme verbal. La prévention de l'engourdissement, des mauvaises pensées ou du silence, je trouve que c'est un peu comme la prévention des incendies et le conseil d'activisme a pour moi tout l'air d'un conseil de pompier : le boyau d'arrosage peut éteindre, mais il ne donnera jamais une seule nouvelle construction. Or, ni le sport, ni la poésie ne sont des oeuvres d'extinction bien que, frappés par un certain activisme d'origine américaine, celui-là soit en train de le devenir et celle-ci ait du mal à percer. Puritanisme et jansénisme auront ici donné ce pouvoir pompier à la balle et au lièvre de Pascal. *Mens extincta in corpore sanissimo !* Car à force de tuer les mauvaises pensées, on aura tué les bonnes aussi et la pensée conceptuelle aura tué la pensée tout court.

Est-il besoin de rappeler que pour les Anciens *mens* et *corpus* se rejoignaient naturellement dans la croyance qu'ils avaient en une beauté formelle dont le canon était précisément celui du corps humain idéalisé ? *Mens* et *corpus* se rejoignaient ainsi dans une belle abstraction qui n'avait rien de morose, ni de puritain, ni de janséniste. Mais c'était une abstraction et c'est grande folie que de vouloir l'entretenir chez nous de nos jours. La crainte que m'inspirait le retour à l'hiver canadien était précisément chez moi la crainte de cette folie, la crainte des pompiers de l'hiver qui éteignent le feu sous la glace et la neige, la crainte du silence mortifiant de ces espaces enneigés, la crainte de l'hiver-absence, de l'hiver-prétexte à l'inaction, de l'hiver-alibi, de l'hiver-confessionnal, de l'hiver-pénitence, de l'hiver-refuge de la mauvaise conscience, de l'hiver-évasion, de l'hiver-bouc émissaire de notre incapacité d'être.

C'est que notre hiver a bon dos. Il nous a bien fidèlement servi — avec les « maudits Anglais » — d'instrument d'auto-flagellation masochiste à la mesure de notre mauvaise morale. Nous nous en sommes fait un beau mythe pour excuser nos retards vis-à-vis de l'histoire, du progrès, de la civilisation, de la culture, de l'art. Petits Sisyphes à la boule de neige qui nous retombe dessus d'un hiver à l'autre, nous avons beau jeu de hausser les épaules dans un geste d'impuissance résignée : « Eh, oui, que voulez-vous, avec un climat comme le nôtre... » Notre hiver nous l'a bien rendu. Il a bien accepté son double rôle de justicier et de justificateur. A son tribunal, notre peur de vivre, notre incapacité d'être, notre manque de poids sur terre trouvent toute leur absolution-condamnation : absolution de tous les manquements d'hier et condamnation simultanée à tous les manquements de demain. Allez en paix, mon fils, et péchez encore ! Notre hiver nous blanchit, sans nous donner le goût de la vraie couleur, mais seulement du chromo.

Certes, notre climat n'est pas facile. Mais était-elle plus facile, cette mer qui des siècles durant déversa en Angleterre l'envahisseur barbare, angle, saxon, scanien, danois, jute et encore, jusqu'à ce que le peuple britannique se mette à fonder sur cette même mer sa vocation et sa grandeur ? Au Canada, pour moi, la question est de savoir ce qu'il y a moyen de fonder sur les glaces et les neiges et la première chose à faire est de regarder l'hiver tel qu'il est, c'est-à-dire démystifié, dépouillé de son double rôle de justicier et de justificateur. En réalité, ne serait-ce pas soi-même qu'il faudrait dépouiller de ces relents de paganisme primitif et superstitieux qui poussent à voir quelque démiurge vengeur dans le travail des éléments de la nature ?

Si le fait d'avoir échappé à six hivers canadiens ne m'avait pas complètement dépouillé d'une certaine crainte que j'ai dite plus haut, je n'en revenais pas moins de l'étranger avec un regard neuf. C'est de ce regard que je pris la mesure de décembre, puis de janvier et de février et que j'y découvris, après certains jours de colère sombre, d'autres jours d'une paix et d'une clarté qui, sans atténuer en rien un froid digne de tous les respects vestimentaires, n'en laissaient quand même pas moins, sur un fond de ciel bleu très pur, toutes ses chances à la lumière. Car nos hivers ne sont pas gris et maussades comme, par exemple, ceux d'Europe. Au contraire, mise à part une minorité (appréciable, il est vrai, mais une minorité quand même) de jours de tempête, nos hivers sont remarquablement clairs et ensoleillés. La température et la neige sont bien nordiques, mais le soleil ne l'est pas, du moins au sens que l'on donne en Europe au mot *nordique*. Il est même plutôt méditerranéen. Or, sous un tel soleil, une fois résolu, comme il l'est, le problème du chauffage, on *peut* penser et non seulement rêver ou se bercer de nostalgie coupable. Penser quoi ? Eh bien, l'espace qu'on occupe, cet espace que Borduas par exemple a su penser, particulièrement dans ses toiles en noir et blanc et ensuite, à la fin de sa vie, dans ses monochromies dont le désert n'est pas celui d'un manque ou d'une absence, mais celui, voulu et organisé, d'une discipline et d'une pauvreté acceptées.

Quand je parle de penser notre espace, je ne veux pas dire le raisonner, l'analyser, le disséquer, le mesurer, l'emprisonner dans l'idée ou le concept. Je ne parle pas de dresser des cadastres. J'emploie ici le verbe *penser* dans son sens dérivé de *pensum,* qui veut dire poids (Denis de Rougemont a déjà dit cela quelque part). Penser notre espace, c'est y peser, y être présent de tout notre poids au lieu de s'en laisser abstraire, retirer, refouler par notre mauvaise morale qui est précisément une morale abstraite, une morale de retraite, une morale de refoulement. Peut-être avons-nous mérité cette morale. En tout cas, nous en avons hérité. Mais à coup sûr, ce pays ne la mérite pas. Car c'est un continent qui demande une morale d'occupation et non de retraite. C'est à nous de changer, pas au pays, pas à son hiver non plus. Je me souviens de quelques jours extrêmement froids de janvier ou février, cet hiver-là que je venais de retrouver après six ans d'absence. Rien dans le ciel n'en troublait la paix et la clarté. Ce ciel n'était absolument pas bouché comme notre morale l'aurait voulu. Ce n'était pas un ciel d'Italie qui reflète trop de mer et dont la luminosité presque tangible s'accroche à tout objet pour éveiller dans l'âme du spectateur le rêve antique de beauté et d'amour. Ce n'était pas un ciel de naissance de Vénus. Ce ciel du Canada, reflétant la neige, était d'un bleu plus pâle qu'en Italie, mais comme translucide à l'infini qui le traversait et en descendait, sollicitant sur terre la présence de l'homme dans un acte de foi. En principe le ciel représente toujours l'infini, mais je tiens qu'il le représente au Canada bien mieux qu'ailleurs. Quoi qu'il en soit, depuis ces jours de février, ces jours d'un hiver enfin compris ou au moins compréhensible, ce ciel m'est devenu tout à fait possible, comme l'hiver, la glace et la neige qui désormais pour moi ont cessé d'être un fardeau, une prison ou un supplice, mais une forme nouvelle de la liberté. Le ciel du désert est aussi une sollicitation par l'infini d'une présence et d'une foi, mais les formes de la liberté y sont celles d'un manque de tout, tandis que dans l'hiver canadien elles sont celles d'un dépouillement et d'un recueillement. En vue de quoi ? En vue de la ruée des eaux à la débâcle, en vue de l'éclatement des bourgeons, en vue de l'explosion printanière. Car chez nous, le printemps est explosif quand, ailleurs, il est plus douce et graduelle éclosion.

Ainsi, puisque c'est dans l'hiver que se prépare cette explosion, la mort, la blancheur, la virginité, à condition de ne plus être comprises comme autant de négations stérilisantes à la façon de la pensée conceptuelle, peuvent être interprétées comme réelles, concrètes et fécondes. D'ailleurs l'hiver, parce qu'il durcit la terre et rend impossible l'inhumation, est un refus de la mort dans ce qu'elle a de fini. L'hiver, c'est la saison du retour à l'infini, à l'inachevé qu'est l'homme quand les fleurs et les fruits, ayant terminé leur carrière, lui laissent la place libre. C'est aussi la saison du retour de l'infini dans le mystère chrétien du Dieu fait homme. Retour à, retour de; ces deux expressions au fond signifient rencontre entre l'infini qui est en Dieu et l'infini qui est en l'homme et qui, en définitive, sont faits pour se rejoindre, se toucher. Or, la rencontre exige la présence. Ici, je reviens au principe d'immaculée-conception dont j'ai parlé dans un chapitre antérieur et je dis qu'il y aura présence et rencontre des deux infinis, de Dieu et de l'homme, dans cette capacité d'immaculée-conception à laquelle j'accroche toute ma définition de notre hiver et la condition indispensable de la fécondité de son être apparent qui est de mort, de blancheur et de virginité.

(*Mon Babel,* 1963)

Fernand Dumont (Né en 1927)

Sociologue par profession, poète, philosophe et théologien par surcroît, ce professeur de l'Université Laval s'intéresse à tout ce qui est de l'homme. Profondément préoccupé par l'aggiornamento, il a réuni ses principaux essais religieux dans *Pour la conversion de la pensée chrétienne,* dont la conclusion est reproduite ici.

EN GUISE DE CONCLUSION

Peut-être faut-il, une fois la route parcourue, dégager brièvement l'intention qui nous a animé. Pour cela, il ne sera pas inutile de rappeler notre itinéraire.

Nous avons trouvé notre départ dans la crise religieuse séculaire. Non pas pour en chercher quelque terme prochain, mais pour en tirer une durable exigence : la réconciliation des structures officielles de l'Eglise et des solidarités humaines, l'intégration des normes religieuses et des requêtes de l'expérience. Si nous nous sommes donné des perspectives historiques, c'était pour éviter les faciles systématisations de principes et bien marquer l'enracinement de nos interrogations dans le présent du christianisme et du monde.

Nous avons essayé de déceler ensuite, dans le chapitre deuxième, comment, au sein de l'histoire toute contemporaine et sous la poussée même de la crise religieuse, le christianisme reprend conscience de son plus profond mystère. Ce qui suffisait pour dénoncer la tentation de la révolte solitaire et pour replacer nos intentions de réforme dans un plus large mouvement de conversion de la communauté. Mais nous nous sommes défendu de tirer de là quelque facile réconfort. La redécouverte est fort loin d'atteindre l'ensemble du milieu chrétien et, par ailleurs, elle indique une tâche plutôt qu'un accomplissement.

C'est pourquoi nous nous sommes engagé dans une confrontation de la morale et de la religion avec la condition humaine d'aujourd'hui. Une psychanalyse de la conscience religieuse doit s'élaborer au regard des situations faites à l'homme par les transformations du milieu. C'est là que les récapitulations historiques que nous avions tentées auparavant trouvaient leur lien avec la recherche de nos vies.

Du même coup, la crise religieuse apparaissait comme la source perpétuelle de nouvelles attitudes religieuses. Nous avons souligné qu'une foi *consciente* est une mise à l'école des signes du temps. Qu'il fallait reconnaître ceux-ci dans la mouvante dialectique du sacré, du profane et de la religion. Qu'il fallait aussi transmuer cette complémentarité effective en une dialectique voulue dont l'engagement, la Parole et la fête sont les coordonnées principales. Pour l'une et l'autre dialectiques, il s'agissait moins, selon nous, de déceler des issues que de dénoncer les échappées des superficielles adaptations.

De l'examen des attitudes, nous sommes passé à celui des structures ecclésiales. La distinction de *la structure de l'Eglise,* du *Peuple de Dieu,* des *structures de la société chrétienne* nous a engagé dans le procès du cléricalisme comme mécanisme superficiel de médiation. Ici encore, nous avons cru que, pour celui qui vit non pas seulement dans l'Eglise mais de l'Eglise, la conscience personnelle ne saurait être immédiatement opposée à l'histoire : l'existence doit trouver sa résonance dans une expérience où se conjuguent la reprise en charge d'un héritage et l'interrogation des situations historiques. Pour l'Eglise, l'affrontement de l'histoire ne s'épuise donc pas dans les leçons de l'empirisme immédiat, bien qu'elle doive s'en inspirer.

De cette conversion sans cesse reprise des attitudes et des structures religieuses, il restait à éclairer, dans notre dernier chapitre, les répercussions sur les intentions de la réflexion religieuse.

De tout cela se dégage sans doute l'impression d'une inlassable critique. Je ne tâcherai pas de dissiper ce sentiment, car il correspond parfaitement à mon intention. J'essaierai plutôt d'en dire, en bref, la raison d'être.

On critique beaucoup dans l'Eglise et, je l'ai rappelé, c'est une tradition immémoriale. Pour une part, je verrais là volontiers un excellent mécanisme de contrôle qui constitue une efficace collaboration à la sagesse du magistère. Mais ces critiques sont le plus souvent fragmentaires et dispersées. Il paraît urgent que, dans l'Eglise, la critique religieuse acquière sa cohérence propre. Pour le chrétien, les velléités de protestation y trouveraient le lieu d'une réforme d'ensemble. Et les oppositions de l'incroyant pourraient mener à un plus large dialogue.

Depuis quelques décades, on a beaucoup insisté sur la nécessité d'une « opinion publique dans l'Eglise ». A mon avis, l'expression est bien vague. J'ai eu l'occasion, à propos de la propagande religieuse, de dire en quoi nos modernes structures sociales ont fait de l'opinion un phénomène superficiel. L'opinion dans l'Eglise, est-ce la réaction dispersée des fidèles aux nouvelles que leur transmettent les moyens d'information, les protestations inefficaces contre le latin ou le sermon du curé que l'on répète au retour de la messe du dimanche, l'éditorial du journaliste catholique, les propos du conférencier habilité par les cercles religieux, les « résolutions » enregistrées au procès-verbal de telle association pieuse ? Quel est le rapport et la pondération que le magistère, le plus attentif et le plus informé soit-il, pourrait établir entre ces manifestations diverses ? Plus encore, où se trouvent la continuité et le fondement de ces critiques dans la condition chrétienne elle-même ? Gouverner en tenant compte des sondages d'opinion est un pis-aller pour des démocraties formelles qui n'ont pas su créer de lien organique entre le peuple et les organisations politiques. Ce ne saurait être l'idéal d'une Eglise qui veut rassembler des consciences libres.

Il faut donc s'entendre, à la fin, sur la notion de *critique*. Un peu comme tout le monde, le célèbre Vocabulaire philosophique de Lalande en distingue deux sens principaux. Pour le langage courant, le terme désigne d'abord « l'objection » et la « désapprobation ». Mais la critique, c'est aussi « l'examen d'un principe ou d'un fait, en vue de porter à son sujet un jugement d'appréciation ». La critique biblique, une plus large critique historique ont déjà pris place dans l'Eglise. La théologie se donne légitimement comme une critique des fondements de la connaissance selon la foi. Pourquoi n'y aurait-il pas une critique systématique de l'expérience et des structures religieuses à la lumière des signes du temps ? C'est la question que nous voudrions reprendre au seuil d'un autre livre et que le présent ouvrage voulait poser. De la même manière que l'épistémologie ne prétend pas dispenser la science des initiatives inattendues de la recherche, de même la critique religieuse ne doit pas ambitionner de remplacer l'inspiration missionnaire, les inventions de la sainteté et, encore moins, les initiatives de l'esprit de Dieu. Mais elle en constitue l'indispensable contrepartie réflexive. Sur le plan personnel, si nous ne confondons pas l'examen de conscience avec la générosité de la charité, nous n'avons pourtant jamais pensé lui substituer la béate quiétude de la naïveté. Il devrait en être ainsi pour la communauté chrétienne tout entière. Là aussi doit s'instaurer une démarche cohérente qui dénonce sans répit les secrets refuges de la bonne conscience religieuse.

Dans cette perspective, il s'agit moins de sortir de la crise religieuse que d'en approfondir sans cesse les implications. Peut-être cela tient-il d'ailleurs à la nature profonde du christianisme. Revenons, une fois encore, à nos propos du début.

Considérée comme rassemblement des hommes, l'Eglise se trouve devant une double possibilité : se constituer elle-même comme société totale au prix d'aménagements qui confinent aux procédés politiques; ne compter que sur la libre initiative de chaque chrétien pour que la communion s'instaure au sein des cités temporelles. L'alternative n'est pourtant qu'apparente. Que le second pôle n'en ait été mis en évidence qu'au cours d'une histoire récente ne doit pas nous égarer. Il s'agit bien, au fond, d'une oscillation. Se déprendre des constructions politiques illustrées par les formes diverses des chrétientés du passé, ce ne peut signifier platement un simple abandon à une religion de l'individu. Ici encore, l'histoire récente peut nous instruire. Depuis quelques siècles surtout, les hommes sont à la recherche d'une société plus rationnelle, qui ne repose plus sur des privilèges arbitraires. En même temps, ils appellent aussi une société qui ne soit pas seulement un vaste système de division du travail, un simple moyen pour la satisfaction de leurs besoins économiques, mais aussi une convergence de leurs intentions les plus hautes, une image de leur amitié. Avec l'extension des communications entre les peuples et l'agonie des colonianismes, la part de la gratuité dans la vie sociale apparaît aussi, à la dimension de la planète, de mieux en mieux circonscrite. L'Eglise n'a pas à s'associer officiellement, comme une force politique parmi d'autres, à ces divers mouvements. Aux chrétiens de le faire selon des adhésions qui requièrent de chacun une hasardeuse lecture de l'histoire. Récusant à la fois la politique chrétienne et l'unique religion du coeur pour poursuivre sa tâche de convocation, il faudrait que l'Eglise apparaisse, à une humanité qui cherche péniblement son unité, comme l'incarnation la plus haute de son désir, comme le Mystère le plus profond de l'histoire. Il nous faudra, à nous chrétiens, beaucoup de tâtonnements et beaucoup de souffrances pour qu'il en soit ainsi.

Il en est de même au sein de l'univers le plus strictement personnel. D'avoir mis quelque peu en évidence une marge séculaire entre les normes religieuses officielles et l'expérience vitale ne doit pas nous précipiter dans quelque hâtif expédient. Il reste à chercher non pas seulement en quoi le christianisme est la rencontre de nos intentions, mais en quoi aussi il est le mystère de nos actions — et de celles des hommes qui ne sont pas officiellement chrétiens. Là encore, de l'inspiration religieuse aux logiques de l'action, la voie n'est pas à sens unique. Il faut en explorer, dans les deux directions, les sentiers incertains.

L'enjeu est décisif. Pour de nombreux fidèles, déjà se pose le cruel dilemne : ou bien j'accepte une tradition de foi, ou bien je me débrouille avec ma foi personnelle ... Il ne s'agit pas de la « tradition dogmatique » : celle-là ne fait guère difficulté, pour la plupart. La tradition dont il s'agit, c'est la communauté qui est derrière nous depuis les origines, avec ses recherches, ses louvoiements, ses compromissions, ses pécheurs et ses saints. On sent de plus en plus intensément que c'est la fidélité envers tout cela, que c'est aussi le procès de tout cela qui constitue la condition chrétienne, et non pas simplement le combat solitaire avec l'Ange. Nous paraît authentique la spiritualité qui accepte de se situer entre l'à priori de la tradition et la spontanéité de la conscience personnelle pour tracer, de l'un à l'autre, les cheminements sans cesse repris de la conversion. A cette jointure, il n'y a pas de position commode; il n'y a pas non plus de normes conventionnelles qui puissent dispenser de l'inquiétude de la foi. C'est en ce sens que la crise religieuse est permanente. Elle attend moins d'être résolue que d'être vécue par chacun de nous.

Dans cette pensée est peut-être aussi l'inspiration la plus essentielle de notre dialogue avec l'incroyant. En tant que chrétiens, il est vrai que nous tenons le sens dernier du monde. Mais nous n'en possédons aucunement la signification plénière. Sinon, à quoi pourrait donc servir d'y vivre, pourquoi Dieu nous aurait-il condamnés à ce long apprentissage ? Regardons du côté de Sartre, de Merleau-Ponty, de Camus — de ceux que l'on qualifie vaguement d'« existentialistes » — et qui expriment sans aucun doute l'obscure recherche d'un grand nombre de nos contemporains. Partis qu'ils sont à la découverte des conditions premières de la spontanéité de l'existence et de la conscience, je les vois aussi chercher une tradition. Celle du marxisme ou celle de la révolte éternelle — peu importe, au fond, les noms qu'ils lui donnent. Chrétiens, nous poursuivons en quelque sorte un chemin inverse, mais qui va peut-être à leur rencontre. De part et d'autre, même si les composantes de l'inquiétude ne sont pas superposables, la ferveur de la recherche doit être égale. Oui, nous tournons en rond sur cette terre, comme nos frères incroyants, dans cette prison qui est aussi la nôtre. Pour l'aménager quelque peu, économiquement ou politiquement, nous n'avons guère de meilleures recettes que les leurs. C'est bien assez déjà de pouvoir offrir notre espérance : qu'après avoir foulé, pétri et réorganisé sans cesse le lieu de l'exil, nous nous présentions devant le Père, debout et les yeux grands ouverts; qu'Il nous explique et nous pardonne, aux uns et aux autres, nos piétinements en cette enceinte qui enclôt nos fureurs et nos amours.

(*Pour la conversion de la pensée chrétienne,* 1964)

Robertson Davies (Born in 1913)

Master of Massey College, University of Toronto, Davies is widely known for his plays, novels, criticism and journalism. His Salterton novels are *A Mixture of Frailties, Tempest-Tost* and *Leaven of Malice,* which won a Leacock Medal. With Tyrone Guthrie he wrote about the Stratford Festival.

A MILLENARY PARALLEL

These are gloomy reflections, and hard-headed readers may think them hare-brained. Let me at once provide them with further evidence of hare-brainedness. We are approaching a millennium; the year 2000 draws on apace. The last time mankind had this experience a chaos comparable to our own was observable in many parts of the world; monsters and portents were reported from all quarters of the globe. We need not believe in these monsters and portents as actualities any more than we need believe the reports of flying saucers today; what is significant is that men yielded to an inner compulsion to fancy such things, and in this sense they were artistic creations rooted in fear much as are the pictures and images which we have been discussing. Journeys to Jerusalem were undertaken, for it was amply clear to the best minds of the time that Christ was going to reappear there when the millennium was completed, and conduct the Last Judgment, preparatory to the end of the world. We have our own dread of the world coming to an end, though the nearest thing we have yet produced to compare with a Last Judgment is a series of Summit Meetings. Such reflections as these, in the words of Dr. C.G. Jung, "come perilously close to those turbid fantasies which becloud the minds of world-improvers and other interpreters of 'signs and portents.' " I advance them not as a millenarian, but simply as one who thinks that historical parallels should neither be exaggerated nor ignored. I refer the curious to Dr. Jung's remarkable little book on *Flying Saucers,* and also to his *The Undiscovered Self.*

This book was not undertaken to explain the world — only to make some comment on literature as it has developed during the past century. But to divorce literature wholly from the world in which it is produced is absurd; it is, indeed, to deny that literature is anything more than a form of entertainment which may, in the hands of finical writers and critics, be lifted to the status of a minor art. But there is nothing minor about it, and when it truly mirrors any part of the soul of the time, it is revelatory and prophetic as nothing else can be in quite the same way.

Is it revelatory and prophetic now? Some of it unquestionably is so, but the task of sifting valid prophecy and revelation from the mass of what is meant only for entertainment, from what is timid, what is purblind, what confuses ignorant romanticism with clear-eyed disillusion, what fears chaos and can discern no hope in it — this is work for which few of our literary critics are fitted, and we must turn to a Toynbee or a Jung for a hint at the answer we seek. The best among our writers are doing their accustomed work of mirroring what is deep in the spirit of our time; if chaos appears in those mirrors, we must have faith that in the future, as always in the past, that chaos will slowly reveal itself as a new aspect of order. And so great is the change in the direction that civilization is taking that we cannot reasonably expect this new order to be welcome or familiar to everyone; the world is full of people whose notion of a satisfactory future is, in fact, a return to an idealized past.

It is for the clerisy* to show themselves more alert, more courageous, and better prepared, so that when the first shafts of the dawn appear in our present night, they will know them for what they are.

* *The "clerisy" is the theme of this book. The author uses the term to mean independent-minded persons, or readers, akin to the laity.*

(A Voice from the Attic)

Walter Gordon (Born in 1906)

Finance Minister in the first Pearson government, Gordon is President of the Privy Council. | Compare the viewpoint stated here with that of Goldwin Smith, which appears earlier in the book.

A CHOICE FOR CANADA

Canadians ask themselves whether they have become free of Britain's colonial influence only to fall under the spell of the United States' economic imperialism. Some businessmen, newspaper publishers, civil servants, economists — and in their hearts, perhaps, even some politicians — go further. They question the wisdom of resisting, or attempting to resist, American financial and economic power and influence. They urge that American and other foreign-capital investments have been profitable for Canada, including the take-over and subsequent modernization of established Canadian business enterprises. Moreover, many of them believe that some kind of merger or integration of the Canadian economy within a North American continental system is inevitable. They ask : If it is to come eventually, why not speed up the process ? These arguments are persuasive and insidious. As an example, here is a quotation from the lead editorial in the Toronto *Globe and Mail* of December 31, 1965 :

« It is probable that we have already advanced too far along the road to economic union with the United States for turning back to be possible. They need our resources, we want their standard of living. Geography weds us, language weds us, culture weds us. To turn back now would be do to drop Canadians far down the scale of prosperity, to retard our development drastically, to invite the mass emigration of Canadians who refused to accept such deprivations, and perhaps to drive the United States into taking by force — economic rather than military — certain of our resources.

"It is not reasonable to suggest turning back. But it is dishonest to refuse to admit where advancing will land us. More, it is dangerous.

"In the next years Canada is almost certain to lose economic and, to a certain extent, political control over large areas of our national being. If we do not admit this, we will not define the extent of the loss, and we will not be in a position to determine what must not be lost."

Defeatist thinking of this sort may unfortunately prevail if enough people who hold contrary views are unwilling or unable to state the case for a proud and independent Canada.

Geographically, Canada can claim to be the second-largest country in the world, with 3,850,000 square miles of territory — about one-third the size of the Soviet Union, and just slightly larger than the United States (North Alaska), China, or Brazil. Statistics, however, can be quite misleading. The fact is that much of Canada's northland is virtually uninhabitable. Three-quarters of the total Canadian population lives in a narrow band about a hundred miles in width north of the United States border.

What is more important than the amount of real estate is the fact that Canada is one of only half-a-dozen areas in the world to possess all. or practically all, the natural resources required by an industrial society. The others are China, the Soviet Union, Western Europe, the United States, and Brazil. This is something Canadians should think about very carefully before they make up their minds to sell their birthright for a mess of pottage — even though the pottage may be rich and tempting.

Canada's population is only twenty million. There are some twenty-four countries with larger populations, but only eight whose total output of goods and services exceeds that of Canada. On a per capita basis, Canada's total output — which can be roughly equated with average living standards — ranks second only to that of the United States.

Canada is enormously rich in raw materials. Already we have the second-highest standard of living in the world. If we play our cards right — and we hold extremely high ones — in the years to come we should be able to narrow the gap that now exists between our standard of living and that of the United States. In doing so, we can, if we so wish, set an example to the world of a people, sprung from many diverse origins, who insist upon equal opportunities for all its citizens. It is within our power to build the necessary facilities and develop educational programmes that will compare favourably with those of any other country. It is within our power to work out a well-balanced and thoroughly integrated system of social security that will inspire the kind of confidence our people need. It is within our power to see that there is a reasonably fair division of incomes both among occupational groups and within all regions of the country.

We can do these things if, first of all, we can manage to work together, regardless of our national backgrounds and origins, regardless of the regions and provinces in which we live. We must learn to think of ourselves as Canadians and not as French Canadians or Irish Canadians or Italian Canadians, as the case may be. And we must learn to believe in Canada instead of thinking primarily and parochially of British Columbia or Nova Scotia or Quebec or Ontario.

We can do these things, secondly, if we insist that Canada will remain free and independent, economically and politically, or as free as it is possible or desirable for any single nation to be in the shrinking and increasingly interdependent world in which we live. Some may think it is unnecessary to continue stressing the need for Canada to retain her independence. But considering the rate at which it is being lost, I believe we should keep on pointing out what is happening. Of far greater importance, we should take steps that will reverse the present trends.

I believe it can be taken for granted that the great majority of Canadians want their country to remain as free and independent as possible. But the pulls and pressures in the other direction are enormous. I was aware of this long before I entered politics. The reports of the Royal Commission on Canada's Economic Prospects, which were published nearly ten years ago, dealt with the subject in some detail. But I had not fully appreciated the depth and strength of these pressures until I became Minister of Finance in April of 1963. During the two-and-one half years I held that office, the influence that financial and business interests in the United States had on Canadian policy and opinion was continually brought home to me. On occasion, this influence was reinforced by representations from the State Department and the American Administration as a whole. It was pressed by those who direct American businesses in Canada, by their professional advisers, by Canadian financiers whose interests were identified directly or indirectly with American investment in Canada, by influential members of the Canadian civil service, by some representatives of the university community and by some sections of the press.

The effects of these pressures on the leaders and spokesmen of all the political parties in Canada are immense — and too often they are effective. I do not suggest that there is anything unnatural or unsavoury about these pressures or the influence they have on Canadian public policy. American citizens and American corporations have enormous investments in Canada and, understandably, they resent any measures that would interfere with or restrict the growth of such investments, or place obstacles in the way of making new ones. I do say, however, that Canadians should not take their independence for granted; they should not underestimate the great difficulties in the way of maintaining it; and they should insist that all public policy be aimed at protecting and preserving the independence of Canada and not eroding it.

(A Choice For Canada)

Edward McCourt (Born in 1907)

McCourt's novels include *The Flaming Hour, The Fasting Friar* and *Music at the Close*. From scholarly works such as *The Canadian West in Fiction,* he has ranged through travel writing in *The Road Across Canada.*

OVERLAND FROM SIGNAL HILL TO VICTORIA

A sharply focused view of the kaleidoscopic pattern of a changing nation as seen from the Trans-Canada Highway

THE EAST

The Trans-Canada Highway begins on Signal Hill high above St. John's, Newfoundland, a good starting point rich in history. John Cabot, loyal Newfoundlanders affirm, entered the narrow-necked

harbour below the hill in 1497 ; and five hundred years earlier Leif
Ericsson may have sighted the craggy summit from far out at sea. Here
in the autumn of 1762 France made her last stand in America against
Great Britain; and nearly one hundred and fifty years later in a tower
on the hill, young Marconi received the first transatlantic wireless
signals.

We had travelled, my wife and I, nearly four thousand miles to
reach our starting point, firm in the belief that all true journeys must
follow the course of the sun.

For the first fifty miles out of St. John's the highway crosses a
wild moorland of rock and pond and tundra (in Newfoundland any
water less than a hundred square miles in area is a pond) — a disheveled
region where the Almighty appears to have assembled the materials
for a large-scale act of creation and then to have quit with the job
barely begun.

In Newfoundland the Trans-Canada Highway is a footpath for
pedestrians, a livestock run, a parking lot six hundred miles long and
thirty feet wide, a playground for children — and lastly, a motor-
vehicle traffic route.

Even where good shoulders exist, Newfoundanders prefer to park
squarely on the pavement — often around a curve or over the top
of a steep hill. All male Newfoundlanders fish (a generalization that
admits of no exceptions) and any hour of the day you must be prepared
to find cars parked in rows on the highway near inviting fishing streams.
Numerous children, who find the highway to be the one piece of level
terrain for miles around, make the fullest use of it from dawn till dusk.

The highway bypasses Gander, the great transatlantic airport and
surely the Siberia of airforce personnel. But Gander is a wonderful
and authentic piece of Americana — a suburbia without a city. Rows
of neat houses radiate from a neat shopping centre, and the house-
wives tripping along the crescents are neat and attractively well-painted,
too, and do more than their share, bless them, to relieve the drabness
of the world they inhabit. [. . .]

ONTARIO

[. . .]
The traveller driving west from Ottawa must choose between two
Trans-Canada routes — the Ottawa Valley route via Highway No. 17
to North Bay and Sudbury, or the Central Ontario and Georgian Bay
routes to Sudbury via Highways Nos. 7, 12, 103 and 69. (I quote these
numbers to suggest the confusion they must create in the mind of the

traveler who finds two Trans-Canada highways bearing five different numbers.) The Ottawa Valley route is to be preferred. For one thing, it is one hundred and fifty miles shorter, and for another, the scenery is consistently more exciting.

At North Bay, a busy town which has fattened on the tourist trade ever since the birth of the Dionne quintuplets in nearby Callander, a further choice of routes confronts the tourist : he may drive northwest to Sudbury and there be reunited with the regular Trans-Canada Highway coming up from Orillia, or he may choose another route and go "over the top" on No. 11, which will take him through Cochrane, Hearst and Longlac, rejoining the regular Trans-Canada at Nipigon.

North from Sault Ste. Marie the traffic intensifies, for we are now on the popular international "circle" drive for which Sault Ste. Marie is the entry and exit at the eastern end. We turned off the highway, found primitive but adequate accommodation in a cabin overlooking a magnificent horseshoe bay, and spent a long sun-mellowed afternoon at ease on the five-mile crescent beach. The water was wonderful; and after an eternity of forest it was a joy to get our eyes laid out straight and watch lake steamers drop out of sight over a remote horizon.

The one-hundred-and-sixty-five-mile stretch of highway from the Agawa River at the south entrance of the Lake Superior Provincial Park to Marathon cost forty million dollars. The builders, working the year round, drove through wild terrain where virtually no trails existed. They blasted through forty miles of rock, bridged twenty-five rivers, surmounted hills rising to sixteen hundred feet.

The Lake Superior Provincial Park will no doubt some day be a model of its kind, since it is the intention of the provincial authorities to preserve the unspoiled wilderness and rigidly limit commercial enterprises within its boundaries. So far the intention has been fully realized; the park at present provides excellent accommodation for campers and not even a gas station for the orthodox tourist.

Nipigon, at the junction of No. 17 and Alternate Route No. 11 coming down through Longlac, is one of our favourite Trans-Canada Highway stopovers. We have found a charming hideout tucked away on Nipigon Bay, and the view from the terraced residential streets of the town embraces the great red cliffs rising up from the water's edge.

Seventy miles west of Nipigon, the Lakehead cities, Port Arthur and Fort William, sit quietly awaiting their destiny. Fifty years ago they were boom towns, fevershly determined to grow up in a hurry. Later they accepted the seemingly inevitable stagnation imposed by isolation from the rest of Canada. But the St. Lawrence Seaway has revived old dreams. A mighty port for ocean-going vessels two thousand miles from salt water — such is the Twin Cities' vision of a not-impossible future. We spent a pleasant night beside Kakabeka Falls, eighteen miles out of Fort William. The picnic area at Kakabeka Falls is enormous and beautifully cared for; it seemed to us the finest we saw all the way across Canada.

Kenora on the north shore of the Lake of the Woods is the centre of a tourist-resort area covering thousands of square miles. Roads in the Lake of the Woods country are few. It is a world of water and rock and forest, a well-balanced combination of the main elements of the Laurentian Shield. It is a world that is a microcosm of roughly one third of all Canada, and it is better approached from the west than the east. For the visitor from the great plains, tall trees and great sheets of clear water exalt the spirit and accelerate the blood flow because they are a combination seldom seen in his own land.

MANITOBA

Manitoba is always spoken of as one of the three prairie provinces, but the Laurentian Shield does not terminate tidily at the border. The highway continues for a hundred miles more through rock and forest muskeg, skirting the Whiteshell Forest Reserve, a recreational area now being developed as a vast provincial playground and tourist attraction. Falcon Lake, alongside the highway just inside the eastern border, is so far the showpiece.

Some miles westward, the highway emerges with shocking suddenness onto the limitless prairie. The sky billows out to twice its former size; eyes accustomed to looking down a green tunnel are unblinkered, and the horizon slips away to a point so remote that it is hard to say where earth ends and sky begins. Some people find the change so abrupt as to feel acute physical and mental upset — like a diver getting the bends from surfacing too quickly.

A pall of smoke obscures the horizon ahead. The highway signs warn us that St. Boniface and Winnipeg are at hand. And with Winnipeg the true West begins.

Of Winnipeg it is hard to say more than that it is bright and lively, with wide streets, handsome public buildings (many of them faced with local Tyndall stone), an admirable motel strip on Highway 75, an expanding university, and many pleasant public parks. The truth is that most Canadian cities — particularly those of the west — impress us, if at all, by reason not of intrinsic qualities but of location.

The highway follows the most direct route from Winnipeg to the Saskatchewan border. Headingly, about fifteen miles out, is the centre of the old White Horse Plain, at one time Métis country and a starting point for the great buffalo hunts that provided the Métis with winter food.

Between Portage la Prairie and the Saskatchewan border the highway passes out of the old Ice-Age Lake Agassiz bed through the Manitoba Escarpment, a line of broken ridges running from the Pasquia Hills in northern Saskatchewan, through the Porcupine Forest Reserve and Riding Mountain National Park to Turtle Mountain near the American border. The escarpment once formed Lake Agassiz' western shore.

SASKATCHEWAN

Saskatchewan's welcome to the tourist is reserved. Only a modest sign informs us that we are now in the Wheat Province. The highway is excellent. Many prosperous farm homes crouch secure behind squat caragana hedges and towering evergreen windbreaks. But deserted farm-steads make the greater impact; they offend the eye and depress the soul.

The sense of depression is unjustified; the deserted farms are not symbols of the triumph of hostile nature over man, but of the fact that farming is fast becoming big business. The homesteader who half a century ago reared a family on one hundred and sixty acres is gone now. The farms with crumbling barns and houses are probably units of a single enterprise spreading over thousands of acres.

Indian Head comes as a pleasant oasis, for it is the centre of the first prairie Experimental Station (established 1888), and the gardens and trees of the town have benefited from the association. Even those of us who, irrationally, love almost everything about Saskatchewan admit that the tourist won't be tempted to linger on the eastern stretch of the highway. Somewhere ahead lies Regina, with the usual tourist amenities — shower baths, air-conditioning, wall-to-wall broadloom, and cool dark taverns. But the wise tourist will eschew the temptations of the flesh; he will leave the Trans-Canada at Indian Head and drive north for twenty miles over Highway No. 56 into a region that seems no part of any familiar world, a region so vast, incongruous, and incomprehensible as to compel the exclamation, "It can't happen here."

Part of the great valley of the Qu'Appelle lies in its total unexpectedness. One moment, we are driving through typical south Saskatchewan landscape; the next, we are hanging on the lip of a miniature Grand Canyon, the floor of the valley as far as the eye can reach a necklace of sky-blue lakes.

Fort Qu'Appelle's buildings are nondescript and the wind funnels eternally down the dusty main street, which seems about half a mile wide. But the valley ramparts rise steeply just behind the town and the lakes stretch into the far distance. Whatever sins abide in the town itself are atoned for by the magnificence of its setting. The Fort Hotel is worth a visit for its cuisine. In most western small-town hotels and restaurants food is served to sustain life ; in the Fort Hotel it also titillates the appetite.

There are some things in Regina worth seeing. The splendid Museum of Natural History is quite properly a source of civic and provincial pride; the RCMP barracks, the western training centre for recruits to the force, draws thousands of visitors during the summer months.

Between Regina and Moose Jaw the great plains stretch uninterrupted to the horizon. This is the authentic wheat country, the original breadbasket of the world.

Moose Jaw squats in a tangle of ravines and valleys at the confluence of the Thunder and Moose Jaw creeks. The immensely wide main street is lined with substantial, reticent, Old World buildings. But the stolid, dignified appearance of the city is at odds with its reputation — in the roaring twenties Moose Jaw roared louder than any other town in the west. River Street was an internationally celebrated criminal hideout, half the city police force were arrested for various misdemeanors, and the Ku Klux Klan — whose Saskatchewan membership in the twenties is said to have numbered forty thousand — made Moose Jaw the centre of its prairie activities.

To the traveller weary of elevators and grain fields and the black ribbon snaking its way forever around low buttes and over sunburned ridges, the attraction of the land now lies to the south. Incredibly, a range of hills has come into view.

The Cypress Hills rise to nearly five thousand feet, the highest point in Canada between Labrador and the Rockies. An island in the last Ice Age — so some geologists theorize — the hills constitute an unglaciated area which has preserved species of fauna and flora found nowhere else in Canada (many of them indigenous to regions hundreds of miles farther south), such exotic and alarming specimens of wildlife as solpugids (a species of scorpion), hog-nose vipers, kangaroo rats, and black widow spiders. Fortunately they are all retiring creatures that live far off the beaten path.

Fort Walsh, named in honour of an early commissioner of the Mounted Police, was built in the valley of the Battle in 1876. None too soon, for 1876 was a bad year in the hills. The great buffalo herds had all but vanished from the plains, and hunger drove the Indians into the hills where a few herds survived. Here the red man made his last stand in the west for the way of life he knew and loved. Here in 1876 came Sitting Bull and his fierce Sioux warriors, fresh from their triumph over the cream of the U.S. Cavalry at Little Big Horn; and here a handful of men in red coats fed the hungry, proclaimed the Queen's law, and compelled white man and Indian alike to accept it.

ALBERTA

The obvious way to enter Alberta is by the Trans-Canada through the border town of Walsh. But travellers who long for a few hours' escape from gas fumes, asphalt and high speeds should do as my wife and I did — make the crossing by way of the winding municipal roads and rutted private trails that haphazardly link the Cypress Hills Provincial Park on the Saskatchewan side with Elkwater Park in Alberta, twenty-five miles south of the highway.

The route — unofficial, mostly unmarked — takes you past Fort Walsh and up on to high bare ridges from which immense vistas open north and south, including on a clear day the Bearpaw Mountains in Montana. It gives you a chance, too, to meet authentic ranchers and cowpokes, for you are sure to get lost several times and have to ask your way. ("Just take that trail over the hill," one weather-beaten cowhand told us. "She'll drop you down the other side into so-and-so's backyard." She did, too. Literally — our faithful car leaning back like a well-trained mustang and digging in her heels all the way down.)

Medicine Hat is a name and a story. Sprawled along the South Saskatchewan River in the middle of a vast semiarid region given over mainly to ranching, Medicine Hat is a cowtown in spirit and in fact, and an industrial centre of some importance because of its unlimited supply of natural gas. But the name and the story are what matter.

In 1907 Rudyard Kipling stopped off in Medicine Hat on a trans-Canada tour. Members of the Cypress Club, mostly old-timers, took Kipling in hand and saved him from the horrors of an orthodox civic reception. The great man showed his immediate appreciation by coining a catchphrase used ever since to describe Medicine Hat : "The city with all hell for a basement." But the really grand gesture was yet to come.

A few years later, dull-spirited newcomers denounced the town's name as an embarrassing absurdity. The city council ordered a plebiscite. Those stout upholders of the ancient ways, the members of the Cypress Club, knowing the outcome to be a foregone conclusion, were disconsolate until at a wake in the clubrooms a member raised from his beer mug a face suddenly illumined with holy joy and said, "Kipling should know of this — he'd flay the hide off those blighters."

The local postmaster, Frank Fatt, wrote an eloquent plea to Kipling, "the Father Confessor of the Empire," to save the town's name. Kipling's reply was a devastating combination of sentiment, logic, and invective : "Believe me, the very name is an asset, and as years go on will become more and more of an asset. It has no duplicate in the world; it makes men ask question ... draws the feet of young men towards it ... What should a city be rechristened that has sold its name ? Judasville."

The Cypress Club saw to it that Kipling's letter was given nation-wide publicity. The advocates of a change of name were silenced. They have remained silent ever since.

Northwest of Medicine Hat, thirty miles off the highway from the town of Brooks, lies a natural wonder which the traveler who relishes the unexpected and spectacular should explore. The road to the Steve-ville Dinosaur Park cuts through irrigated farmlands — then the bad-lands of the Red Deer River burst upon you without the slightest warning. Steveville Dinosaur Park is a Danteesque nightmare, a wild eerie region of eroded hoodoos, fantastically distorted monstrous shapes of earth rising from the valley floor between towering walls.

Four miles off the highway and three miles south of the village of Cluny is a spot splendid to look at, rich in history — the old Black-foot Crossing. Here from time immemorial the Indians of the Blackfoot Confederacy crossed the Bow on their north-south journeyings; here they rendezvoused, plotted war against their ancient enemies the Crees, and sometimes smoked the pipe of peace. And here in 1877 they signed away the land of their ancestors. On a high bluff overlooking the cross-ing a cairn commemorates the Blackfoot Treaty Number Seven. On that day in 1877, four thousand Indians of the confederacy — Black-foot, Blood, Stony, Piegan, Sarcee — met with the commissioners of the Great White Queen. Nearly a hundred members of the North West Mounted Police added to the pageantry. The great Chief Crow-foot, in return for a few scattered reserves and five dollars a year of treaty money, surrendered to the Queen, "for as long as the sun shines and rivers run," the land which is now southwestern Alberta.

The Trans-Canada sideswipes Calgary along her northern flank and it is easy to bypass the city. Few are likely to do so, for Calgary is one of the two glamour cities of Canada. (The other is, of course, Montreal.) Her history is prosaic — a record of steady, sometimes spectacular, growth from Mounted Police fort (1875) to cowtown to oiltown. But the great Calgary Stampede, Canada's most celebrated annual show, has given the city worldwide publicity. (Incidentally, Calgary women are among the most beautiful in Canada, and, outside of Montreal, the best dressed.)

Calgary enjoys perhaps the finest scenic location of all our cities — only Quebec, Montreal, and Vancouver offer serious competition. The Bow and Elbow rivers join near her heart, the foothills roll away in great humpbacked swells on three sides, and on the fourth the wide valley of the Bow reaches back to the mountains sixty miles west, abrupt, massive, snow-capped, a stunning backdrop to the wide sky.

The plainsman like myself is likely to find his first plunge into the mountains on the Calgary-Banff run an alarming experience, because of the sudden feeling of being separated from all famliar things. Before we are aware of what is happening the beautiful but sinister Three Sisters and assorted kinfolk have slipped in behind us and cut off our retreat.

Even the most jaded sophisticate must acknowledge that Banff is one of the loveliest spots on earth. Indeed, looking at the town and its environs from the summit of Sulphur Mountain you get the curious impression that in creating Banff, God assumed the role of a farsighted parks superintendent and designed the area with a view to tourism in the future.

It is a tribute to those in charge of the park that even in the height of the tourist season Banff is a tranquil place. Nightlife is almost non-existent — high altitudes and long walks (which can hardly be resisted) conspire to early and childlike slumber. The smell of evergreen over-powers the gas fumes, and you go to bed nearly everywhere within sound of running water — nature's ultimate soporific.

Lake Louise, forty miles west of Banff, is a place familiar to all Canadians and most Americans even though they have never visited it, for it is surely the most photographed beauty spot on the continent and it looks exactly like its photographs.

BRITISH COLUMBIA

"And what is so great," my wife said, "about the Rogers Pass ?"

"What is so great about the Rogers Pass," I said, "is that we are over it."

The pass, last link of the Trans-Canada Highway to be completed, built at a cost so astronomical that the figures fail to communicate any meaning, is so superbly engineered that after the preceding stretch of up-and-down road from Field to Golden it comes as a distinct anti-climax. No doubt the Rogers Pass Highway was fantastically difficult to build, but it is child's play for even the most timid tourist to drive.

Beyond the Rogers Pass the highway follows a narrow, high-walled valley to Revelstoke, a town celebrated for its heavy snowfall and splendid skiing facilities. Forty-five miles west of Revelstoke, Little Shuswap Lake comes into view — a marvelous expanse of sky-blue water flanked by great hills far enough from the water's edge to allow room for wide sand beaches — and it is possible to breathe freely again.

We liked Salmon Arm, a town scattered casually up and down hill-sides. No one in Salmon Arm appears to have heard of town planning. The town centre is more or less orthodox, but the residential streets and suburbs wander indiscriminately up and down hillsides, disappear completely for no apparent reason, and pop up again on hilltops and in forest clearings. Elsewhere in Canada we diligently prune our shrubs and clip our hedges and shave our lawns, but most British Columbia towns we passed through shared Salmon Arm's slightly ragged look. "Things grow so fast there we can't keep up," one Salmon Arm citizen informed us. "I get the lawn slick as a pooltable one day and she's running wild the next. Discouraging." He didn't look discouraged; he looked contented and well preserved.

The truth is that outside the industrial towns, life in British Colum-bia's is so pleasant that it seems absurd to waste any part of it trying to improve on nature.

Kamloops, at the junction of the North and South Thompson, has some things to commend it, including an admirable scenic location and a lengthy history. David Stuart, a trader with John Astor's Pacific Fur Company, built the original Fort Kamloops in 1812. The following year the Pacific and North West companies merged, and in 1821 were absorbed by the Hudson's Bay Company. Fort Kamloops was thus an important furtrading centre long before any of the coastal cities was founded. Later the settlement enjoyed a brief flurry of excitement during the mid-century gold rush days, before settling down to com-fortable middle-aged respectability.

It is one of the pleasant ironies of history, and cause of hope for all of us, that it is possible for a man to achieve great reputation and even enduring fame by doing something just a little worse than anyone else.

This meditation was prompted by recollections of the almost un-believable trek of a party of tenderfoot gold-seekers across the prairies and through the great mountains to Kamloops in the year 1862. The original Overlanders, as the trekkers were known, were Old Country men who succumbed to the lures of an early travel agency, the Overland Transit Company. For the modest sum of forty-two pounds the company offered transportation from London to the western plains, from whence — so prospective emigrants were assured — it would be an easy journey by stage-coach across the plains and through the Yellowhead Pass two hundred and fifty miles west of Fort Edmonton to the head-waters of the Fraser, the great river of gold. And once on the Fraser it would of course be mere child's play to build rafts and float gently down the river to the gold fields proper.

The Overlanders endured hardships without compare in the history of western Canadian settlement; their rafts were wrecked time and again in the mad waters of the Fraser and North Thompson; they lost most of their supplies and they ate their livestock. Some of the Over-landers drowned and a few may have starved to death, but most of them reached their El Dorado only to find that the gold fields had petered out.

West of Kamloops the country becomes progressively more arid. Kamloops Lake, a magnificent stretch of water twenty miles long, does much to modify the desert aspect of the surrounding terrain; and the village of Savona at the west end of the lake brings to mind an obscure item of local history. In 1885 the village was renamed Van Horne in honor of the great railroad builder, and Van Horne it remained until Sir William actually saw the huddle of shacks — whereupon he insisted that the village take back the old one.

The loneliest places of earth are not those where man has never set foot, but those from which he has withdraw defeated. Walhachin, once the centre of a flourishing agricultural community, lies just off the Trans-Canada Highway about halfway between Savona and Ash-croft. A few ragged, sterile apple trees standing in line across a sun-baked field where nothing else grows, and a few pieces of rotten flume clinging to the hillsides remind us that less than half a century ago Walhachin was one of the showplaces of the interior of British Colum-bia, presided over by the Marquess of Anglesey, who built a fine man-sion complete with swimming pool. But on the outbreak of World War I, nearly all the ablebodied men of the district went off to fight; a year or two later large sections of the flume were swept away in a cloud-burst and there was not sufficient manpower left to repair the damage; blight struck the apple trees; within another ten years the desert had again taken over, leaving only a few scraggly apple trees to survive as melancholy reminders of fair hopes now blasted.

Ashcroft, lying just off the highway near where the Thompson River turns south, was a well-known jumping-off place in the days of the gold rush, but perhaps it will be longest remembered as the centre of a colony of county English, determined to maintain Old Country social customs, including riding to hounds.

The Cornwall brothers, the squirearchy in the colony, imported a pack of foxhounds and democratically invited the local cowboys to join the first fox hunt of the season. The cowboys gave solemn assurances of polite behaviour and agreed to join their hosts in shouting, "Tallyho," at the appropriate times. But when the hounds raised a fox (actually a coyote, for there were no foxes in the Ashcroft country), the cowboys thundered off across the sunbaked flats with mighty yells of "There goes the son of a bitch ! ", overran the hounds and lassoed the coyote.

Whereupon the Englishmen laid away their pink coats and never put them on again.

The canyon of the Fraser River is a wonder and a horror — a nightmarish crack in the earth between three thousand-foot walls through which runs the most ferocious river in all Canada. It breaks from the canyon exhausted, and spews forth its silt to form the great delta on which the cities of New Westminster and Vancouver now stand.

Below Hope the river widens and runs now through the valley of the Fraser, as distinct from the canyon — beautiful, intensively cultivated, rich in market gardens and small fruits and dairy herbs and hay fields. We who have been long immured in the dark canyon suddenly find it possible to lift up our eyes and see something other than a wall of rock, to breathe deeply again without fear of starting an avalanche.

There is much to do and see and marvel at in Vancouver. Her streets are wider than those of most Canadian cities, her parks more luxuriant and numerous, her gardens a glory nearly all the year round, her Chinatown the largest in Canada.

Vancouver is a city that should have grown straight up, like Manhattan, instead of despoiling great mountainsides and blotching fair valleys. The Vancouver that is enduring — not her buildings nor her industries nor her people — is beyond praise or blame because it is no work of man : the firs in Stanley Park, the mountains, the sea, the great ships coming in from far-off places.

The Vancouver Island ferry decants its passengers at Nanaimo, a bustling little town with a harbour full of fishing boats. Duncan, just off the final leg of the highway, is reputed to be populated almost entirely by eccentric Englishmen. Undoubtedly the town has in its time enjoyed its full share of younger sons, remittance men, retired rear-admirals, major-generals, and gentleman farmers who left the cows unmilked to finish a cricket match. Certainly Vancouver Island is a world in which men frequently acquire a brand-new set of values. That the rest of Canada is hard-working and virtuous is no reason why the citizens of Duncan and similar communities should be denied their cakes and ale. Thus they reason and thus they live.

The city of Victoria has perpetrated the most successful hoax in the history of tourism : it has persuaded the rest of the world that it is indeed a little bit of old England. Perhaps there was some warrant for this half a century ago, but there is none now. Victoria has, of course, rather more than its share of tweedy old gentlemen and even tweedier ladies who haunt such mausoleums as the Empress Hotel and the Union Club where tea and port are drunk in silence; but a day or two in the city convinces those of us of clear eye and level head that we are being exposed to a wonderfully entertaining — and for the city wonderfully profitable — piece of stagecraft. Victoria is self-consciously and deliberately Old Country, hence not Old Country at all.

For us, journey's end was a motel shaded by great evergreens on the outskirts of Victoria, where under the evergreens or in deck chairs beside the swimming pool we relaxed and absorbed the sunshine and thought of all the people we should talk to, the sights we should see, the things we should do, and dismissed them all from our minds as irrelevant and inconsequential.

(Maclean's)

Solange Chaput-Rolland (Née en 1919)

Journaliste, elle a publié avec Gwethalyn Graham leur échange de lettres portant sur la différence de mentalité et de culture des Canadiens anglais et des Canadiens français *(Chers ennemis,* 1963); puis ses impressions de voyage à travers le Canada *(Mon pays, Québec ou le Canada?,* 1966).

SAINT-JERÔME, le 16 juillet 1963

Chère Gwen,

Me voici donc au terme de notre dialogue. Que de choses j'aurais encore à vous dire, mais puisqu'il faut terminer cet échange de vues, laissez-moi résumer succinctement mes espoirs de Canadienne française. Ils sont précis et catégoriques.

Je ne veux plus être considérée citoyenne de seconde classe dans mon pays.

Je ne veux plus penser à mes compatriotes vivant hors du Québec et luttant héroïquement pour parler et prier en français.

Je ne veux plus penser aux sacrifices injustes consentis par les parents pour donner à leurs enfants une éducation française, lorsque leur nombre justifie la construction d'écoles catholiques françaises dans un milieu anglais. Je pense particulièrement à la question des écoles séparées qui dans toutes les provinces du Canada, sauf au Québec, dressent les uns contre les autres Canadiens français et anglais.

Je ne puis accepter que mon fils, par exemple, occupe un poste subalterne au service de son pays, simplement parce que son camarade de carrière, de service civil ou d'armée possède sur lui le rare avantage de ne pas dire un seul mot de français.

Je ne veux plus croire qu'il existera au Canada, en 1967, des endroits où il sera défendu de parler français.

Je ne veux plus devoir prouver dans un livre, une causerie, une conversation ou un article de journal, que le Québec ne vit plus selon le mot de Goldwin Smith : "Like an antediluvian animal preserved in Siberian ice".

Je refuse d'envisager l'heure où un de mes enfants me reviendra brisé, meurtri, parce qu'il se sera fait dire à son tour : "Speak white".

Je n'accepte plus d'être mal servie, où que ce soit au Canada, si je m'exprime en français; je ne demande pas d'être comprise, mais je ne tolèrerai ni le mépris ni la grossièreté ni l'ironie si je m'exprime en ma langue devant vos compatriotes. Si le Canadien français ne comprend guère les rouages de la démocratie dont vous vous affirmez les fidèles défenseurs, vous nous en donnez un triste exemple.

Peut-être aurait-il fallu pour rendre justice à nos griefs respectifs que toutes deux fûssions spécialisées en histoire, en sociologie et en politique. Si les avocats, les professeurs et les politiciens sont qualifiés pour étudier et pratiquer les refontes à la Constitution, les Canadiens moyens subissent, sans tellement savoir pourquoi, les résultats des décisions intempestives prises par nos grands hommes au nom des petits. Or, je suis de cette classe de Canadiens ne comprenant guère les ramifications juridiques des réformes constitutionnelles. Nos politiciens ont fait et défait la Confédération. Ce mystérieux document, parfois impénétrable dans ses desseins, mériterait d'être relégué dans les archives de notre Parlement. Les vrais penseurs de 1967 auront-ils le courage de rédiger une Constitution dictée par le seul désir d'unir les Canadiens de toutes les races et de toutes les langues dans un même souci démocratique de respecter les droits collectifs, minoritaires et individuels des citoyens du Canada ? Sans une préoccupation véritablement nationale et biculturelle, dépouillée de l'envie mesquine de limiter les droits de celui-ci au profit de celui-là, le Canadien anonyme français ou anglais, n'ayant jamais voix au chapitre des hautes décisions politiques, pourra se dire ces vers de Saint-Denys-Garneau : « Je marche à côté d'une joie, d'une joie qui n'est pas pour moi. »

Or, cette joie fut à moi, durant notre dialogue. Si d'autres autour de nous le continuent, ce sera dans la joie d'une mission accomplie que je signerai avec toute mon amitié et tout mon amour pour ce merveilleux pays.

Solange

(Chers Ennemis)

Gwethalyn Graham (1913-1965)

Educated in Switzerland, the U. S. and Canada, Miss Graham was acutely concerned with foreign affairs and inter-racial problems.

She wrote two novels, *Swiss Sonata* and *Earth and High Heaven,* both of which received Governor-General's awards.

GO HOME BAY, ONTARIO, August 15, 1963

Dear Solange :

"The arguments brought against . . . the obvious inference were peculiarly masculine. They were tainted with that decadence which befalls all human activities, art, literature, science, medicine, and law, when the game becomes less important than the rules." This is a quotation from Rebecca West's *The Meaning of Treason* which strikes me as being singularly apt in the circumstances. The "obvious inference" of our present Canadian dilemma is the logical impossibility of bringing about even a minimum of bilingualism and biculturalism in this country without the intervention of the federal government in some aspects of education. If French Canada is going to continue to insist that matters of education are exclusively the business of the provinces, then it will indeed be arguing that the rules are more important than the game. Our motto is to be "Provincial autonomy at all costs." The other nine provinces are each, individually and on their own, to go out and become bilingual and bicultural without any help from French Canada by some sort of process of distant osmosis coupled with the large-scale purchase of books called *How To Teach Yourself French.*

It is doubtless a limitation of the feminine as opposed to the masculine view of things that the English-Canadian mother, informed that her children can't have French-Canadian teachers to teach them French because Quebec can't afford to train them in such numbers and the federal government isn't allowed to, will *not* bow her head before the majesty of the law, but will say, "If the law is as silly and illogical as that, then get rid of it."

To speak a second language is a lesson in humility, and there is no reason why that lesson should be confined to French Canadians. I have seen you come back from presiding over a conference which lasted from nine in the morning till midnight, entirely in English, and you were so tired you could hardly keep your head up. I know that the same thing happens to me when I am obliged to listen, think, and speak in French all day long. What English Canada has done to French Canada on the federal level and in a major segment of industry is, in effect, to force French Canadians to speak English for their entire working lives. I am not proud of a people who would illegally, unconstitutionally, and inhumanely force another people who are supposed to be their equals to undergo the strain of being perpetually obliged to express themselves in a language other than their own. I have often thought that a failure of imagination has far wider significance than most of those acts which we usually refer to as sins. How many crimes would be committed if all of us made use of our full measure of sympathetic imagination ? Surely almost all of them would become unthinkable, and so would most of the small meannesses and cruelties of everyday life.

You have made some harsh remarks about your fellow-nationals; I have saved up the worst of mine for this final letter. A tendency to regard people who speak other languages as either peculiar or slightly subhuman is an abiding and disastrous characteristic of the English-speaking peoples. It plagued the English all through their days of empire; it is plaguing the Americans in the world of today. Because I do regard a failure of sympathetic imagination as the root of most evil, when I say that English Canadians sin against French Canadians by the very fact of their refusal to recognize the equality of the French language in Canada, and to learn it when they can, I am accusing them of a stupidity and an inhumanity far surpassing anything you or I have said against French Canadians.

So much has been written about the reinterpretation of Confederation; about bilingualism in the civil service and Crown corporations and on the federal political level, as well as in those English-owned industries doing business in Quebec; about the importance of creating a bilingual training college for federal civil servants; about the importance of establishing a royal commission on bilingualism and biculturalism in order to learn more facts and to go less on guesswork — that I can see no reason for repeating any of it. It is all obvious, and obviously necessary if we are to survive as a single, united country and not to fall apart into two separate banana republics.

I am also convinced that, with the exception of the royal commission, every one of these problems can only be viewed as a result, and that, in order to understand why solutions have been so long in coming, we have to go to the bottom of our educational structure to find the causes. It is a truism to say that if you have a poorly constructed house with a defective foundation you can't hope to achieve much by rebuilding from the second floor up.

At the base of the whole problem described by that one word "bilingualism" are the elementary and high schools of English Canada. The French language should be regarded as a compulsory subject from Grade I, and I would hope that the Tan-Gau method would be adopted across the country, because it is at once the easiest and most effective way of teaching small children another language yet devised, so far as I know — they simply learn by listening, the way they learned English as babies. As Dr. Wilder Penfield has pointed out over and over again (in proper neurological language, not in my garbled version), it is anatomically easier to learn a second language before the age of twelve, when those paths in the brain most receptive to language, which have been open till then, begin to close. If the neurological argument is not convincing, there is the added psychological fact that language habits become more fixed year by year. You speak much better English than I do French, I think most probably because you started speaking English as a small child while I only began speaking French when I was sixteen.

Across English Canada, then, French should be a compulsory subject through university. If English Canadians want to lapse back into unilingualism after that, it will be their affair, but if they are intending to go into business, federal politics, or the federal civil service, they will be making a serious mistake in the first instance and a fatal one in the second and third. A bilingual federal government will have no use for employees, and the Canadian people no use for politicians, who can't speak French. As for the future businessmen, French is one of the languages of the Common Market and a sister language to the Spanish and Portuguese of all Latin America. It would seem a great pity for them deliberately to abandon their inherent advantage of having been born in an Anglo-French nation.

And the French departments of the schools and universities of English Canada must be staffed by French Canadians. This, if you like, is the price your people are going to have to pay as their *due* share in the continuance of the pact of Confederation.

I do not think there is any other solution.

Gwen

(Dear Enemies)

INDEX

ACHEVÉ

D'IMPRIMER

SUR LES PRESSES

DE LA

LIBRAIRIE

BEAUCHEMIN

LIMITÉE

À MONTRÉAL

LE SIXIÈME

JOUR D'OCTOBRE

MIL NEUF CENT

SOIXANTE-SEPT